AUTOMATIC
CONTROL SYSTEMS

PRENTICE-HALL INTERNATIONAL, INC., *London*
PRENTICE-HALL OF AUSTRALIA, PTY. LTD., *Sydney*
PRENTICE-HALL OF CANADA, LTD., *Toronto*
PRENTICE-HALL OF INDIA PRIVATE LTD., *New Delhi*
PRENTICE-HALL OF JAPAN, INC., *Tokyo*

AUTOMATIC
CONTROL SYSTEMS

Second Edition

BENJAMIN C. KUO

Professor of Electrical Engineering
University of Illinois

PRENTICE-HALL, INC.
Englewood Cliffs, N.J.

© 1967 by
PRENTICE-HALL, INC
Englewood Cliffs, N.J.

Current Printing (Last Digit):
10   9   8   7   6   5   4   3   2   1

Library of Congress Catalog Card Number 67-16388
Printed in the United States of America

Preface

The primary aim of this book is to give the reader a reasonably complete understanding of the various principles and techniques utilized in the analysis and design of feedback control systems. The book is intended as a text for an undergraduate course on control systems in the engineering curriculum. The book is also an outgrowth of the material used by the author for many years in a senior control systems course at the University of Illinois.

The second edition represents a modernized version of the original book which was published in 1962. The two major changes in this new edition are the inclusion of the state variable technique and the integration of the discrete-data systems with the continuous-data systems. The chapter on nonlinear systems has been deleted. The author feels that a comprehensive treatment on the subject of nonlinear systems cannot be made successfully in a text at the introductory level, and with limited space.

Since modern control systems theory relies heavily on the state variable technique, the author feels that the latter subject should be included in even an introductory course on control systems. Today, the practicing engineer may find it extremely difficult to read modern advanced texts and professional journals without the background on the state description of linear systems.

Digital transducers and digital computers have become increasingly important as elements in control systems. Since most of the principles and techniques for the analysis and design of continuous-data systems can be extended to the study of discrete-data systems, a unified treatment of these topics should be advantageous. Therefore, in this new edition material on discrete-data systems is integrated with that of the continuous-data systems. The reader may find that in the new edition the material on discrete-data systems appears as sections at the end of several chapters. However, if time does not allow to cover these topics in a specific course, these sections may be omitted without any loss of continuity.

Chapter 1 presents the basic concept of control systems and mathematical preliminaries. The Fourier transform, the Laplace transform, and the z-transform are discussed. Chapter 2 includes the foundation of linear systems analysis using the transfer function and impulse response concepts. The signal flow graph and the block diagram techniques are discussed. These concepts and techniques are extended to discrete-data systems and multivariable systems. Frequency domain plots of transfer functions are also included in this chapter. Chapter 3 introduces the state variable description of linear systems. Emphasis is also placed on the comparison and relationships between the transfer function and the state variable approach. In Chapter 4, the transfer function and state variable descriptions of control systems components are developed. This material represents some practical examples on the applications of the methods presented in Chapters 2 and 3. Chapter 5 covers the basic feedback theory. Chapters 6, 7, 8, and 9 deal with topics on time response, stability, root locus, and frequency response of feedback control systems. These four chapters contain the major material on the analysis of control systems. The stability analysis and the root locus technique have been expanded from the original edition.

In Chapter 10, the design of control systems is effected by both the frequency domain technique and the root locus technique. This material essentially still represents the conventional cut-and-try principle.

Chapter 11 gives an introduction to the ideas of optimal control theory. The concepts of controllability and observability are discussed, and the chapter ends with the optimum design of digital control systems.

The author wishes to express his sincere appreciation to Dean W. L. Everitt, Professors E. C. Jordan and W. E. Miller, of the University of Illinois for their encouragement and interest in the preparation of the manuscript. The author also owes a debt of gratitude to Professor T. J. Higgins of the University of Wisconsin for his thorough review of the manusript.

Benjamin C. Kuo

Contents

AUTOMATIC
CONTROL SYSTEMS

1

Introduction
and
Mathematical Preliminaries

1.1 The Control Systems

In recent years, automatic control systems have assumed an increasingly important role in the development and advancement of modern civilization and technology. Domestically, automatic controls in heating and air conditioning systems regulate the temperature and the humidity of modern homes for comfortable living. Industrially, automatic control systems are employed in numerous applications, such as quality control of manufactured products, inventory control, machine tooling, etc. In modern space technology and weapon systems, control systems appear in the form of guidance systems, fire-control systems, etc.

The basic control system problem may be described by the simple block diagram shown in Fig. 1-1. The main objective of the system is to control

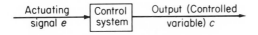

FIG. 1-1. The basic control system.

the variable c in some prescribed manner by an actuating signal e through the elements of the controlled process. For instance, in the steering system of an automobile the direction of the two front wheels is regarded as the controlled variable c. The position of the steering wheel is the actuating

1

signal *e*. The controlled process in this case is composed of the steering mechanisms, including the dynamics of the wheels. As another illustrative example, consider the temperature control in a home where the room temperature is to be regulated at a desirable level. In this case, the room temperature is the controlled variable *c*. In order to regulate *c* in a desired manner, an appropriate signal, or actuating signal *e*, must be applied to the heating system.

Open-loop Control Systems (*Nonfeedback Systems*)

Not any type of control systems can provide satisfactory control of the controlled variable. The basic system described in Fig. 1-1 is a typical open-loop control system which represents the simplest and most economical type of control system. The control adjustment of an open-loop system must depend on human judgment and estimate. For instance, consider the home furnace control problem described earlier. Let us assume that the furnace is equipped only with a timing device, which controls the periods of on and off of the furnace. Then, in order to regulate the temperature, the human operator must estimate the amount of time required for the furnace to stay on in order to reach the desired temperature and then set the time accordingly. When the preset time is up, the furnace is turned off automatically. However, it is quite likely that the room temperature is either above or below the desired value. It is quite apparent that this type of control system is inaccurate and quite unreliable. One reason for the inaccuracy lies in the fact that one may not know the exact characteristics of the furnace; the other factor is that one has no control over the outdoor temperature which has a detrimental effect on the indoor temperature. Therefore, another important disadvantage in the performance of an open-loop system is that the system does not adapt to variations in environmental conditions or to external disturbances. Perhaps an experienced person can estimate correctly the exact amount of operating time for the furnace to provide a certain temperature in the house, but if the doors or windows are opened and closed intermittently during the operating period, the final temperature of the house definitely will not be the desired temperature.

An "automatic" washing machine is also an open-loop system, because the amount of wash time is entirely determined by the judgment and estimation of the human operator. A truly automatic washer would check the cleanliness of the clothes constantly and turn itself off when the desired degree of cleanliness was reached.

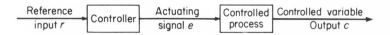

FIG. 1-2. A block diagram of an open-loop system.

In general, the block diagram of a typical open-loop control system is shown in Fig. 1-2. An input signal, or command r, is applied to the controller whose output acts as the actuating signal e; the actuating signal then actuates the controlled process and hopefully will drive the controlled variable c to the desired value.

Closed-loop Control Systems (Feedback Control Systems)

What is missing in the open-loop control system for more accurate control is a link or feedback path between the output and the input of the system. In order to obtain more accurate control, the controlled signal $c(t)$ must be fed back and compared with the command or reference input, and an actuating signal proportional to the difference of the output and the input must be sent through the system to correct the error. A system with a feedback path like that just described is called a closed-loop system. Human beings are probably the most complicated and sophisticated feedback control system in existence. For instance, when a person reaches for a book on the desk, his brain sends out a signal to his arms to reach for the book. His eyes serve as a sensing device which feeds back the exact position of his hand continuously. The distance between his hand and the book is the error. However, if he is told to reach for the book and then is blindfolded, he can only reach toward it, estimating its exact position. It is quite possible that he may miss the book by a large margin. With his eyes blindfolded, the feedback loop is broken, and he is operating as an

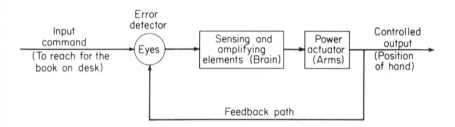

FIG. 1-3. Block diagram of human being as a closed-loop system.

open-loop system. The example of a human being as a feedback control system is described by the block diagram shown in Fig. 1-3.

Figure 1-4 shows the block diagram of another closed-loop system whose function is to position a load. In this case, a pair of potentiometers are used to detect the error between the actual position of the load (output) and the reference input, which is the desired position of the load. The error voltage $e(t)$ which appears at the potentiometer terminals is amplified and then sent to cause the motor to rotate in such a direction that the error

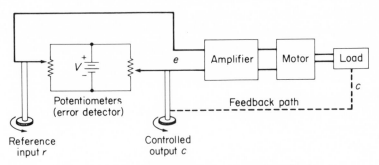

FIG. 1-4. A closed-loop system for positioning a load.

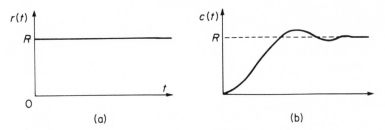

FIG. 1-5. Typical step response of a feedback control system. (a)
Step displacement input; (b) Output system response.

signal is eventually reduced to zero. If the reference input shaft is suddenly given an angular displacement of R units, as shown in Fig. 1-5a, the typical output response of the system as a function of time is as shown in Fig. 1-5b. Because of electrical and mechanical inertia, the output displacement cannot respond instantaneously, but will, rather, move gradually toward and sometimes oscillate about the desired position before reaching its final steady state.

Although a closed-loop system can offer more accuracy in control than an open-loop system, it is also capable of being unstable. In most feedback control systems, if the gain is too high, the system may tend to "overcorrect" the error, and its output may oscillate without bound. An unstable linear system is considered useless. Another important consideration is that the final output of a feedback control system usually does not exactly equal the reference input. In other words, because of friction and the features of feedback, the system may have a steady-state error. It will be shown later that the steady-state error can usually be reduced by increasing the gain of the system. In a very rough sense, we can say that to design feedback control systems essentially is to find a compromise between two contradictory factors: *stability* and *accuracy*.

The foregoing discussion of the significance and effects of feedback is, of course, oversimplified. From feedback amplifier theories, it is known that feedback also has significant effects on such system characteristics as bandwidth, impedance, sensitivity, and distortion, as well as stability and accuracy. In fact, in the analysis and design of feedback control systems, all these factors are important and should be considered. A more quantitative discussion of feedback theory will be given in Chapter 5.

1.2 Basic Elements of a Feedback Control System

From the basic concept of closed-loop control systems, a feedback control system may be defined as *a system comprising one or more feedback loops which compare the controlled signal c with the command signal r; the difference (e = r — c) is used to drive c into correspondence with r.*

In the literature on feedback control systems, the term *servomechanisms*, or *servo* for short, has been used quite often. Strictly speaking, servomechanisms merely represent a particular group of feedback control systems whose controlled outputs are mechanical positions.* However, since servomechanism and servo have been frequently used in a very broad sense, in this text *servo system* and *feedback control system* are used interchangeably.

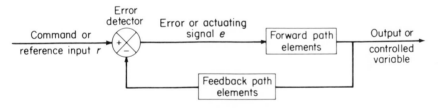

FIG. 1-6. Basic block diagram of a servo system.

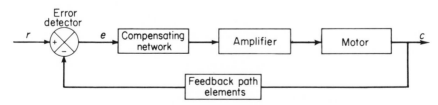

FIG. 1-7. Block diagram illustrating the basic components of a servo system.

*"IRE Standards on Terminology for Feedback Control Systems," *Proc. IRE*, January, 1956.

The elements of a basic control system can be schematically represented by the closed-loop block diagram shown in Fig. 1-6. The block diagram consists of a forward path, a feedback path, and an error-sensing device. A more detailed diagram of a control system is illustrated in Fig. 1-7. In general, the forward path of a control system may consist of the following elements: (1) error-sensing device (error detector), (2) amplifier, (3) servo-motor, (4) compensating networks, etc. The feedback path usually consists of transducers and compensating networks. The error detector compares the reference input with the actual output or some function of the output signal, and sends out a signal proportional to the difference. Compensating networks are often needed in the forward path, the feedback path, or both, to improve the performance of the system. A servo system with only its minimum required components seldom gives satisfactory performance.

1.3 Types of Feedback Control Systems

Feedback control systems may be classified in a number of ways. According to the method of analysis and design, feedback control systems may be classified as linear and nonlinear. Strictly speaking, linear systems do not exist in practice, since all physical systems are nonlinear to some extent. Therefore, linear feedback control systems are idealized systems which are fabricated merely for the simplicity of analysis and design. When the magnitudes of the actuating signals are limited to a range in which system components are considered linear, these components may be represented by their linear models and counterparts. But when the actuating signals are extended outside the range of linear operations, the feedback control system becomes nonlinear. For instance, electronic servo amplifiers often possess saturation effect when the applied signal becomes too large; the magnetic fields of servo motors also have saturation properties. There are other inherent nonlinearities, such as backlash between gears and the hysteresis effects in some components, whose occurence does not depend entirely on the size of the actuating signals. The relay-type (on-off type) control systems represent a class of systems in which a nonlinearity is intentionally introduced to improve the performance of the system.

In terms of the type of signals found in the systems, feedback control systems can be classified as continuous-data systems and discrete-data or sampled-data systems.

(1) Continuous-data Feedback Control Systems

A continuous-data system is one in which the signals at various parts of the system are all functions of the continuous time variable t. In general, the continuous data may be either modulated, in which case the system

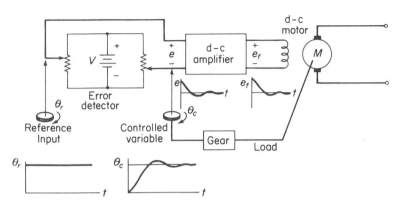

FIG. 1-8. A typical d-c servo system and its signals.

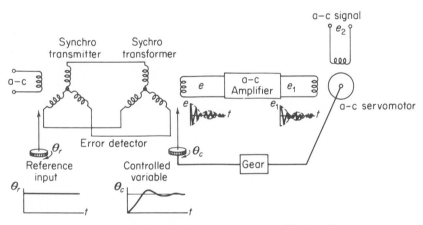

FIG. 1-9. A typical a-c servo system and its signals.

is referred to as an a-c carrier system,[1,2]* or unmodulated, then the system is called a d-c system. The schematic diagram of a simple d-c servo system is shown in Fig. 1-8. Typical waveforms of the system in response to a step function input are shown in the figure. Notice that all the signals are of the low frequency and are unmodulated. Typical components of a d-c servo system include potentiometers, d-c amplifiers, d-c motors, d-c tachometers, etc. The schematic diagram of a typical a-c servo system is shown in Fig. 1-9. In this case, the signals in the system are of the suppressed-carrier

*Superscripts refer to the numbered references at the end of the chapter.

modulated type. The actual signal of the control system appears as the envelope of the carrier signal. Typical components of the a-c servo system are synchros, a-c amplifier, and a-c motor. The synchros act as a modulator which converts the reference input signal into a modulated signal. The motor in this case serves as a demodulator which converts the modulated signal into an unmodulated signal as the output. Therefore, basically, the two systems in Figs. 1-8 and 1-9 may serve the same purpose; only the signals inside the systems are different.

In practice not all servo systems are strictly of the d-c or the a-c type. Many systems may incorporate a mixture of a-c and d-c components, using modulators and demodulators to match the signals at various points of the system.

(2) Sampled-data and Discrete-data Control Systems[3, 4, 5]

Sampled-data and digital-data control systems differ from the continuous-data systems in that the signal in one or more sections of the system is in the form of either a pulse train or a numerical code. Usually, sampled-data systems refer to a more general class of systems whose signals are in the form of pulsed data, whereas the term digital control systems implies the use of a digital computer or digital sensing element in a system. In this text, the term *discrete-data control systems* is used to describe both types of systems.

In general, a discrete-data system receives data or information only intermittently at some specific instants of time. For instance, the error signal in a control system may be supplied only intermittently in the form of pulses, in which case the control system receives no information about the

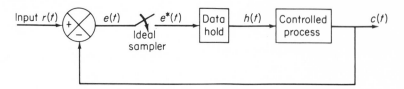

FIG. 1-10. Block diagram of a sampled-data control system.

error signal during the periods between two consecutive pulses. Figure 1-10 illustrates how a sampled-data control system operates. A continuous input signal $r(t)$ is applied to the system. The continuous error signal $e(t)$ is sampled by a sampling device, the sampler, and the output of the sampling device is a sequence of pulses. Usually the sampler has a uniform sampling rate. However, in general, the sampling schemes may take any form. Some of the sampling schemes may be periodic, cyclic, multirate, skip-rate, random, and pulse-width modulated. The most common variations are single-rate and multirate samplings.

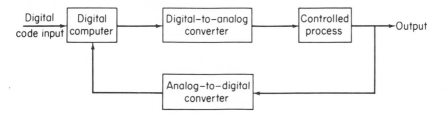

FIG. 1-11. A typical digital control system.

A digital control system is shown in block diagram form in Fig. 1-11. The appearance of digital signals (such as binary numbers) in part of the system requires the use of digital-to-analog as well as analog-to-digital converters.

The output of a sampler contains a train of pulses; the amplitude of each pulse follows the amplitude of the input time function during the pulse width. However, the exact analysis of sampled-data systems with finite pulse widths is quite complex. Usually, the sampler is replaced by an "ideal sampler" whose output contains a train of impulses. If the pulse width of the sampler output is very small compared to the dominant time constant of the continuous part of the system and to the sampling period, the pulse

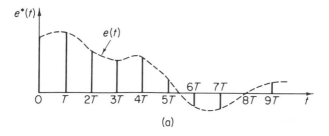

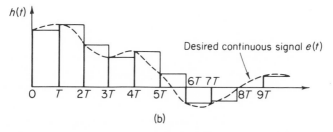

FIG. 1-12. (a) Input signal $e(t)$ and sampled signal $e^*(t)$; (b) Output waveform of zero-order hold circuit.

of finite pulse width can be approximated by an impulse train. If the input to the sampler is a continuous function $e(t)$, the output of the ideal sampler, $e^*(t)$, is given by

$$e^*(t) = \sum_{n=0}^{\infty} e(nT)\delta(t - nT) \tag{1-1}$$

This expression implies that the output of the ideal sampler is a train of impulses whose respective impulse areas (strengths) are equal to the magnitudes of $e(t)$ at the corresponding sampling instants $t = nT$.

In most sampled-data control systems, a data hold device is used to reconstruct the continuous signal from the sampled data, as shown in the block diagram of Fig. 1-10. A hold device commonly used in practice is the *zero-order hold*[3] whose input-output relationship is shown in Fig. 1-12. In other words, the mathematical description of the zero-order hold is simply

$$h(t) = e(nT) \quad \text{for } nT \leq t < (n + 1)T \tag{1-2}$$

where T is the sampling period.

1.4 Complex Variable and the s-Plane[6]

The analysis and design of feedback control systems rely to a great extent on the application of the complex variable theory.

A complex variable s is considered to have two components: a real component σ, and an imaginary component ω. Graphically, the σ component is represented in the horizontal direction, and the ω component is measured on the vertical axis in the complex s-plane. In other words, a complex variable is always defined by a point in a plane which has a σ

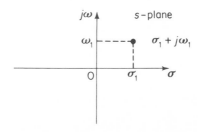

FIG. 1-13. The complex s-plane.

axis and a $j\omega$ axis. Figure 1-13 illustrates the complex s-plane, in which any arbitrary point $s = s_1$ is defined by the coordinates $\sigma = \sigma_1$, and $\omega = \omega_1$, or $s_1 = \sigma_1 + j\omega_1$.

Function of a Complex Variable

The function $G(s)$ is said to be a function of the complex variable s, if for every value of s there is a corresponding value (or values) of $G(s)$. Since s has real and imaginary parts, the function $G(s)$ is also represented by its real and imaginary parts; that is,

$$G(s) = Re\ G + jIm\ G \tag{1-3}$$

Thus, the function $G(s)$ can also be represented by a complex G-plane, whose horizontal axis represents $Re\ G$ and whose vertical axis measures the imaginary component of $G(s)$. If, for every value of s (every point in the s-plane), there is only one corresponding value for $G(s)$ (one corresponding point in the $G(s)$-plane), $G(s)$ is said to be a "single-valued function," and the mapping (correspondence) from points in the s-plane into points in the

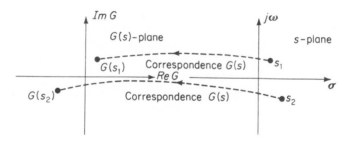

FIG. 1-14. One-to-one mapping from s-plane to $G(s)$-plane.

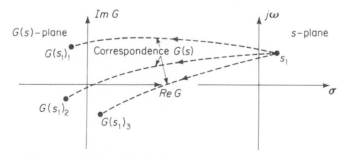

FIG. 1-15. One-to-three mapping from s-plane to $G(s)$-plane illustrating that the function $G(s)$ is multi-valued.

$G(s)$-plane is described as "one-to-one" (Fig. 1-14). If, for every point in the s-plane, there is more than one corresponding point in the $G(s)$-plane

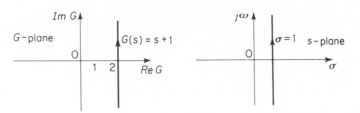

FIG. 1-16. Mapping from the s-plane into the $G(s)$-plane.

(mapped by the function $G(s)$), then $G(s)$ is called a "multivalued function" (Fig. 1-15).

Figure 1-16 illustrates the mapping of the function $G(s) = s + 1$ from the given s-plane locus ($s = 1$); the correspondence is apparently one-to-one. The arrows on the s-plane locus and on the G-plane locus indicate the corresponding directions of the two loci.

Analytic Functions

Definition. A function of complex variable $G(s)$ is analytic in a region if the function and all its derivatives exist in the region. For instance, the function $G(s) = 1/(s + a)$ is analytic at every point in the s-plane except at the point $s = -a;$ the function $G(s) = s + 2$ is analytic at every point in the finite s-plane.

Singularities and Poles of a Function

The singularities of a function are the points in the s-plane at which the function (or its derivatives) does not exist. A *pole* is the simplest type of singularity, and plays a very important role in the analysis and design of feedback control systems.

Definition of a Pole. If a function $G(s)$ is analytic and single-valued in the neighborhood of s_i except at s_i, it is said to have a pole of order r at $s = s_i$ if the limit

$$\lim_{s=s_i} [(s - s_i)^r G(s)] \tag{1-4}$$

has a finite, nonzero value. In other words, the denominator of $G(s)$ must include the factor $(s - s_i)^r$, and when $s = s_i$, the function becomes infinite. If $r = 1$, the pole at $s = s_i$ is called a "simple pole." For instance, the function

$$G(s) = \frac{10(s + 2)}{s(s + 1)(s + 3)^2} \tag{1-5}$$

has a pole of order two at $s = -3$, and simple poles at $s = 0$ and $s = -1$. The function is analytic in the s-plane except at these poles.

Zero of a Function

Definition. If the function $G(s)$ is analytic at $s = s_i$, it is said to have a zero of order r at $s = s_i$ if the limit

$$\lim_{s = s_i} [(s - s_i)^{-r} G(s)] \tag{1-6}$$

has a finite, nonzero value. Or, simply, $G(s)$ has a zero of order r at $s = s_i$ if $1/G(s)$ has an rth order pole at $s = s_i$. The function in Eq. (1-5), for instance, has a simple zero at $s = -2$.

If the function under consideration is a rational function, the total number of poles equals the total number of zeros (counting the multiple poles and zeros) if the poles and zeros at infinity and zero are taken into account. The function in Eq. (1-5) has four finite poles at $s = 0, -1, -3, -3$; there is one finite zero at $s = -2$, but there are three zeros at infinity, for

$$\lim_{s \to \infty} G(s) = \lim_{s \to \infty} 10/s^3 = 0 \tag{1-7}$$

1.5 The Laplace Transform[7, 8]

The Laplace transformation is one of the major mathematical tools used in the solution of ordinary linear differential equations. For complex

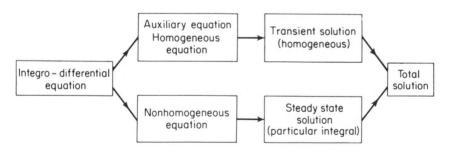

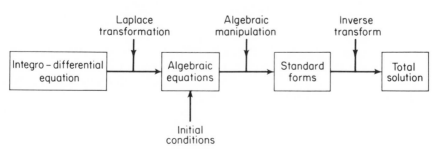

FIG. 1-17. Flow diagram comparing classical and Laplace transformation methods in solving differential equations.

systems, the method of Laplace transform has a definite advantage over the classical method. The philosophy behind the Laplace transform and its comparison with the classical method are illustrated by the flow diagram shown in Fig. 1-17.

In order to understand the properties and definitions of the Laplace transformation, it is necessary to examine first the properties of the Fourier series and the Fourier integral.

The Fourier Series and the Fourier Integral

Let $f_T(t)$ be a single-valued periodic function of t with period T. Then $f_T(t)$ may be expanded into a Fourier series of the following form [if $f_T(t)$ satisfies certain additional mathematical conditions]:

$$f_T(t) = \frac{a_0}{T} + \frac{2}{T} \sum_{n=1}^{\infty} (a_n \cos \omega_n t + b_n \sin \omega_n t) \qquad (1\text{-}8)$$

where

$$\omega_n = \frac{2\pi n}{T} = \text{angular frequency} \qquad (1\text{-}9)$$

and the coefficients a_0, a_n, and b_n are defined by

$$a_n = \int_{-T/2}^{T/2} f_T(t) \cos \omega_n t \, dt \quad n = 0, 1, 2, 3, \ldots \qquad (1\text{-}10)$$

$$b_n = \int_{-T/2}^{T/2} f_T(t) \sin \omega_n t \, dt \quad n = 1, 2, 3, \ldots \qquad (1\text{-}11)$$

Since a_n and b_n are functions of frequency but not of time, Eq. (1-8) expresses $f_T(t)$ in terms of all its frequency components. The amplitude of a frequency component is given by $\sqrt{a_n^2 + b_n^2}$ and the phase is measured by $\tan^{-1}(-b_n/a_n)$. Specification of the amplitude and phase of all frequency components is thus entirely equivalent to a description of the time function $f_T(t)$.

A more compact expression may be obtained for the Fourier series in the complex form. Equation (1-8) can be written

$$f_T(t) = \frac{a_0}{T} + \frac{2}{T} \sum_{n=1}^{\infty} \left[\frac{a_n}{2}(e^{j\omega_n t} + e^{-j\omega_n t}) - j\frac{b_n}{2}(e^{j\omega_n t} - e^{-j\omega_n t}) \right] \qquad (1\text{-}12)$$

or

$$f_T(t) = \frac{a_0}{T} + \frac{1}{T} \sum_{n=1}^{\infty} [(a_n - jb_n)e^{j\omega_n t} + (a_n + jb_n)e^{-j\omega_n t}] \qquad (1\text{-}13)$$

Using Eqs. (1-10) and (1-11), we obtain

$$a_n - jb_n = \int_{-T/2}^{T/2} f_T(t)e^{-j\omega_n t} \qquad (1\text{-}14)$$

and

$$a_n + jb_n = \int_{-T/2}^{T/2} f_T(t)e^{j\omega_n t} \tag{1-15}$$

Since ω_n is given by Eq. (1–9), we see that Eqs. (1–14) and (1–15) differ by a sign in n; i.e.,

$$(a_n - jb_n) = [(a_n + jb_n)]_{n=-n} \tag{1-16}$$

Equation (1–13) can be written as

$$f_T(t) = \frac{1}{T} \sum_{n=-\infty}^{\infty} \left\{ \int_{-T/2}^{T/2} f_T(t)e^{-j\omega_n t}\, dt \right\} e^{j\omega_n t} \tag{1-17}$$

or

$$f_T(t) = \frac{1}{T} \sum_{n=-\infty}^{\infty} C_n e^{j\omega_n t} \tag{1-18}$$

where

$$C_n = \int_{-T/2}^{T/2} f_T(t)e^{-j\omega_n t} dt \tag{1-19}$$

Equation (1–18) gives the complex Fourier series of $f_T(t)$, and C_n is the complex Fourier coefficient. As an example of the utility of the complex

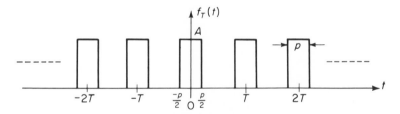

FIG. 1-18. A periodic pulse train.

Fourier series, let us consider the train of periodic pulses shown in Fig. 1-18. The complex Fourier coefficient of the periodic wave is

$$C_n = \int_{-p/2}^{p/2} A\, e^{-j\omega_n t}\, dt = -\frac{A}{j\omega_n} e^{-j\omega_n t} \Big|_{-p/2}^{p/2} = \frac{2A}{\omega_n} \sin \frac{\omega_n p}{2} \tag{1-20}$$

Equation (1–20) can also be written as

$$C_n = Ap \left(\frac{\sin \dfrac{\omega_n p}{2}}{\dfrac{\omega_n p}{2}} \right) \tag{1-21}$$

The plot of C_n for values of frequency ranging from $-\infty$ to $+\infty$ is shown in Fig. 1-19. The envelope of C_n follows the well-known function $\sin \theta/\theta$. The spacing between successive lines in the C_n plot is equal to

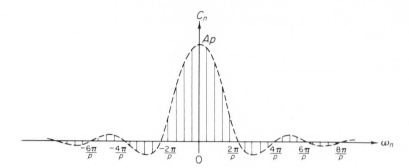

FIG. 1-19. The complex Fourier coefficient for the pulse train of Fig. 1-18.

$$\Delta\omega_n = \frac{2\pi}{T} \tag{1-22}$$

Therefore, the number of lines between the interval $n\pi$ and $(n + 1)\pi$ depends on the period T; more lines for higher T. As T approaches infinity, C_n approaches a continuous function, described by the envelope shown in Fig. 1-19.

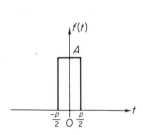

FIG. 1-20. A pulse signal.

Many functions of interest in our work are not periodic and, therefore, cannot be represented by a Fourier series. However, we shall use the Fourier integral to represent this type of function. Let us consider the non-periodic function $f(t)$ shown in Fig. 1-20. We can certainly construct a periodic function $f_T(t)$, using $f(t)$ as the fundamental function during a period. The Fourier series of the periodic function $f_T(t)$ can be written, and, as the period of $f_T(t)$ approaches infinity, $f_T(t)$ approaches $f(t)$. Therefore the Fourier series of $f_T(t)$ as T approaches infinity is a sufficient representation of $f(t)$. Using Eq. (1-22), we can write Eq. (1-18) as

$$f_T(t) = \frac{1}{2\pi} \sum_{n=-\infty}^{\infty} C_n e^{j\omega_n t} \Delta\omega_n \tag{1-23}$$

If we take the limit as T approaches infinity, then $\omega_n \to 0$, and the discrete lines in the C_n spectrum merge into a continuous frequency spectrum, as shown in Fig. 1-21. We have

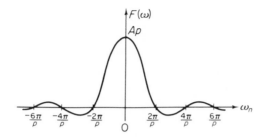

FIG. 1-21. The Fourier transformation of the pulse signal of Fig. 1-20.

$$\lim_{\substack{T \to \infty \\ \omega_n \to 0}} f_T(t) = \lim_{\substack{T \to \infty \\ \omega_n \to 0}} \frac{1}{2\pi} \sum_{n=-\infty}^{\infty} C_n e^{j\omega_n t} \, \Delta\omega_n$$

$$= \frac{1}{2\pi} \int_{-\infty}^{\infty} C_n e^{j\omega t} \, d\omega \qquad (1\text{-}24)$$

Also, as $T \to \infty$,

$$C_n = \int_{-\infty}^{\infty} f(t) e^{-j\omega t} \, dt = F(\omega) \qquad (1\text{-}25)$$

which is defined as the *Fourier transform* of the nonperiodic function $f(t)$ and is designated by $F(\omega)$. The condition for the existence of the Fourier transform of the time function $f(t)$ is that $f(t)$ satisfies the following condition:

$$\int_{-\infty}^{\infty} |f(t)| \, dt < \infty \qquad (1\text{-}26)$$

Therefore, before the Fourier integral (transform) of a time function is taken, it is essential to find out if the function satisfies the absolute convergence condition stated in Eq. (1–26).

As an example, let us consider the time function

$$f(t) = e^{at} \quad \text{for } t > 0$$

$$= 0 \quad \text{for } t < 0 \qquad (1\text{-}27)$$

where a is considered to be a constant. The Fourier transform of $f(t)$ is obtained by use of Eq. (1–25). Thus,

$$F(\omega) = \int_{-\infty}^{\infty} e^{at} e^{-j\omega t} \, dt = \frac{e^{at} e^{-j\omega t}}{a - j\omega} \bigg|_0^{\infty} \qquad (1\text{-}28)$$

If a is a negative number, substitution of the upper limit in the last equation will result in zero; therefore, Eq. (1–28) becomes

$$F(\omega) = \frac{-1}{a - j\omega} \qquad a < 0 \qquad (1\text{-}29)$$

However, if $a > 0$, $|F(\omega)|$ becomes infinite at the upper limit and the Fourier transform does not exist. We could have obtained the same conclusion from Eq. (1–26) since for $a > 0$, $f(t)$ diverges as $t \to \infty$.

Although the Fourier transform is applicable to a large variety of functions, and is widely used as a mathematical tool in engineering science, because of the restriction stated by Eq. (1–26), many time functions which are of interest in engineering work cannot be handled by the Fourier transform method. For instance, the Fourier transform of a unit-step function is not defined; other functions, such as t, t^2, etc., are also not Fourier transformable. In order to handle functions of this type, we modify our transformation by introducing a convergence factor $e^{-\sigma t}$, where σ is a real number large enough to insure absolute convergence. Therefore,

$$F(c, \omega) = \int_0^\infty f(t)\, e^{-\sigma t}\, e^{-j\omega t}\, dt \qquad (1\text{–}30)$$

The lower limit of the integral is forced to be taken as zero rather than $-\infty$, since for $\sigma > 0$, the convergence factor $e^{-\sigma t}$ will diverge when $t \to -\infty$. The transformation in Eq. (1–30) now ignores all information contained in $f(t)$ prior to $t = 0$. This does not put any serious limitation upon the new transformation, since in the usual transient studies, time reference is normally chosen at the instant $t = 0$. If we let $s = \sigma + j\omega$, Eq. (1–30) becomes

$$F(s) = \int_0^\infty f(t)e^{-st}\, dt \qquad (1\text{–}31)$$

$F(s)$ is called the Laplace transform of $f(t)$, and is denoted by

$$F(s) = \mathscr{L}[f(t)] \qquad (1\text{–}32)$$

Also, the condition for the Laplace transform to exist is changed from that of Eq. (1–26) to

$$\int_{-\infty}^\infty |f(t)e^{-\sigma t}|\, dt < \infty \qquad (1\text{–}33)$$

for some finite σ.

Example 1-1. If $f(t)$ is a unit-step function (defined for $t > 0$),

$$f(t) = u(t) \qquad (1\text{–}34)$$

The Laplace transform of $f(t)$ is

$$F(s) = \mathscr{L}[f(t)] = \int_0^\infty u(t)e^{-st}\, dt$$

$$= -\frac{1}{s}[e^{-st}]_0^\infty = \frac{1}{s} \qquad (1\text{–}35)$$

if $Re(s) = \sigma > 0$. Therefore, the Laplace transform of a step function is defined only in the right half of the s-plane.

Example 1-2. If

$$f(t) = e^{-at} \quad \text{for} \qquad\qquad t > 0 \quad (1\text{–}36)$$

$$F(s) = \int_0^\infty e^{-at} e^{-st} dt = \left[\frac{e^{-(s+a)t}}{s+a} \right]_0^\infty = \frac{1}{s+a} \tag{1-37}$$

if $Re(s) > -a$. Therefore, the Laplace transform of $f(t)$ exists in the region to the right of the line $Re(s) = -a$ in the s-plane.

Inverse Laplace Transformation

A function $f(t)$ can be obtained from its Laplace transform by the relation

$$f(t) = \mathscr{L}^{-1}[F(s)] = \frac{1}{2\pi} \int_{c-j\infty}^{c+j\infty} F(s)e^{st} ds \tag{1-38}$$

where c is a real constant greater than the real part of any singularity of $F(s)$. Although the evaluation of the integral in Eq. (1-38) is usually difficult, the inverse transformations are usually performed by referring to the Laplace transform tables.

Important Theorems of the Laplace Transformation

Some of the important theorems of the Laplace transformation are given in the following:

(1) *The Laplace transform of the product of a constant A and a time function $f(t)$ is the constant A multiplied by the Laplace transform of $f(t)$;* that is,

$$\mathscr{L}[Af(t)] = AF(s) \tag{1-39}$$

where $F(s)$ is the Laplace transform of $f(t)$.

(2) *The Laplace transform of the sum (or difference) of two time functions is the sum (or difference) of the Laplace transforms of the time functions;* that is,

$$\mathscr{L}[f_1(t) \pm f_2(t)] = F_1(s) \pm F_2(s) \tag{1-40}$$

where $F_1(s)$ and $F_2(s)$ are the Laplace transforms of $f_1(t)$ and $f_2(t)$, respectively.

(3) *The Laplace transform of the first derivative of a time function $f(t)$ is s times the Laplace transform of $f(t)$ minus the limit of $f(t)$ as $t \to 0^+$;* that is,

$$\mathscr{L}\left[\frac{df(t)}{dt}\right] = sF(s) - \lim_{t \to 0+} f(t) = sF(s) - f(0^+) \tag{1-41}$$

In general, we have

$$\mathscr{L}\left[\frac{d^n f(t)}{dt^n}\right] = s^n F(s) - \lim_{t \to 0^+}\left[s^{n-1} f(t) + s^{n-2}\frac{df(t)}{dt} + \cdots + \frac{d^{n-1} f(t)}{dt^{n-1}} \right]$$

$$= s^n F(s) - s^{n-1} f(0^+) - s^{n-2} f'(0^+) - \cdots - f^{(n-1)}(0^+) \tag{1-42}$$

(4) *The Transform of Integral. The Laplace transform of the first integral of a function $f(t)$ with respect to time is the Laplace transform of $f(t)$ divided by s;* that is,

$$\mathscr{L}\left[\int_0^t f(\tau)\,d\tau\right] = \frac{F(s)}{s} \tag{1-43}$$

In general, for nth order integration,

$$\mathscr{L}\left[\int_0^{t_1}\int_0^{t_2}\cdots\int_0^{t_n} f(\tau)\,d\tau\,dt_1\cdots dt_{n-1}\right] = \frac{F(s)}{s^n} \tag{1-44}$$

(5) *Shifting Theorem.* The Laplace transform of a time function $f(t)$ delayed by time T is equal to the Laplace transform of $f(t)$ multiplied by e^{-sT}; that is,

$$\mathscr{L}[f(t-T)\cdot u(t-T)] = e^{-sT}F(s) \tag{1-45}$$

where $u(t)$ is a unit-step function.

(6) *Initial Value Theorem.* If the Laplace transform of $f(t)$ is $F(s)$, and $f(t)$ is Laplace transformable, then

$$\lim_{t\to 0} f(t) = \lim_{s\to\infty} sF(s) \tag{1-46}$$

if the time limit exists.

(7) *Final Value Theorem.* If the Laplace transform of $f(t)$ is $F(s)$, and if $sF(s)$ is analytic on the imaginary axis and in the right half of the s-plane, then

$$\lim_{t\to\infty} f(t) = \lim_{s\to 0} sF(s) \tag{1-47}$$

The final value theorem is a very useful relation in the analysis and design of feedback control systems, since it gives the final value of a time function by determining the behavior of its Laplace transform as s tends to zero. However, the final value theorem is not valid if the denominator of $sF(s)$ contains any zero whose real part is zero or positive, which is equivalent to the analytic requirement of $sF(s)$ given above.

Example 1-3. Let

$$F(s) = \frac{5}{s(s^2 + s + 2)} \tag{1-48}$$

Since $sF(s)$ is analytic on the imaginary axis and in the right half of the s-plane, the final value theorem may be applied.

$$\lim_{t\to\infty} f(t) = \lim_{s\to 0} sF(s) = \lim_{s\to 0} \frac{5}{(s^2 + s + 2)} = \frac{5}{2} \tag{1-49}$$

Example 1-4. Let

$$F(s) = \frac{\omega}{s^2 + \omega^2} \tag{1-50}$$

The function $sF(s)$ has two poles on the imaginary axis; thus, although the final value theorem gives a final value of zero for $f(t)$, the result is incorrect, because the theorem cannot be applied in this case.

Application of Laplace Transforms to Solving Differential Equations

With the aid of the theorems concerning Laplace transforms given in the last section and a table of transforms, linear differential equations can now be solved by the Laplace transform method.

Example 1-5. Consider the equation

$$\frac{d^2x}{dt^2} + 3\frac{dx}{dt} + 2x = 5 \qquad (1\text{-}51)$$

with initial conditions: $x'(0^+) = 2$, $x(0^+) = -1$. Taking the Laplace transform of both sides of Eq. (1-51), we have

$$s^2 X(s) - sx(0^+) - x'(0^+) + 3sX(s) - 3x(0^+) + 2X(s) = \frac{5}{s} \quad (1\text{-}52)$$

Substituting the values of $x'(0^+)$ and $x(0^+)$ into Eq. (1-52) and solving for $X(s)$, we have

$$X(s) = \frac{-s^2 - s + 5}{s(s^2 + 3s + 2)} = \frac{-s^2 - s + 5}{s(s + 1)(s + 2)} \qquad (1\text{-}53)$$

Equation (1-53) is expanded by partial fraction expansion.

$$X(s) = \frac{5}{2s} - \frac{5}{s + 1} + \frac{3}{2(s + 2)} \qquad (1\text{-}54)$$

The inverse transform of Eq. (1-54) is

$$x(t) = \frac{5}{2} - 5e^{-t} + \frac{3}{2}e^{-2t} \qquad (t > 0) \qquad (1\text{-}55)$$

The first term of Eq. (1-55) is the steady-state solution, and the last two terms are the transient solution. Unlike the classical method, the Laplace transform gives the total solution of a differential equation in one operation. In the last example, if only the magnitude of the steady-state solution is of interest, the final value theorem may be applied; thus,

$$\lim_{t\to\infty} x(t) = \lim_{s\to 0} sX(s) = \lim_{s\to 0}\frac{-s^2 - s + 5}{(s^2 + 3s + 2)} = \frac{5}{2} \qquad (1\text{-}56)$$

Example 1-6. Consider the equation

$$\frac{d^3x}{dt^3} + 5\frac{d^2x}{dt^2} + 8\frac{dx}{dt} = 0 \qquad (1\text{-}57)$$

The initial conditions are as follows: at $t = 0$, $x(0^+) = 5$, but the second derivative is zero. Taking the Laplace transform of both sides of Eq. (1-57), we have

$$s^3 X(s) - s^2 x(0^+) - sx'(0^+) - x''(0^+) + 5s^2 X(s) - 5sx(0^+) - 5x'(0^+)$$
$$+ 8sX(s) - 8x(0^+) = 0 \qquad (1\text{-}58)$$

Substituting the initial conditions yields

$$(s^3 + 5s^2 + 8s)X(s) = (s^2 + 5s + 8)5 \tag{1-59}$$

or

$$X(s) = 5/s \tag{1-60}$$

The inverse transform of $X(s)$ is simply

$$x(t) = x(0^+) = 5 \qquad\qquad (t \geqslant 0) \tag{1-61}$$

At first glance, it is hard to believe that the solution is correct since the system essentially stays at its initial condition. However, from the physical point of view, the differential equation represents a system with no element for potential energy storage (no spring or capacitance); thus, with no external disturbance, the system can only stay in its initial state $x(0^+)$.

1.6 Partial Fraction Expansions

Example 1–5 indicates that, in applying the inverse Laplace transformation, it is usually necessary to expand the algebraic transfer function $X(s)$ into simple terms of standard forms whose inverse transforms may be found in the Laplace transform table. The usual form of the Laplace transform solution of a differential equation is a quotient of polynomials in s; that is,

$$X(s) = \frac{p(s)}{q(s)} \tag{1-62}$$

The denominator of the polynomial, $q(s)$, may be written as

$$\begin{aligned} q(s) &= a_0 s^n + a_1 s^{n-1} + \cdots + a_{n-1}s + a_n \\ &= a_0(s + s_1)(s + s_2) \cdots (s + s_n) \end{aligned} \tag{1-63}$$

If the coefficients $a_0, a_1, a_2, \ldots, a_n$ are real numbers, the zeros of $q(s)$ must be real or in complex conjugate pairs; in simple or multiple order.

The methods of partial fraction expansion will now. be given for (1) simple zeros, (2) multiple zeros, (3) complex zeros of $q(s)$.

Partial Fraction Expansion When All the Zeros of $q(s)$ Are Simple

If all the zeros of $q(s)$ are simple, Eq. (1–62) may be written as

$$\begin{aligned} X(s) = \frac{p(s)}{q(s)} &= \frac{p(s)}{(s + s_1)(s + s_2)(s + s_3) \cdots (s + s_n)} \\ &= \frac{K_{s1}}{(s + s_1)} + \frac{K_{s2}}{(s + s_2)} + \cdots + \frac{K_{sn}}{(s + s_n)} \end{aligned} \tag{1-64}$$

Any of the coefficients $K_{s1}, K_{s2}, \ldots K_{sn}$ can be evaluated by multiplying $X(s)$ in Eq. (1–64) by the corresponding denominator factor and setting s equal to the zero. Thus, to find the coefficient K_{s1}, for instance,

$$K_{s1} = \left[(s + s_1)\frac{p(s)}{q(s)} \right]_{s=-s_1} = \frac{p(-s_1)}{(s_2 - s_1)(s_3 - s_1) \cdots (s_n - s_1)} \qquad (1\text{–}65)$$

As an example, consider the function

$$X(s) = \frac{5s + 3}{(s + 1)(s + 2)(s + 3)} \qquad (1\text{–}66)$$

which may be written in the partial-fraction form

$$X(s) = \frac{K_{-1}}{s + 1} + \frac{K_{-2}}{s + 2} + \frac{K_{-3}}{s + 3} \qquad (1\text{–}67)$$

Then,

$$K_{-1} = [(s + 1)X(s)]_{s=-1} = \frac{5(-1) + 3}{(2 - 1)(3 - 1)} = -1 \qquad (1\text{–}68)$$

$$K_{-2} = [(s + 2)X(s)]_{s=-2} = \frac{5(-2) + 3}{(1 - 2)(3 - 2)} = 7 \qquad (1\text{–}69)$$

$$K_{-3} = [(s + 3)X(s)]_{s=-3} = \frac{5(-3) + 3}{(1 - 3)(2 - 3)} = -6 \qquad (1\text{–}70)$$

Hence,

$$X(s) = \frac{-1}{s + 1} + \frac{7}{s + 2} + \frac{6}{s + 3} \qquad (1\text{–}71)$$

Partial Fraction Expansion When Some Zeros of q(s) Are of Multiple Order

If r of the n zeros of $q(s)$ are alike, the function $X(s)$ becomes

$$X(s) = \frac{p(s)}{q(s)} = \frac{p(s)}{(s + s_1)(s + s_2) \cdots (s + s_i)^r(s + s_n)} \qquad (1\text{–}72)$$

which is expanded as

$$X(s) = \frac{K_{s1}}{s + s_1} + \frac{K_{s2}}{s + s_2} + \cdots + \frac{K_{sn}}{s + s_n}$$

$$\longmapsto \quad (n-r) \quad \text{terms} \quad \text{of} \quad \text{simple} \quad \text{zeros} \quad \longmapsto$$

$$+ \frac{A_1}{s + s_i} + \frac{A_2}{(s + s_i)^2} + \cdots + \frac{A_r}{(s + s_i)^r} \qquad (1\text{–}73)$$

$$\longmapsto \quad r \quad \text{terms} \quad \text{of} \quad \text{repeated} \quad \text{zeros} \quad \longmapsto$$

The $n - r$ coefficients, corresponding to the simple zeros $K_{s1}, K_{s2}, \ldots, K_{sn}$, may be evaluated by the method described by Eq. (1–65).

The following equations may be used for the evaluation of the coefficients of repeated zeros.

$$A_r = \left[(s + s_i)^r \frac{p(s)}{q(s)} \right]_{s=-s_i} \qquad (1\text{–}74)$$

$$A_{r-1} = \frac{d}{ds} \left[(s + s_i)^r \frac{p(s)}{q(s)} \right]_{s=-s_i} \qquad (1\text{–}75)$$

$$A_{r-2} = \frac{1}{2!}\frac{d^2}{ds^2}\left[(s + s_i)^r\frac{p(s)}{q(s)}\right]_{s = -s_i} \tag{1-76}$$

$$A_1 = \frac{1}{(r - 1)!}\frac{d^{r-1}}{ds^{r-1}}\left[(s + s_i)^r\frac{p(s)}{q(s)}\right]_{s = -s_i} \tag{1-77}$$

Example 1-7. Let

$$X(s) = \frac{p(s)}{q(s)} = \frac{1}{s(s + 1)^3(s + 2)} \tag{1-78}$$

Then,

$$X(s) = \frac{K_0}{s} + \frac{K_{-2}}{s + 2} + \frac{A_1}{s + 1} + \frac{A_2}{(s + 1)^2} + \frac{A_3}{(s + 1)^3} \tag{1-79}$$

From Eq. (1-65),

$$K_0 = [sX(s)]_{s=0} = \tfrac{1}{2} \tag{1-80}$$

$$K_{-2} = [(s + 2)X(s)]_{s=-2} = \tfrac{1}{2} \tag{1-81}$$

The coefficients of the repeated zeros at $s = -1$ are

$$A_3 = [(s + 1)^3 X(s)]_{s=-1} = -1 \tag{1-82}$$

$$A_2 = \frac{d}{ds}[(s + 1)^3 X(s)]_{s=-1} = \frac{d}{ds}\left[\frac{1}{s(s + 2)}\right]_{s=-1}$$

$$= \left[\frac{-(2s + 2)}{s^2(s + 2)^2}\right]_{s=-1} = 0 \tag{1-83}$$

$$A_1 = \frac{1}{2!}\frac{d^2}{ds^2}[(s + 1)^3 X(s)]_{s=-1} = \frac{1}{2}\frac{d}{ds}\left[\frac{-2(s + 1)}{s^2(s + 2)^2}\right]_{s=-1}$$

$$= \left[-\frac{1}{s^2(s + 2)^2} + \frac{2(s + 1)}{s^2(s + 2)^3} + \frac{2(s + 1)}{s^3(s + 2)^2}\right]_{s=-1} = -1 \tag{1-84}$$

The complete expansion is

$$X(s) = \frac{1}{2s} + \frac{1}{2(s + 2)} - \frac{1}{s + 1} - \frac{1}{(s + 1)^3} \tag{1-85}$$

Partial Fraction Expansion of Complex Conjugate Zeros

Suppose that $q(s)$ contains a pair of complex zeros:

$$s = -\alpha + j\omega \quad \text{and} \quad s = -\alpha - j\omega$$

Since these zeros are simple, the corresponding coefficients are

$$K_{-\alpha+j\omega} = (s + \alpha - j\omega)\frac{p(s)}{q(s)}\bigg|_{s=-\alpha+j\omega} \tag{1-86}$$

$$K_{-\alpha-j\omega} = (s + \alpha + j\omega)\frac{p(s)}{q(s)}\bigg|_{s=-\alpha-j\omega} \tag{1-87}$$

For example, consider the function

$$X(s) = \frac{\omega_n^2}{s(s^2 + 2\delta\omega_n s + \omega_n^2)} = \frac{K_0}{s} + \frac{K_{-\alpha+j\omega}}{(s+\alpha-j\omega)} + \frac{K_{-\alpha-j\omega}}{(s+\alpha+j\omega)}$$

(1-88)

where $\alpha = \delta\omega_n$ and $\omega = \omega_n\sqrt{1-\delta^2}$.

Then

$$K_0 = [sX(s)]_{s=0} = 1$$

(1-89)

$$K_{-\alpha-j\omega} = [(s + \alpha - j\omega)X(s)]_{s=-\alpha+j\omega}$$

$$= \frac{\omega_n^2}{2j\omega(-\alpha+j\omega)} = \frac{\omega_n}{2\omega}e^{-j(\theta+\pi/2)}$$

(1-90)

where $\theta = \tan^{-1}(-\omega/\alpha)$.

(1-91)

Also,

$$K_{-\alpha-j\omega} = [(s + \alpha + j\omega)X(s)]_{s=-\alpha-j\omega}$$

$$= \frac{\omega_n^2}{-2j\omega(-\alpha-j\omega)} = \frac{\omega_n}{2\omega}e^{j(\theta+\pi/2)}$$

(1-92)

The complete expansion is

$$X(s) = \frac{1}{s} + \frac{\omega_n}{2\omega}\left[\frac{e^{-j(\theta+\pi/2)}}{(s+\alpha-j\omega)} + \frac{e^{j(\theta+\pi/2)}}{(s+\alpha+j\omega)}\right]$$

(1-93)

The inverse transform of $X(s)$ is

$$x(t) = 1 + \frac{\omega_n}{2\omega}[e^{-j(\theta+\pi/2)}e^{(-\alpha+j\omega)t} + e^{j(\theta+\pi/2)}e^{(-\alpha-j\omega)t}]$$

$$= 1 + \frac{\omega_n}{2\omega}e^{-\alpha t}[e^{j[(\omega t-\theta)-\pi/2]} + e^{-j[(\omega t-\theta)-\pi/2]}]$$

$$= 1 + \frac{\omega_n}{\omega}e^{-\alpha t}\sin(\omega t - \theta)$$

(1-94)

or

$$x(t) = 1 + \frac{1}{\sqrt{1-\delta^2}}e^{-\delta\omega_n t}\sin(\omega_n\sqrt{1-\delta^2}t - \theta)$$

(1-95)

1.7 The z-Transform[3]

The Laplace transform method is a basic tool for the analysis and design of linear control systems with continuous data. Similarly, the z-transform method is convenient for the study of control systems with discrete data.

Definition of the z-Transform

The Laplace transform of the output signal of an ideal sampler may be obtained by taking the Laplace transform of Eq. (1-1). Therefore,

$$E^*(s) = \sum_{n=0}^{\infty} e(nT)e^{-nTs}$$

(1-96)

It is apparent that the exponential term e^{-nTs} in the expression of Eq. (1–96) will generally introduce nonalgebraic functions in discrete-data systems. Therefore, it is convenient to introduce a change in variable by setting

$$z = e^{Ts} \tag{1–97}$$

where s is the Laplace transform variable and T is the sampling period. Equation (1–96) is now written as

$$E^*\left(s = \frac{1}{T}\ln z\right) = E(z) = \sum_{n=0}^{\infty} e(nT)z^{-n} \tag{1–98}$$

or

$$E(z) = z\text{-transform of } e(t) = \mathscr{Z}[e(t)]$$
$$= [\text{Laplace transform of } e^*(t)]_{s=1/T \ln z} \tag{1–99}$$

Evidently, the z-transform of the time function $e(t)$ is the same as the Laplace transform of $e^*(t)$, though disguised by the change in variable from s to z. In general, any continuous function which possesses a Laplace transform also has a z-transform.

Example 1-8. Given

$$e(t) = e^{-at}$$

then

$$e(nT) = e^{-anT}$$

From Eq. (1–96),

$$E^*(s) = \sum_{n=0}^{\infty} e^{-anT}e^{-nTs} = \frac{1}{1 - e^{-(s+a)T}} \tag{1–100}$$

The z-transform of $e(t)$ is

$$E(z) = [E^*(s)]_{z=e^{Ts}} = \frac{1}{1 - e^{-aT}z^{-1}} = \frac{z}{z - e^{-aT}} \tag{1–101}$$

Example 1-9. Find the z-transform of $e(t) = \sin \omega t$.
From Eq. (1–98),

$$E(z) = \sum_{n=0}^{\infty} \sin \omega nT\, z^{-n} = \sum_{n=0}^{\infty} \frac{e^{jn\omega T} - e^{-jn\omega T}}{2j} z^{-n}$$

$$= \frac{1}{2j}\left(\frac{1}{1 - e^{j\omega T}z^{-1}} - \frac{1}{1 - e^{-j\omega T}z^{-1}}\right)$$

$$= \frac{z \sin \omega T}{z^{-2} - 2z^{-1}\cos \omega T + 1} \tag{1–102}$$

Hence,

$$E(z) = \frac{z \sin \omega T}{z^2 - 2z \cos \omega T + 1} \tag{1–103}$$

The z-transforms of some common time functions are given in Table 1-1.

Table 1-1

TABLE OF z-TRANSFORMS

Laplace transform	Time function	z-Transform
1	Unit impulse $\delta(t)$	1
$\dfrac{1}{s}$	Unit step $u(t)$	$\dfrac{z}{z-1}$
$\dfrac{1}{1-e^{-Ts}}$	$\delta_T(t) = \sum\limits_{n=0}^{\infty} \delta(t-nT)$	$\dfrac{z}{z-1}$
$\dfrac{1}{s^2}$	t	$\dfrac{Tz}{(z-1)^2}$
$\dfrac{1}{s^3}$	$\dfrac{t^2}{2}$	$\dfrac{T^2 z(z+1)}{2(z-1)^3}$
$\dfrac{1}{s^{n+1}}$	$\dfrac{t^2}{n!}$	$\lim\limits_{a\to 0} \dfrac{(-1)^n}{n!} \dfrac{\partial^n}{\partial a^n}\left(\dfrac{z}{z-e^{-aT}}\right)$
$\dfrac{1}{s+a}$	e^{-at}	$\dfrac{z}{z-e^{-aT}}$
$\dfrac{1}{(s+a)^2}$	te^{-at}	$\dfrac{Tze^{-aT}}{(z-e^{-aT})^2}$
$\dfrac{a}{s(s+a)}$	$1-e^{-at}$	$\dfrac{(1-e^{-aT})z}{(z-1)(z-e^{-aT})}$
$\dfrac{\omega}{s^2+\omega^2}$	$\sin \omega t$	$\dfrac{z\sin\omega T}{z^2 - 2z\cos\omega T + 1}$
$\dfrac{\omega}{(s+a)^2+\omega^2}$	$e^{-at}\sin\omega t$	$\dfrac{ze^{-aT}\sin\omega T}{z^2 e^{2aT} - 2ze^{aT}\cos\omega T + 1}$
$\dfrac{s}{s^2+\omega^2}$	$\cos\omega t$	$\dfrac{z(z-\cos\omega T)}{z^2 - 2z\cos\omega T + 1}$
$\dfrac{s+a}{(s+a)^2+\omega^2}$	$e^{-at}\cos\omega t$	$\dfrac{z^2 - ze^{-aT}\cos\omega T}{z^2 - 2ze^{-aT}\cos\omega T + e^{-2aT}}$

The Inverse z-Transformation

Just as in the Laplace transform method, it is often desirable to obtain the time-domain response from the z-transform expression. The inverse z-transformation can be effected by one of the following methods:

(1) The z-transform is manipulated into a partial-fraction expression and the z-transform table is used to find the corresponding time function.

(2) The z-transform $E(z)$ is expanded into a power series in powers of z^{-1}. The coefficient of z^{-n} corresponds to the value of the time function $e(t)$ at the nth sampling instant. The above statement is apparent in view of Eq. (1–98).

(3) The time function $e(t)$ may be obtained from $E(z)$ by the real inversion integral. The values of $e(t)$ at the sampling instants $t = nT$ can be obtained by the following formula:

$$e(nT) = \frac{1}{2\pi j} \oint_\Gamma E(z) z^{n-1}\, dz \qquad (1\text{–}104)$$

where Γ is a circle of radius $z = e^{cT}$ centered at the origin in the z-plane, and c is of such a value that all the poles of $E(z)$ are enclosed by the circle.

It must be emphasized here that only the values of $e(t)$ at the sampling instants can be obtained from $E(z)$, since $E(z)$ does not contain any information on $e(t)$ between sampling instants.

Example 1-10. Given the z-transform

$$E(z) = \frac{(1 - e^{-aT})z}{(z - 1)(z - e^{-aT})} \tag{1–105}$$

find the inverse z-transform $e^*(t)$.

(1) *Partial-Fraction Expansion Method*

Equation (1–105) may be written as

$$E(z) = \frac{z}{z - 1} - \frac{z}{z - e^{-aT}} \tag{1–106}$$

From the z-transform table (Table 1-1), the corresponding time function at the sampling instants is

$$e(nT) = 1 - e^{-anT} \tag{1–107}*$$

Hence

$$e^*(t) = \sum_{n=0}^{\infty} e(nT)\delta(t - nT)$$

$$= \sum_{n=0}^{\infty} (1 - e^{-anT})\delta(t - nT) \tag{1–108}$$

(2) *Power Series Expansion*

Expanding $E(z)$ into a power series in z^{-1} by long division, we have

$$E(z) = (1 - e^{-aT})z^{-1} + (1 - e^{-2aT})z^{-2} + (1 - e^{-3aT})z^{-3} + \cdots$$
$$+ (1 - e^{-naT})z^{-n} + \cdots \tag{1–109}$$

Correspondingly,

$$e^*(t) = 0\delta(t) + (1 - e^{-aT})\delta(t - T)$$
$$+ (1 - e^{-2aT})\delta(t - 2T) + \cdots + (1 - e^{-naT})\delta(t - nT) + \cdots$$
$$= \sum_{n=0}^{\infty} (1 - e^{-anT})\delta(t - nT) \tag{1–110}$$

(3) *Real Inversion Integral Method*

From Eq. (1–104) we have

---

*It is seen that the inverse z-transform of $z/(z - 1)$ is not unique; it could be either a unit step function or a unit impulse train. In other words, the definition of the z-transform implies that the sampling of an impulse still results in an impulse of the same strength. The sampler output will still be a unit impulse train, regardless of whether the input to the sampler is a unit step function or a unit impulse train of period T.

$$e(nT) = \frac{1}{2\pi j} \oint_\Gamma E(z)z^{n-1}\, dz = \sum \text{Residues of } E(z)z^{n-1} \text{ at poles of } E(z)$$

$$= 1 - e^{-aT}e^{-anT}e^{aT} = 1 - e^{-anT} \qquad (1\text{–}111)$$

hence, the same result for $e^*(t)$ is obtained.

It is important to remember that the inverse of the z-transform is not unique. For any given $E(z)$, the inverse of $E(z)$ found by any of the above-mentioned methods is not unique, since $e^*(t)$ may represent any time function $e(t)$ having the same values at the sampling instants.

Some Important Theorems of the z-Transforms

(1) *Addition and Subtraction*

If $e_1(t)$ and $e_2(t)$ are Laplace transformable, and

$$E_1(z) = \mathscr{Z}[e_1(t)] \qquad E_2(z) = \mathscr{Z}[e_2(t)]$$

then

$$\mathscr{Z}[e_1(t) \pm e_2(t)] = E_1(z) \pm E_2(z) \qquad (1\text{–}112)$$

Proof: By definition,

$$\mathscr{Z}[e_1(t) \pm e_2(t)] = \sum_{n=0}^{\infty} [e_1(nT) \pm e_2(nT)]z^{-n}$$

$$= \sum_{n=0}^{\infty} e_1(nT)z^{-n} \pm \sum_{n=0}^{\infty} e_2(nT)z^{-n}$$

$$= E_1(z) \pm E_2(z) \qquad (1\text{–}113)$$

(2) *Multiplication by a Constant*

$$\mathscr{Z}[ae(t)] = aZ[e(t)] = aE(z) \qquad (1\text{–}114)$$

where a is a constant.

Proof: $\quad \mathscr{Z}[ae(t)] = \sum_{n=0}^{\infty} ae(nT)z^{-n} = a \sum_{n=0}^{\infty} e(nT)z^{-n} = aE(z) \qquad (1\text{–}115)$

(3) *Real Translation*

If $e(t)$ is Laplace transformable and has the z-transform $E(z)$, then

$$\mathscr{Z}[e(t - nT)] = z^{-n}E(z) \qquad (1\text{–}116)$$

and

$$\mathscr{Z}[e(t + nT)] = z^n \left[E(z) - \sum_{k=0}^{n-1} e(kT)z^{-k} \right] \qquad (1\text{–}117)$$

where n is a positive integer.

Proof: By definition,

$$\mathscr{Z}[e(t - nT)] = \sum_{k=0}^{\infty} e(kT - nT)z^{-k} = \sum_{k=0}^{\infty} e(kT - nT)z^{-(k-n)}z^{-n}$$

$$= z^{-n} \sum_{k=0}^{\infty} e(kT - nT)z^{-(k-n)} = z^{-n}E(z) \qquad (1\text{–}118)$$

To prove Eq. (1–117), we write

$$\mathscr{L}[e(t+nT)] = \sum_{k=0}^{\infty} e(kT+nT)z^{-k} = z^n \sum_{k=0}^{\infty} e(kT+nT)z^{-(k+n)} \quad (1\text{–}119)$$

Now letting $m = k + n$, Eq. (1–119) becomes

$$\mathscr{L}[e(t+nT)] = z^n \sum_{m=n}^{\infty} e(mT)z^{-m}$$

$$= z^n \left[\sum_{m=0}^{\infty} e(mT)z^{-m} - \sum_{m=0}^{n-1} e(mT)z^{-m} \right] \quad (1\text{–}120)$$

which is identical to Eq. (117).

(4) *Complex Translation*

$$\mathscr{L}[e^{\mp at}e(t)] = \mathscr{L}[E(s \pm a)] = E(ze^{\pm aT}) \quad (1\text{–}121)$$

Proof: By definition,

$$\mathscr{L}[e^{\mp aT}e(t)] = \sum_{n=0}^{\infty} e(nT)e^{\mp anT}z^{-n} \quad (1\text{–}122)$$

If we let $z_1 = ze^{\pm aT}$, Eq. (1–122) becomes

$$\mathscr{L}[e^{\mp at} e(t)] = \sum_{n=0}^{\infty} e(nT)z_1^{-n} = E(z_1) \quad (1\text{–}123)$$

Hence,

$$\mathscr{L}[e^{\mp at} e(t)] = E(z\,e^{\pm aT}) \quad (1\text{–}124)$$

Example 1-11. Apply the complex translation theorem to find the z-transform of te^{-at}.

If we let $e(t) = t$, then

$$E(z) = \mathscr{L}[t] = \frac{Tz}{(z-1)^2} \quad (1\text{–}125)$$

From Theorem 4,

$$\mathscr{L}[te^{-at}] = E(ze^{aT}) = \frac{T(ze^{aT})}{(ze^{aT}-1)^2}$$

$$= \frac{T(ze^{-aT})}{(z-e^{-aT})^2} \quad (1\text{–}126)$$

(5) *Initial Value Theorem*

If the function $e(t)$ has the z-transform $E(z)$, and $\lim E(z)$ exists, then

$$\lim_{t \to 0} e^*(t) = \lim_{z \to \infty} E(z) \quad (1\text{–}127)$$

(6) *Final Value Theorem*

If the function $e(t)$ has the z-transform $E(z)$, and $(1 - z^{-1})E(z)$ has no pole on or outside the unit circle centered at the origin in the z-plane, then

$$\lim_{t \to \infty} e^*(t) = \lim_{z \to 1} (1 - z^{-1})E(z) \quad (1\text{–}128)$$

Example 1-12. Given

$$E(z) = \frac{0.792z^2}{(z-1)(z^2 - 0.416z + 0.208)} \tag{1-129}$$

determine the final value of $e^*(t)$.
Since

$$(1 - z^{-1})E(z) = \frac{0.792z}{(z^2 - 0.416z + 0.208)} \tag{1-130}$$

which does not have a pole on or outside the unit circle in the z-plane, the final-value theorem can be applied. Hence,

$$\lim_{t \to \infty} e^*(t) = \lim_{n \to \infty} e(nT) = \lim_{z \to 1} \frac{0.792z}{z^2 - 0.416z + 0.208}$$

$$= \frac{0.792}{1 - 0.416 + 0.208} = 1 \tag{1-131}$$

This result can readily be checked by expanding $E(z)$ in powers of z^{-1}.

$$E(z) = \frac{0.792z^2}{(z-1)(z^2 - 0.416z + 0.208)} = 0.792z^{-1} + 1.12z^{-2}$$

$$+ 1.091z^{-3} + 1.01z^{-4} + 0.983z^{-5} + 0.989z^{-6} + 0.99z^{-7} + \cdots \tag{1-132}$$

The coefficients of this series converge rapidly to its final steady-state value of 1.

REFERENCES

1. J. T. Tou, "Analysis of Feedback Control Systems Containing Carrier Frequency Circuits," *Proc. National Electronics Conf.*, Vol. 11, pp. 1012–1016, 1955.

2. A. Sobszyk, *Carrier Frequency Servomechanisms*, 3 parts, J. Franklin Inst., 1948.

3. B. C. Kuo, *Analysis and Synthesis of Sampled-data Control Systems*, Prentice-Hall, Inc., Englewood Cliffs, N. J., 1963.

4. J. T. Tou, *Digital and Sampled-data Control Systems*, McGraw-Hill Book Company, New York, N.Y., 1959.

5. J. R. Ragazzini and G. F. Franklin, *Sampled-data Control Systems*, McGraw-Hill Book Company, New York, N.Y., 1958.

6. R. V. Churchill, *Introduction to Complex Variables and Applications*, McGraw-Hill Book Company, New York, N.Y., 1948.

7. C. R. Wylie, Jr., *Advanced Engineering Mathematics*, 2nd ed., McGraw-Hill Book Company, New York, N.Y., 1960.

8. R. Legros and A. V. J. Martin, *Transform Calculus for Electrical Engineers*, Prentice-Hall, Inc., Englewood Cliffs, N.J., 1961.

PROBLEMS

1-1. Find the poles and zeros of the following functions (include the ones at infinity):

(a) $G(s) = \dfrac{5(s + 1)}{s^2(s + 2)(s + 5)}$

(b) $G(s) = \dfrac{s^2(s + 1)}{(s + 2)(s^2 + 2s + 2)}$

(c) $G(s) = \dfrac{K(2s + 1)}{s(s^2 + s + 1)(s + 0.5)}$

1-2. Find the Laplace transforms of the following functions:

(a) $g(t) = te^{-2t}$

(b) $g(t) = t \cos 5t$

(c) $g(t) = e^{-t} \sin \omega t$

(d) $g(t) = t^n e^{0.5t}$

1-3. Solve the following differential equations by means of Laplace transformation:

$$\frac{d^2f(t)}{dt^2} + 5\frac{df(t)}{dt} + 4f(t) = e^{-t}u(t)$$

$$f(0^+) = 0, \quad \frac{df(0^+)}{dt} = 0.$$

1-4. Given that the Laplace transform of $f(t)$ is $F(s)$, prove that

$$\mathscr{L}\left[\int_{t_0}^{t} f(\tau)\,d\tau\right] = \frac{F(s)}{s} + \frac{\int_{t_0}^{0} f(\tau)\,d\tau}{s}$$

1-5. Find the inverse Laplace transforms of the following functions:

(a) $G(s) = \dfrac{1}{(s + 2)(s + 3)}$

(b) $G(s) = \dfrac{1}{(s + 1)^2(s + 4)}$

(c) $G(s) = \dfrac{10}{s(s^2 + 4)(s + 1)}$

(d) $G(s) = \dfrac{5(s + 10)}{s^2(s + 3)(s + 5)}$

(e) $G(s) = \dfrac{2(s + 1)}{s(s^2 + s + 2)}$

1-6. The following signals are sampled by an ideal sampler with sampling period T. Determine the sampler output $f^*(t)$ and evaluate the Laplace transform of $f^*(t)$, $F^*(s)$. Express $F^*(s)$ in closed form.

(a) $f(t) = te^{-at}$

(b) $f(t) = e^{-at} \sin \omega t$ (a and ω are constants)

1-7. Derive the z-transform of the following functions:

(a) $\dfrac{1}{(s + a)^n}$

(b) $\dfrac{1}{s^n}$

(c) $\dfrac{1}{(s + a)^3}$

1-8. Find the z-transforms of the following functions:

(a) $\dfrac{1}{s^3(s + 2)}$

(b) $\dfrac{1}{s(s + 5)^2}$

1-9. Find the z-transforms of the following functions:
(a) $t^2 e^{-2t}$
(b) $t \sin \omega t$

1-10. Find the inverse z-transform of

$$G(z) = \frac{z(z^2 + 2z + 1)}{(z^2 - z + 1)(z^2 + z + 2)}$$

by means of the following methods:
(a) the real inversion formula
(b) the partial fraction expansion
(c) power series expansion.

2

Transfer Function
and
Graphical Descriptions
of Linear Systems

2.1 Introduction

The first step in the process of analysis of a physical system is to derive a mathematical model from which the characteristics of the system may be studied. In a very broad sense, a model may be regarded as a means of representing the interrelationships between system components and ideas. Generally speaking, a model of a physical system may take any appropriate form. The following categories are the most useful and common:

(1) Direct analog: Scaled or unscaled replicas and analog models.

(2) Graphical representation: Block diagrams, signal flow graphs.

(3) Mathematical representation: Differential equations, state equations, transfer function relations, matrix representations, etc.

A direct analog is a scaled or unscaled replica of a physical system; the necessity of this representation stems from many situations in which circumstances make direct study of the actual system virtually impossible.

Representation of a physical system by mathematical expressions and pictorial means allows the control engineer to use the available mathematical and topological tools, such as differential equations and block diagrams. In practice, circumstances usually do not allow an exact mathematical representation of a complex system, but if valid assumptions are made on the system properties, much valuable information on the system can be gained from the approximated treatment. To clarify the statement just made, we should realize that all physical systems are nonlinear to some extent, and the mathematical treatment of nonlinear systems is extremely difficult. Therefore, it is often necessary to assume that the system under study behaves linearly over the range of operation. In some cases, the assumption of linearity is quite valid over a large operating range. Under certain conditions, however, the assumption of linearity may depart greatly from the actual happenings. Strictly speaking, a linear system simply does not exist; it is only for the sake of simplifying the mathematics involved that the linear equivalence of a physical system is introduced.

Once the physical system is replaced by its linear model, the system equations are derived by applying various appropriate physical laws. For electrical systems, there are, for instance, Ohm's law, Kirchhoff's laws, Lenz's law, etc.; in mechanics, there are Newton's laws of motion.

The equations describing a physical system may assume many different forms. For an electric network, for instance, the network equations may be written in the form of loop equations, node equations, and state equations.[1,2,3] Depending on the network configuration and the information

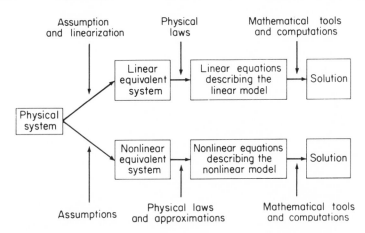

FIG. 2-1. Flow diagram describing the process of linear and non-linear study of physical systems.

required, one of these mathematical representations may be more preferable under a given situation. In more general terms, a conventional way of describing a physical system is the use of integro-differential equations, which involve integrals and differentials of the dependent variables. In modern control theory it is often desirable to use a set of first-order differential equations, called the state equations, to describe a physical system.

Once the systems equations are obtained, the solutions of the equations may be obtained by the classical method, the operational (transform) method, or the computer method. The general steps involved in the study of physical systems by linear and nonlinear analysis can be described by the flow diagram shown in Fig. 2-1.

2.2 Transfer Functions of Linear Systems

A well-known method of characterizing a linear system is by its input-output relationship. Consider that a linear system with a single input and output is described by the following nth order differential equation with constant coefficients:

$$a_0 \frac{d^n c(t)}{dt^n} + a_1 \frac{d^{n-1} c(t)}{dt^{n-1}} + \cdots + a_{n-1} \frac{dc(t)}{dt} + a_n c(t) = b_0 \frac{d^m r(t)}{dt^m}$$

$$+ b_1 \frac{d^{m-1} r(t)}{dt^{m-1}} + \cdots + b_{m-1} \frac{dr(t)}{dt} + b_m r(t) \qquad (2-1)$$

where $c(t)$ is the output variable and $r(t)$ is the input variable, and the a's and the b's are constants.

The differential equation in Eq. (2-1) provides a complete description of the system behavior between the input and the output. Once the input and the initial conditions of the system are specified, the output response is obtained by solving Eq. (2-1). However, it is apparent that the differential equation method of describing a system is rather cumbersome and of little practical use in design.

A simplification of linear system description is possible if the "transfer function" and the "impulse response" concepts are introduced. These modes of description are simply related, and each offers advantages in different fields of application and circumstances.

Taking the Laplace transform on both sides of Eq. (2-1) and assuming zero initial conditions, we have

$$(a_0 s^n + a_1 s^{n-1} + \cdots + a_{n-1} s + a_n) C(s) = (b_0 s^m + b_1 s^{m-1} + \cdots$$

$$+ b_{m-1} s + b_m) R(s) \quad (2-2)$$

According to definition, the transfer function of the system is the ratio of $C(s)$ to $R(s)$; therefore,

$$G(s) = \frac{C(s)}{R(s)} = \frac{b_0 s^m + b_1 s^{m-1} + \cdots + b_{m-1} s + b_m}{a_0 s^n + a_1 s^{n-1} + \cdots + a_{n-1} s + a_n} \qquad (2-3)$$

The characteristics of a linear system depend solely on the properties of system elements; therefore, the transfer function $G(s)$ is a property of the system elements only, and is independent of excitation and initial conditions. It should be pointed out that the transfer function is not defined for a nonlinear system, although with certain approximations, "pseudo-linear transfer functions" may be defined for particular types of nonlinearities.

In the analysis problem, the transfer function of a system is known and the transformed output response is found from the equation

$$C(s) = G(s)R(s) \tag{2-4}$$

The output time response is obtained by taking the inverse Laplace transform of $C(s)$.

It is noticed that the transfer function of a linear system as defined in Eq. (2–3) is analogous to the gain of an electronic amplifier:

$$A = \frac{e_o}{e_i} \tag{2-5}$$

where e_o is the output voltage, e_i, the input voltage, and A is the voltage gain of the amplifier.

The following example is given to show how transfer functions for single variable linear systems are derived.

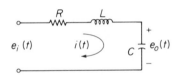

FIG. 2-2. A series RLC network.

Example 2-1. A series RLC network is shown in Fig. 2-2. The loop equation of the network is

$$e_i(t) = Ri(t) + L\frac{di(t)}{dt} + \frac{1}{C}\int_{0^+}^t i(t)\, dt + e_o(0^+) \tag{2-6}$$

where $e_o(0^+)$ is the initial voltage across the capacitor C.

Taking the Laplace transform on both sides of Eq. (2–6) and assuming zero initial conditions, we have

$$E_i(s) = \left(R + Ls + \frac{1}{Cs}\right)I(s) \tag{2-7}$$

If we regard the current $i(t)$ as an output variable, the transfer function between $e_i(t)$ and $i(t)$ is simply

$$\frac{I(s)}{E_i(s)} = \frac{1}{R + Ls + \dfrac{1}{Cs}} = \frac{Cs}{1 + RCs + LCs^2} \tag{2-8}$$

If the voltage $e_o(t)$ is considered as output, the transfer function between e_i and e_o is obtained by substituting

$$E_o(s) = \frac{1}{Cs}I(s) \tag{2-9}$$

into Eq. (2–7). Therefore,

$$\frac{E_o(s)}{E_i(s)} = \frac{1}{1 + RCs + LCs^2} \tag{2-10}$$

The definition of transfer function can be extended to a system with multiple inputs and outputs. This type of system is often referred to as the multivariable system. In a multivariable system, a differential equation of the form of Eq. (2–1) may be needed to describe the relationship between each pair of input and output. Similarly, the transfer function of Eq. (2–3) can be modified to show the interactions between the various inputs and outputs of the system. As a simple example of the multivariable system, we may consider the control problem of a turbopropeller engine.[4] In this case, the input variables are the fuel rate and the propeller blade angle. The output variables are the speed of rotation of the engine and the turbine-inlet temperature. In general, either one of the outputs is affected by the changes in both inputs. Similarly, both outputs are affected by a change in either of the inputs. For instance, when the blade angle of the propeller is increased, the speed of rotation of the engine will decrease and the temperature usually increases. Therefore, the following transfer relations may be written from steady-state tests performed on the system:

$$C_1(s) = G_{11}(s)R_1(s) + G_{12}(s)R_2(s) \tag{2-11}$$

$$C_2(s) = G_{21}(s)R_1(s) + G_{22}(s)R_2(s) \tag{2-12}$$

where

$C_1(s) =$ transformed variable of speed of rotation.

$C_2(s) =$ transformed variable of turbine-inlet temperature.

$R_1(s) =$ transformed variable of fuel rate.

$R_2(s) =$ transformed variable of propeller blade angle.

All these variables are assumed to be measured from some reference levels as zero references.

Since Eqs. (2–11) and (2–12) are written with the assumption that the system is linear, the principal of superposition holds. Therefore, $G_{12}(s)$ represents the transfer function between the speed of engine rotation and the propeller blade angle with the fuel rate held at the reference level ($R_1 = 0$). Similar statements can be made for the other transfer functions.

In general, if a linear system has p inputs and q outputs, the transfer function between the ith output and jth input is defined as

$$G_{ij}(s) = \frac{C_i(s)}{R_j(s)}\bigg|_{\substack{r_k=0,\, k=1,2,\dots\, p \\ k \neq j}} \tag{2-13}$$

Note that Eq. (2–13) is defined with only the jth input in effect, while the other inputs are assumed to be zero. The ith output transform of the system is related to all the input transforms by

$$C_i(s) = G_{11}(s)R_1(s) + G_{12}(s)R_2(s) + \cdots + G_{1p}(s)R_p(s)$$

$$= \sum_{j=1}^{p} G_{ij}(s)R_j(s) \qquad (i = 1, 2, \cdots, q) \tag{2–14}$$

where $G_{ij}(s)$ is defined in Eq. (2–13).

It is convenient to represent Eq. (2–14) by a matrix equation

$$\mathbf{C}(s) = \mathbf{G}(s)\mathbf{R}(s) \tag{2–15}$$

where

$$\mathbf{C}(s) = \begin{bmatrix} C_1(s) \\ C_2(s) \\ \cdot \\ \cdot \\ \cdot \\ C_q(s) \end{bmatrix} \tag{2–16}$$

is a $q \times 1$ matrix and is called the *transformed output vector;*

$$\mathbf{R}(s) = \begin{bmatrix} R_1(s) \\ R_2(s) \\ \cdot \\ \cdot \\ \cdot \\ R_p(s) \end{bmatrix} \tag{2–17}$$

is a $p \times 1$ matrix and is called the *transformed input vector;*

$$\mathbf{G}(s) = \begin{bmatrix} G_{11}(s) & G_{12}(s) & \cdots & G_{1p}(s) \\ G_{21}(s) & G_{22}(s) & \cdots & G_{2p}(s) \\ \cdot \\ \cdot \\ \cdot \\ G_{q1}(s) & G_{q2}(s) & \cdots & G_{qp}(s) \end{bmatrix} \tag{2–18}$$

is a $q \times p$ matrix and is called the *transfer function matrix.*

2.3 Impulse Response of Linear Systems

If the input signal of a linear system with a single input and output is a unit impulse function, $r(t) = \delta(t)$, the output transform of the system is given by

$$C(s) = G(s) \tag{2–19}$$

since the Laplace transform of the unit impulse function is unity.

Taking the inverse Laplace transform on both sides of Eq. (2–19) yields

$$c(t) = g(t) \tag{2–20}$$

where $g(t)$ is the inverse Laplace transform of $G(s)$ and is called the *impulse response* (or weighting function) of the linear system. Therefore, when a unit impulse is applied to a linear system, the output is the impulse response of the system. *The Laplace transform of the impulse response gives the transfer function G(s).* This means that if a linear system is initially quiescent (zero initial conditions), theoretically, the system can be described by exciting it with an impulse function and measuring the output response. In practice, although a true impulse cannot be generated physically, a pulse with a very narrow pulse width (much less than the significant time constants of the system) usually provides a suitable approximation.

For a multiple number of inputs and outputs, or, simply, a multivariable system, the *impulse response matrix* is given by

$$\mathbf{g}(t) = \mathscr{L}^{-1}[\mathbf{G}(s)] \tag{2-21}$$

where the inverse Laplace transform (or the Laplace transform) of a matrix function implies the operation on each term of the matrix.

The derivation of $G(s)$ in Eq. (2–3) is based on the knowledge of the system differential equation, and the solution of $C(s)$ from Eq. (2–4) also assumes that $R(s)$ and $G(s)$ are all available in analytical forms. This is not always possible, for quite often the input signal $r(t)$ is not Laplace transformable or is only available in the form of experimental data. If such a situation should occur, in order to analyze the system we would have no alternatives but to work with the time functions $r(t)$ and $g(t)$. Let us consider

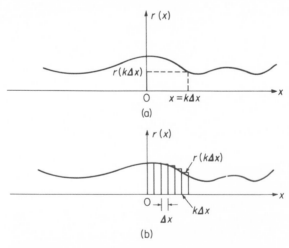

FIG. 2-3. (a) Input signal of a linear system; (b) Input signal represented by sum of rectangular pulses.

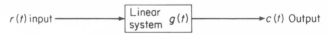

FIG. 2-4. Linear system.

that the excitation function sketched in Fig. 2-3a is applied to a linear system as shown in Fig. 2–4; the output response $c(t)$ is to be determined. In Fig. 2–3, the input signal is denoted as a function of x, which is a dummy time variable; this is necessary since t is considered to be a fixed quantity in the process. For all practical purposes, we may assume that the signal extends from minus infinity to plus infinity in time. Now consider that the signal is approximated by the sequence of pulses of pulse width Δx, as shown in Fig. 2-3b. In the limit, as Δx approaches zero, these pulses become a sequence of impulses, and the impulse at time $k \Delta x$ has a strength (area) $\Delta x \cdot r(k \Delta x)$, which is the area of the pulse at $k \Delta x$. Also when we let Δx become smaller, we have to increase k proportionally, so that the value $k \Delta x$ stays constant and equals x, which is a particular point on the time axis. We now compute the response of the linear system, using this impulse approximated signal. When only the impulse at time $x = k \Delta x$ is considered, the system response is given by

$$\Delta x \cdot r(k \Delta x)g(t - k \Delta x) \qquad (2\text{--}22)$$

which is the impulse strength multiplied by the system impulse response, delayed by $k \Delta x$. By use of the superposition principle, the total response due to $r(t)$ is obtained by adding the responses to each of the impulses from $-\infty$ to $+\infty$. Therefore,

$$c(t) = \lim_{\substack{\Delta x \to 0 \\ N \to \infty}} \sum_{k=-N}^{N} r(k \Delta x)g(t - k \Delta x) \Delta x \qquad (2\text{--}23)$$

or

$$c(t) = \int_{-\infty}^{\infty} r(x)g(t - x) \, dx \qquad (2\text{--}24)$$

For all physical systems,

$$g(t) = 0 \qquad t < 0 \qquad (2\text{--}25)$$

That is, response does not precede excitation. Therefore,

$$g(t - x) = 0 \qquad (x > t) \qquad (2\text{--}26)$$

The response for a physically realizable system now becomes

$$c(t) = \int_{-\infty}^{t} r(x)g(t - x) \, dx \qquad (2\text{--}27)$$

Further, if $r(t) = 0$ for $t < 0$, the integral of Eq. (2–27) becomes

$$c(t) = \int_{0}^{t} r(x)g(t - x) \, dx \qquad (2\text{--}28)$$

The expressions in Eqs. (2–27) and (2–28) are called the *convolution integral*[2,5] and are denoted by

$$c(t) = r(t) * g(t) \qquad (2\text{--}29)$$

or

$$c(t) = r(t) \text{ convolves into } g(t) \qquad (2\text{–}30)$$

The time functions $r(t)$ and $g(t)$ in the convolution process may be interchanged, since basically there is no difference between the two. The convolution integral can also be written as

$$c(t) = g(t) * r(t) = \int_{-\infty}^{t} g(x)r(t - x)\,dx \qquad (2\text{–}31)$$

and for physically realizable systems $g(t)$ satisfies Eq. (2–25); it can be shown that

$$c(t) = \int_{0}^{t} g(x)r(t - x)\,dx \qquad (2\text{–}32)$$

The evaluation of the impulse response of the controlled process or system is an important step in a class of systems called the "adaptive control systems."[6] From a critical point of view, the dynamic characteristics of most control systems vary to some extent during the lifetime of the control operation. This may be caused by simple deterioration of components due to wear and tear, drift in operating environments, etc. For instance, the transfer characteristic of a guided missile in flight will vary in time because of the change of mass and atmospheric conditions. Thus the control system designed under the assumption of known transfer characteristic may fail to provide satisfactory guidance, should the dynamic characteristic variation become large. In order that the system may have the ability of self-modification or self-adjustment in accordance with varying parameters and environment, it is necessary that the system's transfer characteristic be identified at all times. One of the methods of identification is to measure the impulse response of the controlled process continuously, so that design parameters may be adjusted accordingly to attain optimum control at all times.

In the two preceding sections the definitions of transfer functions and impulse responses of physical systems have been presented. The two functions are closely related through the Laplace transformation, and they contain essentially the same information about the system. However, we must reiterate that transfer function and impulse response are significant only for linear systems and that the initial conditions are assumed to be zero.

2.4 Block Diagrams

Because detailed schematic diagrams are difficult to draw for complex systems, a shorthand symbol called the *block diagram* is often used by control engineers. The combination of block diagram and transfer function of a physical system provides a pictorial representation of the cause-and-effect relationship between the input and output of the system. For instance, the block diagram representation of the transfer relation in Eq. (2–4) is shown in Fig. 2-5. The arrows on the diagram imply that the block diagram has a unilateral property (just as an electronic amplifier); that is, signals can only pass in the direction of the arrows.

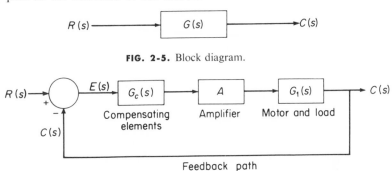

FIG. 2-5. Block diagram.

FIG. 2-6. Block diagram of a feedback control system.

Although all systems (with one input and one output) may be denoted by a single block connected between the input and the output, the advantage of the block diagram concept lies in the fact that feedback control systems are composed of many noninteracting elements whose transfer functions are determined independently. An entire system may, then, be represented by the interconnection of the blocks of the individual elements, so that their contributions to the over-all performance of the system may be evaluated. The simple configuration shown in Fig. 2-5 is actually the basic building block of a complex block diagram. For instance, the block diagram of a typical feedback control system is shown in Fig. 2-6. Each block in the diagram represents an independent element of the system.

Block Diagrams of Feedback Control Systems

One of the important elements of a feedback control system is the sensing device, which often acts as a junction point, and it operates on signals coming

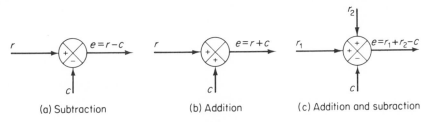

(a) Subtraction   (b) Addition   (c) Addition and subtraction

FIG. 2-7. Block diagrams of sensing devices.

from different parts of the system. Common examples of the sensing device include potentiometers,[7] synchros,[7] and resolvers.[7] For linear systems, the sensing operation usually consists of addition and subtraction of signals, and the block diagram notations are illustrated by some examples in Fig. 2-7. In each case the output of the sensing device is shown to be equal to the algebraic sum of the input signals.

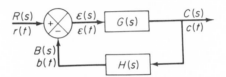

FIG. 2-8. Basic block diagram of a feedback control system.

Some of the important terminology used in the block diagrams of feedback control systems are defined with reference to Fig. 2-8.

$R(s)$ = reference input

$C(s)$ = output signal (controlled variable)

$B(s)$ = feedback signal

$\mathscr{E}(s)$ = actuating signal

$G(s) = C(s)/\mathscr{E}(s)$ = forward path transfer function, or open-loop transfer function

$M(s) = C(s)/R(s)$ = closed-loop transfer function

$H(s)$ = feedback path transfer function

$G(s)H(s)$ = loop transfer function

The closed-loop transfer function, $M(s) = C(s)/R(s)$, can be expressed as a function of $G(s)$ and $H(s)$. From Fig. 2-8, we have

$$C(s) = G(s)\mathscr{E}(s) \qquad (2\text{--}33)$$

and

$$B(s) = H(s)C(s) \qquad (2\text{--}34)$$

The actuating signal is given by

$$\mathscr{E}(s) = R(s) - B(s) \qquad (2\text{--}35)$$

Substituting Eq. (2–35) into Eq. (2–33) yields

$$C(s) = G(s)R(s) - G(s)B(s) \qquad (2\text{--}36)$$

Substituting Eq. (2–34) into Eq. (2–36), we have

$$C(s) = G(s)R(s) - G(s)H(s)C(s) \qquad (2\text{--}37)$$

from which, the closed-loop transfer function is given by

$$M(s) = \frac{C(s)}{R(s)} = \frac{G(s)}{1 + G(s)H(s)} \qquad (2\text{-}38)$$

The block diagram of a complex feedback control system usually contains many feedback loops, and the valuation of the system transfer function by means of the algebraic method described above may be tedious. Theoretically, a complex block diagram can always be reduced to the basic form of Fig. 2-8 by using the block diagram reduction technique,[8,9] and then the transfer function is written from Eq. (2–38). However, we shall show later in Sec. 2.7 that the transfer function of any linear system can be obtained from its block diagram by use of the signal flow graph gain formula.

Block Diagrams of Multivariable Systems

Two common block diagram representations of multivariable systems are shown in Fig. 2-9. However, these simple diagrams merely portray the matrix transfer relation given by Eq. (2–15); that is,

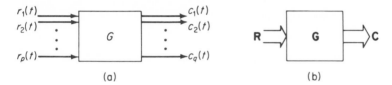

(a)   (b)

FIG. 2-9. Block diagram representation of multivariable systems.

$$\mathbf{C}(s) = \mathbf{G}(s)\mathbf{R}(s) \qquad (2\text{-}39)$$

Therefore, the block diagrams in Fig. 2-9 are useful only when the transfer relationships between the inputs and the outputs are given concurrently. If the block diagram is to carry all the mathematical description of the system as in the single variable case, a more detailed diagram is necessary.

Consider that a linear system has two inputs, $r_1(t)$ and $r_2(t)$, and two outputs, $c_1(t)$ and $c_2(t)$. The transfer relation between the input and output is described by

$$\begin{bmatrix} C_1(s) \\ C_2(s) \end{bmatrix} = \begin{bmatrix} G_{11}(s) & G_{12}(s) \\ G_{21}(s) & G_{22}(s) \end{bmatrix} \begin{bmatrix} R_1(s) \\ R_2(s) \end{bmatrix} \qquad (2\text{-}40)$$

In view of the fact that Eq. (2–40) is a matrix representation of Eq. (2–14) with $p = q = 2$, a block diagram of the multivariable system may be drawn as shown in Fig. 2-10. Notice that this block diagram alone is able to specify the transfer relationships between the inputs and the outputs.

It is apparent that for complex multivariable systems, block diagrams

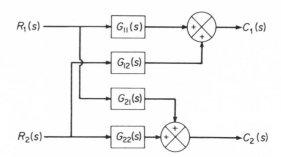

FIG. 2-10. Block diagram representation of a multi-variable system with two inputs and two outputs.

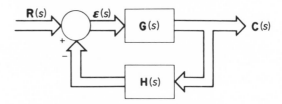

FIG. 2-11. Block diagram representation of a multivariable feedback control system.

of the form of Fig. 2-10 are quite involved. Therefore, the simplified versions of Fig. 2-9 still prove to be useful. For instance, a multivariable feedback control system may be portrayed by the block diagram shown in Fig. 2-11. The transfer relations of the system are defined as follows:

$$\mathbf{C}(s) = \mathbf{G}(s)\mathbf{E}(s) \tag{2-41}$$

$$\mathbf{E}(s) = \mathbf{R}(s) - \mathbf{B}(s) \tag{2-42}$$

$$\mathbf{B}(s) = \mathbf{H}(s)\mathbf{C}(s) \tag{2-43}$$

Substituting Eq. (2–43) into Eq. (2–42) and then from Eq. (2–42) into Eq. (2–41) yields

$$\mathbf{C}(s) = \mathbf{G}(s)\mathbf{R}(s) - \mathbf{G}(s)\mathbf{H}(s)\mathbf{C}(s) \tag{2-44}$$

Solving for $\mathbf{C}(s)$ from Eq. (2–44) gives

$$\mathbf{C}(s) = [\mathbf{I} + \mathbf{G}(s)\mathbf{H}(s)]^{-1}\mathbf{G}(s)\mathbf{R}(s) \tag{2-45}$$

provided that $\mathbf{I} + \mathbf{G}(s)\mathbf{H}(s)$ is nonsingular; $\mathbf{I}$ is the *unit matrix*.[10]

We notice that although the development here is similar to the derivation of Eq. (2–38), which is for the single variable case, Eq. (2–45) is actually obtained by using the laws of *matrix algebra* rather than those of real algebra. Therefore, in the present case it is meaningless to speak of the ratio $\mathbf{C}(s)/\mathbf{R}(s)$, although it is still possible to define a closed-loop transfer matrix

$$\mathbf{M}(s) = [\mathbf{I} + \mathbf{G}(s)\mathbf{H}(s)]^{-1}\mathbf{G}(s) \tag{2-46}$$

Then, Eq. (2–45) can be written as

$$\mathbf{C}(s) = \mathbf{M}(s)\mathbf{R}(s) \tag{2–47}$$

Example 2-2. Consider that a multivariable feedback control system is represented by the block diagram of Fig. 2-11. The transfer matrices of the system are

$$\mathbf{G}(s) = \begin{bmatrix} \dfrac{1}{s+1} & -\dfrac{1}{s} \\ 2 & \dfrac{1}{s+2} \end{bmatrix} \tag{2–48}$$

and

$$\mathbf{H}(s) = \begin{bmatrix} 1 & 0 \\ 0 & 1 \end{bmatrix} \tag{2–49}$$

The closed-loop transfer matrix of the system is defined by Eq. (2–46) and is evaluated as follows:

$$\mathbf{I} + \mathbf{G}(s)\mathbf{H}(s) = \begin{bmatrix} 1 + \dfrac{1}{s+1} & -\dfrac{1}{s} \\ 2 & 1 + \dfrac{1}{s+2} \end{bmatrix} = \begin{bmatrix} \dfrac{s+2}{s+1} & -\dfrac{1}{s} \\ 2 & \dfrac{s+3}{s+2} \end{bmatrix} \tag{2–50}$$

The determinant of $\mathbf{I} + \mathbf{G}(s)\mathbf{H}(s)$ is

$$\Delta_M = |\mathbf{I} + \mathbf{G}(s)\mathbf{H}(s)| = \frac{s+3}{s+1} + \frac{2}{s} = \frac{s^2 + 5s + 2}{s(s+1)} \tag{2–51}$$

which is nonsingular if $s \neq 0$, $s \neq -1$.

Therefore,

$$\mathbf{M}(s) = [\mathbf{I} + \mathbf{G}(s)\mathbf{H}(s)]^{-1}\mathbf{G}(s) = \frac{1}{\Delta_M} \begin{bmatrix} \dfrac{s+3}{s+2} & \dfrac{1}{s} \\ -2 & \dfrac{s+2}{s+1} \end{bmatrix} \begin{bmatrix} \dfrac{1}{s+1} & -\dfrac{1}{s} \\ 2 & \dfrac{1}{s+2} \end{bmatrix}$$

$$= \frac{s(s+1)}{s^2 + 5s + 2} \begin{bmatrix} \dfrac{3s^2 + 9s + 4}{s(s+1)(s+2)} & -\dfrac{1}{s} \\ 2 & \dfrac{3s+2}{s(s+1)} \end{bmatrix} \tag{2–52}$$

2.5 Transfer Functions of Discrete-data Systems[16]

The signals in a discrete-data or sampled-data system are in the form of pulse trains. Therefore, the transfer functions defined for continuous-data systems cannot be used adequately to describe discrete-data systems.

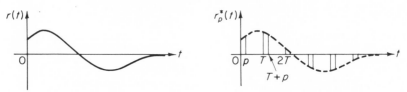

FIG. 2-12. A discrete-data system with a finite-pulsewidth sampler.

$r(t)$ ↑

O ───────────────────────→ t

$r_p^*(t)$ ↑

O p T $2T$
   $T+p$ ──────────────→ t

FIG. 2-13. Input and output signals of a finite-pulsewidth sampler.

Figure 2-12 illustrates a system G whose input is the output of a sampler. The sampler S_1 closes for a very short duration of p second once every T second, and it is said to have a sampling duration of p second and a sampling period of T second. A typical set of input and output signals of the sampler is shown in Fig. 2-13.

We shall show that if the sampling duration is much less than the sampling period; i.e., $p \ll T$, the train of pulses in Fig. 2-13 can be approximated by a train of impulses. Then, the finite-pulsewidth sampler can be approximated by an ideal sampler which has zero sampling duration and a cascade gain element p.

The pulse signal of Fig. 2-13 can be regarded as the product of $r(t)$ and a train of pulses each with unit amplitude, pulsewidth p, and are spaced T second apart. Therefore,

$$r_p^*(t) = r(t) \sum_{k=0}^{\infty} [u(t - kT) - u(t - kT - p)] \qquad (p \ll T) \quad (2\text{-}53)$$

where $u(t)$ is the unit step function.

Equation (2–53) can be written as

$$r_p^*(t) \cong \sum_{k=0}^{\infty} r(kT)[u(t - kT) - u(t - kT - p)] \qquad (2\text{-}54)$$

Taking the Laplace transform on both sides of Eq. (2–54) yields

$$R_p^*(s) = \mathscr{L}[r_p^*(t)] \cong \sum_{k=0}^{\infty} r(kT)\frac{1 - e^{-ps}}{s} e^{-kTs} \qquad (2\text{-}55)$$

Now we expand e^{-ps} into a power series, and since p is very small, only the first two terms of the series are considered significant. Equation (2–55) becomes

$$R_p^*(s) \cong \sum_{k=0}^{\infty} r(kT)\frac{1 - (1 - ps)}{s} e^{-kTs}$$

$$= \sum_{k=0}^{\infty} p r(kT) e^{-kTs} \qquad (2\text{-}56)$$

However, it is easy to see that the right-hand side of Eq. (2–56) rep the product of p and the Laplace transform of a train of impulses w strength (or area) of each impulse equal to the value of $r(t)$ at the corresponding sampling instant. Therefore, Eq. (2–56) is written as

$$R_p^*(s) \cong p\,R^*(s) \qquad (2-57)$$

where

$$R^*(s) = \sum_{k=0}^{\infty} r(kT)e^{-kTs} \qquad (2-58)$$

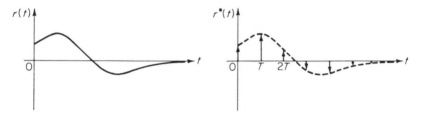

FIG. 2-14. A discrete-data system approximating the system of Fig. 2-12 using an ideal sampler.

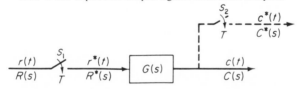

FIG. 2-15. Input and output signals of an ideal sampler.

FIG. 2-16. A discrete-data system with an ideal sampler.

The discrete-data system of Fig. 2-12 is now approximated by the system shown in Fig. 2-14. The sampler used in the system of Fig. 2-14 has a zero sampling duration, and is called an *ideal sampler*. Typical signals at the input and output of the ideal sampler are shown in Fig. 2-15. The length of an arrow is used to indicate the strength or area of an impulse, since the amplitude of an impulse function is infinite.

Normally, it is assumed that the factor p is included in the transfer function of the linear process. Therefore, the block diagram of a typical open-loop discrete-data system is shown in Fig. 2-16.

When $r^*(t)$ is a unit impulse function, the output of G is the impulse response $g(t)$. If a fictitious sampler S_2 which is synchronized with S_1 and has the same sampling period as that of S_1 is placed at the output of G, as shown in Fig. 2-16, the output of S_2 is

$$c^*(t) = g^*(t) = \sum_{k=0}^{\infty} c(kT)\delta(t - kT) \tag{2-59}$$

where $c(kT) = g(kT)$ is defined as the *weighting sequence* of the linear system G. In other words, the sampled version of the impulse response (weighting function) is the weighting sequence. Taking the Laplace transform on both sides of Eq. (2-59) yields

$$G^*(s) = \mathscr{L}[g^*(t)] = \sum_{k=0}^{\infty} g(kT)e^{-kTs} \tag{2-60}$$

which is defined as the *pulsed transfer function* of the system G.

We can sum up our findings about the description of the discrete-data system shown in Fig. 2-16 as follows: *When a unit impulse function is applied to the linear system G, the output is simply the impulse response of G; the output of the fictitious sampler S_2 is called the weighting sequence of the system G. The Laplace transform of the weighting sequence impulse train gives the pulsed transfer function $G^*(s)$.*

Once the weighting sequence of a system G is defined, the output $c(t)$ and $c^*(t)$ of the system corresponding to any arbitrary input can be obtained by means of the principle of superposition.

Consider that an arbitrary function $r(t)$ is applied to the system of Fig. 2-16 at $t = 0$. The input to G is the impulse train $r^*(t)$, where

$$r^*(t) = \sum_{k=0}^{\infty} r(kT)\delta(t - kT) \tag{2-61}$$

By means of superposition, the output of G is written as

$$c(t) = r(0)g(t) + r(T)g(t - T) + \cdots + r(kT)g(t - kT) + \cdots \tag{2-62}$$

At $t = kT$, Eq. (2-62) becomes

$$c(kT) = r(0)g(kT) + r(T)g[(k - 1)T] + \cdots + r[(k - 1)T]g(T) + r(kT)g(0) \tag{2-63}$$

where it is assumed that $g(t)$ is zero for all $t < 0$, since G is a physical system.

Multiplying both sides of the last equation by e^{-kTs}, and taking the summation from $k = 0$ to ∞, we have

$$\sum_{k=0}^{\infty} c(kT)e^{-kTs} = \sum_{k=0}^{\infty} r(0)g(kT)e^{-kTs} + \sum_{k=0}^{\infty} r(T)g[(k - 1)T]e^{-kTs} + \cdots$$

$$+ \sum_{k=0}^{\infty} r[(k - 1)T]g(T)e^{-kTs} + \sum_{k=0}^{\infty} r(kT)g(0)e^{-kTs} \tag{2-64}$$

Again using the fact that $g(t)$ is zero for negative time, we can write Eq. (2-64) as

$$\sum_{k=0}^{\infty} c(kT)e^{-kTs} = [r(0) + r(T)e^{-Ts} + r(2T)e^{-2Ts} + \cdots] \sum_{k=0}^{\infty} g(kT)e^{-kTs}$$

$$(2\text{-}65)$$

or

$$\sum_{k=0}^{\infty} c(kT)e^{-kTs} = \sum_{k=0}^{\infty} r(kT)e^{-kTs} \sum_{k=0}^{\infty} g(kT)e^{-kTs} \qquad (2\text{-}66)$$

Therefore, from Eq. (2–60), we have

$$C^*(s) = R^*(s)G^*(s) \qquad (2\text{-}67)$$

which is the transfer relationship for the discrete-data system shown in Fig. 2-16. The z-transform relationship is obtained directly from the definition of the z-transform. Since $z = e^{Ts}$, Eq. (2–66) is also written as

$$\sum_{k=0}^{\infty} c(kT)z^{-k} = \sum_{k=0}^{\infty} r(kT)z^{-k} \sum_{k=0}^{\infty} g(kT)z^{-k} \qquad (2\text{-}68)$$

Therefore, defining the z-*transfer function* of G as

$$G(z) = \sum_{k=0}^{\infty} g(kT)z^{-k} \qquad (2\text{-}69)$$

Eq. (2–68) corresponds to

$$C(z) = R(z)G(z) \qquad (2\text{-}70)$$

Equation (2–69) defines the z-transfer function $G(z)$ of a linear system as *the z-transform of the weighting sequence g(kT) of the system.*

It is important to point out that the output $c(t)$ of the discrete-data system is continuous with respect to time. However, the pulsed transform of the output, $C^*(s)$, and the z-transform of the output, $C(z)$, specify the values of $c(t)$ only at the sampling instants. If $c(t)$ is a well-behaved function between sampling instants, $c^*(t)$ and $C(z)$ give an accurate description of the true output; otherwise, the z-transform method may give misleading results.

The pulse transfer relation given by Eq. (2–67) can also be obtained by using the relation in Eq. (2–72) between $C^*(s)$ and $C(s)$ which is given in the literature.[16,17] From Fig. 2-16, the Laplace transform of the continuous output is

$$C(s) = G(s)R^*(s) \qquad (2\text{-}71)$$

Substituting the last equation into

$$C^*(s) = \frac{1}{T} \sum_{n=-\infty}^{\infty} C(s + jn\omega_s) \qquad (2\text{-}72)^{[16]}$$

gives

$$C^*(s) = \frac{1}{T} \sum_{n=-\infty}^{\infty} G(s + jn\omega_s)R^*(s + jn\omega_s) \qquad (2\text{-}73)$$

where ω_s is the sampling frequency in radians per second, and $\omega_s = 2\pi/T$.

In Eq. (2–73), we can write $R^*(s + jn\omega_s)$ as

$$R^*(s + jn\omega_s) = \sum_{k=0}^{\infty} r(kT)e^{-kT(s+jn\omega_s)} \tag{2-74}$$

using Eq. (2–58). Since for integral k and n,

$$e^{-jnT\omega_s k} = e^{-j2\pi nk} = 1 \tag{2-75}$$

Eq. (2–74) becomes

$$R^*(s + jn\omega_s) = \sum_{k=0}^{\infty} r(kT)e^{-kTs} = R^*(s) \tag{2-76}$$

Therefore, Eq. (2–73) becomes

$$C^*(s) = \frac{1}{T} R^*(s) \sum_{n=-\infty}^{\infty} G(s + jn\omega_s) \tag{2-77}$$

or

$$C^*(s) = R^*(s)G^*(s) \tag{2-78}$$

where

$$G^*(s) = \frac{1}{T} \sum_{n=-\infty}^{\infty} G(s + jn\omega_s) \tag{2-79}$$

Transfer Functions of Discrete-data Systems with Cascaded Elements

Figure 2-17 illustrates two different situations of a discrete-data system which contains two cascaded elements. In the system of Fig. 2-17a, the two elements are separated by a second sampler S_2 which is synchronized to S_1, and the two samplers have the same sampling period. The two elements G_1 and G_2 of the system in Fig. 2-17b are connected together directly.

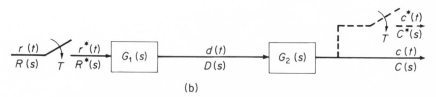

(a)

(b)

FIG. 2-17. (a) A discrete-data system with cascaded elements and sampler separates the two elements; (b) discrete-data system with cascaded elements with no sampler between the two elements.

In discrete-data systems, it is important to distinguish these two cases when deriving the pulse transfer functions.

Let us consider the system of Fig. 2-17a first. The output signal of G_1 is

$$D(s) = G_1(s)R^*(s) \qquad (2\text{-}80)$$

and the system output is

$$C(s) = G_2(s)D^*(s) \qquad (2\text{-}81)$$

Taking the pulsed transform of Eq. (2–80) and substituting the result into Eq. (2–81) yields

$$C(s) = G_2(s)G_1^*(s)R^*(s) \qquad (2\text{-}82)$$

Taking the pulsed transform on both sides of the last equation gives

$$C^*(s) = G_2^*(s)G_1^*(s)R^*(s) \qquad (2\text{-}83)$$

The corresponding z-transform expression of the last equation is

$$C(z) = G_2(z)G_1(z)R(z) \qquad (2\text{-}84)$$

Therefore, we conclude that *the z-transform of two linear elements separated by a sampling switch is equal to the product of the z-transforms of the two individual elements.*

The Laplace transform of the output of the system in Fig. 2-17b is

$$C(s) = G_1(s)G_2(s)R^*(s) \qquad (2\text{-}85)$$

The pulsed transform of $C(s)$ is

$$C^*(s) = [G_1(s)G_2(s)]^* R^*(s) \qquad (2\text{-}86)$$

where

$$[G_1(s)G_2(s)]^* = \frac{1}{T} \sum_{n=-\infty}^{\infty} G_1(s + jn\omega_s)G_2(s + jn\omega_s) \qquad (2\text{-}87)$$

For simplicity, we define the following notation:

$$[G_1(s)G_2(s)]^* = G_1G_2^*(s) \qquad (2\text{-}88)$$

Then, Eq. (2–86) becomes

$$C^*(s) = G_1G_2^*(s)R^*(s) \qquad (2\text{-}89)$$

The z-transform of Eq. (2–89) is

$$C(z) = G_1G_2(z)R(z) \qquad (2\text{-}90)$$

where $G_1G_2(z)$ is defined as the z-transform of the product of $G_1(s)$ and $G_2(s)$. It should be noted that, in general,

$$G_1G_2^*(s) \neq G_1^*(s)G_2^*(s) \qquad (2\text{-}91)$$

and

$$G_1G_2(z) \neq G_1(z)G_2(z) \qquad (2\text{-}92)$$

Therefore, we conclude that *the z-transform of two cascaded elements with no sampler between them is equal to the z-transform of the product of the Laplace transform of the two elements.*

Transfer Functions of Closed-loop Discrete-data Systems

The transfer function of a closed-loop discrete-data system can be obtained by the procedure used in the last section.

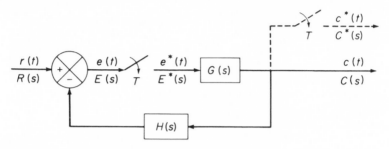

FIG. 2-18. A closed-loop discrete-data system.

Consider the closed-loop system shown in Fig. 2-18. The output transform is

$$C(s) = G(s)E^*(s) \tag{2–93}$$

The Laplace transform of the continuous error function is

$$E(s) = R(s) - H(s)C(s) \tag{2–94}$$

Substituting Eq. (2–93) into Eq. (2–94) yields

$$E(s) = R(s) - G(s)H(s)E^*(s) \tag{2–95}$$

Now taking the pulsed transform on both sides of the last equation gives

$$E^*(s) = R^*(s) - GH^*(s)E^*(s) \tag{2–96}$$

from which

$$E^*(s) = \frac{R^*(s)}{1 + GH^*(s)} \tag{2–97}$$

The output transform $C(s)$ is obtained by substituting $E^*(s)$ from Eq. (2–97) into Eq. (2–93); hence,

$$C(s) = \frac{G(s)}{1 + GH^*(s)}R^*(s) \tag{2–98}$$

The transform of $c^*(t)$ is

$$C^*(s) = G^*(s)E^*(s) = \frac{G^*(s)}{1 + GH^*(s)}R^*(s) \tag{2–99}$$

Therefore, the z-transform of the output is

$$C(z) = \frac{G(z)}{1 + GH(z)}R(z) \tag{2–100}$$

The closed-loop transfer function of the system is

$$\frac{C(z)}{R(z)} = \frac{G(z)}{1 + GH(z)} \tag{2-101}$$

As another example of attempting to derive the closed-loop transfer

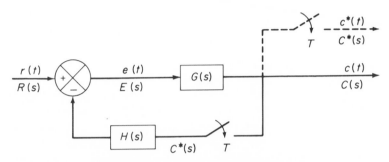

FIG. 2-19. A closed-loop discrete-data system.

function of a discrete-data system, consider the system shown in Fig. 2-19. The output transforms $C(s)$ and $C(z)$ are derived as follows:

$$C(s) = G(s)E(s) \tag{2-102}$$

$$E(s) = R(s) - H(s)C^*(s) \tag{2-103}$$

Substituting Eq. (2–103) into Eq. (2–102) yields

$$C(s) = G(s)R(s) - G(s)H(s)C^*(s) \tag{2-104}$$

Taking the pulsed transform of the last equation gives

$$C^*(s) = GR^*(s) - GH^*(s)C^*(s) \tag{2-105}$$

Notice now that the input R and the transfer function $G(s)$ are combined as one function $GR^*(s)$ which cannot be separated.

The pulsed transform of the output is obtained from Eq. (2–105) as

$$C^*(s) = \frac{GR^*(s)}{1 + GH^*(s)} \tag{2-106}$$

To determine the transform of the continuous output, $C(s)$, we substitute $C^*(s)$ from Eq. (2–106) into Eq. (2–104). Thus,

$$C(s) = G(s)R(s) - \frac{G(s)H(s)}{1 + GH^*(s)} GR^*(s) \tag{2-107}$$

The z-transform of the output is obtained directly from Eq. (2–106).

$$C(z) = \frac{GR(z)}{1 + GH(z)} \tag{2-108}$$

An important feature of this problem is that because of the location of the sampler, it is no longer possible to derive a transfer function of the discrete-data system. The output transforms, $C^*(s)$ and $C(z)$, are expressed as functions of the system transfer functions and the input. This represents one important difference in the transform analysis of the discrete-data systems and continuous-data systems.

For more complicated discrete-data systems, the algebraic method just described becomes tedious. We shall show in Sec. 2.8 that a signal flow graph method may be used to simplify the procedure.

2.6 Signal Flow Graphs[11, 12, 13]

Because block diagrams require more time to construct, in general, they are used mostly for the portrayal of interactions of signals between large element blocks. However, the blocks in a block diagram may contain such complicated transfer functions that detailed study of the system—in regard to the flow of signals from point to point, and the effects of variations in system parameters on such system performance functions as gain, impedance, and sensitivity—frequently cannot be made directly.

The signal flow graph introduced by S. J. Mason[11] is capable of giving a more detailed representation of a complex system than a block diagram. For feedback systems, the signal flow graph not only illustrates the passage of signals through the systems, but also gives a clear indication of the feedback paths in the system.

What is a signal flow graph? We can state simply that a signal flow graph is a graphical representation of the relationships between the variables of a set of linear algebraic equations. A signal flow graph of a system is a *network* with junction points called *nodes;* the nodes are connected by paths, called *branches,** which have directions. A signal travels along a branch only in the direction of the arrow.

Consider that a system is described by the set of equations**

$$x_j = \sum_{k=1}^{N} t_{kj} x_k \qquad (j = 1, 2, \cdots, N) \qquad (2\text{–}109)$$

where the coefficient t_{kj} is called the "transmission" or "transmission function" representing the contribution of variable x_k to the value of variable

---

*It is important to note that the terms, *network*, *node*, and *branch*, used here do not have the same meaning as those used in network analysis.

**The set of equations may represent integro-differential equations; i.e., x_j and x_k either are functions of time, or they may be transformed equations in which case x_j and x_k and t_{kj} are functions of s, and should be capitalized. It should also be noted that, in the present case, the system equations are written in the form:

Effect at $j = \sum$ (transmission from k to j)(cause at k)

These are unlike the network equations we wrote in the past, whose form is

Excitation (cause) at $k = \sum$ (transmittance from k to j) (response at j)

x_j. If the variables are represented as nodes, and t_{kj} as directed branches, Eq. (2-109) implies that the system equations may be portrayed by a signal flow graph. The construction of the flow graph is basically a matter of following the *cause* and *effect* relations through the system relating each variable in terms of itself and the other variables. For instance, the equation

$$x_2 = t_{12}x_1 \qquad (2\text{-}110)$$

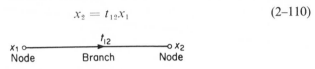

FIG. 2-20. Signal flow graph for $x_2 = t_{12}x_1$.

is represented by the signal flow graph shown in Fig. 2-20. Node x_1 and node x_2 represent the variables x_1 and x_2 respectively, and the branch directing from node x_1 to node x_2 expresses the dependence of x_2 upon x_1 (but not the

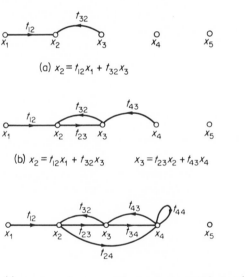

(a) $x_2 = t_{12}x_1 + t_{32}x_3$

(b) $x_2 = t_{12}x_1 + t_{32}x_3$ $x_3 = t_{23}x_2 + t_{43}x_4$

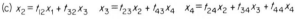

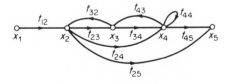

(c) $x_2 = t_{12}x_1 + t_{32}x_3$ $x_3 = t_{23}x_2 + t_{43}x_4$ $x_4 = t_{24}x_2 + t_{34}x_3 + t_{44}x_4$

(d) Complete signal flow graph

FIG. 2-21. Construction of signal flow graph for Eq. 2-111.

reverse). The branch may also be interpreted as a unilateral amplifier of gain t_{12}, so that when a signal x_1 appears at its input, the signal is multiplied by the gain of the branch t_{12}, and a signal of strength $t_{12}x_1$ is delivered at node x_2.

As another example, consider the set of equations of a certain system:

$$x_2 = t_{12}x_1 + t_{32}x_3$$
$$x_3 = t_{23}x_2 + t_{43}x_4$$
$$x_4 = t_{24}x_2 + t_{34}x_3 + t_{44}x_4$$
$$x_5 = t_{25}x_2 + t_{45}x_4$$

$$(2-111)$$

The signal flow graph for the system is constructed as shown in Fig. 2-21. The nodes x_1, x_2, x_3, x_4, and x_5 are located in order from left to right. The first equation states that x_2 depends upon two signals, $t_{12}x_1$ and $t_{32}x_3$; the signal flow graph representing this equation is shown in Fig. 2-21a. The second equation states that x_3 depends upon $t_{23}x_2$ and $t_{43}x_4$; on the flow graph shown in Fig. 2-21a, a branch of gain t_{23} is drawn from node x_2 to x_3, and a branch of gain t_{43} is drawn from x_4 to x_3 with the directions of the branches indicated by the arrows (Fig. 2-21b). Similarly, with the consideration of the third equation, Fig. 2-21c is obtained. The complete signal flow graph is shown in Fig. 2-21d. The loop with gain t_{44} represents the dependence of x_4 upon itself.

Basic Properties of Signal Flow Graphs

At this point, it is best to summarize some of the important properties of the signal flow graph.

(1) The nodes represent variables of a system. Normally, the nodes are arranged from left to right, following a succession of causes and effects through the system.

(2) The branch directing from node x_k to x_j represents the dependence of the variable x_j upon x_k, but not the reverse.

(3) Signals travel along branches only in the direction described by the arrows of the branches.

(4) A signal x_k traveling along a branch between nodes x_k and x_j is multiplied by the gain of the branch t_{kj}, so that a signal of $t_{kj}x_k$ is delivered at node x_j.

Definitions for Signal Flow Graphs

The following terms are frequently used in connection with the signal flow graphs:

(1) *Input node* (*source*): A node which has only outgoing branches. (Example: node x_1 in Fig. 2-21.)

(2) *Output node* (*sink*): A node which has only incoming branches. (Example: node x_5 in Fig. 2-21d.) However, this condition is not always met by an output node. For instance, the signal flow graph shown in Fig. 2-22a illustrates that the output node also has an outgoing branch. In order to meet the specified condition, it is necessary to introduce an additional branch of unit gain and an additional variable x_3, as shown in Fig. 2-22b.

This simply means that any noninput node of a signal flow graph can always be made an output node by the aforementioned operation. However, one cannot convert a noninput node into an input node by using a similar

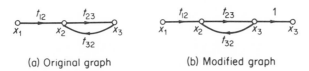

(a) Original graph   (b) Modified graph

FIG. 2-22. Realization of signal flow graph in which no branch leaves the output node.

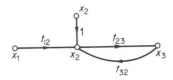

FIG. 2-23. An attempt to make x_2 an input node.

operation. For instance, node x_2 of the signal flow graph of Fig. 2-22 does not satisfy the condition of an input node. If we attempt to convert it into an input node by adding an incoming branch of unit gain from another identical node x_2, the graph in Fig. 2-23 results. However, the equation at node x_2 now reads

$$x_2 = x_2 + t_{12}x_1 + t_{32}x_3 \qquad (2\text{--}112)$$

which is different from the original equation

$$x_2 = t_{12}x_1 + t_{32}x_3 \qquad (2\text{--}113)$$

Therefore, the conclusion is that the only way that x_2 can be made an input node is to rewrite the original system equations so that x_2 appears only on the right-hand side of the equations.

(3) *Path*: Any continuous, unidirectional, succession of branches traversed in the indicated branch directions. (Example: x_1-x_2-x_3-x_4-x_5; x_2-x_3-x_4; x_2-x_3-x_2; etc. in Fig. 2-21d.)

(4) *Forward path*: A path from the input node to the output node, along which no node is encountered more than once. (Example: x_1-x_2-x_3-x_4-x_5; x_1-x_2- through t_{24}-x_4-x_5, or x_1-x_2- through t_{25}-x_5 in Fig. 2-21d.)

(5) *Feedback path* (*loop*): A path which originates and terminates on the

same node, along which no node is encountered more than once. (Example: x_2-x_3-x_2; x_3-x_4-x_3; x_4-x_4 through t_{44}; however, x_2-x_3-x_4-x_3-x_2 is not a feedback path, since x_3 is encountered twice in Fig. 2-21d.)

(6) *Path gain*: The product of the branch gains encountered in traversing the path. (Example: $t_{12}t_{23}t_{34}$ for path x_1-x_2-x_3-x_4 in Fig. 2-21d.)

(7) *Loop gain*: The product of all the branch gains of the branches forming that loop. (Example: $t_{23}t_{32}$ for loop x_2-x_3-x_2; $t_{34}t_{43}$ for loop x_3-x_4-x_3; and t_{44} for loop x_4-x_4 in Fig. 2-21d.)

Simple Signal Flow Graph Algebra

(1) *Addition*

(a) The value of the variable represented by a node is equal to the sum of all the signals entering the node. In Fig. 2-24a, the value of x_j is

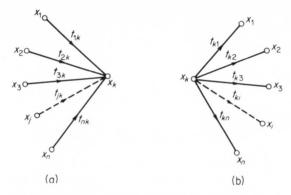

(a)   (b)

FIG. 2-24. (a) Node as a summing point; (b) Node as a transmitting point.

equal to the sum of the signals transmitted through the n incoming branches; i.e.,

$$x_k = \sum_{j=1}^{n} t_{jk} x_j \qquad (2\text{--}114)$$

(b) The value of the variable represented by any node is transmitted on all branches leaving the node. In Fig. 2-24b, the signal flow graph shows that the signal x_k is transmitted to all n branches which are leaving the node. Thus

$$x_1 = t_{k1} x_k$$
$$x_2 = t_{k2} x_k$$
$$\cdot$$
$$\cdot \qquad\qquad (2\text{--}115)$$
$$\cdot$$
$$x_n = t_{kn} x_k$$

(2) Multiplication

A series connection of branches with gains $t_{12}, t_{23}, t_{34}, \ldots, t_{(n-1)n}$, as shown in Fig. 2-25a, can be replaced by a single branch with gain equal to $t_{12}t_{23}t_{34} \cdots t_{(n-1)n}$; or

$$x_n = t_{12}t_{23}t_{34} \cdots t_{(n-1)n}x_1 \tag{2-116}$$

We shall use the following examples to illustrate the construction of the signal flow graphs of linear systems.

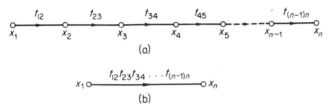

(a)

(b)

FIG. 2-25. (a) Signal flow graph with $n-1$ cascaded branches. (b) Equivalent signal flow graph of (a). Signal flow graphs showing the multiplication of branch gains.

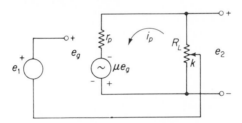

FIG. 2-26. Linear incremental equivalent of a feedback amplifier.

Example 2-3. A vacuum-tube feedback amplifier.

The linear incremental equivalent circuit for a feedback amplifier is shown in Fig. 2-26. One set of cause-and-effect equations describing the circuit may be written as

$$e_g = e_1 - e_f \tag{2-117}$$

$$e_f = \frac{\mu k R_L}{r_p + R_L} e_g \tag{2-118}$$

$$e_2 = -\frac{e_f}{k} \tag{2-119}$$

In these equations, we have chosen the variables e_1, e_g, e_f, and e_2, and the corresponding signal flow graph is drawn in Fig. 2-27a. In this signal flow graph, the feedback path from e_f to e_g clearly indicates the effect of the feedback voltage signal directed from the output to the input of the grid.

Normally, the equations for any physical system may take on various

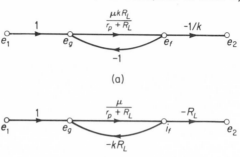

(a)

(b)

FIG. 2-27. (a) Signal flow graph portraying Eqs. (2-117)–(2-119). (b) Signal flow graph portraying Eqs. (2-120)–(2-122). Signal flow graphs for the feedback amplifier in Example 2-3.

forms, depending on the choice of the dependent variables. In this same problem, if we choose a new set of variables, $e_1, e_g, i_p,$ and e_2, the circuit equations become

$$e_g = e_1 - kR_L i_p \qquad (2\text{-}120)$$

$$i_p = \frac{\mu e_g}{r_p + R_L} \qquad (2\text{-}121)$$

$$e_2 = -R_L i_p \qquad (2\text{-}122)$$

The signal flow graph corresponding to these equations is drawn as shown in Fig. 2-27b. This simply shows that the signal flow graph of a given system is never unique. It is possible to construct a number of different signal flow graphs for the same system, depending on how the system equations are written.

Example 2-4. A passive ladder network.

The passive network shown in Fig. 2-28a is considered to consist of R, L, C elements so that the network elements can be represented by impedance functions or admittance functions, $Z(s)$ or $Y(s)$, respectively. The Laplace transform of the input voltage is denoted by $E_{in}(s)$, and that of the output voltage is $E_0(s)$. If we use the branch currents and node voltages designated as shown in the circuit, one set of independent equations representing cause-and-effect relation is

$$I_1 = (E_{in} - E_2)Y_1 \qquad (2\text{-}123)$$

$$E_2 = (I_1 - I_2)Z_2 \qquad (2\text{-}124)$$

$$I_3 = (E_2 - E_4)Y_3 \qquad (2\text{-}125)$$

$$E_0 = Z_4 I_3 \qquad (2\text{-}126)$$

where all functions are understood to be of s. With the variables $E_{in}, I_1,$

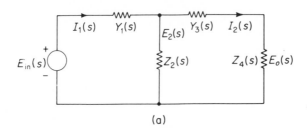

(a)

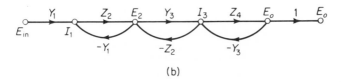

(b)

FIG. 2-28. (a) A passive ladder network; (b) Signal flow graph for the network.

E_2, I_3, and E_0 arranged from left to right in order, the signal flow graph of the network is constructed as shown in Fig. 2-28b.

From these two simple illustrations, we found that the equations that are proper for signal flow graphs are not the loop equations or the node equations generally used for network analysis. In the second case, we showed that a combination of branch current and node voltage equations are written so that the signal flow graph can be drawn directly from these equations. On the other hand, if the loop or node equations are already given, and they are the only source of information, since they are not in the correct form of cause-and-effect relations, we must first rearrange the terms of the equations so that all the "effects" appear on the left-hand side and all the "causes" appear on the right-hand side of the equations, before constructing the signal flow graph. In fact, a second look at Eqs. (2–120), (2–121), and (2–122) reveals that these are indeed obtained by rearranging the loop equations of the network.

We can readily show that only two loop equations are needed to describe the ladder network of Fig. 2-28a. The signal flow graph drawn from the rearranged loop equations would have fewer nodes and branches than the graph in Fig 2-28b, but the branch gains would be more complex. In fact, the advantage of the signal flow graph of Fig. 2-28b is that each branch contains a gain related to only one impedance or admittance element.

A General Gain Formula for Signal Flow Graph

In solving for the functional relation between the input and output variables (nodes) on a signal flow graph, a general gain formula[14] has been derived which permits writing down the functional relation by inspection. The formula is

$$M = \frac{x_{\text{out}}}{x_{\text{in}}} = \sum_k \frac{M_k \Delta_k}{\Delta} \qquad (2\text{-}127)$$

where $M_k = $ gain of the kth forward path, x_{out} is an *output node* variable, and x_{in} is an *input node* variable.

$$\Delta = 1 - \sum_m P_{m1} + \sum_m P_{m2} - \sum_m P_{m3} + \cdots \qquad (2\text{-}128)$$

$P_{mr} = $ gain product of the mth possible combination of r nontouching loops. $\qquad (2\text{-}129)$

Or $\Delta = 1 - $ (sum of all individual loop gains) $+$ (sum of gain products of all possible combinations of two non-touching loops) $-$ (sum of the gain products of all possible combinations of 3 nontouching loops) $+ \cdots$ $\qquad (2\text{-}130)$

$\Delta_k = $ the value of Δ for that part of the graph not touching* the kth forward path. $\qquad (2\text{-}131)$

This general gain formula may seem formidable to use at first glance, but the following examples will show that the actual application of the formula is quite straightforward. It must be emphasized, however, that the gain formula is valid only between an *input node* and an *output node*. Therefore, it cannot be used to evaluate the gain between the nodes x_2 and x_3 of the signal flow graphs in Fig. 2-22.

Example 2-5. Consider, in Fig. 2-28, that the functional relation between E_{out} and E_{in} is to be determined by using the general gain formula. The signal flow graph for the ladder network shown in Fig. 2-28a is redrawn in Fig. 2-29a. The following conclusions are obtained by inspection from the given signal flow graph:

(1) There is only one forward path (Fig. 2-29b); the forward path gain is

$$M_1 = Y_1 Z_2 Y_3 Z_4 \qquad (2\text{-}132)$$

(2) There are three individual feedback loops (Fig. 2-29c); the loop gains are

$$P_{11} = -Z_2 Y_1 \qquad (2\text{-}133)$$

$$P_{21} = -Z_2 Y_3 \qquad (2\text{-}134)$$

$$P_{31} = -Z_4 Y_3 \qquad (2\text{-}135)$$

(3) There are two nontouching loops, as shown in Fig. 2-29d. The loop gains of these two loops are

$$-Z_2 Y_1 \quad \text{and} \quad -Z_4 Y_3 \qquad (2\text{-}136)$$

*Two loops or two parts of a signal flow graph are said to be nontouching if they do not have any common nodes.

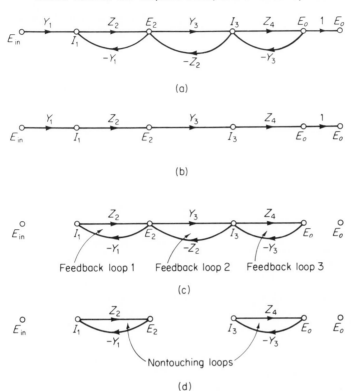

FIG. 2-29. (a) Signal flow graph of passive ladder network; (b) The forward path; (c) The three individual feedback loops; (d) The two nontouching loops; Identification of quantities in the general gain formula for the signal flow graph of Fig. 2-28.

Hence

P_{12} = gain product of the first (and only) possible combination of two nontouching loops = $Z_2Z_4Y_1Y_3$.

(4) There are no three nontouching loops, four nontouching loops, etc.; thus

$$P_{m3} = 0, \qquad P_{m4} = 0, \ldots$$

From Eq. (2–128),

$$\Delta = 1 - (-Z_2Y_1 - Z_2Y_3 - Z_4Y_3) + (Z_2Z_4Y_1Y_3) \qquad (2\text{–}137)$$

(5) All the three feedback loops are in touch with the forward path; hence

$$\Delta_1 = 1 \qquad (2\text{–}138)$$

Substituting the quantities in Eqs. (2–132) through (2–138) into Eq. (2–127), we obtain the output-input voltage relation of the ladder network as

$$\frac{E_{\text{out}}}{E_{\text{in}}} = M = \frac{M_1 \Delta_1}{\Delta} = \frac{Y_1 Y_3 Z_2 Z_4}{1 + Z_2 Y_1 + Z_2 Y_3 + Z_4 Y_3 + Z_2 Z_4 Y_1 Y_3}$$

$$(2\text{-}139)$$

Example 2-6. As a second example, consider the signal flow graph shown

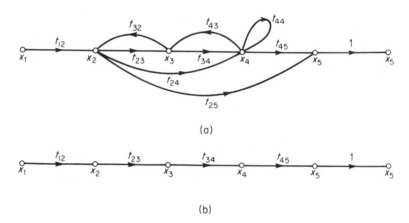

(a)

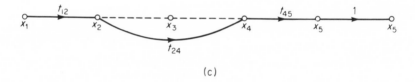

(b)

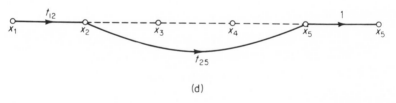

(c)

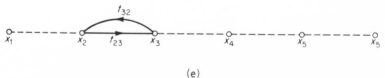

(d)

(e)

FIG. 2-30. (a) Signal flow graph; (b) Forward path with gain M_1; (c) Forward path with gain M_2. (d) Forward path with gain M_3; (e) Feedback loop P_{11}. Signal flow graph showing the application of the general flow graph gain formula.

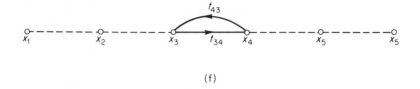

(f)

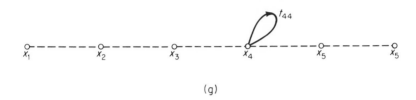

(g)

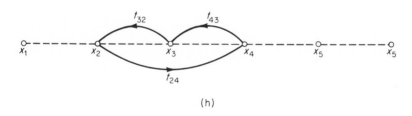

(h)

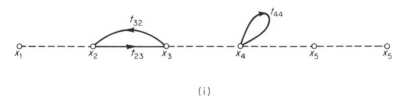

(i)

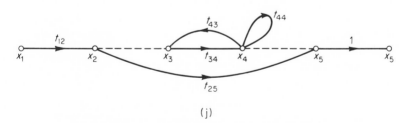

(j)

Fig. 2-30 (*cont.*) (f) Feedback loop P_{21}; (g) Feedback loop P_{31}; (h) Feedback loop P_{41}; (i) The two nontouching loops of the signal flow graph; (j) Feedback loops not touching forward path M_3. Signal flow graphs showing the application of the general flow graph gain formula.

in Fig. 2-21d, which is redrawn in Fig. 2-30a. The functional relation between the output variable x_5 and the input variable x_1 is to be determined by means of the general gain formula. The following conclusions are obtained by inspection from the given signal flow graph:

(1) There are three forward paths (Figs. 2-30b, c, d); the forward path gains are

$$M_1 = t_{12}t_{23}t_{34}t_{45} \quad \text{(for } x_1\text{-}x_2\text{-}x_3\text{-}x_4\text{-}x_5) \tag{2-140}$$

$$M_2 = t_{12}t_{24}t_{45} \quad \text{(for } x_1\text{-}x_2\text{-}x_4\text{-}x_5) \tag{2-141}$$

$$M_3 = t_{12}t_{25} \quad \text{(for } x_1\text{-}x_2\text{-}x_3) \tag{2-142}$$

(2) There are four individual feedback loops (Figs. 2-30b, c, d); with loop gains

$$P_{11} = t_{23}t_{32} \quad \text{(for } x_2\text{-}x_3\text{-}x_2) \tag{2-143}$$

$$P_{21} = t_{34}t_{43} \quad \text{(for } x_3\text{-}x_4\text{-}x_3) \tag{2-144}$$

$$P_{31} = t_{44} \quad \text{(for } x_4\text{-}x_4) \tag{2-145}$$

$$P_{41} = t_{24}t_{43}t_{32} \quad \text{(for } x_2\text{-}x_4\text{-}x_3\text{-}x_2) \tag{2-146}$$

(3) There are two nontouching loops, as shown in Fig. 2-30i. The loop gains of these two loops are

$$t_{23}t_{32} \quad \text{and} \quad t_{44}$$

Hence

$P_{12} =$ gain product of the first (and only) possible combination

of two nontouching loops $= t_{23}t_{32}t_{44}$ $\qquad$ (2-147)

(4) There are no three nontouching loops, four nontouching loops, etc.; hence

$$P_{m3} = P_{m4} = \cdots = 0 \tag{2-148}$$

From Eq. (2-128),

$$\Delta = 1 - (t_{23}t_{32} + t_{34}t_{43} + t_{44} + t_{24}t_{43}t_{32}) + t_{23}t_{32}t_{44} \tag{2-149}$$

(5) The first forward path (path gain $= M_1$) is in touch with all the four feedback loops; hence $\Delta_1 = 1$. The second forward path (path gain $= M_2$) is also in touch with all the four feedback loops; hence $\Delta_2 = 1$. The third forward path (path gain $= M_3$) is not in touch with the two feedback loops, $x_3\text{-}x_4\text{-}x_3$ (loop gain $= t_{34}t_{43}$), and $x_4\text{-}x_4$ (loop gain $= t_{44}$), but is in touch with the other two loops (Fig. 2-30j); hence

$$\Delta_3 = 1 - (t_{34}t_{43} + t_{44}) \tag{2-150}$$

Substituting the quantities obtained in Eq. (2-140) through Eq. (2-150) into the general gain formula, we find that the expression for x_5/x_1 is

$$M = \frac{x_5}{x_1} = \frac{M_1\Delta_1 + M_2\Delta_2 + M_3\Delta_3}{\Delta}$$

$$= \frac{t_{12}t_{23}t_{34}t_{45} + t_{12}t_{24}t_{45} + t_{12}t_{25}(1 - t_{34}t_{43} - t_{44})}{1 - t_{23}t_{32} - t_{34}t_{43} - t_{44} - t_{24}t_{43}t_{32} + t_{23}t_{32}t_{44}} \tag{2-151}$$

2.7 Application of Signal Flow Graph Gain
Formula to Block Diagrams

Because of the similarity in the topology of the block diagram and the signal flow graph, it is possible to apply the general gain formula in Eq. (2–127) directly to a block diagram. In fact, given any block diagram, there is always an equivalent signal flow graph.

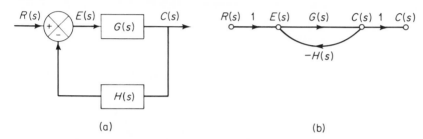

(a)   (b)

FIG. 2-31. Equivalent signal flow graph of a block diagram of a simple feedback control system. (a) Block diagram; (b) Signal flow graph.

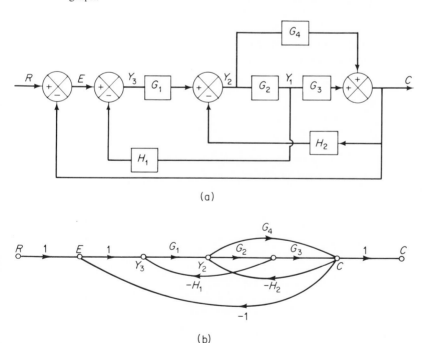

(a)

(b)

FIG. 2-32. A block diagram and its equivalent signal flow graph. (a) Block diagram; (b) Signal flow graph.

To illustrate how the signal flow graph and the block diagram are related, the equivalent models for a simple feedback control system are shown in Fig. 2-31. Note that since a node on the signal flow graph is interpreted as a summing point of all incoming signals to the node, the negative feedback in this case is represented by assigning a negative sign for the feedback path gain H.

The block diagram of a more complex system is shown in Fig. 2-32a. The equivalent signal flow graph for this block diagram is shown in Fig. 2-32b. The closed-loop transfer function of this feedback control system is obtained by applying the general gain formula to either the block diagram or the signal flow graph.

$$\frac{C(s)}{R(s)} = M(s) = \frac{G_1 G_2 G_3 + G_1 G_4}{1 + G_1 G_2 H_1 + G_2 G_3 H_2 + G_1 G_2 G_3 + G_4 H_2 + G_1 G_4}$$

$$(2\text{--}152)$$

2.8 Signal Flow Graphs of Discrete-data Systems

It is reasonable to expect that for discrete-data systems with more complicated system configurations than those shown in Fig. 2-18 and Fig. 2-19, the derivation of the output transforms by means of the algebraic method will be quite tedious. One probably would immediately consider the possibility of using Mason's signal flow graph formula, which is successfully applied to the block diagrams of continuous-data control systems. However, an attempt to apply Mason's formula to the block diagram or the equivalent signal flow graph of a system with sampled data will encounter immediate

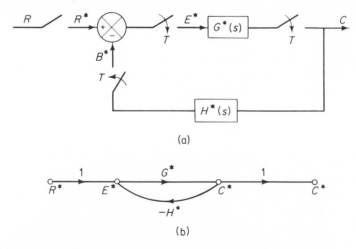

(a)

(b)

FIG. 2-33. (a) An all-sampled-data system; (b) Equivalent signal flow graph of sampled-data system in Fig. (a).

difficulty, since the gain formula does not know how to treat samplers. The conventional signal flow graph algebra cannot handle systems with samplers, unless all the signals in the discrete-data system are of the discrete form. For instance, the signals at all points of the system shown in Fig. 2-33a are discrete with respect to time. The signal flow graph of the system is shown in Fig. 2-33b. Since no continuous data are found in the system, the samplers are omitted from the equivalent signal flow graph, and all the signals and transfer functions are starred quantities. Therefore, applying the gain formula to Fig. 2-33b, we obtain the closed-loop transfer function of the system as

$$\frac{C^*(s)}{R^*(s)} = \frac{G^*(s)}{1 + G^*(s)H^*(s)} \qquad (2\text{--}153)$$

Therefore, we conclude that *the gain formula for signal flow graphs can be applied only when the signal flow graph contains nodes representing either all continuous signals or all discrete signals.* However, a great majority of the systems with discrete data contain both sampled and continuous data. Therefore, the samplers cannot be left out of the signal flow graph.

A method of determining the output transforms of a system with both sampled and continuous data using Mason's gain formula is described in the following:

(1) Using the block diagram as the starting point, we draw the signal flow graph of the system. For instance, the signal flow graph of the system in Fig. 2-18 is shown in Fig. 2-34.

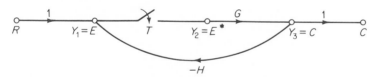

FIG. 2-34. Signal flow graph of the discrete-data system of Fig. 2-18.

(2) The *discrete signal flow graph* is constructed from information obtained from the signal flow graph of the system. This step will need some explanation.

Let us consider the signal flow graph of Fig. 2-34. Notice that the signal flow graph still contains the sampling switch, so the transfer relationships of the system cannot be obtained in one operation by applying Mason's gain formula. If an artificial source E^* is added at the output of the sampler, the sampler can be deleted from the signal flow graph. Now the signal flow graph has two inputs in $R(s)$ and $E^*(s)$. The following equations are written by inspection from the signal flow graph of Fig. 2-34:

$$Y_1 = E = R - GHY_1^* \qquad (2\text{--}154)$$

$$Y_2 = E^* = Y_1^* \qquad (2\text{--}155)$$

$$Y_3 = C = GY_1^* \qquad (2\text{-}156)$$

where, for simplicity, $E^*(s)$ is represented by E^*, $R(s)$ by R, $H(s)$ by H, etc. In essence, Eqs. (2-154), (2-155), and (2-156) are obtained by applying Mason's gain formula to Fig. 2-34, with R and E^* ($= Y_1^*$) as input nodes, and Y_1, Y_2, and Y_3 as output nodes.

Taking the pulsed transform on both sides of the last three equations yields

$$Y_1^* = R^* - (GH)^* Y_1^* \qquad (2\text{-}157)$$

$$Y_2^* = Y_1^* \qquad (2\text{-}158)$$

$$Y_3^* = G^* Y_1^* \qquad (2\text{-}159)$$

Since these three equations now contain only discrete variables, the signal flow graph drawn from these equations is called the *discrete signal flow graph*, and is shown in Fig. 2-35. Applying Mason's gain formula directly to this discrete signal flow graph, we have

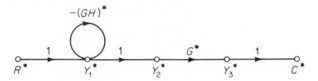

FIG. 2-35. Discrete signal flow graph of the system in Fig. 2-18.

$$C^*(s) = \frac{G^*(s)}{1 + GH^*(s)} R^*(s) \qquad (2\text{-}160)$$

which agrees with the result obtained earlier in Eq. (2-99).

In general, if a multiloop discrete-data system contains several synchronized samplers, by deleting the samplers and adding the artificial signal sources at the nodes where the output of the samplers are connected, a set of equations similar to Eqs. (2-154) through (2-156) may be written. For instance, if the node variables of the signal flow graph are represented by Y, the following equation may be written for the variable Y_j of node j:

$$Y_j = \sum_i a_{ij} Y_i^* + \sum_k b_{kj} R_k \qquad (2\text{-}161)$$

where it is assumed that a sampler is located between nodes i and j, and that the signal is transmitted from node i to node j. Therefore, Y_i^* is the sampled signal from the sampler following node i which will flow to node j; a_{ij} represents the transmission between node i and node j; b_{kj} denotes the transmission from node k to node j; R_k is the signal applied at node k which will flow to node j. Taking the pulsed transform of both sides of Eq. (2-161) yields

$$Y_j^* = \sum_i a_{ij}^* Y_i^* + \sum_k (b_{kj} R_k)^* \qquad (2\text{-}162)$$

In general, it is possible to combine the application of Mason's formula and the pulsed transformation into one step so that one gets Eq. (2–162) without Eq. (2–161).

In Eq. (2–162), all the variables are of the discrete form. Therefore, the discrete signal flow graph may be constructed, which represents the functional relationship between the sampled variables Y_1^*, Y_2^*, ..., Y_i^*, ... of the system.

(3) In the last step we demonstrated how the sampled variables of a discrete-data system can be evaluated from the discrete signal flow graph by direct use of Mason's gain formula. However, the discrete signal flow graph does not contain the unsampled variables Y_1, Y_2, ... Since the actual output response of most discrete-data control systems does not take the form of a pulse train, it is necessary to determine the expression of the continuous response $C(s)$. For this purpose, we shall define a *composite signal flow graph*, which is the composition of the original signal flow graph and the discrete signal flow graph, with the sampling switches in the original signal flow graph deleted. The sampling operation is described by drawing a branch of unity gain from node Y_i^* of the discrete signal flow graph to node Y_j on the original signal flow graph (since if a sampler is located between node i and node j and the signal is transmitted from i to j, the branch of unity gain simply describes the relation $Y_j = Y_i^*$). From this composite signal flow graph, *all the discrete and continuous output responses can be determined as functions of the input signal by means of Mason's formula*. Actually, once the composite signal flow graph is constructed, there is no need to construct a separate discrete signal flow graph, because the former will contain all the information about the discrete and the continuous signals.

Let us use the simple discrete-data system shown in Fig. 2-18 to illustrate

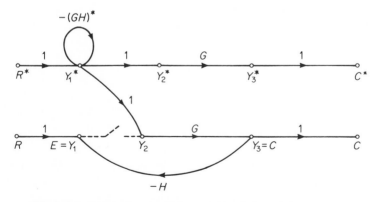

FIG. 2-36. Composite signal flow graph of discrete-data system given in Fig. 2-18.

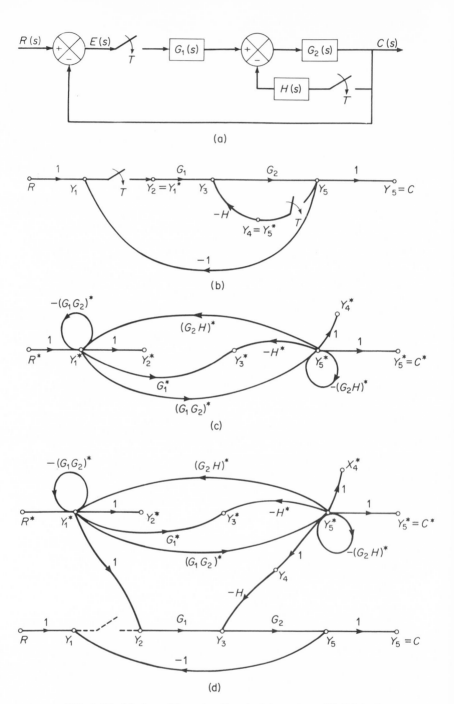

FIG. 2-37. (a) A multisampler discrete-data system; (b) Original signal flow graph of system in Fig. 2-37 (a); (c) Discrete flow graph for the system of Fig. 2-37(a); (d) Composite signal flow of system in Fig. 2-37(a).

the construction of the composite signal flow graph. The signal flow graph of the system is shown in Fig. 2-34, and the discrete signal flow graph is already obtained, as shown in Fig. 2-35. It is apparent that the variables in the two signal flow graphs are related by $Y_2 = Y_1^*$. Therefore, the composite signal flow graph is constructed by drawing a branch of unity gain from node Y_1^* of the discrete signal flow graph to node Y_2 of the signal flow graph, as shown in Fig. 2-36. Using Mason's gain formula, we obtain the continuous output response of the system as

$$C(s) = \frac{G(s)}{1 + GH^*(s)} R^*(s) \tag{2-163}$$

which agrees with the result obtained earlier in Eq. (2–98). The continuous signal $R(s)$ does not appear in the expression for $C(s)$, since there is no forward path from R to C. In a similar manner, the continuous error is obtained as

$$E(s) = \frac{1}{1 + GH^*(s)} R(s) \tag{2-164}$$

It is easy to see that the discrete functions $C^*(s)$ and $E^*(s)$ can also be derived directly from the composite signal flow graph simply by use of the gain formula.

Example 2-7. In this example, the discrete and continuous output responses of the discrete-data system shown in Fig. 2-37a will be evaluated by use of the signal flow graph technique. Following the steps outlined in the last section, we have

(1) The signal flow graph of the system is drawn as shown in Fig. 2-37b.

(2) From the signal flow graph, the following equations are written in accordance with the form of Eq. (2–161):

$$Y_1 = -G_1 G_2 Y_1^* + G_2 H Y_5^* + R \tag{2-165}$$

$$Y_2 = Y_1^* \tag{2-166}$$

$$Y_3 = G_1 X_1^* - H X_5^* \tag{2-167}$$

$$Y_4 = Y_5^* \tag{2-168}$$

$$Y_5 = -G_2 H Y_5^* + G_1 G_2 Y_1^* \tag{2-169}$$

Taking the pulsed transform on both sides of Eqs. (2–165) through (2–169) yields

$$Y_1^* = -(G_1 G_2)^* Y_1^* + (G_2 H)^* Y_5^* + R^* \tag{2-170}$$

$$Y_2^* = Y_1^* \tag{2-171}$$

$$Y_3^* = G_1^* Y_1^* - H^* Y_5^* \tag{2-172}$$

$$Y_4^* = Y_5^* \tag{2-173}$$

$$Y_5^* = (G_1 G_2)^* Y_1^* - (G_2 H)^* Y_5^* \tag{2-174}$$

Based on these equations, the discrete signal flow graph is constructed as shown in Fig. 2-37c. The composite signal flow graph is obtained by connecting nodes Y_1^* and Y_5^* of the discrete signal flow graph to nodes Y_2 and Y_4 on the signal flow graph, respectively, by branches with unity gains. (see Fig. 2–37d.) The discrete and continuous output transforms are obtained by applying Mason's formula to the composite signal flow graph.

$$C^* = Y_5^* = \frac{(G_1G_2)^*R^*}{1 + (G_1G_2)^* + (G_2H)^* - (G_1G_2)^*(G_2H)^* + (G_1G_2)^*(G_2H)^*}$$

$$= \frac{(G_1G_2)^*R^*}{1 + (G_1G_2)^* + (G_2H)^*} \tag{2-175}$$

and

$$C = Y_5 = \frac{G_1G_2[1 + (G_2H)^*] - (G_1G_2)^*G_2H}{1 + (G_1G_2)^* + (G_2H)^*} R^* \tag{2-176}$$

2.9 The Polar Plots of Transfer Functions

Generally speaking, the analysis and design of control systems can be carried out in either the time domain or the frequency domain. The essential feature of the frequency-domain method is that the description of a system is given in terms of its response to a sinusoidally varying input signal. If the system is linear, the output will be a sine wave of the same frequency as the input; if the system is nonlinear, the output will, in addition, contain higher harmonics, and sometimes subharmonics. Another important feature of the frequency response method is that the transfer function describing the sinusoidal steady-state behavior of the system can be obtained from the transfer function simply by replacing the Laplace operator s with $j\omega$. The sinusoidal transfer function is thus a complex function of complex variables, and, in general, can be represented by a magnitude and a phase angle. Therefore, it is often convenient to represent a transfer function graphically in terms of its magnitude and phase angle when the frequency is varied from zero to infinity.

In control system studies, the plots of the open-loop transfer function $G(j\omega)$ or that of the loop transfer function $G(j\omega)H(j\omega)$ are often made and the performance of the closed-loop system is predicted from these plots.

Consider that $G(s)$ is the open-loop transfer function of a certain feedback control system. The sinusoidal transfer function is $G(j\omega)$ and can be written as

$$G(j\omega) = [G(s)]_{s=j\omega} = |G(j\omega)|\,\underline{/\phi(j\omega)} \tag{2-177}$$

where $|G(j\omega)|$ denotes the magnitude of $G(j\omega)$, and $\underline{/\phi(j\omega)}$ is the angle of $G(j\omega)$.

The following methods of plotting the transfer function $G(j\omega)$ are most useful in the analysis and design of feedback control systems in the frequency domain:

(1) *Polar plot.* A plot of magnitude versus phase on polar coordinates as ω is varied from zero to infinity.

(2) *Bode plot* (*corner plot*). A plot of magnitude in decibel versus log ω (or ω) and phase angle versus log ω (or ω) in rectangular (or semilog) coordinates.

(3) *Magnitude versus phase angle plot.* A plot of magnitude in decibel versus phase angle of $G(j\omega)$ on rectangular coordinates with frequency as a varying parameter on the curve.

The polar plot of a transfer function $G(s)$ is a plot of the magnitude versus phase of $G(j\omega)$ on polar coordinates as ω is varied from zero to infinity. From a mathematical viewpoint, the process is regarded as a mapping of the positive half of the imaginary axis of the plane of the complex variable s onto the plane of the function $G(j\omega)$ as shown in Fig. 2-38.

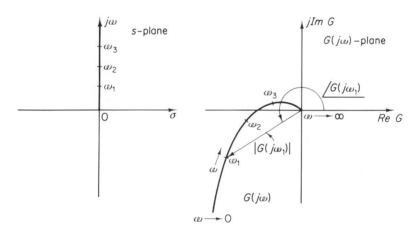

FIG. 2-38. Polar plot shown as a mapping of the positive half of the $j\omega$ axis in the s-plane onto the $G(j\omega)$ plane.

For any frequency $\omega = \omega_1$, the magnitude and phase of $G(j\omega_1)$ are represented by a phasor with the corresponding magnitude and phase angle, which originates from the origin of the $G(j\omega)$-plane. In measuring the phase, counterclockwise is referred to as positive and clockwise as negative.

To illustrate the plotting of the transfer function $G(j\omega)$ curve on polar coordinates, consider the function

$$G(s) = \frac{C(s)}{E(s)} = \frac{1}{1 + sT} \qquad (2\text{--}178)$$

where T is the time constant.

Putting $s = j\omega$, we have

$$G(j\omega) = \frac{C(j\omega)}{E(j\omega)} = \frac{1}{1 + j\omega T} \qquad (2\text{–}179)$$

In terms of magnitude and phase shift, the last equation can be written as

$$G(j\omega) = \frac{1}{\sqrt{1 + \omega^2 T^2}} \underline{/-\tan^{-1}\omega T} \qquad (2\text{–}180)$$

When ω is zero, the magnitude of $G(j\omega)$ is unity, and the phase of $G(j\omega)$ is zero degree. Thus, at $\omega = 0$, $G(j\omega)$ is represented by a phasor of unit length directed in the zero degree direction. As ω increases, the magnitude of $G(j\omega)$ decreases and the phase angle also becomes more negative. Thus the length of the phasor decreases and the phasor rotates in the clockwise direction as ω increases. When ω approaches infinity, the magnitude of $G(j\omega)$ becomes zero, and the phase is -90 deg. This is represented by a phasor of zero length directed along the -90-deg axis in the $G(j\omega)$-plane. By substituting other finite values of ω into Eq. (2–180), the exact locus of $G(j\omega)$ is depicted in Fig. 2-39 as a semicircle.

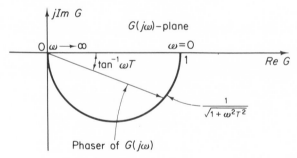

FIG. 2-39. The polar plot of $G(j\omega) = \dfrac{1}{1 + j\omega T}$.

As a second example, consider the transfer function

$$G(j\omega) = \frac{1 + j\omega T_a}{1 + j\omega T_1} \qquad (2\text{–}181)$$

where T_a and T_1 are time constants. Equation (2–181) can also be written as

$$G(j\omega) = \sqrt{\frac{1 + \omega^2 T_a^2}{1 + \omega^2 T_1^2}} \underline{/\tan^{-1}\omega T_a - \tan^{-1}\omega T_1} \qquad (2\text{–}182)$$

The polar plot of $G(j\omega)$, in this case, apparently depends upon the relative magnitudes of T_a and T_1. If $T_a > T_1$, the magnitude of $G(j\omega)$ is always greater than unity as ω is varied from zero to infinity, and the phase shift of $G(j\omega)$ is always positive. If $T_a < T_1$, the magnitude of $G(j\omega)$ is always less than unity, and the phase shift is always negative. The transfer function

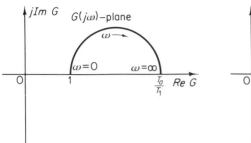

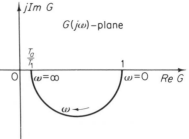

FIG. 2-40. Polar plot of
$$G(j\omega) = \frac{1 + j\omega T_a}{1 + j\omega T_1}(T_a > T_1).$$

FIG. 2-41. Polar plot of
$$G(j\omega) = \frac{1 + j\omega T_a}{1 + j\omega T_1}(T_a < T_1).$$

loci of $G(j\omega)$ corresponding to the two different situations are plotted in Figs. 2-40 and 2-41, respectively.

It is apparent that the plotting of the polar plots of transfer functions is generally a tedious process, except perhaps in a few trivial cases. In practice, a digital computer can be used to give data or even the final figure of the polar plots of a wide class of transfer functions. However, the major use of the polar plot in feedback control systems is in conjunction with the graphical study of the stability of the system. As will be shown later, the polar plot of the loop transfer function of a closed-loop system forms the main part of the Nyquist plot from which the stability of the over-all system is determined. For stability study, only the general shape of the Nyquist plot of $G(s)H(s)$ is needed, and for all practical purposes, a rough sketch of the polar plot is usually quite adequate.

In general, the sketching of the polar plot is facilitated by the following information:

(1) The behavior of the magnitude and phase of the transfer function at $\omega = 0$ and at $\omega = \infty$.

(2) The possible points of intersections of the polar plot with the real and imaginary axes of the s-plane and the values of ω at these intersections.

Example 2-8. Consider that it is desired to make a rough sketch of the polar plot for the transfer function

$$G(s) = \frac{10}{s(s + 1)} \qquad (2\text{-}183)$$

Substituting $s = j\omega$ in Eq. (2-183), the magnitude and phase of $G(j\omega)$ at $\omega = 0$ and $\omega = \infty$ are computed as follows:

$$\lim_{\omega \to 0} |G(j\omega)| = \lim_{\omega \to 0} \frac{10}{\omega} = \infty \qquad (2\text{-}184)$$

$$\lim_{\omega \to \infty} |G(j\omega)| = \lim_{\omega \to \infty} \frac{10}{\omega^2} = 0 \qquad (2\text{-}185)$$

$$\lim_{\omega \to 0} \underline{/G(j\omega)} = \lim_{\omega \to 0} \left/ \frac{10}{j\omega} \right. = -90° \qquad (2\text{-}186)$$

$$\lim_{\omega \to \infty} \underline{/G(j\omega)} = \lim_{\omega \to \infty} \left/ \frac{10}{(j\omega)^2} \right. = -180° \qquad (2\text{-}187)$$

Thus, the behavior of the polar plot of $G(s)$ at $\omega = 0$ and $\omega = \infty$ is ascertained. Next, it is necessary to determine if $G(j\omega)$ intersects any of the axes of the $G(j\omega)$-plane.

If the polar plot of $G(j\omega)$ intersects the real axis, at the point of intersection, the imaginary part of $G(j\omega)$ is zero; i.e.,

$$\text{Im}\,[G(j\omega)] = 0 \qquad (2\text{-}188)$$

$G(j\omega)$ can be rationalized by multiplying its numerator and denominator by the complex conjugate of its denominator. Therefore,

$$G(j\omega) = \frac{10(-j\omega - \omega^2)}{(j\omega - \omega^2)(-j\omega - \omega^2)} = \frac{-10\omega^2}{\omega^4 + \omega^2} - j\frac{10\omega}{\omega^4 + \omega^2} \qquad (2\text{-}189)$$

and

$$\text{Im}[G(j\omega)] = \frac{-10\omega}{\omega^4 + \omega^2} = \frac{-10}{\omega(\omega^2 + 1)} \qquad (2\text{-}190)$$

When Im $[G(j\omega)] = 0$, $\omega = \infty$, meaning the only intersect that the $G(j\omega)$ plot has with the real axis of the $G(j\omega)$-plane is at $\omega = \infty$, and from the result of Eq. (2–185), this intersect is at the origin.

Similarly, the intersection with the imaginary axis is found by setting

$$\text{Re}\,[G(j\omega)] = 0 \qquad (2\text{-}191)$$

Thus, from Eq. (2–189),

$$\text{Re}\,[G(j\omega)] = \frac{-10}{\omega^2 + 1} = 0$$

when $\omega = \infty$, which also implies that the only intersection is at the origin of the $G(j\omega)$-plane.

From these calculations, a rough sketch of the polar plot of $G(j\omega)$ is made as shown in Fig. 2-42.

Example 2-9. Consider that a rough sketch of the polar plot of the transfer function

$$G(s) = \frac{10}{s(s+1)(s+2)} \qquad (2\text{-}192)$$

is desired.

The following calculations are made:

$$\lim_{\omega \to 0} |G(j\omega)| = \lim_{\omega \to 0} \frac{10}{\omega} = \infty \qquad (2\text{-}193)$$

$$\lim_{\omega \to \infty} |G(j\omega)| = \lim_{\omega \to \infty} \frac{10}{\omega^3} = 0 \qquad (2\text{-}194)$$

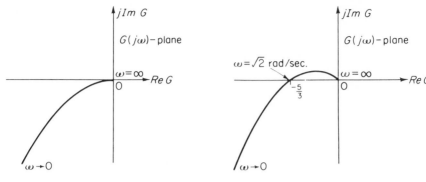

FIG. 2-42. A sketch of the polar plot of
$$G(s) = \frac{10}{s(s + 1)}$$

FIG. 2-43. A sketch of the polar plot of
$$G(s) = \frac{10}{s(s + 1)(s + 2)}$$

$$\lim_{\omega \to 0} \underline{/G(j\omega)} = \lim_{\omega \to 0} \underline{/\frac{10}{j\omega}} = -90° \qquad (2\text{-}195)$$

$$\lim_{\omega \to \infty} \underline{/G(j\omega)} = \lim_{\omega \to \infty} \underline{/\frac{10}{(j\omega)^3}} = -270° \qquad (2\text{-}196)$$

Rationalizing $G(j\omega)$ gives

$$G(j\omega) = \frac{10[-3\omega^2 - j\omega(2 - \omega^2)]}{[-3\omega^2 + j\omega(2 - \omega^2)][-3\omega^2 - j\omega(2 - \omega^2)]}$$

$$= \frac{-30\omega^2}{9\omega^4 + \omega^2(2 - \omega^2)^2} - \frac{j10\omega(2 - \omega^2)}{9\omega^4 + \omega^2(2 - \omega^2)^2} \qquad (2\text{-}197)$$

Thus,

$$\mathrm{Re}\,[G(j\omega)] = \frac{-30}{9\omega^2 + (2 - \omega^2)^2} = 0$$

gives

$$\omega = \infty$$

which means that the $G(j\omega)$ plot intersects the imaginary axis only at the origin.

Also, when

$$\mathrm{Im}[G(j\omega)] = \frac{-10(2 - \omega^2)}{9\omega^3 + \omega(2 - \omega^2)^2} = 0 \qquad (2\text{-}198)$$

$$\omega^2 = 2 \qquad (2\text{-}199)$$

which gives the intersection on the real axis of $G(j\omega)$ at $\omega = \pm\sqrt{2}$ rad/sec. Substituting $\omega = \sqrt{2}$ rad/sec into Eq. (2-197) gives the intersect at

$$G(j\omega) = \frac{-30 \times 2}{9 \times 4} = -\frac{5}{3} \qquad (2\text{-}200)$$

The result of $\omega = -\sqrt{2}$ rad/sec has no meaning physically, but mathematically it simply represents a mapping point on the negative $j\omega$ axis of the s-plane. In general, if $G(s)$ is a rational function of s (a quotient of two polynomials of s), the plot of $G(j\omega)$ for negative ω is the mirror image of that for positive ω, with the mirror placed on the real axis in the $G(j\omega)$-plane.

With the information collected above, it is now possible to make a sketch of the polar plot for $G(j\omega)$, and the sketch is shown in Fig. 2–43.

Although the method of obtaining the rough sketch of the polar plot described above is quite general, it is evident that for complex transfer functions which may have multiple crossings on the real and imaginary axes in the transfer function plane, the algebraic manipulation may again be quite involved. We shall show in the next section that information on the polar plot can always be obtained from the Bode plot, which is usually sketched with ease. Thus, for more complex transfer functions, sketches of the polar plots are preferably obtained with the help of the Bode plots.

2.10 The Bode Plot[15] (Corner Plot) of a Transfer Function

Another useful form of the transfer function plots is the *Bode plot*, which ordinarily contains two graphs—one with the magnitude of the sinusoidal transfer function $G(j\omega)$ plotted in decibel versus $\log \omega$ or ω, and the other with the phase angle of $G(j\omega)$ in degrees as a function of $\log \omega$ or ω. The *Bode plot* is also known sometimes as the *corner plot* or simply the *logarithmic plot* of the transfer function $G(s)$.

The Bode plot has the following unique characteristics:

(1) The product factors in the expression of $G(j\omega)$ become additive terms, since logarithms are used.

(2) The shape of the corner plot for most control systems makes it possible to represent approximately the exact function plot by straight line asymptotes.

(3) Since the corner plots are easy to construct, the data necessary for the construction of the polar plot and the magnitude in decibels versus phase shift plot (Sec. 2.11) can be obtained directly from the corner plot.

In general, we can represent the open-loop transfer function of a feed-back control system (if the system does not have pure time lag in the forward path) by the following equation:

$$G(s) = \frac{K'(s + z_1)(s + z_2)\dots(s + z_m)}{(s + p_1)(s + p_2)\dots(s + p_n)} \qquad (2\text{–}201)$$

where K' is a constant. The z's and the p's may be zero, real, or complex conjugate numbers. Hence, Eq. (2–201) can also be written

$$G(s) = \frac{K' \displaystyle\prod_{i=1}^{\mu} (s + \sigma_i) \prod_{k=1+\mu}^{m} \left(\frac{s^2}{\omega_{nk}^2} + \frac{2\delta_k}{\omega_{nk}}s + 1\right)}{\displaystyle\prod_{q=1}^{v} (s + \sigma_q) \prod_{r=1+v}^{n} \left(\frac{s^2}{\omega_{nr}^2} + \frac{2\delta_r}{\omega_{nr}}s + 1\right)} \qquad (2\text{–}202)$$

where σ_i and σ_q are real numbers. Under sinusoidal steady-state conditions, $s = j\omega$, Eq. (2-202) becomes

$$G(j\omega) = \frac{K' \prod\limits_{i=1}^{\mu} (j\omega + \sigma_i) \prod\limits_{k=1+\mu}^{m} \left[\left(\frac{j\omega}{\omega_{nk}}\right)^2 + \left(\frac{2\delta_k}{\omega_{nk}}\right) j\omega + 1 \right]}{\prod\limits_{q=1}^{v} (j\omega + \sigma_q) \prod\limits_{r=1+v}^{n} \left[\left(\frac{j\omega}{\omega_{nr}}\right)^2 + \left(\frac{2\delta_r}{\omega_{nr}}\right) j\omega + 1 \right]} \qquad (2\text{-}203)$$

which can also be written

$$G(j\omega) = \frac{K \prod\limits_{i=1}^{\mu} (1 + j\omega T_i) \prod\limits_{k=1+\mu}^{m} (-\mu_k^2 + j2\delta_k\mu_k + 1)}{\prod\limits_{q=1}^{v} (1 + j\omega T_q) \prod\limits_{r=1+v}^{n} (-\mu_r^2 + j2\delta_r\mu_r + 1)} \qquad (2\text{-}204)$$

where

$$K = \frac{K' \prod\limits_{i=1}^{\mu} \sigma_i}{\prod\limits_{q=1}^{v} \sigma_q}$$

$$T_i = \frac{1}{\sigma_i}$$

$$T_q = \frac{1}{\sigma_q}$$

$$\mu_k = \frac{\omega}{\omega_{nk}}$$

and

$$\mu_r = \frac{\omega}{\omega_{nr}}$$

The magnitude of $G(j\omega)$ in decibels is obtained by multiplying the logarithm to the base 10 of $|G(j\omega)|$ by 20; we have

$$20 \log_{10} |G(j\omega)| = 20 \log_{10} |K| + 20 \sum_{i=1}^{\mu} \log_{10} |1 + j\omega T_i| + 20 \sum_{k=1+\mu}^{m} \log_{10} |1$$

$$+ j2\delta_k\mu_k - \mu_k^2| - 20 \sum_{q=1}^{v} \log_{10} |1 + j\omega T_q|$$

$$- 20 \sum_{r=1+v}^{n} \log_{10} |1 + j2\delta_r\mu_r - \mu_r^2| \qquad (2\text{-}205)$$

The phase of $G(j\omega)$ is

$$\mathrm{Arg}\, G(j\omega) = \mathrm{Arg}\,|K| + \sum_{i=1}^{\mu} \mathrm{Arg}\,(1 + j\omega T_i) + \sum_{k=1+\mu}^{m} \mathrm{Arg}\,(1 + j2\delta_k\mu_k - \mu_k^2)$$

$$- \sum_{q=1}^{v} \mathrm{Arg}\,(1 + j\omega T_q) - \sum_{r=1+v}^{n} \mathrm{Arg}\,(1 + j2\delta_r\mu_r - \mu_r^2)$$

$$\qquad (2\text{-}206)$$

where $\mathrm{Arg}\, K = 0$ if $K > 0$ and $\mathrm{Arg}\, K = \pi$ if $K < 0$.

The last two equations show that the magnitude and phase of an open-loop transfer function $G(j\omega)$ are composed of four simple types of factors, which are as follows:

(1) Constant K

(2) Poles or zeros at the origin (σ_i or $\sigma_q = 0$) $(j\omega)^{\pm n}(n = 1, 2, \ldots)$

(3) Simple pole or zero $(1 + j\omega T)^{\pm 1}$

(4) Quadratic pole or zero $(1 + 2j\delta\mu - \mu^2)^{\pm 1}$

The advantage of the logarithmic plot is quite apparent, since each of the four kinds of factors may be considered as a separate plot. The plots are then added or subtracted accordingly to yield the magnitude and phase of $G(j\omega)$. The curves may be plotted on either semilog paper or linear rectangular coordinate paper.

With semilog paper: linear scale—decibel gain $|G|$ db

                         logarithmic scale—frequency ω

With linear rectangular paper: vertical scale—decibel gain $|G|$ db

                         horizontal scale—$\log_{10} \omega$

The four different kinds of factors are now to be investigated separately.

(1) *The Constant Term K*

Since

$$K_{db} = 20 \log_{10} |K| = \text{constant} \tag{2-207}$$

and

$$\text{Arg } K = 0 \text{ deg or } 180 \text{ deg} \tag{2-208}$$

the gain in decibels and the zero phase shift are plotted in Fig. 2-44 on semilog paper.

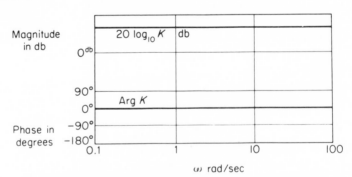

FIG. 2-44. Gain in decibel and phase shift of constant K.

(2) *Poles or Zeros at the Origin* $(j\omega)^{\pm n}$

The magnitude of $(j\omega)^{\pm n}$ in decibels is

$$20 \log_{10} |(j\omega)^{\pm n}| = \pm 20n \log_{10} \omega \text{ db} \tag{2-209}$$

which is the equation of a straight line in either semi-logarithmic coordinates or rectangular coordinates. The slopes of these straight lines may be obtained by taking the derivative of Eq. (2–209) with respect to $\log_{10} \omega$; that is,

$$\frac{d20 \log |(j\omega)^{\pm n}|}{d \log_{10} \omega} = \pm 20n \text{ db} \qquad (2\text{–}210)$$

Hence, in the rectangular coordinates a unit change in $\log_{10} \omega$ will correspond to a change of $\pm 20n$ db. Furthermore, a unit change in $\log_{10} \omega$ is equivalent to a change of 1 to 10, 10 to 100, etc., in the logarithmic scale. Thus the slopes of these straight lines are described by

$$20n \text{ decibel per decade of frequency} \qquad (2\text{–}211)$$

Sometimes the unit *octave* is used to represent the separation of two frequencies. The frequencies ω_1 and ω_2 are separated by an octave if $\omega_2/\omega_1 = 2$. The number of octaves between any two frequencies is defined by

$$\text{Number of octaves} = \frac{\log_{10} \dfrac{\omega_2}{\omega_1}}{\log_{10} 2} \qquad (2\text{–}212)$$

The number of decades between any two frequencies is defined by

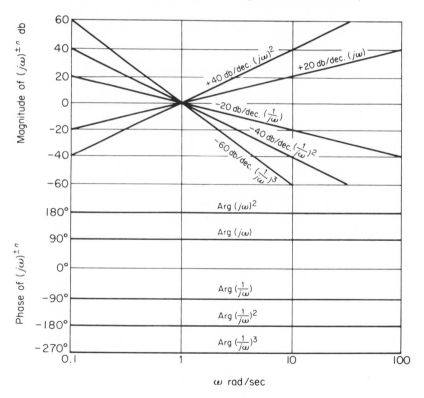

FIG. 2-45. Bode plot of magnitude and phase of the factor $(j\omega)^{\pm n}$.

$$\text{Number of decades} = \frac{\log_{10} \frac{\omega_2}{\omega_1}}{\log_{10} 10} \qquad (2\text{-}213)$$

For one decade of frequency, $\omega_2/\omega_1 = 10$; the relation between *octaves* and *decades* is

$$\text{Number of octaves} = \frac{1}{\log_{10} 2} = \frac{1}{0.301} \text{ decade} \qquad (2\text{-}214)$$

Hence $\pm 20n \text{ db/decade} = \pm 20n \times 0.301 = \pm 6n \text{ db/octave} \qquad (2\text{-}215)$

For a single pole at the origin ($s = 0$), the slope of the magnitude curve is -20 db/decade of frequency or -6 db/octave of frequency. The phase shift of $(j\omega)^{\pm n}$ is

$$\text{Arg}(j\omega)^{\pm n} = \pm n \times 90 \text{ deg} \qquad (2\text{-}216)$$

The magnitude and phase shift curves of the term $(j\omega)^{\pm n}$ are shown in Fig. 2–45 for several values of n.

(3) *Simple Pole or Zero* $(1 + j\omega T)^{\pm 1}$

(a) *Simple zero:* Let

$$G(j\omega) = 1 + j\omega T \qquad (2\text{-}217)$$

Taking the logarithm of the magnitude of the last equation, we have

$$20 \log_{10} |G(j\omega)| = 20 \log_{10} \sqrt{1 + T^2 \omega^2} \qquad (2\text{-}218)$$

Also

$$\text{Arg } G(j\omega) = \tan^{-1} \omega T \qquad (2\text{-}219)$$

A linear asymptotic approximation is normally used in plotting the magnitude curve. At very low frequencies, $\omega T \ll 1$.

$$20 \log_{10} |G(j\omega)| = 20 \log_{10} \sqrt{1 + \omega^2 T^2} \cong 20 \log_{10} 1 = 0 \text{ db} \qquad (2\text{-}220)$$

At very high frequencies, $\omega T \gg 1$.

$$20 \log_{10} |G(j\omega)| = 20 \log_{10} \sqrt{\omega^2 T^2} = 20_{10} \log \omega T = 20 \log_{10} \omega + 20 \log_{10} T \qquad (2\text{-}221)$$

Equation (2–221) represents a straight line with a slope of $+20$ db per decade of frequency (or 6 db/octave). The intersection of the low frequency and the high frequency asymptotes is found by equating Eq. (2–220) to Eq. (2–221); that is,

$$20 \log_{10} \omega T = 0 \text{ db} \qquad (2\text{-}222)$$

from which

$$\omega = 1/T \qquad (2\text{-}223)$$

The frequency ω obtained in Eq. (2–223) is sometimes known as the "positive corner frequency" of the plot. The actual magnitude curve, however, is a smooth curve, but deviates only slightly from the straight line asymptotes. The magnitude and phase shift of the factor $(1 + j\omega T)$ are given in Table 2-1 for various values of ωT. In Table 2-2 is a comparison of the actual magnitude and the straight line asymptotes at some significant frequencies.

Table 2-1

ωT	$\log_{10}\omega T$	$|1 + j\omega T|$	$|1 + j\omega T|$ db	Arg $(1 + j\omega T)$
0.01	-2	1	0	0.5°
0.1	-1	1.04	0.043	5.7°
0.5	-0.3	1.12	1	26.6°
0.76	-0.12	1.26	2	37.4°
1.0	0	1.41	3	45.0°
1.31	0.117	1.65	4.3	52.7°
1.73	0.238	2.0	6.0	60.0°
2.0	0.3	2.23	7.0	63.4°
5.0	0.7	5.1	14.2	78.7°
10.0	1.0	10.4	20.3	84.3°

Table 2-2

ωT		Magnitude of $(1 + j\omega T)$ in db	Asymptotic values of magnitude (db)	Error (db)
0.1	One decade below corner freq.	0.3	0	$+0.3$
0.5	One octave below corner freq.	1.0	0	$+1$
0.76	At the corner freq.	2	0	$+2$
1.0	At the corner freq.	3	0	$+3$
1.31		4.3	2.3	$+2$
2.0	One octave above corner freq.	7	6	$+1$
10	One decade above corner freq.	20.3	20	$+0.3$

(b) *Simple pole:* When

$$G(j\omega) = \frac{1}{1 + j\omega T} \qquad (2\text{--}224)$$

it is easy to see that negative signs are added to Eq. (2–220) and Eq. (2–221). The low frequency asymptote of the magnitude curve is still a straight line of zero slope and the high frequency asymptote is a straight line which has a slope of -20 db/decade. The intersection of these two straight lines is still the same as in the simple zero case; i.e., $\omega = 1/T$. This corner frequency, however, is usually called the "negative corner frequency." The phase shift is the negative of all the values given in Table 2-1.

The magnitude curves and the error between the actual and the asymp-

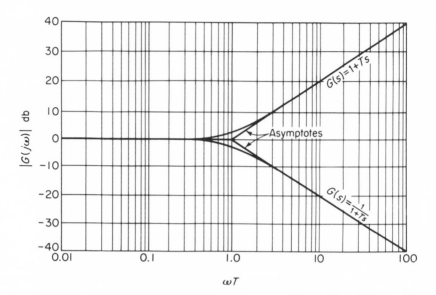

FIG. 2-46. Magnitude versus frequency of the Bode plots of
$G(s) = 1 + Ts$ and $G(s) = \dfrac{1}{1 + Ts}$.

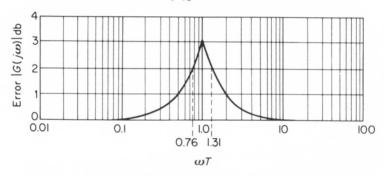

FIG. 2-47. Error in magnitude versus frequency in the Bode plots of
$G(s) = 1 + Ts$ and $G(s) = 1/(1 + Ts)$.

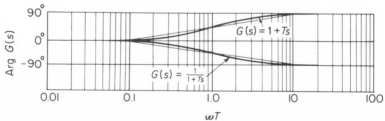

FIG. 2-48. Phase angle versus frequency for the Bode plots of
$G(s) = 1 + Ts$ and $G(s) = \dfrac{1}{1 + Ts}$.

totic curves are plotted in Fig. 2-46 and Fig. 2-47, respectively. The phase shift curves for the simple pole and zero are plotted in Fig. 2-48 in semi-logarithmic coordinates.

It is interesting to note that the error between the actual magnitude curve and the asymptotic plot is symmetrical with respect to the corner frequency $1/T$. Furthermore, the error is 3 db at the corner frequency, and 1 db at one octave above and below the corner frequency. At one decade above and below the corner frequency, the error is about 0.3 db. From these known facts, the procedure in plotting the corner plot for the linear factor $(1 + j\omega T)^{\pm 1}$ may be outlined as follows:

(1) Locate the corner frequency $\omega = 1/T$.

(2) Draw the 6 db/octave straight line asymptotes through the corner frequency ($+6$ db/octave for positive corner, and -6 db/octave for negative corner).

(3) The actual curve is obtained by locating the points given in Table 2-2. Usually a smooth curve can be sketched by locating the 3 db point at the corner frequency and the 1 db points at one octave above and below the corner frequency.

Similarly, a straight line can be used to approximate the phase shift curve. The line is drawn from 0 deg at one decade below the corner frequency to ± 90 deg at one decade above the corner frequency. It is seen that the maximum deviation of the straight line approximation from the actual curve is about 6 deg. Table 2-3 gives the error between the actual phase shift curve and the straight line approximation.

Table 2-3

ωT	Actual Arg $(1 + j\omega T)$	Straight line approximation	Error
0.1	5.7°	0°	+5.7°
0.3	16.7°	21.7°	−5°
0.5	26.6°	31.6°	−5°
1.0	45°	45°	0°
2.0	63.4°	58.4°	+5°
3.0	71.6°	66.6°	+5°
10.0	84.3°	90.0°	−5.7°

(4) *Quadratic Poles and Zeros*

Consider the second-order transfer function:

$$G(s) = \frac{\omega_n^2}{s^2 + 2\delta\omega_n s + \omega_n^2} = \frac{1}{\dfrac{s^2}{\omega_n^2} + \dfrac{2\delta}{\omega_n}s + 1} \tag{2–225}$$

If we let $s = j\omega$, the last equation becomes

$$G(j\omega) = \frac{1}{\left[1 - \left(\dfrac{\omega}{\omega_n}\right)^2\right] + j\omega\dfrac{2\delta}{\omega_n}} \tag{2–226}$$

The magnitude of $G(j\omega)$ in decibels is

$$20 \log_{10} |G(j\omega)| = -20 \log_{10}\sqrt{\left[1 - \left(\frac{\omega}{\omega_n}\right)^2\right]^2 + \left(\frac{2\delta\omega}{\omega_n}\right)^2} \qquad (2\text{-}227)$$

The phase shift of $G(j\omega)$ is

$$\operatorname{Arg} G(j\omega) = -\tan^{-1}\left(\frac{\dfrac{2\delta\omega}{\omega_n}}{1 - \left(\dfrac{\omega}{\omega_n}\right)^2}\right) \qquad (2\text{-}228)$$

At very low frequencies, $\dfrac{\omega}{\omega_n} \ll 1$; Eq. (2-227) may be written as

$$20 \log |G(j\omega)| \cong -20 \log_{10} 1 = 0 \text{ db} \qquad (2\text{-}229)$$

Hence, the low frequency asymptote for the second-order factor plot is, again, a straight line with zero slope.

At very high frequencies, $\dfrac{\omega}{\omega_n} \ll 1$; the magnitude of $G(j\omega)$ in decibels becomes

$$20 \log_{10} |G(j\omega)| = -20 \log_{10}\sqrt{\left[1 - \left(\frac{\omega}{\omega_n}\right)^2\right]^2 + \left(2\delta\frac{\omega}{\omega_n}\right)^2}$$

$$\cong -20 \log_{10}\sqrt{\left(\frac{\omega}{\omega_n}\right)^4} = -40 \log\left(\frac{\omega}{\omega_n}\right) \text{ db} \qquad (2\text{-}230)$$

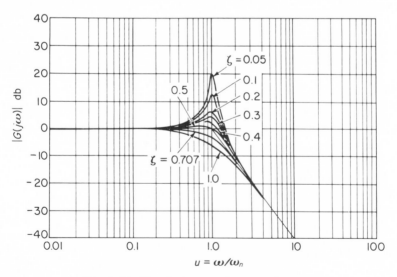

FIG. 2-49. Magnitude versus frequency for

$$G(s) = \frac{1}{1 + 2\delta(s/\omega_n) + (s/\omega_n)^2}.$$

The last equation represents the equation of a straight line with slope of -40 db/decade in the semi-logarithmic coordinates.

The intersection of the two asymptotes is found by equating

$$-40 \log_{10} \left(\frac{\omega}{\omega_n} \right) = 0 \text{ db} \tag{2-231}$$

from which

$$\omega = \omega_n \tag{2-232}$$

Hence, the frequency $\omega = \omega_n$ is considered to be the corner frequency of

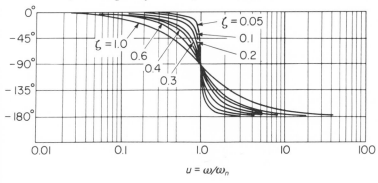

FIG. 2-50. Phase angle versus frequency for
$$G(s) = \frac{1}{1 + 2\delta(s/\omega_n) + (s/\omega_n)^2}.$$

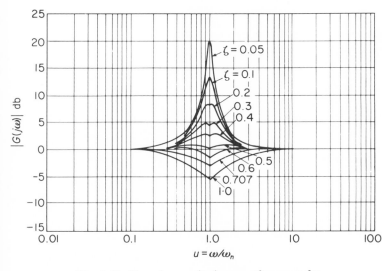

FIG. 2-51. Error in magnitude versus frequency for
$$G(s) = \frac{1}{1 + 2\delta(s/\omega_n) + (s/\omega_n)^2}.$$

the second-order factor. The actual magnitude plot in this case, however, differs strikingly from the asymptotic lines. The reason for this is that the amplitude and phase curves depend not only on the corner frequency ω_n (same as the natural undamped frequency), but also on the damping ratio δ. The actual magnitude plot and the phase shift plot are plotted in Fig. 2-49 and Fig. 2-50, respectively. The error between the curves shown in Fig. 2-49 and the asymptotic straight lines are plotted in Fig. 2-51. Usually, if a transfer function of the quadratic form is given, first, the values of δ and ω_n are determined; then, by using the sets of curves shown in Fig. 2-51, the magnitude and phase shift versus frequency curve may be plotted.

Example 2-10. Consider that the transfer function of a linear system is given by

$$G(s) = \frac{10(s + 10)}{s(s + 5)(s + 2)} \tag{2-233}$$

It is desired to sketch the Bode plot of $G(j\omega)$. The first step is to replace s by $j\omega$ and transform the transfer function into the form of Eq. (2–204). Thus, Eq. (2–233) becomes

$$G(j\omega) = \frac{10(1 + 0.1j\omega)}{j\omega(1 + 0.2j\omega)(1 + 0.5j\omega)} \tag{2-234}$$

It is observed that the transfer function has a positive corner frequency at $\omega = 10$ rad/sec, and two negative corner frequencies at $\omega = 2$ rad/sec and $\omega = 5$ rad/sec. The pole at the origin corresponds to a magnitude curve which is a straight line with a slope of -20 db/decade and passing through the $\omega = 1$ rad/sec (or $\log_{10} \omega = 0$ if the $\log_{10} \omega$ axis is used) point

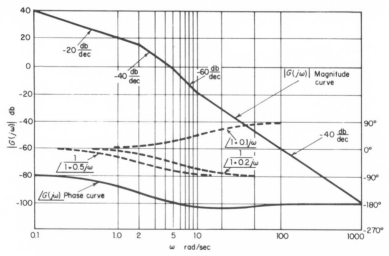

FIG. 2-52. Bode plot of $G(s) = \dfrac{10(s + 10)}{s(s + 5)(s + 2)}$.

on the frequency axis at 0 db magnitude. The component plots of each of the basic factors are sketched as shown in Fig. 2-52, and the total plot, obtained through adding the curves algebraically point by point, is also shown in the same figure.

The actual magnitude plot of $G(j\omega)$ may be obtained by considering the errors of asymptotic curves at the various corner frequencies according to Fig. 2-47. However, in practice, the accuracy attained by the asymptotic sketches is satisfactory for most control problems.

The accuracy of the Bode plots at $\omega = 0$ and $\omega = \infty$ can be checked easily by a limiting process. From Eq. (2–234), we have

$$\lim_{\omega \to 0} |G(j\omega)| = \lim_{\omega \to 0} \frac{10}{\omega} \qquad (2\text{–}235)$$

which means that at zero frequency the slope of the magnitude Bode plot should be -20 db/decade. Similarly, at $\omega = \infty$,

$$\lim_{\omega \to \infty} |G(j\omega)| = \lim_{\omega \to \infty} \frac{10}{\omega^2} \qquad (2\text{–}236)$$

This implies that as $\omega \to \infty$, the slope of the magnitude Bode plot should be -40 db/decade.

For the phase angle plot,

$$\lim_{\omega \to 0} \underline{/G(j\omega)} = \lim_{\omega \to 0} \underline{/\frac{10}{j\omega}} = -90 \text{ deg} \qquad (2\text{–}237)$$

$$\lim_{\omega \to \infty} \underline{/G(j\omega)} = \lim_{\omega \to \infty} \underline{/\frac{10}{(j\omega)^2}} = -180 \text{ deg} \qquad (2\text{–}238)$$

These results are supported by the Bode plot shown in Fig. 2-52.

2.11 The Magnitude Versus Phase Plot

As mentioned in the introduction section of this chapter, the magnitude versus phase plot is a plot of the magnitude of the transfer function $G(s)$ in decibels versus its phase in degrees with frequency as a parameter on the curves. The main advantage of using this set of coordinates is that the plot can be superposed on the Nichols chart (see Chapter 10) to determine the relative stability and the frequency response of the closed-loop system. When the gain constant K of the transfer function $G(j\omega)$ is varied, the plot is raised or lowered vertically according to the logarithmic scale. However, the unique property of adding the individual plot for cascaded terms in the corner plot does not carry over to this case. The magnitude versus phase plots are usually obtained by first plotting the corner plot and then transferring the data to the decibel versus phase coordinates. As an example, the corner plots of the second-order transfer function shown in Figs. 2-49 and 2-50 are transferred to the magnitude versus phase plot, as shown in Fig. 2-53. The normalized frequency ω/ω_n is used as a parameter on the curves.

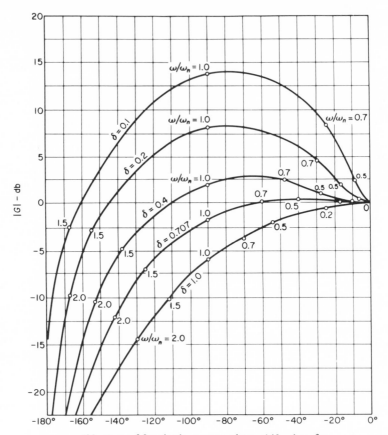

FIG. 2-53. Magnitude versus phase shift plots for

$$G(s) = \frac{\omega_n^2}{s^2 + 2\delta\omega_n s + \omega_n^2}.$$

2.12 Relationships Between Polar, Bode, and Magnitude Versus Phase Plots

Since the various types of transfer function plots discussed in the previous sections are all considered as mappings of the points on the positive part of the $j\omega$ axis of the s-plane onto the functional $G(j\omega)$-plane, they must be closely related. As an example, the three types of plots of the function

$$G(s) = \frac{10(s + 10)}{s(s + 2)(s + 5)} \tag{2–239}$$

are sketched in Fig. 2-54. The Bode plot shown in Fig. 2-54b is apparently the easiest one to sketch; thus the others are usually obtained by transferring the data from the Bode plot to the other respective coordinates. The relationships between the plots are easily established by comparing these figures without using detailed explanation. However, it is convenient to define the following terms:

Gain Crossover: the point at which the magnitude of $G(j\omega)$ is unity.

This definition is interpreted in terms of the various types of plots as follows:

Polar plot: the point or points at which $|G(j\omega)| = 1$. Or, the point(s) where the $G(j\omega)$ curve intersects a circle with unit radius and centered at the origin of the $G(j\omega)$-plane.

Bode plot: the point or points at which the magnitude curve of $G(j\omega)$ crosses the zero db axis.

Magnitude versus phase plot: the point or points at which the $G(j\omega)$ plot crosses the zero db axis.

Phase Crossover: the point(s) at which the phase of $G(j\omega)$ is 180 degrees.

Polar plot: the point(s) at which the $G(j\omega)$ plot intersects the negative real axis of the $G(j\omega)$-plane.

Bode plot: the phase shift curve crosses the 180 deg axis.

Magnitude versus phase plot: the point(s) at which the $G(j\omega)$ plot intersects the 180 deg axis.

These special points of interest are illustrated on the sketches shown in Fig. 2-54.

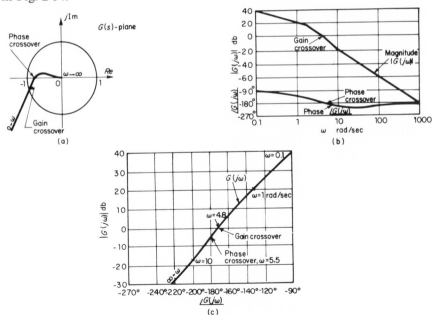

FIG. 2-54. (a) Polar plot; (b) Bode diagram; (c) Magnitude versus phase plot.

$$G(s) = \frac{10(s + 10)}{s(s + 5)(s + 2)}$$

The frequencies at the gain crossover and the phase crossover are referred to as the *gain-crossover frequency* and the *phase-crossover frequency*, respectively. It will be shown later that the gain crossover and the phase crossover are detrimental in the graphical stability study of feedback control systems.

2.13 Minimum Phase and Nonminimum Phase Transfer Functions

Observing that the Bode plot contains two separate plots while the polar plot and the magnitude versus phase plot each contain only a single plot suggests that there must be a unique relationship between the Bode magnitude and phase plots. In other words, once the magnitude characteristic is given, the corresponding phase characteristic is uniquely specified. However, the statement just made is not true in general. Based on whether a unique relation exists between the magnitude and phase characteristics or not, a transfer function belongs to one of the following two classes: *minimum phase function*, and *nonminimum phase function*.

A minimum phase transfer function has the property that its magnitude and phase are uniquely related, whereas a nonminimum phase transfer function lacks the property. Strictly, a minimum phase function is defined, as its name implies, as *a function which goes through a minimum amount of phase change in the negative direction (phase lag) when frequency is varied from zero to infinity. A nonminimum phase function, of course, is one that does not have the minimum-phase property.* Alternatively, one can define a minimum phase transfer function as one which *does not have any poles or zeros in the right-hand half of the s-plane. If a transfer function has at least one pole or zero that is located in the right-hand half of the s-plane, it is a nonminimum phase function.* For example, the transfer function

$$G(s) = \frac{10(s + 10)}{s(s + 5)(s + 2)} \qquad (2\text{--}240)$$

is a minimum phase function since it does not have any pole or zero in the right-hand half of the *s*-plane. The Bode plot of $G(s)$ in Fig. 2-52 shows that the net phase loss between $\omega = 0$ and $\omega = \infty$ is -90 deg; that is, the phase shift of $G(j\omega)$ goes through a total of 90 deg in the clockwise direction as ω is varied from zero to infinity. On the other hand, the transfer function

$$G(s) = \frac{10(s - 10)}{s(s + 5)(s + 2)} \qquad (2\text{--}241)$$

is a nonminimum phase. The function has a zero located in the right-hand half of the *s*-plane, and, moreover,

$$\lim_{\omega \to 0} \underline{/G(j\omega)} = \lim_{\omega \to 0} \underline{/\frac{-10}{j\omega}} = 90° \qquad (2\text{--}242)$$

$$\lim_{\omega \to \infty} \underline{/G(j\omega)} = \lim_{\omega \leftarrow \infty} \underline{/\frac{10}{(j\omega)^2}} = 180° \qquad (2\text{--}243)$$

indicating that there is a "phase gain" of 90 deg when ω is varied from zero to infinity. The irrational transfer function $e^{-Ts}G(s)$ is also a common example of the nonminimum phase function, since it is possible to decrease the phase of the function by increasing T, without changing the magnitude characteristics. This transfer function is often encountered in control systems with pure transportation-lag or time delay.

REFERENCES

1. B. C. Kuo, *Linear Networks and Systems*, McGraw-Hill Book Company, New York, N. Y., 1967.

2. R. J. Schwarz and B. Friedland, *Linear Systems*, McGraw-Hill Book Company, New York, N. Y., 1965.

3. C. A. Desoer, "An Introduction to State Space Techniques in Linear Systems," Workshop on State Space Techniques for Control Systems, *Proceedings*, Joint Automatic Control Conference, Boulder, Colorado, 1962.

4. H. S. Tsien, *Engineering Cybernetics*, McGraw-Hill Book Company, New York, N. Y., 1954.

5. S. Seshu and N. Balabanian, *Linear Network Analysis*, John Wiley & Sons, Inc., New York, N. Y., 1959.

6. E. Mishkin and L. Brown, *Adaptive Control Systems*, McGraw-Hill Book Company, New York, N. Y., 1961.

7. J. E. Gibson and F. B. Tuteur, *Control System Components*, McGraw-Hill Book Company, New York, N. Y., 1958.

8. T. D. Graybeal, "Block Diagram Network Transformation," *Elec. Eng.*, Vol. 70, pp. 985–990, 1951.

9. R. A. Bruns and R. M. Saunders, *Analysis of Feedback Control Systems*, McGraw-Hill Book Company, pp. 259–290, 1955.

10. R. Bellman, *Introduction to Matrix Analysis*, McGraw-Hill Book Company, New York, N. Y., 1960.

11. S. J. Mason, "Feedback Theory—Some Properties of Signal Flow Graphs," *Proceedings of the IRE*, Vol. 41, No. 9, pp. 1144–1156, September, 1953.

12. L. P. A. Robichand, M. Boisvert, and J. Robert, *Signal Flow Graphs and Applications*, Prentice-Hall, Inc., Englewood Cliffs, N. J., 1962.

13. S. J. Mason and H. J. Zimmerman, *Electronic Circuits, Signals, and Systems*, Chaps. 4 and 5, John Wiley & Sons, Inc., New York, N. Y., 1960.

14. S. J. Mason, "Feedback Theory—Further Properties of Signal Flow Graphs," *Proceedings of the IRE*, Vol. 44, No. 7, pp. 920–926, July, 1956.

15. H. W. Bode, *Network Analysis and Feedback Amplifier Design*, D. Van Nostrand Company, Inc., Princeton, N. J., 1945.

16. B. C. Kuo, *Analysis and Synthesis of Sampled-Data Control Systems*, Prentice-Hall, Inc., Englewood Cliffs, N. J., 1963.

17. J. T. Tou, *Digital and Sampled-Data Control Systems*, McGraw-Hill Book Company, New York, N. Y., 1959.

PROBLEMS

2-1. The following differential equations are used to describe linear systems, where $r(t)$ is the input and $c(t)$ is the output. Find the transfer function of each of the systems.

(a) $\dfrac{d^3c(t)}{dt^3} + 3\dfrac{d^2c(t)}{dt^2} + 4\dfrac{dc(t)}{dt} + c(t) = 2\dfrac{dr(t)}{dt} + r(t)$

(b) $\dfrac{d^2c(t)}{dt^2} + 10\dfrac{dc(t)}{dt} + 2c(t) = r(t-2)$

2-2. The block diagram of a multivariable feedback control system is shown in Fig. 2P-2. The transfer matrices of the system are:

$$\mathbf{G}(s) = \begin{bmatrix} \dfrac{1}{s} & \dfrac{1}{s+2} \\ 5 & \dfrac{1}{s+1} \end{bmatrix}$$

$$\mathbf{H}(s) = \begin{bmatrix} 1 & 0 \\ 0 & 1 \end{bmatrix}$$

Find the closed-loop transfer function matrix for the system.

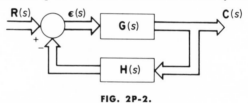

FIG. 2P-2.

2-3. Determine the following transfer relationships from the block diagram shown in Fig. 2P-3:

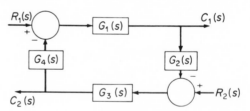

FIG. 2P-3.

$$\left.\frac{C_2(s)}{R_1(s)}\right|_{R_2=0}, \quad \left.\frac{C_2(s)}{R_2(s)}\right|_{R_1=0}, \quad \left.\frac{C_1(s)}{R_1(s)}\right|_{R_2=0}, \quad \left.\frac{C_1(s)}{R_2(s)}\right|_{R_1=0}$$

Write the transfer function matrix for the system in the form of

$$\mathbf{C}(s) = \mathbf{G}(s)\mathbf{R}(s)$$

2-4. Find the transfer function $C(z)/R(z)$ of the discrete-data system shown in Fig. 2P-4. The sampling period T is 1 second.

$$r(t) \;\;\times\!\!\!\!\!\!\!\diagup\;\; \boxed{\dfrac{1}{s(s+2)}} \;\; c(t)$$
$$T$$

FIG. 2P-4.

2-5. Find the transfer functions of the discrete-data systems shown in Fig. 2P-5. Compare the answers.

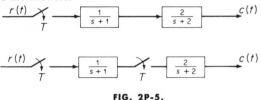

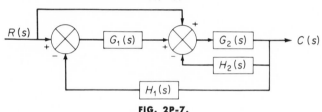

FIG. 2P-5.

2-6. Draw a signal flow graph for the following set of linear equations:

$$3y_1 + y_2 + 5y_3 = 0$$
$$y_1 + 2y_2 - 4y_3 = 2$$
$$-y_2 - y_3 = 0$$

2-7. Draw an equivalent signal flow graph for the block diagram in Fig. 2P-7 and find the transfer function $C(s)/R(s)$.

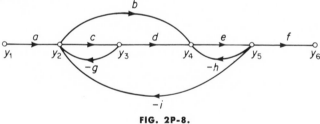

FIG. 2P-7.

2-8. Find the gains, y_6/y_1, y_3/y_1, and y_5/y_2 for the signal flow graph shown in Fig. 2P-8.

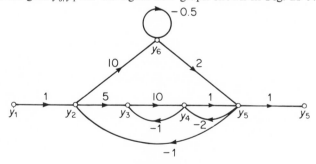

FIG. 2P-8.

2-9. Find the gain y_5/y_1 for the signal flow graph shown in Fig. 2P-9.

FIG. 2P-9.

2-10. Draw a signal flow graph for the electric circuit shown in Fig. 2P-10. Find the transfer function relation $E_0(s)/E_i(s)$ from the signal flow graph.

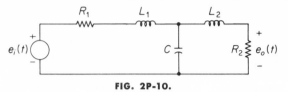

FIG. 2P-10.

2-11. In the circuit of Fig. 2P-11, $e_s(t)$, $e_d(t)$, and $i_s(t)$ are ideal sources. Find the value of a so that the voltage e_0 is not affected by the source e_d.

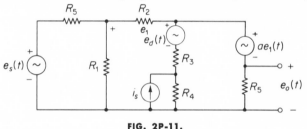

FIG. 2P-11.

2-12. A linear system is characterized by the following matrix equation:

$$\begin{bmatrix} 2 \\ 1 \\ 0 \\ 0 \end{bmatrix} = \begin{bmatrix} 1 & 1 & -1 & 0 \\ 4 & 1 & 0 & -1 \\ 1 & 0 & 1 & 0 \\ -4 & 0 & 2 & 1 \end{bmatrix} \begin{bmatrix} y_1 \\ y_2 \\ y_3 \\ y_4 \end{bmatrix}$$

2-13. One of the problems associated with the operation of sensitive d-c amplifiers is the erratic drift in output voltage caused by random changes in cathode

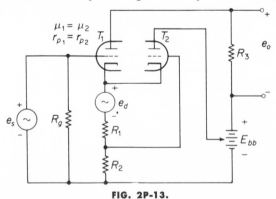

FIG. 2P-13.

emission. The Miller compensation circuit shown in Fig. 2P-13 provides a means of overcoming cathode drift in the d-c amplifier. The drift is simulated here by an equivalent random-drift generator e_d in the common cathode lead of the two tubes. By means of the signal flow graph technique, determine the optimum value of R_2 necessary to render cathode drift ineffective. What is the voltage gain of the d-c amplifier under the no-drift condition?

2-14. Construct an equivalent signal flow graph for the block diagram of Fig. 2P-14 and evaluate C/R by use of Mason's gain formula.

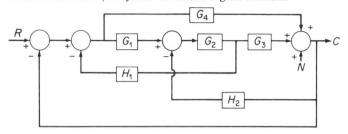

FIG. 2P-14.

2-15. In the system of Fig. 2P-14, determine the relation between the transfer functions G_1, G_2, G_3, G_4, H_1, and H_2 so that the output C is not affected by the disturbance N. The system is assumed to be stable.

2-16. Construct the original signal flow graph, the sampled signal flow graph, and the composite signal flow graph for the systems shown in Fig. 2P-16. Find $C(s)$ and $C^*(s)$ from the flow graphs.

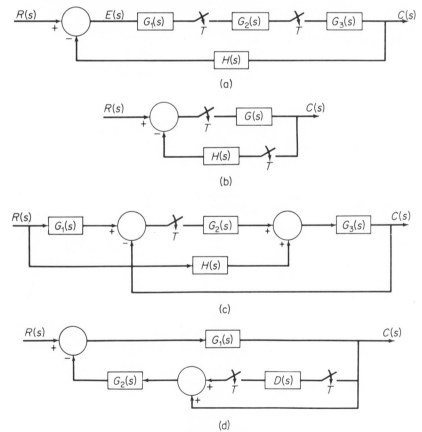

(a)

(b)

(c)

(d)

FIG. 2P-16.

2-17. Sketch the polar plots for the following transfer functions:

(a) $G(s) = \dfrac{s}{1 + Ts}$

(b) $G(s) = \dfrac{K}{s(1 + Ts)}$

(c) $G(s) = \dfrac{K}{(1 + T_1 s)(1 + T_2 s)}$

(d) $G(s) = \dfrac{K}{s^2(1 + Ts)}$

(e) $G(s) = \dfrac{K}{s(1 + T_1 s)(1 + T_2 s)}$

(f) $G(s) = \dfrac{K(s + 1)}{s(1 + 0.2s)(1 + 0.5s)}$

(g) $G(s) = \dfrac{K(1 + 0.1s)}{s(1 + 0.2s)(1 + 0.5s)}$

2-18. Sketch the Bode plots in magnitude and phase versus frequency for the following functions.

(a) $G(s) = \dfrac{1 + T_1 s}{1 + T_2 s}$

(b) $G(s) = \dfrac{K}{s(1 + Ts)}$

(c) $G(s) = \dfrac{K(1 + 3s)}{s^2(1 + 2s)}$

(d) $G(s) = \dfrac{10(1 + 0.5s)}{s(1 + 0.1s)(1 + 0.2s)}$

2-19. The magnitude curves of the open-loop transfer function $G(s)$ of certain feedback control systems are given in Fig. 2P-19. In each case, determine the transfer function $G(s)$, and sketch the corresponding phase versus frequency curve. Sketch corresponding polar plots. Assume that the systems are of the minimum phase type.

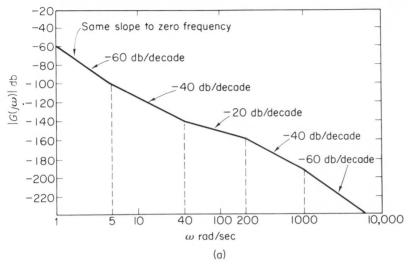

(a)

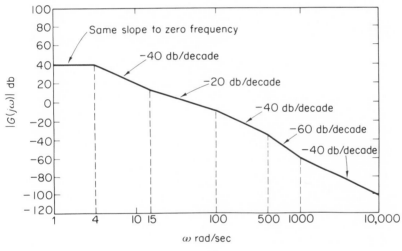

(b)

FIG. 2P-19.

3

State Variable
Characterization
of Linear Systems

3.1 Introduction to the State Concept

In the preceding chapter the classical method of describing a linear system by transfer function, impulse response, and block diagram is presented. An important feature of this type of representation is that the system dynamics are described by the input-output relations. The transfer function method is very convenient in the frequency-domain analysis of a system. However, the method suffers a major disadvantage in that all the initial conditions of the system are neglected. Therefore, when one is interested in the time-domain solution, which depends to a great deal on the past history of the system, the transfer function method becomes inadequate. Further, the conventional frequency-domain design of control systems leads to a trial-and-error procedure which guarantees neither a solution nor that the solution is optimum. The modern control systems design is usually carried out in the time domain, and, therefore, a different way of characterizing a system is deemed necessary.

The modern way, or an alternative to the transfer function method of describing a linear system, is to use the *state variables*[1,2] and *state equations*. The "state" of a system refers to the *past*, *present*, and *future* of the system. It represents all the information that one cares to know about the behavior of the system.

Let us assume that a set of variables, $x_1(t)$, $x_2(t)$, ..., $x_n(t)$, are chosen to describe the dynamic behavior of a linear system. These variables at any given instant of time $t = t_0$ completely describe the past history of the system up to time t_0. Therefore, the numbers $x_1(t_0)$, $x_2(t_0)$, $\ldots$, $x_n(t_0)$ define the *initial state* of the system at $t = t_0$. The set of variables, x_1, x_2, $\ldots$, x_n also have the characteristic that once the inputs for $t \geq t_0$ are specified, together with the knowledge on the initial state, the future behavior of the system is completely defined.

In a loose sense, the set of variables just described are called the *state variables*. More formally, the state variables of a linear system may be defined as *a minimal set of variables, $x_1(t)$, $x_2(t)$, $\ldots$, $x_n(t)$, such that knowledge of these variables at any time t_0 plus information on the input excitation subsequently applied is sufficient to determine the state of the system at any time $t \geq t_0$.*

One should not confuse the state variables with the outputs of a system. An output is a system variable which can be *measured* or *observed*, but a state variable does not always and often does not satisfy this requirement. Sometimes a state variable can be regarded as an output if it is *measurable* or *observable*.

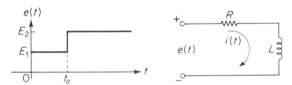

FIG. 3-1. An RL network.

As an example, consider the simple *RL* network shown in Fig. 3-1. Regardless of what the input excitation prior to the time $t = 0^+$ is, the history of the network is completely specified by the initial current $i(0^+)$ of the inductor. The loop equation of the network is

$$e(t) = Ri(t) + L\frac{di(t)}{dt} \tag{3-1}$$

Taking the Laplace transform on both sides of Eq. (3–1) gives

$$E(s) = (R + Ls)I(s) - Li(0^+) \tag{3-2}$$

Solving for $I(s)$ from the last equation yields

$$I(s) = \frac{E(s)}{R + Ls} + \frac{Li(0^+)}{R + Ls} \tag{3-3}$$

The current $i(t)$ for $t \geq 0$ is obtained by taking the inverse Laplace transform of both sides of Eq. (3–3). Assuming that the input voltage for $t \geq 0$ is a step function of E_1 volts, we have

$$i(t) = \frac{E_1}{R}(1 - e^{-(Rt/L)}) + i(0^+)e^{-(Rt/L)} \qquad (t \geq 0) \tag{3-4}$$

which describes the current behavior of the network for $t \geq 0$ once the initial condition of the network at $t = 0^+$ and the input for $t \geq 0$ are given. Therefore, it is apparent that the current $i(t)$ in this case satisfies the basic requirements as a state variable. It will be shown later that in network analysis, *the currents in inductors and the voltages across capacitors are usually selected as state variables.*

To generalize the initial time from $t = 0$ to $t = t_0 \geq 0$, we set $t = t_0$ in Eq. (3–4). Therefore,

$$i(t_0) = \frac{E_1}{R}(1 - e^{-(Rt_0/L)}) + i(0^+)e^{-(Rt_0/L)} \tag{3-5}$$

Solving for $i(0^+)$ in Eq. (3–5) gives

$$i(0^+) = \left[i(t_0) - \frac{E_1}{R}(1 - e^{-(Rt_0/L)}) \right] e^{Rt_0/L} \tag{3-6}$$

Now if the initial state of the network is considered to be at $t = t_0$, Eq. (3–6) is substituted into Eq. (3–3). The Laplace transform of $i(t)$ for $t \geq t_0$ is

$$I(s) = \frac{E(s)}{R + Ls} + \frac{L}{R + Ls} \left[i(t_0) - \frac{E_1}{R}(1 - e^{-(Rt_0/L)}) \right] e^{Rt_0/L} \tag{3-7}$$

where $E(s)$ now represents the Laplace transform of the input voltage applied at $t = t_0$. Notice that information on the input condition prior to t_0 is no longer necessary for the determination of $i(t)$ for $t \geq t_0$ once the initial condition $i(t_0)$ is given.

Assume that an input step voltage of magnitude $E_2 - E_1$ is applied at $t = t_0$. Then

$$E(s) = \frac{E_2 - E_1}{s} \qquad t \geq t_0 \tag{3-8}$$

Taking the inverse Laplace transform on both sides of Eq. (3–7) and simplifying gives

$$i(t) = \frac{E_2}{R}[1 - e^{-(R/L)(t-t_0)}] + e^{-(R/L)(t-t_0)}i(t_0) \tag{3-9}$$

for $t \geq t_0$.

The evolution of the system from $t = 0$ to t_0 and then from t_0 to any time beyond is considered as a "transition" of state.

Therefore, Eqs. (3–4) and (3–9) are referred to as the *state transition equations* of the *RL* network for the periods $0 \leq t \leq t_0$, and $t \geq t_0$, respectively.

The network equation of Eq. (3–1) can be rearranged as

$$L\frac{di(t)}{dt} = -Ri(t) + e(t) \qquad (3\text{-}10)$$

This first-order differential equation is usually referred to as the *state equation*. It can be shown in general that the state equations of a linear system can be written as a set of first-order differential equations similar to that of Eq. (3-10). A general form of the state equations is defined in the next section.

3.2 State Equations of Linear Continuous-data Systems

Consider that the block diagram shown in Fig. 3-2 represents a linear continuous-data system with p inputs and q outputs. Let us assume that the system dynamics are characterized by the following set of n first-order differential equations, called *state equations:*

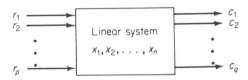

FIG. 3-2. A linear system with p inputs, q outputs, and n state variables.

$$\frac{dx_i(t)}{dt} = f_i[x_1(t), x_2(t), \ldots, x_n(t), r_1(t), r_2(t), \ldots, r_p(t)] \qquad (i = 1, 2, \ldots, n)$$

$$(3\text{-}11)$$

where $x_1(t), x_2(t), \ldots, x_n(t)$ are the state variables, $r_1(t), r_2(t), \ldots, r_p(t)$ are the inputs, and f_i denotes the ith linear functional relationship.

The outputs of the system are related to the state variables and the inputs through the following expression:

$$c_k(t) = g_k[x_1(t), x_2(t), \ldots, x_n(t), r_1(t), r_2(t), \ldots, r_p(t)] \qquad (k = 1, 2, \ldots, q)$$

$$(3\text{-}12)$$

where g_k denotes the kth linear functional relationship.

Equation (3-12) is often called the *output equation* of the system. The state equations and the output equations together form the *dynamic equations* of the system.

As a simple example, let us consider that a linear system with single input and output is described by the following differential equation:

$$\frac{d^3c(t)}{dt^3} + 2\frac{d^2c(t)}{dt^2} + 3\frac{dc(t)}{dt} + c(t) = 2r(t) \qquad (3\text{-}13)$$

where $c(t)$ is the output and $r(t)$ is the input.

At this point it may be mentioned that the transfer function description of the system is easily obtained by taking the Laplace transform on both sides of Eq. (3–13) and assuming zero initial conditions. Therefore, the transfer function of the system is

$$\frac{C(s)}{R(s)} = \frac{2}{s^3 + 2s^2 + 3s + 1} \tag{3–14}$$

We proceed to show that the system can also be described by a set of dynamic equations which includes the state equations and output equations. Let us define the state variables as follows:

$$x_1(t) = c(t) \tag{3–15}$$

$$x_2(t) = \frac{dx_1(t)}{dt} = \frac{dc(t)}{dt} \tag{3–16}$$

$$x_3(t) = \frac{dx_2(t)}{dt} = \frac{dc^2(t)}{dt^2} \tag{3–17}$$

Equation (3–13) can be rearranged so that the highest-order derivative term appears on one side of the equation. Therefore,

$$\frac{d^3c(t)}{dt^3} = -2\frac{d^2c(t)}{dt^2} - 3\frac{dc(t)}{dt} - c(t) + 2r(t) \tag{3–18}$$

Now using Eqs. (3–16) and (3–17) and substituting the defining relations of the state variables into Eq. (3–18), we find that the state equations are

$$\frac{dx_1(t)}{dt} = x_2(t)$$

$$\frac{dx_2(t)}{dt} = x_3(t) \tag{3–19}$$

$$\frac{dx_3(t)}{dt} = -x_1(t) - 3x_2(t) - 2x_3(t) + 2r(t)$$

where it is recognized that only the third equation is equivalent to the original differential equation; the first two state equations are merely the defining equations of the state variables. Equation (3–19) is also called the *normal form state equation* of the system in Eq. (3–13).

In the case just considered the output $c(t)$ is also defined as the state variable $x_1(t)$. Thus Eq. (3–15) is also the output equation.

In general, if the approach described above is used, the nth order differential equation

$$\frac{d^nc(t)}{dt^n} + a_1\frac{d^{n-1}c(t)}{dt^{n-1}} + a_2\frac{d^{n-2}c(t)}{dt^{n-2}} + \cdots + a_{n-1}\frac{dc(t)}{dt} + a_nc(t) = r(t) \tag{3–20}$$

is represented by the following state equations:

$$\frac{dx_1(t)}{dt} = x_2(t)$$

$$\frac{dx_2(t)}{dt} = x_3(t)$$

$$\cdot$$
$$\cdot \qquad\qquad\qquad\qquad (3\text{--}21)$$
$$\cdot$$

$$\frac{dx_{n-1}(t)}{dt} = x_n(t)$$

$$\frac{dx_n(t)}{dt} = -a_n x_1(t) - a_{n-1} x_2(t) - \cdots - a_2 x_{n-1}(t)$$
$$- a_1 x_n(t) + r(t)$$

where the first $n - 1$ equations define the state variables.

The output equation is simply

$$c(t) = x_1(t) \qquad\qquad\qquad (3\text{--}22)$$

It is important to realize that, in general, the definition of the state variable relations is not unique. The pattern set in the foregoing examples is convenient merely for the particular type of differential equations described by Eq. (3–20). The nonuniqueness of the choice of state variables is illustrated by citing the fact that either the current i or the flux linkage λ in an inductor can be defined as a state variable.

The method of defining state variables described above is inappropriate when the right-hand side of Eq. (3–20) also includes derivatives of $r(t)$. For an nth-order differential equation, we have

$$\frac{d^n c(t)}{dt^n} + a_1 \frac{d^{n-1} c(t)}{dt^{n-1}} + a_2 \frac{d^{n-2} c(t)}{dt^{n-2}} + \cdots + a_{n-1} \frac{dc(t)}{dt} + a_n c(t)$$

$$= b_0 \frac{d^n r(t)}{dt^n} + b_1 \frac{d^{n-1} r(t)}{dt^{n-1}} + \cdots + b_{n-1} \frac{dr(t)}{dt} + b_n r(t) \qquad (3\text{--}23)$$

It will be shown that, in this case, the relations between state variables must also include the input function $r(t)$.

By trial and error,[1] the state variables are defined as follows:

$$x_1(t) = c(t) - b_0 r(t)$$

$$x_2(t) = \frac{dx_1(t)}{dt} - h_1 r(t)$$

$$x_3(t) = \frac{dx_2(t)}{dt} - h_2 r(t) \qquad\qquad\qquad (3\text{--}24)$$

$$\cdot$$
$$\cdot$$
$$\cdot$$

$$x_k(t) = \frac{dx_{k-1}(t)}{dt} - h_k r(t) \qquad (k = 2, 3, \ldots, n)$$

where

$$h_1 = b_1 - a_1 b_0$$

$$h_2 = (b_2 - a_2 b_0) - a_1 h_1$$

$$h_3 = (b_3 - a_3 b_0) - a_2 h_1 - a_1 h_2 \qquad\qquad (3\text{-}25)$$

.

.

.

$$h_k = (b_k - a_k b_0) - a_{k-1} h_1 - a_{k-2} h_2 - \cdots - a_2 h_{k-1} - a_1 h_k$$

Using Eqs. (3-24) and (3-25), we resolve the nth order differential equation in Eq. (3-23) into the following n state equations in normal form:

$$\frac{dx_1(t)}{dt} = x_2(t) + h_1 r(t)$$

$$\frac{dx_2(t)}{dt} = x_3(t) + h_2 r(t)$$

.

.   (3-26)

.

$$\frac{dx_{n-1}(t)}{dt} = x_n(t) + h_{n-1} r(t)$$

$$\frac{dx_n(t)}{dt} = -a_n x_1(t) - a_{n-1} x_2(t) - \cdots - a_2 x_{n-1}(t) - a_1 x_n(t) + h_n r(t)$$

The output equation is obtained from the first expression in Eq. (3-24); i.e.,

$$c(t) = x_1(t) + b_0 r(t) \qquad\qquad (3\text{-}27)$$

There are other ways of representing Eq. (3-23) by state equations; the reader may refer to the literature.[1]

3.3 Matrix Representation of State Equations

The state equations of a dynamic system can usually be written in matrix form. The use of matrix representation is particularly desirable in the case of complex systems, since it provides a condensed form for complicated equations. The matrix-vector form of the n linear state equations given by Eq. (3-11) is simply

$$\frac{d\mathbf{x}(t)}{dt} = \mathbf{A}\mathbf{x}(t) + \mathbf{B}\mathbf{r}(t) = \mathbf{f}[\mathbf{x}(t), \mathbf{r}(t)] \qquad\qquad (3\text{-}28)$$

where $\mathbf{x}(t)$ is a column matrix for the state variables and is usually called the *state vector*; $\mathbf{r}(t)$ is a column matrix for the input variables and is called the *input vector*. In other words,

$$\mathbf{x}(t) = \begin{bmatrix} x_1(t) \\ x_2(t) \\ \cdot \\ \cdot \\ \cdot \\ x_n(t) \end{bmatrix} \quad \text{and} \quad \mathbf{r}(t) = \begin{bmatrix} r_1(t) \\ r_2(t) \\ \cdot \\ \cdot \\ \cdot \\ r_p(t) \end{bmatrix} \tag{3-29}$$

$\mathbf{A}$ is an $n \times n$ square matrix given by

$$\mathbf{A} = \begin{bmatrix} a_{11} & a_{12} & \cdots & a_{1n} \\ a_{21} & a_{22} & \cdots & a_{2n} \\ \cdot & \cdot & \cdots & \cdot \\ \cdot & & & \\ a_{n1} & a_{n2} & \cdots & a_{nn} \end{bmatrix} \; n \text{ rows} \tag{3-30}$$

$$n \text{ columns}$$

$\mathbf{B}$ is an $n \times n$ matrix given by

$$\mathbf{B} = \begin{bmatrix} b_{11} & b_{12} & \cdots & b_{1p} \\ b_{21} & b_{22} & \cdots & b_{2p} \\ \cdot & \cdot & \cdots & \cdot \\ \cdot & & & \\ b_{n1} & b_{n2} & \cdots & b_{np} \end{bmatrix} \; n \text{ rows} \tag{3-31}$$

$$p \text{ columns}$$

$\mathbf{A}$ and $\mathbf{B}$ are sometimes referred to as the $\mathbf{A}$ *matrix* and the $\mathbf{B}$ *matrix*, respectively, of the system.

Similarly, the q equations in Eq. (3–12) can also be represented by a single matrix-vector equation,

$$\mathbf{c}(t) = \mathbf{D}\mathbf{x}(t) + \mathbf{E}\mathbf{r}(t) = \mathbf{g}[\mathbf{x}(t), \mathbf{r}(t)] \tag{3-32}$$

where $\mathbf{D}$ is a $q \times n$ matrix whose elements are denoted by d_{kj}, and $\mathbf{E}$ is a $q \times p$ matrix whose elements are defined by e_{kh}.

For instance, the state equations of Eq. (3–21) are written in the matrix form,

$$\begin{bmatrix} \dfrac{dx_1(t)}{dt} \\ \dfrac{dx_2(t)}{dt} \\ \cdot \\ \cdot \\ \cdot \\ \dfrac{dx_n(t)}{dt} \end{bmatrix} = \begin{bmatrix} 0 & 1 & 0 & 0 & 0 & \cdots & 0 \\ 0 & 0 & 1 & 0 & 0 & \cdots & 0 \\ 0 & 0 & 0 & 1 & 0 & \cdots & 0 \\ & & & & & & \\ 0 & 0 & 0 & 0 & \cdots\cdots & 1 \\ -a_n & -a_{n-1} & \cdots\cdots\cdots\cdots & -a_1 \end{bmatrix} \begin{bmatrix} x_1(t) \\ x_2(t) \\ \cdot \\ \cdot \\ \cdot \\ x_n(t) \end{bmatrix} + \begin{bmatrix} 0 \\ 0 \\ \cdot \\ \cdot \\ \cdot \\ 1 \end{bmatrix} r(t)$$

$$\tag{3-33}$$

When Eq. (3-33) is compared with Eq. (3-28), the matrices **A** and **B** are easily identified. In this case, the output equation in Eq. (3-22) is a scalar equation; thus,

$$\mathbf{D} = [1 \quad 0 \quad 0 \quad \cdots \quad 0] \tag{3-34}$$

and

$$\mathbf{E} = \mathbf{0} \text{ (null matrix)} \tag{3-35}$$

Similarly, **A**, **B**, **C**, and **D** matrices for the differential equation in Eq. (3-23) are

$$\mathbf{A} = \begin{bmatrix} 0 & 1 & 0 & 0 & \cdots & 0 \\ 0 & 0 & 1 & 0 & \cdots & 0 \\ 0 & 0 & 0 & 1 & \cdots & 0 \\ & \cdot & \cdot & \cdot & \cdot & \\ -a_n & -a_{n-1} & \cdots\cdots\cdots & -a_1 \end{bmatrix} \tag{3-36}$$

$$\mathbf{B} = \begin{bmatrix} h_1 \\ h_2 \\ \cdot \\ \cdot \\ \cdot \\ h_n \end{bmatrix} \tag{3-37}$$

$$\mathbf{D} = [1 \quad 0 \quad 0 \quad \cdots \quad 0] \tag{3-38}$$

$$\mathbf{E} = [b_0] \tag{3-39}$$

3.4 The State Transition Equation

The solution of the state equations is called the *state transition equation*. It is possible to solve the state equation

$$\frac{d\mathbf{x}(t)}{dt} = \mathbf{A}\mathbf{x}(t) + \mathbf{B}\mathbf{r}(t) \tag{3-40}$$

by using either the classical method[3] or the transform method. The transform method of solution is presented in the following.

Taking the Laplace transform on both sides of Eq. (3-40) gives

$$s\mathbf{X}(s) - \mathbf{x}(0^+) = \mathbf{A}\mathbf{X}(s) + \mathbf{B}\mathbf{R}(s) \tag{3-41}$$

where $\mathbf{x}(0^+)$ is the initial state vector evaluated at $t = 0^+$. Solving for $\mathbf{X}(s)$ in Eq. (3-41) yields

$$\mathbf{X}(s) = (s\mathbf{I} - \mathbf{A})^{-1}\mathbf{x}(0^+) + (s\mathbf{I} - \mathbf{A})^{-1}\mathbf{B}\mathbf{R}(s) \tag{3-42}$$

where **I** denotes the unity matrix and $(s\mathbf{I} - \mathbf{A})^{-1}$ is the matrix inverse of $(s\mathbf{I} - \mathbf{A})$. It is assumed that $(s\mathbf{I} - \mathbf{A})$ is nonsingular so that its matrix inverse exists.

The following identity can be proved by multiplying both sides of the equation by $(s\mathbf{I} - \mathbf{A})$.

$$(s\mathbf{I} - \mathbf{A})^{-1} = \frac{\mathbf{I}}{s} + \frac{\mathbf{A}}{s^2} + \frac{\mathbf{A}^2}{s^3} + \cdots \tag{3-43}$$

The inverse Laplace transform of $(s\mathbf{I} - \mathbf{A})^{-1}$ is obtained as

$$\mathscr{L}^{-1}[(s\mathbf{I} - \mathbf{A})^{-1}] = \mathbf{I} + \mathbf{A}t + \frac{\mathbf{A}^2 t^2}{2!} + \cdots + \frac{\mathbf{A}^n t^n}{n!} + \cdots \tag{3-44}$$

for $t \geq 0$.

By definition, the last expression is written as

$$\mathscr{L}^{-1}[(s\mathbf{I} - \mathbf{A})^{-1}] = e^{\mathbf{A}t} = \mathbf{\Phi}(t) \qquad t \geq 0 \tag{3-45}$$

where $\mathbf{\Phi}(t)$ is called the *state transition matrix* of $\mathbf{A}$.

Several important properties of the state transition matrix $\mathbf{\Phi}(t)$ are given below:

(1) $\mathbf{\Phi}(0) = \mathbf{I}$ (3-46)

(2) $\mathbf{\Phi}(t_2 - t_1)\mathbf{\Phi}(t_1 - t_0) = \mathbf{\Phi}(t_2 - t_0)$ for any t_0, t_1, t_2 (3-47)

(3) $\mathbf{\Phi}^{-1}(t) = \mathbf{\Phi}(-t)$ (3-48)

The proofs of these properties may be found in the literature.[1,3]

When Eq. (3-45) is used, the inverse Laplace transform of Eq. (3-42) becomes

$$\mathbf{x}(t) = \mathbf{\Phi}(t)\mathbf{x}(0^+) + \mathscr{L}^{-1}[(s\mathbf{I} - \mathbf{A})^{-1}\mathbf{B}\mathbf{R}(s)] \tag{3-49}$$

or

$$\mathbf{x}(t) = \mathbf{\Phi}(t)\mathbf{x}(0^+) + \int_0^t \mathbf{\Phi}(t - \tau)\mathbf{B}\mathbf{r}(\tau)\,d\tau \qquad t \geq 0 \tag{3-50}$$

where the integral on the right-hand side of Eq. (3-50) is recognized as the convolution integral. Equation (3-50) is known as the *state transition equation* for the system characterized by Eq. (3-40), for the time interval between 0 and $t(> 0)$.

The state transition equation of Eq. (3-50) is useful only when the initial state is defined to be at $t = 0$. In the study of control systems, especially sampled-data control systems, it is desirable to use a more general initial time, t_0. Thus, the initial state is represented by $\mathbf{x}(t_0)$, and it is assumed that the input signal $\mathbf{r}(t)$ is given for $t \geq t_0$.

Letting $t = t_0$ in Eq. (3-50), and solving for $\mathbf{x}(0^+)$, we get

$$\mathbf{x}(0^+) = \mathbf{\Phi}(-t_0)\mathbf{x}(t_0) - \mathbf{\Phi}(-t_0)\int_0^{t_0} \mathbf{\Phi}(t_0 - \tau)\mathbf{B}\mathbf{r}(\tau)\,d\tau \tag{3-51}$$

where the property in Eq. (3-48) has been used.

Substituting Eq. (3-51) into Eq. (3-50) gives

$$\begin{aligned}
\mathbf{x}(t) &= \mathbf{\Phi}(t)\mathbf{\Phi}(-t_0)\mathbf{x}(t_0) - \mathbf{\Phi}(t)\mathbf{\Phi}(-t_0)\int_0^{t_0} \mathbf{\Phi}(t_0 - \tau)\mathbf{B}\mathbf{r}(\tau)\,d\tau \\
&\quad + \int_0^t \mathbf{\Phi}(t - \tau)\mathbf{B}\mathbf{r}(\tau)\,d\tau \\
&= \mathbf{\Phi}(t - t_0)\mathbf{x}(t_0) + \int_{t_0}^t \mathbf{\Phi}(t - \tau)\mathbf{B}\mathbf{r}(\tau)\,d\tau \qquad (t \geq t_0) \tag{3-52}
\end{aligned}$$

where in arriving at the expression, the properties of $\Phi(t)$ are used.

Equation (3–52) is known as the state transition equation of the system described by Eq. (3–40) for $t \geq t_0$. If we compare Eq. (3–52) with Eq. (3–50), it is possible to show by substituting $\tau_1 = \tau + t_0$ into Eq. (3–52) that the *state vector* $\mathbf{x}(t)$ for $t \geq t_0$ can be obtained from Eq. (3–50) simply by replacing t by $t - t_0$ and $\mathbf{x}(0^+)$ by $\mathbf{x}(t_0^+)$. In other words,

$$
\begin{aligned}
\mathbf{x}(t) &= \Phi(t - t_0)\mathbf{x}(t_0) + \int_{t_0}^{t} \Phi(t - \tau)\mathbf{Br}(\tau)\,d\tau \\
&= \Phi(t - t_0)\mathbf{x}(t_0) + \int_{0}^{t-t_0} \Phi(t - t_0 - \tau)\mathbf{Br}(\tau)\,d\tau \qquad t \geq t_0 \\
&= \left[\Phi(t)\mathbf{x}(0^+) + \int_{0}^{t} \Phi(t - \tau)\mathbf{Br}(\tau)\,d\tau \right]\Big|_{\substack{t=t-t_0 \\ \mathbf{x}(0^+)=\mathbf{x}(t_0^+)}}
\end{aligned}
\tag{3–53}
$$

Once the state transition equation is found, the output vector can be expressed as a function of the initial state and the input vector simply by substituting $\mathbf{x}(t)$ from Eq. (3–53) into Eq. (3–32). Thus the output vector is

$$
\mathbf{c}(t) = \mathbf{D}\Phi(t - t_0)\mathbf{x}(t_0) + \int_{t_0}^{t} \mathbf{D}\Phi(t - \tau)\mathbf{Br}(\tau)\,d\tau + \mathbf{Er}(t) \qquad (t \geq t_0) \tag{3–54}
$$

The following example illustrates how the state transition equation of a linear system is obtained by using Eq. (3–53).

Example 3-1. Consider that a linear system is described by the differential equation

$$
\frac{d^2 c(t)}{dt^2} + 3\frac{dc(t)}{dt} + 2c(t) = r(t) \tag{3–55}
$$

where $c(t)$ is the output. The input $r(t)$ is a unit step function.

The state equations of the system are determined by using the method described in Sec. 3.2. In matrix form, the state equations are written as

$$
\begin{bmatrix} \dfrac{dx_1(t)}{dt} \\[2mm] \dfrac{dx_2(t)}{dt} \end{bmatrix} = \begin{bmatrix} 0 & 1 \\ -2 & -3 \end{bmatrix}\begin{bmatrix} x_1(t) \\ x_2(t) \end{bmatrix} + \begin{bmatrix} 0 \\ 1 \end{bmatrix} r(t) \tag{3–56}
$$

where it is given that $r(t) = u(t)$.

The output equation of the system is simply

$$
c(t) = x_1(t) \tag{3–57}
$$

Comparing Eq. (3–56) with Eq. (3–40), we may write the $\mathbf{A}$ and $\mathbf{B}$ matrices of the system.

$$
\mathbf{A} = \begin{bmatrix} 0 & 1 \\ -2 & -3 \end{bmatrix} \qquad \mathbf{B} = \begin{bmatrix} 0 \\ 1 \end{bmatrix}
$$

Therefore,

$$
(s\mathbf{I} - \mathbf{A}) = \begin{bmatrix} s & 0 \\ 0 & s \end{bmatrix} - \begin{bmatrix} 0 & 1 \\ -2 & -3 \end{bmatrix} = \begin{bmatrix} s & -1 \\ 2 & s+3 \end{bmatrix} \tag{3–58}
$$

The matrix inverse of $(s\mathbf{I} - \mathbf{A})$ is

$$(s\mathbf{I} - \mathbf{A})^{-1} = \frac{1}{s^2 + 3s + 2}\begin{bmatrix} s + 3 & 1 \\ -2 & s \end{bmatrix} \qquad (3\text{-}59)$$

The state transition matrix of $\mathbf{A}$ is found from the inverse transform of $(s\mathbf{I} - \mathbf{A})^{-1}$. Thus,

$$\Phi(t) = \mathscr{L}^{-1}(s\mathbf{I} - \mathbf{A})^{-1} = \mathscr{L}^{-1}\left\{\frac{1}{s^2 + 3s + 2}\begin{bmatrix} s + 3 & 1 \\ -2 & s \end{bmatrix}\right\}$$

$$= \begin{bmatrix} 2e^{-t} - e^{-2t} & e^{-t} - e^{-2t} \\ -2e^{-t} + 2e^{-2t} & -e^{-t} + 2e^{-2t} \end{bmatrix} \qquad (t \geq 0) \qquad (3\text{-}60)$$

Now substituting Eq. (3–60), $\mathbf{B}$, and $r(t)$ into Eq. (3–50) gives

$$\mathbf{x}(t) = \Phi(t)\mathbf{x}(0^+) + \int_{0^+}^{t}\begin{bmatrix} 2e^{-(t-\tau)} - e^{-2(t-\tau)} & e^{-(t-\tau)} - e^{-2(t-\tau)} \\ -2e^{-(t-\tau)} + 2e^{-2(t-\tau)} & -e^{-(t-\tau)} + 2e^{-2(t-\tau)} \end{bmatrix}$$

$$\times \begin{bmatrix} 0 \\ 1 \end{bmatrix} u(\tau)\, d\tau = \Phi(t)\mathbf{x}(0^+) + \begin{bmatrix} \frac{1}{2}u(t) - e^{-t} + \frac{1}{2}e^{-2t} \\ e^{-t} - e^{-2t} \end{bmatrix} \qquad (t \geq 0) \quad (3\text{-}61)$$

where $\Phi(t)$ is given in Eq. (3–60).

For any initial time $t = t_0$, the state transition equation can be generalized by using Eq. (3–53). Thus, for $t \geq t_0$

$$\mathbf{x}(t) = \begin{bmatrix} x_1(t) \\ x_2(t) \end{bmatrix} = \begin{bmatrix} 2e^{-(t-t_0)} - e^{-2(t-t_0)} & e^{-(t-t_0)} - e^{-2(t-t_0)} \\ -2e^{-(t-t_0)} + 2e^{-2(t-t_0)} & -e^{-(t-t_0)} + 2e^{-2(t-t_0)} \end{bmatrix}\begin{bmatrix} x_1(t_0^+) \\ x_2(t_0^+) \end{bmatrix}$$

$$+ \begin{bmatrix} \frac{1}{2}u(t - t_0) - e^{-(t-t_0)} + \frac{1}{2}e^{-2(t-t_0)} \\ e^{-(t-t_0)} - e^{-2(t-t_0)} \end{bmatrix} \qquad (3\text{-}62)$$

The output of the system is already expressed in terms of $x_1(t)$ in Eq. (3–57).

3.5 State Equations of Linear Discrete-data Systems

Similar to the continuous-data case, a modern way of describing a discrete-data system is by means of discrete state equations. As described earlier, when dealing with discrete-data control systems, we often encounter two different situations. The first one is that the components of the system are still continuous basically, but the signals at certain points of the system are discrete or discontinuous, because of the sample-and-hold operation. In this case, the components of the system are still described by differential equations, but because of the discrete nature of the signal, a set of difference equations may be generated from the original differential equation. The second situation involves systems which are completely discrete, in the sense that they receive and send out discrete data only, such as in the case of a digital controller or digital computer. Under this condition, the system dynamics should be described by difference equations.

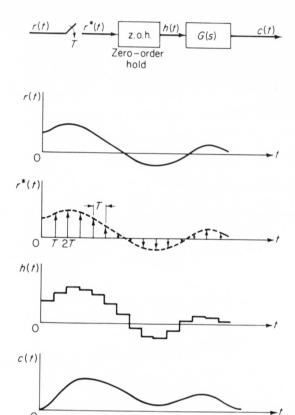

FIG. 3-3. A discrete-data system with sample-and-hold.

Let us consider the open-loop discrete-data system with sample-and-hold device, shown in Fig. 3-3. Typical signals that appear at various points in the system are also shown in the figure. The output, $c(t)$, ordinarily is a continuous function of time. The output of the zero-order hold, $h(t)$, is a train of steps. Therefore,

$$h(kT) = r(kT) \qquad (k = 0, 1, 2, \ldots) \qquad (3\text{–}63)$$

Let the linear system G be described by the set of state equation and output equation,

$$\frac{d\mathbf{x}(t)}{dt} = \mathbf{A}\mathbf{x}(t) + \mathbf{B}h(t) \qquad (3\text{–}64)$$

$$c(t) = \mathbf{D}\mathbf{x}(t) + \mathbf{E}h(t) \qquad (3\text{–}65)$$

where $\mathbf{x}(t)$ is the state vector, and $h(t)$ and $c(t)$ are the scalar input and output variables, respectively, since there is only one input and one output. **A, B, D,** and $\mathbf{E}$ are matrices which have been defined in the last section. From Eq. (3–52), the state transition equation of the system is obtained as

$$\mathbf{x}(t) = \mathbf{\Phi}(t - t_0)\mathbf{x}(t_0) + \int_{t_0}^{t} \mathbf{\Phi}(t - \tau)\mathbf{B}h(\tau)\,d\tau \qquad (3\text{–}66)$$

for $t \geq t_0$.

If we are interested only in the responses at the sampling instants, just as in the case of the z-transform solution, we let $t = (k + 1)T$ and $t_0 = kT$. Then Eq. (3–66) becomes

$$\mathbf{x}[(k + 1)T] = \mathbf{\Phi}(T)\mathbf{x}(kT) + \int_{kT}^{(k+1)T} \mathbf{\Phi}[(k + 1)T - \tau]\mathbf{B}h(\tau)\,d\tau \qquad (3\text{–}67)$$

where $\mathbf{\Phi}(t)$ is defined in Eq. (3–45).

Since $h(t)$ is piecewise constant, and $h(kT) = r(kT)$ for $kT \leq t < (k + 1)T$, the input function $h(\tau)$ can be replaced by $r(kT)$ and can be taken outside of the integral sign in Eq. (3–67). Therefore,

$$\mathbf{x}[(k + 1)T] = \mathbf{\Phi}(T)\mathbf{x}(kT) + \int_{kT}^{(k+1)T} \mathbf{\Phi}[(k + 1)T - \tau]\mathbf{B}\,d\tau\, r(kT) \qquad (3\text{–}68)$$

or

$$\mathbf{x}[(k + 1)T] = \mathbf{\Phi}(T)\mathbf{x}(kT) + \mathbf{\Theta}(T)r(kT) \qquad (3\text{–}69)$$

where

$$\mathbf{\Theta}(T) = \int_{kT}^{(k+1)T} \mathbf{\Phi}[(k + 1)T - \tau]\mathbf{B}\,d\tau \qquad (3\text{–}70)$$

Equation (3–69) is of the form of a linear difference equation in vector-matrix form. Since it represents a set of first-order difference equations, it is referred to as the *discrete state equation*.

The discrete state equation in Eq. (3–69) can be solved by means of a simple recursion procedure. Setting $k = 0, 1, 2, \ldots$ in Eq. (3–69), we find that the following equations result:

$$k = 0 \qquad \mathbf{x}(T) = \mathbf{\Phi}(T)\mathbf{x}(0) + \mathbf{\Theta}(T)r(0) \qquad (3\text{–}71)$$

$$k = 1 \qquad \mathbf{x}(2T) = \mathbf{\Phi}(T)\mathbf{x}(T) + \mathbf{\Theta}(T)r(T) \qquad (3\text{–}72)$$

$$k = 2 \qquad \mathbf{x}(3T) = \mathbf{\Phi}(T)\mathbf{x}(2T) + \mathbf{\Theta}(T)r(2T) \qquad (3\text{–}73)$$

$$\vdots \qquad \vdots \qquad \vdots \qquad \vdots$$

$$k = k - 1 \qquad \mathbf{x}(kT) = \mathbf{\Phi}(T)\mathbf{x}[(k - 1)T] + \mathbf{\Theta}(T)r[(k - 1)T] \qquad (3\text{–}74)$$

Substituting Eq. (3–71) into Eq. (3–72), and then, Eq. (3–72) into Eq. (3–73), ..., and so on, we obtain the following solution for Eq. (3–69):

$$\mathbf{x}(kT) = \mathbf{\Phi}^k(T)\mathbf{x}(0) + \sum_{i=0}^{k-1} \mathbf{\Phi}^{k-i-1}(T)\mathbf{\Theta}(T)r(iT) \qquad (3\text{–}75)$$

Equation (3–75) is defined as the *discrete state transition equation* of the discrete-data system. It is interesting to note that Eq. (3–75) is analogous to its continuous counterpart in Eq. (3–50). In fact, the state transition equation of Eq. (3–50) describes the state of the system of Fig. 3-3 for any time $t \geq 0$, with or without sampling. The discrete state transition equation of Eq. (3–75) is more restrictive in that it describes the state only at $t = kT$ ($k = 0, 1, 2, \ldots$), and only if for a system with a sample-and-hold device.

With kT considered as the initial state, a discrete state transition equation similar to that of Eq. (3–52) can be obtained as

$$\mathbf{x}[(k + N)T] = \mathbf{\Phi}^N(T)\mathbf{x}(kT) + \sum_{i=0}^{N-1} \mathbf{\Phi}^{N-i-1}(T)\mathbf{\Theta}(T)r[(k + i)T] \quad (3\text{–}76)$$

where N is a positive integer. The derivation of Eq. (3–76) is left to the reader.

The output of the system at the sampling instants is obtained by substituting $t = kT$ and Eq. (3–75) into Eq. (3–65), yielding

$$c(kT) = \mathbf{D}\mathbf{x}(kT) + \mathbf{E}h(kT)$$

$$= \mathbf{D}\mathbf{\Phi}^k(T)\mathbf{x}(0) + \mathbf{D}\sum_{i=0}^{k-1} \mathbf{\Phi}^{k-i-1}(T)\mathbf{\Theta}(T)r(iT) + \mathbf{E}h(kT) \quad (3\text{–}77)$$

An important advantage of the state variable method over the z-transform method is that it can be modified easily to describe the state and the output between sampling instants. In Eq. (3–66), if we let $t = (k + \Delta)T$, where $0 < \Delta \leq 1$, and $t_0 = kT$, we get

$$\mathbf{x}[(k + \Delta)T] = \mathbf{\Phi}(\Delta T)\mathbf{x}(kT) + r(kT)\int_{kT}^{(k+\Delta)T} \mathbf{\Phi}[(k + \Delta)T - \tau]\mathbf{B}\,d\tau$$

$$= \mathbf{\Phi}(\Delta T)\mathbf{x}(kT) + \mathbf{\Theta}(\Delta T)r(kT) \quad (3\text{–}78)$$

By varying the value of Δ between 0 and 1, the information between the sampling instants is completely described by Eq. (3–78).

One of the interesting properties of the state transition matrix $\mathbf{\Phi}(t)$, is that

$$\mathbf{\Phi}^k(T) = \mathbf{\Phi}(kT) \quad (3\text{–}79)$$

which is easily proved as follows.

Using the homogeneous solution of the state equation,

$$\mathbf{x}(t) = \mathbf{\Phi}(t - t_0)\mathbf{x}(t_0) \quad (3\text{–}80)$$

we let $t = kT$, and $t_0 = 0$. Therefore,

$$\mathbf{x}(kT) = \mathbf{\Phi}(kT)\mathbf{x}(0) \quad (3\text{–}81)$$

Also, by recursion, with $t = (k + 1)T$ and $t_0 = kT$, Eq. (3–80) leads to

$$\mathbf{x}(kT) = \mathbf{\Phi}^k(T)\mathbf{x}(0) \quad (3\text{–}82)$$

Hence, Eq. (3–79) is established.

In view of Eq. (3–79), the state transition equations in Eq. (3–75) and Eq. (3–76) are written as

$$\mathbf{x}(kT) = \mathbf{\Phi}(kT)\mathbf{x}(0) + \sum_{i=0}^{k-1} \mathbf{\Phi}[(k - i - 1)T]\mathbf{\Theta}(T)r(iT) \quad (3\text{–}83)$$

$$\mathbf{x}[(k + N)T] = \mathbf{\Phi}(NT)\mathbf{x}(kT) + \sum_{i=0}^{N-1} \mathbf{\Phi}[(N - i - 1)T]\mathbf{\Theta}(T)r[(k + i)T] \quad (3\text{–}84)$$

These two equations can be extended to the multi-input case simply by changing the input r into a vector $\mathbf{r}$.

When a linear system deals strictly with discrete data, the system can be described by a set of discrete state equations

$$\mathbf{x}[(k + 1)T] = \mathbf{A}\mathbf{x}(kT) + \mathbf{B}\mathbf{r}(kT) \tag{3-85}$$

and output equations

$$\mathbf{c}(kT) = \mathbf{D}\mathbf{x}(kT) + \mathbf{E}\mathbf{r}(kT) \tag{3-86}$$

where $\mathbf{A}$, $\mathbf{B}$, $\mathbf{D}$, and $\mathbf{E}$ are coefficient matrices of the appropriate dimensions. Notice that Eq. (3–85) is basically of the same form as Eq. (3–69). The only difference in the two cases is the starting point. In the case of Eq. (3–69), the starting point is the continuous state equations of Eq. (3–64); $\mathbf{\Phi}(T)$ and $\mathbf{\Theta}(T)$ are determined from the $\mathbf{A}$ and $\mathbf{B}$ matrices taken from Eq. (3–64). In the case of Eq. (3–85), the equation itself represents the starting point for the description of the discrete-data system which has only discrete signals.

The solution of Eq. (3–85) follows directly from that of Eq. (3–69). Therefore, the discrete state transition equation of Eq. (3–85) is

$$\mathbf{x}(kT) = \mathbf{A}^k\mathbf{x}(0) + \sum_{i=0}^{k-1} \mathbf{A}^{k-i-1}\mathbf{B}\mathbf{r}(iT) \tag{3-87}$$

where

$$\mathbf{A}^k = \underbrace{\mathbf{A}\mathbf{A}\mathbf{A}\mathbf{A}\mathbf{A} \cdots \mathbf{A}}_{k} \tag{3-88}$$

3.6 z-Transform Solution of Discrete State Equations

The discrete state equations

$$\mathbf{x}[(k + 1)T] = \mathbf{A}\mathbf{x}(kT) + \mathbf{B}\mathbf{r}(kT) \tag{3-89}$$

can be solved by means of the z-transform method. Taking the z-transform of both sides of Eq. (3–89) yields

$$z\mathbf{X}(z) - z\mathbf{x}(0) = \mathbf{A}\mathbf{X}(z) + \mathbf{B}\mathbf{R}(z) \tag{3-90}$$

Solving for $\mathbf{X}(z)$ from the last equation gives

$$\mathbf{X}(z) = (z\mathbf{I} - \mathbf{A})^{-1}z\mathbf{x}(0) + (z\mathbf{I} - \mathbf{A})^{-1}\mathbf{B}\mathbf{R}(z) \tag{3-91}$$

The inverse z-transform of the last equation is

$$\mathbf{x}(kT) = \mathscr{Z}^{-1}[(z\mathbf{I} - \mathbf{A})^{-1}z]\mathbf{x}(0) + \mathscr{Z}^{-1}[(z\mathbf{I} - \mathbf{A})^{-1}\mathbf{B}\mathbf{R}(z)] \tag{3-92}$$

The z-transform of $\mathbf{A}^k$ is, by definition,

$$\mathscr{Z}(\mathbf{A}^k) = \sum_{k=0}^{\infty} \mathbf{A}^k z^{-k} = \mathbf{I} + \mathbf{A}z^{-1} + \mathbf{A}^2 z^{-2} + \cdots \tag{3-93}$$

Premultiplying both sides of Eq. (3–93) by $\mathbf{A}z^{-1}$ and subtracting the result from Eq. (3–93), we have

$$(\mathbf{I} - \mathbf{A}z^{-1})\mathcal{Z}(\mathbf{A}^k) = \mathbf{I} \tag{3–94}$$

Therefore,

$$\mathcal{Z}(\mathbf{A}^k) = (\mathbf{I} - \mathbf{A}z^{-1})^{-1} = (z\mathbf{I} - \mathbf{A})^{-1}z \tag{3–95}$$

or

$$\mathbf{A}^k = \mathcal{Z}^{-1}[(z\mathbf{I} - \mathbf{A})^{-1}z] \tag{3–96}$$

Equation (3–96) also represents a way of finding $\mathbf{A}^k$ by using the z-transform method. Similarly, we can prove that

$$\mathcal{Z}^{-1}[(z\mathbf{I} - \mathbf{A})^{-1}\mathbf{B}\mathbf{R}(z)] = \sum_{i=0}^{k-1} \mathbf{A}^{k-i-1}\mathbf{B}\mathbf{r}(iT) \tag{3–97}$$

Now substituting Eqs. (3–96) and (3–97) into Eq. (3–92), we get

$$\mathbf{x}(kT) = \mathbf{A}^k\mathbf{x}(0) + \sum_{i=0}^{k-1} \mathbf{A}^{k-i-1}\mathbf{B}\mathbf{r}(iT) \tag{3–98}$$

which is identical to Eq. (3–87).

3.7 Relationships Between State Equations and Transfer Functions

Now that the two ways of describing a linear system with transfer functions and state equations have been presented, it is interesting to investigate the relations between the two methods.

In Eq. (2–3), the transfer function of a continuous-data system with a single input and output is defined in terms of the coefficients of the system's differential equations. Equation (2–15) gives the matrix transfer function relationship for a multivariable system. Now consider that a system is characterized by the state equations of Eq. (3–40). Substituting $\mathbf{X}(s)$ of Eq. (3–42) into the transformed version of Eq. (3–32) gives

$$\mathbf{C}(s) = \mathbf{D}\mathbf{X}(s) + \mathbf{E}\mathbf{R}(s)$$
$$= \mathbf{D}(s\mathbf{I} - \mathbf{A})^{-1}\mathbf{x}(0) + \mathbf{D}(s\mathbf{I} - \mathbf{A})^{-1}\mathbf{B}\mathbf{R}(s) + \mathbf{E}\mathbf{R}(s) \tag{3–99}$$

Since the definition of the transfer function calls for the assumption of zero initial conditions, $\mathbf{x}(0) = \mathbf{0}$. Thus, Eq. (3–99) becomes

$$\mathbf{C}(s) = [\mathbf{D}(s\mathbf{I} - \mathbf{A})^{-1}\mathbf{B} + \mathbf{E}]\mathbf{R}(s) \tag{3–100}$$

Hence, the transfer function matrix is defined as

$$\mathbf{G}(s) = \mathbf{D}(s\mathbf{I} - \mathbf{A})^{-1}\mathbf{B} + \mathbf{E} \tag{3–101}$$

provided that the matrix $s\mathbf{I} - \mathbf{A}$ is nonsingular.

Similarly, it can be shown easily that the transfer function matrix of a discrete-data system is

$$\mathbf{G}(z) = \mathbf{D}(z\mathbf{I} - \mathbf{A})^{-1}\mathbf{B} + \mathbf{E} \tag{3–102}$$

for the system which is described by Eqs. (3–85) and (3–86). Of course, the matrix $z\mathbf{I} - \mathbf{A}$ must not be singular.

3.8 The Characteristic Equation

The characteristic equation of a linear system can be defined with respect to the system's differential equation (difference equation), transfer function, or the state equations. Consider that a linear continuous-data system is described by the differential equation

$$\frac{d^n c(t)}{dt^n} + a_1 \frac{d^{n-1} c(t)}{dt^{n-1}} + a_2 \frac{d^{n-2} c(t)}{dt^{n-2}} + \cdots + a_{n-1} \frac{dc(t)}{dt} + a_n c(t)$$

$$= b_0 \frac{d^n r(t)}{dt^n} + b_1 \frac{d^{n-1} r(t)}{dt^{n-1}} + \cdots + b_{n-1} \frac{dr(t)}{dt} + b_n r(t) \qquad (3\text{--}103)$$

The transfer function of the system is

$$G(s) = \frac{C(s)}{R(s)} = \frac{b_0 s^n + b_1 s^{n-1} + \cdots + b_{n-1} s + b_n}{s^n + a_1 s^{n-1} + \cdots + a_{n-1} s + a_n} \qquad (3\text{--}104)$$

The characteristic equation is defined as *the equation obtained by equating the denominator of the transfer function to zero; that is,*

$$s^n + a_1 s^{n-1} + \cdots + a_{n-1} s + a_n = 0 \qquad (3\text{--}105)$$

We also notice that the characteristic equation is a polynomial which contains only the coefficients of the homogeneous part of the differential equation of the system.

The characteristic equation can also be defined in terms of the state equations of the system. Referring to Eq. (3–101), we can write the equation as

$$\mathbf{G}(s) = \mathbf{D} \frac{[\Delta_{ij}]'}{|s\mathbf{I} - \mathbf{A}|} \mathbf{B} + \mathbf{E}$$

$$= \frac{\mathbf{D}[\Delta_{ij}]'\mathbf{B} + |s\mathbf{I} - \mathbf{A}|\,\mathbf{E}}{|s\mathbf{I} - \mathbf{A}|} \qquad (3\text{--}106)$$

where Δ_{ij} represents the cofactor of the ijth element of the matrix $s\mathbf{I} - \mathbf{A}$, and $[\Delta_{ij}]'$ is the matrix transpose of $[\Delta_{ij}]$.

Setting the denominator of the transfer function matrix $\mathbf{G}(s)$ to zero gives

$$|s\mathbf{I} - \mathbf{A}| = 0 \qquad (3\text{--}107)$$

which is the characteristic equation of the system described by Eq. (3–103).

The roots of the characteristic equation are often called the *eigenvalues* of the matrix $\mathbf{A}$, since they depend only on $\mathbf{A}$.

A linear discrete-data system can be described by the following linear constant-coefficient difference equation:

$$c[(k + n)T] + a_1 c[(k + n - 1)T] + a_2 c[(k + n - 2)T] + \cdots$$

$$+ a_{n-1} c[(k + 1)T] + a_n c(kT) = b_0 r[(k + n)]T$$

$$+ b_1 r[(k + n - 1)T] + \cdots + b_{n-1} r[(k + 1)T] + b_n r(kT) \qquad (3\text{--}108)$$

The discrete state equations of the system can be written as

$$\mathbf{x}[(k + 1)T] = \mathbf{Ax}(kT) + \mathbf{Br}(kT) \qquad (3\text{-}109)$$

and the output equation is

$$\mathbf{c}(kT) = \mathbf{Dx}(kT) + \mathbf{Er}(kT) \qquad (3\text{-}110)$$

The coefficient matrices $\mathbf{A}$, $\mathbf{B}$, $\mathbf{D}$, and $\mathbf{E}$ can be obtained as functions of the coefficients of Eq. (3-108) by using the method similar to that given by Eqs. (3-24) and (3-25).

The characteristic equation of the discrete-data system is defined as

$$z^n + a_1 z^{n-1} + a_2 z^{n-2} + \cdots + a_{n-1} z + a_n = 0 \qquad (3\text{-}111)$$

which depends only on the coefficients of the homogeneous part of Eq. (3-108). It is also obtained by setting the denominator of $\mathbf{G}(z)$ to zero; or

$$|z\mathbf{I} - \mathbf{A}| = 0 \qquad (3\text{-}112)$$

Example 3-2. As an illustrative example, let us derive the characteristic equation for the system which is described by the differential equation in Eq. (3-13). The equation is repeated below.

$$\frac{d^3 c(t)}{dt^3} + 2\frac{d^2 c(t)}{dt^2} + 3\frac{dc(t)}{dt} + c(t) = 2r(t) \qquad (3\text{-}113)$$

The transfer function of the system is

$$\frac{C(s)}{R(s)} = \frac{2}{s^3 + 2s^2 + 3s + 1} \qquad (3\text{-}114)$$

Thus, the characteristic equation is

$$s^3 + 2s^2 + 3s + 1 = 0 \qquad (3\text{-}115)$$

The $\mathbf{A}$ matrix of the system is

$$\mathbf{A} = \begin{bmatrix} 0 & 1 & 0 \\ 0 & 0 & 1 \\ -1 & -3 & -2 \end{bmatrix} \qquad (3\text{-}116)$$

Thus, Eq. (3-107) gives

$$|s\mathbf{I} - \mathbf{A}| = \begin{vmatrix} s & -1 & 0 \\ 0 & s & -1 \\ 1 & 3 & s+2 \end{vmatrix} = s^2(s + 2) + 1 + 3s \qquad (3\text{-}117)$$

$$= s^3 + 2s^2 + 3s + 1 = 0$$

which agrees with Eq. (3-115).

Similarly, it is easy to show that the characteristic equation of the system described by Eq. (3-55) is

$$s^2 + 3s + 2 = 0 \qquad (3\text{-}118)$$

and the eigenvalues are $s = -1$ and $s = -2$.

Example 3-3. Consider that a discrete-data system is described by the difference equation

$$c(k + 2) + 5c(k + 1) + 3c(k) = r(k + 1) + 2r(k) \qquad (3\text{--}119)$$

Taking the z-transform on both sides of the difference equation and assuming zero initial conditions, we have

$$z^2 C(z) + 5z C(z) + 3C(z) = z R(z) + 2R(z) \qquad (3\text{--}120)$$

Therefore, the transfer function of the system is

$$\frac{C(z)}{R(z)} = \frac{z + 2}{z^2 + 5z + 3} \qquad (3\text{--}121)$$

Setting the denominator of $C(z)/R(z)$ to zero, we have the characteristic equation of the system as

$$z^2 + 5z + 3 = 0 \qquad (3\text{--}122)$$

By defining the state variables as follows,

$$x_1(k) = c(k) \qquad (3\text{--}123)$$

$$x_2(k) = x_1(k + 1) - r(k) \qquad (3\text{--}124)$$

the difference equation of Eq. (3–119) is resolved into two state equations

$$x_1(k + 1) = x_2(k) + r(k) \qquad (3\text{--}125)$$

$$x_2(k + 1) = -3x_1(k) - 5x_2(k) - 3r(k) \qquad (3\text{--}126)$$

Therefore, the **A** matrix of the system is

$$\mathbf{A} = \begin{bmatrix} 0 & 1 \\ -3 & -5 \end{bmatrix} \qquad (3\text{--}127)$$

The characteristic equation of the discrete-data system is also obtained from Eq. (3–112). Thus,

$$|z\mathbf{I} - \mathbf{A}| = \begin{vmatrix} z & -1 \\ 3 & z + 5 \end{vmatrix} = z^2 + 5z + 3 = 0 \qquad (3\text{--}128)$$

which agrees with the result obtained in Eq. (3–122).

3.9 State Transition Signal Flow Graphs[1,4]

The signal flow graph discussed in Sec. 2.5 applies only to algebraic equations. In this section we shall present the idea of the *state transition signal flow graph* which may be used to portray state equations or differential equations. A significant contribution of the state transition signal flow graph is that it resembles the analog computer block diagram. Therefore, once the state transition signal flow graph is drawn, the problem may be programmed on an analog computer.

Basic Analog Computer Elements[5]

It is helpful to discuss the linear elements of an analog computer before we take up the subject of state transition signal flow graphs.

The fundamental linear operations that can be performed on an analog computer are *multiplication by constants, addition,* and *integration.*

(1) *Multiplication by a constant:* Multiplication of a machine variable by a constant is done by potentiometers and amplifiers. Consider the operation

$$x_2(t) = ax_1(t) \qquad (3\text{–}129)$$

where a is a constant. If a lies between zero and unity, a potentiometer is used for the purpose. An operational amplifier is used to simulate Eq.(3–129) if a is a negative integer less than -1. This is because the output voltage of the amplifier is usually 180 deg out of phase with respect to the input.

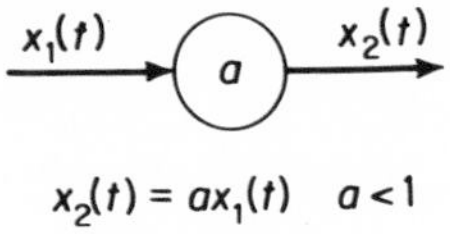

$$x_1(t) \longrightarrow \bigcirc a \longrightarrow x_2(t)$$

$$x_2(t) = ax_1(t) \quad a < 1$$

FIG. 3-4. Block diagram symbol of a potentiometer.

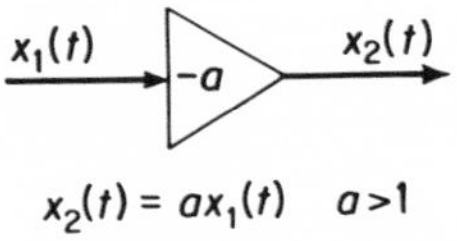

$$x_1(t) \longrightarrow \triangleright -a \longrightarrow x_2(t)$$

$$x_2(t) = ax_1(t) \quad a > 1$$

FIG. 3-5. Block diagram symbol of an operational amplifier.

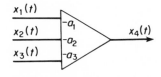

$$x_4(t) = a_1x_1(t) + a_2x_2(t) + a_3x_3(t)$$

FIG. 3-6. The operational amplifier used as a summer.

The computer block diagram symbols of the potentiometer and the operational amplifier are shown in Figs. 3-4 and 3-5, respectively.

(2) *Algebraic sum of two or more machine variables:* The algebraic sum of two or more machine variables is obtained by means of an operational amplifier as shown in Fig. 3-6; e.g.,

$$x_4(t) = a_1x_1(t) + a_2x_2(t) + a_3x_3(t) \qquad (3\text{–}130)$$

(3) *Integration:* The integration of a machine variable on an analog computer is achieved by means of a computer element called the *integrator.*

If $x_1(t)$ is the output of the integrator with initial condition $x_1(t_0)$ given at $t = t_0$, and $x_2(t)$ is the output, the integrator performs the following operation:

$$x_1(t) = \int_{t_0}^{t} a x_2(\tau)\, d\tau + x_1(t_0) \tag{3-131}$$

Te block diagram symbol of the integrator is shown in Fig. 3-7. The integrator can also serve simultaneously as a summing device, and an amplifier.

We shall now show that these computer operations can be portrayed by state transition signal flow graph elements.

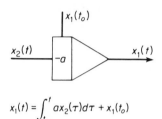

$$x_1(t) = \int_{t_0}^{t} a x_2(\tau)\, d\tau + x_1(t_0)$$

FIG. 3-7. Block diagram of an integrator.

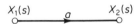

FIG. 3-8. Signal flow graph representation of $X_2(s) = aX_1(s)$.

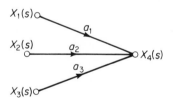

FIG. 3-9. Signal flow graph representation of $X_4(s) = aX_1(s) + a_2X_2(s) + a_3X_3(s)$.

The Laplace transform of Eq. (3–129) reads

$$X_2(s) = aX_1(s) \tag{3-132}$$

where a is a constant. A flow graph representation of Eq. (3–132) is shown in Fig. 3-8. For the summing operation, Eq. (3–130) leads to

$$X_4(s) = a_1X_1(s) + a_2X_2(s) + a_3X_3(s) \tag{3-133}$$

which is portrayed by the flow graph shown in Fig. 3-9.

Now taking the Laplace transform on both sides of Eq. (3–131) gives

$$X_1(s) = a\frac{X_2(s)}{s} + a\int_{t_0}^0 x_2(\tau)\,d\tau + \frac{x_1(t_0)}{s} \qquad (3\text{--}134)$$

Since the past history of the integrator is represented by $x_2(t_0)$, and the state transition starts from $t = t_0$, $x_2(\tau) = 0$ for $0 < \tau < t_0$. Thus, Eq. (3–134) becomes

$$X_1(s) = \frac{aX_2(s)}{s} + \frac{x_1(t_0)}{s} \qquad (t \geq t_0) \qquad (3\text{--}135)$$

However, it should be emphasized that the transformed equation of Eq. (3–135) is defined only for the period $t \geq t_0$. Therefore, the inverse Laplace transform of $X_1(s)$ should read

$$x_1(t) = \mathscr{L}^{-1}[X_1(s)] = a\int_0^t x_2(\tau)u(-t_0)\,d\tau + x_1(t_0)$$

$$= a\int_{t_0}^t x_2(\tau)d\tau + x_1(t_0) \qquad (3\text{--}136)$$

which is identical to Eq. (3–131).

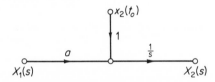

FIG. 3-10. A signal flow graph representation of
$$X_2(s) = \frac{aX_1(s)}{s} + \frac{x_2(t_0)}{s}.$$

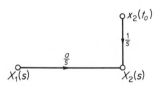

FIG. 3-11. A signal flow graph representation of
$$X_2(s) = \frac{aX_1(s)}{s} + \frac{x_2(t_0)}{s}.$$

The signal flow graph representation of Eq. (3–136) is shown in Fig. 3-10. Another parallel representation with fewer numbers of nodes and branches is shown in Fig. 3-11.

Thus we have established a correspondence between the analog computer elements and the signal flow graph representation of the computer operations. Since these flow graph elements include initial conditions and can be used to solve state equations, they form the basic elements of the *state transition signal flow graph*. The correspondence of the analog computer elements and

Potentiometer (attenuation)

Amplification and phase reversal

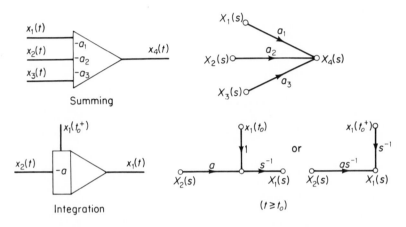

Analog computer operations   State transition signal flow graph elements

FIG. 3-12. Correspondence of analog computer elements and state transition signal flow graph elements.

the state transition signal flow graph elements is illustrated in Fig. 3-12. The following example illustrates the construction of the state transition signal flow graph of a linear system.

Example 3-4. Consider that a linear system is described by the following differential equation:

$$\frac{d^2 c(t)}{dt^2} + 3\frac{dc(t)}{dt} + 2c(t) = r(t) \qquad (3\text{--}137)$$

where $c(t)$ is the output and $r(t)$ is the input. The state equations of the system are

$$\frac{dx_1(t)}{dt} = x_2(t) \qquad (3\text{--}138)$$

$$\frac{dx_2(t)}{dt} = -2x_1(t) - 3x_2(t) + r(t) \qquad (3\text{--}139)$$

The output equation is simply

$$c(t) = x_1(t) \tag{3-140}$$

Integrating both sides of Eq. (3–138) from t_0^+ to t gives

$$x_1(t) = \int_{t_0^+}^t x_2(\tau)\, d\tau + x_1(t_0^+) \tag{3-141}$$

which is similar to the expression in Eq. (3–131). Therefore, the signal flow graph element of Fig. 3–10 or Fig. 3–11 may be used to portray Eq. (3–138). The expression in Eq. (3–139) simply describes a summing operation. Thus, a state transition signal flow graph of the system is drawn as shown in Fig. 3-13a. An analog computer block diagram of the system is constructed in Fig. 3-13b. The final practical version of the block diagram may be somewhat different, since scaling of the numerical values of the signals at various points of the system may be necessary.

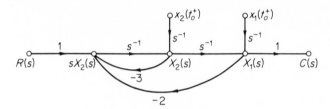

(a) State transition flow graph for Eq. (3–137).

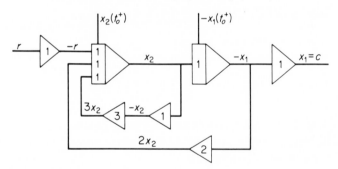

FIG. 3-13. (b) An analog computer block diagram for the system described by Eq. (3–137).

It is necessary to reiterate here that the initial states being defined at $t = t_0$ implies that the signal flow graph and the block diagram are valid only for $t \geq t_0$. This must be kept in mind when the state transition equation of the system is derived.

The transformed state transition equations of the system are obtained from the state transition signal flow graph by using Mason's gain formula.

Thus, from Fig. 3-13a,

$$X_1(s) = \frac{s^{-1}(1 + 3s^{-1})}{\Delta}\, x_1(t_0^+) + \frac{s^{-2}}{\Delta}\, x_2(t_0^+) + \frac{s^{-2}}{\Delta}\, R(s) \tag{3-142}$$

$$X_2(s) = \frac{-2s^{-2}}{\Delta} x_1(t_0^+) + \frac{s^{-1}}{\Delta} x_2(t_0^+) + \frac{s^{-1}}{\Delta} R(s) \qquad (3\text{-}143)$$

where

$$\Delta = 1 + 3s^{-1} + 2s^{-2} \qquad (3\text{-}144)$$

After simplification, Eqs. (3-142) and (3-143) are presented below in matrix form:

$$\begin{bmatrix} X_1(s) \\ X_2(s) \end{bmatrix} = \frac{1}{(s+1)(s+2)} \begin{bmatrix} s+3 & 1 \\ -2 & s \end{bmatrix} \begin{bmatrix} x_1(t_0^+) \\ x_2(t_0^+) \end{bmatrix} + \begin{bmatrix} \dfrac{1}{(s+1)(s+2)} \\ \dfrac{s}{(s+1)(s+2)} \end{bmatrix} R(s)$$

$$(3\text{-}145)$$

The state transition equation for $t \geq t_0$ is obtained by taking the inverse Laplace transform on both sides of Eq. (3-145).

If the input $r(t)$ is a unit step function $u(t)$, $R(s) = 1/s$, the inverse transform of Eq. (3-145) gives

$$\begin{bmatrix} x_1(t) \\ x_2(t) \end{bmatrix} = \begin{bmatrix} 2e^{-(t-t_0)} - e^{-2(t-t_0)} & e^{-(t-t_0)} - e^{-2(t-t_0)} \\ -2e^{-(t-t_0)} + 2e^{-2(t-t_0)} & -e^{-(t-t_0)} + 2e^{-2(t-t_0)} \end{bmatrix} \begin{bmatrix} x_1(t_0^+) \\ x_2(t_0^+) \end{bmatrix}$$

$$+ \begin{bmatrix} \frac{1}{2}u(t-t_0) - e^{-(t-t_0)} + \frac{1}{2}e^{-2(t-t_0)} \\ e^{-(t-t_0)} - e^{-2(t-t_0)} \end{bmatrix} \qquad (3\text{-}146)$$

for $t \geq t_0$, and is identical to the result in Eq. (3-62).

Notice that in deriving the last equation, the following inverse Laplace transform relations have been used:

$$\mathscr{L}^{-1}\left(\frac{1}{s}\right) = u(t - t_0) \qquad\qquad (t \geq t_0) \qquad (3\text{-}147)$$

$$\mathscr{L}^{-1}\left(\frac{1}{s+a}\right) = e^{-a(t-t_0)}u(t - t_0) \qquad (t \geq t_0) \qquad (3\text{-}148)$$

These results agree with the discussion given in Sec. 3.4 and Eq. (3-53).

The transfer function and the characteristic equation of the system can also be determined directly from the state transition signal flow graph. Assuming zero initial conditions, we obtain the transfer function from Eq. (3-142). Thus,

$$\frac{C(s)}{R(s)} = \frac{X_1(s)}{R(s)} = \frac{1}{s^2 + 3s + 2} \qquad (3\text{-}149)$$

The characteristic equation is

$$s^2 + 3s + 2 = 0 \qquad (3\text{-}150)$$

and its roots are at $s = -1$ and $s = -2$.

Discrete State Transition Signal Flow Graphs

When a discrete-data system is described by difference equations or discrete state equations, a discrete state transition signal flow graph may be constructed for the system. In contrast to the similarity between an analog computer diagram and a continuous-data state transition flow graph, the elements of a discrete state transition flow graph resemble the computing elements of a digital computer.

Some of the operations of a digital computer are multiplication by a constant, addition of several machine variables, time delay, or shifting. The mathematical descriptions of these basic digital computations and their corresponding z-transform expressions are given below:

(1) Multiplication by a constant

$$x_2(kT) = ax_1(kT) \qquad\qquad (3\text{-}151)$$

$$X_2(z) = aX_1(z) \qquad\qquad (3\text{-}152)$$

(2) Summing

$$x_2(kT) = x_0(kT) + x_1(kT) \qquad\qquad (3\text{-}153)$$

$$X_2(z) = X_0(z) + X_1(z) \qquad\qquad (3\text{-}154)$$

(3) Shifting or time delay

$$x_2(kT) = x_1[(k + 1)T] \qquad\qquad (3\text{-}155)$$

$$X_2(z) = zX_1(z) - zx_1(0^+) \qquad\qquad (3\text{-}156)$$

or

$$X_1(z) = z^{-1}X_2(z) + x_1(0^+) \qquad\qquad (3\text{-}157)$$

The state transition signal flow graph representations of these operations

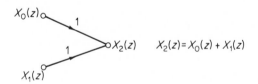

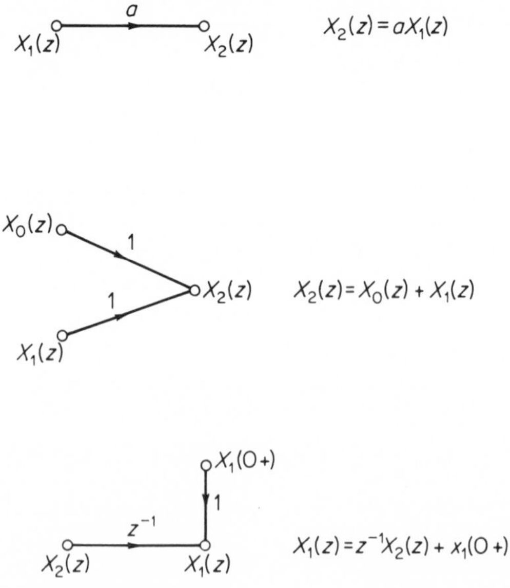

$$X_2(z) = aX_1(z)$$

$$X_2(z) = X_0(z) + X_1(z)$$

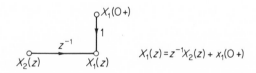

$$X_1(z) = z^{-1}X_2(z) + x_1(0^+)$$

FIG. 3-14. Basic elements of a discrete state transition signal flow graph.

are illustrated in Fig. 3-14. The initial time $t = 0^+$ in Eq. (3–157) can be generalized to $t = t_0^+$. Then Eq. (3-157) becomes

$$X_1(z) = z^{-1}X_2(z) + x_1(t_0^+) \qquad (3\text{–}158)$$

which is valid for $t \geq t_0^+$.

Example 3-5. Consider again the difference equation of Eq. (3–119), which is

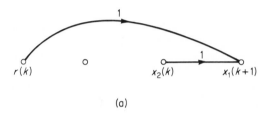

(a)

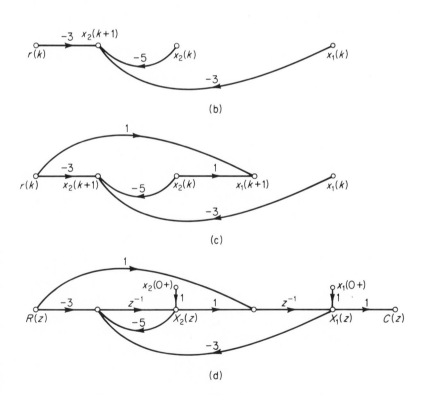

(b)

(c)

(d)

FIG. 3-15. Discrete state transition signal flow graph of the system described by Eq. (3–159).

$$c(k + 2) + 5c(k + 1) + 3c(k) = r(k + 1) + 2r(k) \qquad (3\text{-}159)$$

One way of constructing the discrete state transition signal flow graph for the system is to start with the state equations, which are given by Eqs. (3-125) and (3-126), and are repeated below:

$$x_1(k + 1) = x_2(k) + r(k) \qquad (3\text{-}160)$$

$$x_2(k + 1) = -3x_1(k) - 5x_2(k) - 3r(k) \qquad (3\text{-}161)$$

A method using Eq. (3-159) directly will be described in the next section.

First, the three nodes representing $x_1(k + 1)$, $x_2(k)$ and $r(k)$ are arranged and connected according to Eq. (3-160), as shown in Fig. 3-15a. Next, Fig. 3-15b shows the signal flow graph of Eq. (3-161). The combination of the signal flow graphs in Figs. 3-15a and 3-15b is shown in Fig. 3-15c. As seen from the shifting relationship between $x_1(k + 1)$ and $x_1(k)$, defined by the signal flow graph of Fig. 3-14, the delay units, z^{-1}, and the initial states are added to the flow graph of Fig. 3-15c. The complete discrete state transition signal flow graph of the system is shown in Fig. 3-15d. Notice that in this case the state variables appear as outputs of the delay units on the state transition flow graph.

The state transition equation of the system can be obtained directly from the signal flow graph by applying Mason's gain formula to Fig. 3-15d. Referring to $X_1(z)$ and $X_2(z)$ as output nodes, and $x_1(0^+)$, $x_2(0^+)$, and $R(z)$ as input nodes, we have

$$\begin{bmatrix} X_1(z) \\ X_2(z) \end{bmatrix} = \frac{1}{\Delta} \begin{bmatrix} 1 + 5z^{-1} & z^{-1} \\ -3z^{-1} & 1 \end{bmatrix} \begin{bmatrix} x_1(0^+) \\ x_2(0^+) \end{bmatrix} + \frac{1}{\Delta} \begin{bmatrix} z^{-1}(1 + 5z^{-1}) - 3z^{-2} \\ -3z^{-1} - 3z^{-2} \end{bmatrix} R(z)$$

$$(3\text{-}162)$$

where

$$\Delta = 1 + 5z^{-1} + 3z^{-2} \qquad (3\text{-}163)$$

Equation (3-162) is the state transition equation, which is generally of the form

$$\mathbf{X}(z) = (z\mathbf{I} - \mathbf{A})^{-1}z\mathbf{x}(0) + (z\mathbf{I} - \mathbf{A})^{-1}\mathbf{B}R(z) \qquad (3\text{-}164)$$

One advantage of using the state transition flow graph is that Eq. (3-162) is obtained simply by use of Mason's gain formula. This saves the effort of performing the matrix inverse of $(z\mathbf{I} - \mathbf{A})$ which is required in Eq. (3-164).

The transfer function of the system can be obtained directly from Eq. (3-162). Therefore,

$$\frac{C(z)}{R(z)} = \frac{X_1(z)}{R(z)} = \frac{z^{-1} + 2z^{-2}}{1 + 5z^{-1} + 3z^{-2}} = \frac{z + 2}{z^2 + 5z + 3} \qquad (3\text{-}165)$$

which checks with the result obtained earlier in Eq. (3-121).

3.10 Decomposition of Transfer Functions

In Chapter 2 and the preceding sections of this chapter, various methods of characterizing a linear system have been discussed. It is advantageous to summarize briefly and gather thoughts at this point, before proceeding to the main topics of this section.

It has been shown that the starting point of the description of a linear system may be the system's differential equation(s), difference equation(s), transfer function(s), or a set of state or dynamic equations. The solutions may be in the form of a time-domain expression or a frequency response of the output or the state transition equation. It is clear that these various methods of linear system characterizations are indeed closely related. Further, the state transition signal flow graph is shown to be a useful tool which not only can lead to the solutions, but also acts as a vehicle of translation from one type of description to the others.

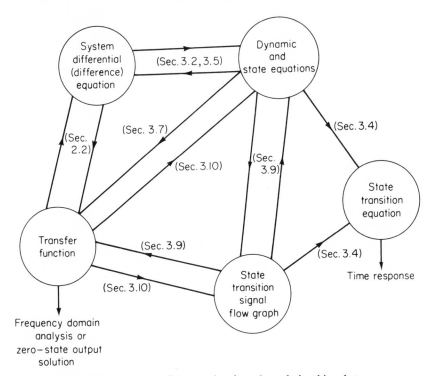

FIG. 3-16. A flow diagram showing the relationships between various methods of describing and solving linear systems.

In summarizing the various ways of describing a linear system and their interrelationships, a flow diagram is constructed in Fig. 3-16. The diagram shows that starting, for instance, with the differential equation of a system, one can get the solution to the output by use of the classical method or the Laplace transform method of solving differential equations. As an alternative, the differential equations can be transformed into a set of state equations, and eventually the solution is obtained in the form of the state transition equation. Or one may use the transfer function approach, starting with either the differential equation or the dynamic equations.

The discussions given thus far on the characterization of linear systems still leave us with several unclarified points. For instance, given a differential equation or difference equation, what is a convenient way of choosing the state variables? It is clear that Eqs. (3–24) and (3–25) are awkward and inconvenient for this purpose, although they are quite general. Another question is concerned with the construction of the state transition signal flow graph, given the differential equation or the difference equation. The state transition signal flow graphs for Examples 3-3 and 3-4 have been drawn from the state equations. However, it would be helpful if these flow graphs could be constructed directly from the differential equation or the difference equation. Then, in general, it is essential to learn the relation between transfer functions, state equations, state transition signal flow graphs, and the system's differential or difference equation. In this section we shall discuss how a differential (difference) equation is transformed to a transfer function, and then how the transfer function will lead to the state equations and the state transition signal flow graph.

The process of going from the transfer function to the state equations or the state transition signal flow graph is called the *decomposition* of a transfer function. The process of decomposition is extremely important in the study of feedback control systems, since in practice many control systems and components are often described by transfer functions obtained through experimental means. For instance, it has been a standard practice to represent the voltage-displacement transfer function of a two-phase servomotor by

$$\frac{\Theta(s)}{E(s)} = \frac{K}{s(1 + Ts)} \tag{3–166}$$

In general, there are three different ways of decomposing a transfer function. We shall show in the following that each of these three schemes of decomposition has its own advantage and is best suited for a particular situation.

Decomposition of Continuous-data Transfer Functions

(1) *Direct Decomposition*

Consider that a system is described by the following transfer function:

$$\frac{C(s)}{R(s)} = \frac{a_0 s^2 + a_1 s + a_2}{b_0 s^2 + b_1 s + b_2} \qquad (3\text{-}167)$$

It is desired to find the state equations and the state transition signal flow graph of the system. Let us multiply the numerator and the denominator of the right-hand side of Eq. (3–167) by $s^{-2} X(s)$, where $X(s)$ is an auxiliary variable. Equation (3–167) now reads

$$\frac{C(s)}{R(s)} = \frac{(a_0 + a_1 s^{-1} + a_2 s^{-2}) X(s)}{(b_0 + b_1 s^{-1} + b_2 s^{-2}) X(s)} \qquad (3\text{-}168)$$

Equating the numerators on both sides of Eq. (3–168) gives

$$C(s) = (a_0 + a_1 s^{-1} + a_2 s^{-2}) X(s) \qquad (3\text{-}169)$$

The same operation on the denominator brings

$$R(s) = (b_0 + b_1 s^{-1} + b_2 s^{-2}) X(s) \qquad (3\text{-}170)$$

In order to construct a signal flow graph, Eq. (3–170) must first be written in a cause-and-effect relation. Solving for $X(s)$ in Eq. (3–170) gives

$$X(s) = \frac{1}{b_0} R(s) - \frac{b_1}{b_0} s^{-1} X(s) - \frac{b_2}{b_0} s^{-2} X(s) \qquad (3\text{-}171)$$

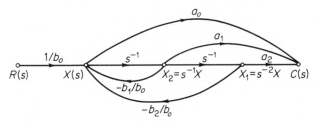

FIG. 3-17. State transition signal flow graph of the transfer function of Eq. (3–167) by direct decomposition.

The state transition signal flow graph is now drawn in Fig. 3-17 following through the cause-and-effect relationships stated in Eqs. (3–169) and (3–171). For simplicity, the initial conditions are not included on the flow graph. The state variables are now defined as the output variables of the integrators, and the state equations are written as

$$\frac{dx_1(t)}{dt} = x_2(t) \qquad (3\text{-}172)$$

$$\frac{dx_2(t)}{dt} = -\frac{b_2}{b_0} x_1(t) - \frac{b_1}{b_0} x_2(t) + \frac{1}{b_0} r(t) \qquad (3\text{-}173)$$

The output equation is obtained from Fig. 3-17 by writing $c(t)$ as a function of $x_1(t)$, $x_2(t)$, and $r(t)$. Therefore,

$$c(t) = \left(a_2 - \frac{a_0 b_2}{b_0}\right) x_1(t) + \left(a_1 - \frac{a_0 b_1}{b_0}\right) x_2(t) + \frac{a_0}{b_0} r(t) \qquad (3\text{-}174)$$

The procedure just described is typical for the direct decomposition and can be easily generalized to transfer functions of any order. In general, the scheme is more suitable when the transfer function is not in factored form.

(2) *Cascade Decomposition*

Consider that the transfer function of Eq. (3-167) is factored in the following form:

$$\frac{C(s)}{R(s)} = \frac{a_0}{b_0}\left(\frac{s + q_1}{s + p_1}\right)\left(\frac{s + q_2}{s + p_2}\right) \tag{3-175}$$

Then it is possible to treat the function as the product of two first-order transfer functions. The state transition flow graph of each of the first-order transfer functions is realized by using the direct decomposition method, and the complete graph is obtained by cascading the two graphs as shown in Fig. 3-18.

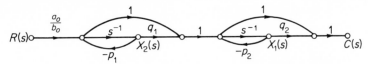

FIG. 3-18. State transition signal flow graph of the transfer function of Eq. (3–167) by cascade decomposition.

The output variables of the integrators are assigned as the state variables. The state equations are

$$\frac{dx_1(t)}{dt} = -p_2 x_1 + (q_1 - p_1)x_2 + \frac{a_0}{b_0}r(t) \tag{3-176}$$

$$\frac{dx_2(t)}{dt} = -p_1 x_2 + \frac{a_0}{b_0}r(t) \tag{3-177}$$

and the output equation is

$$c(t) = (q_2 - p_2)x_1 + (q_1 - p_1)x_2 + \frac{a_0}{b_0}r(t) \tag{3-178}$$

The reader can verify the flow graph by showing that the transfer function of Eq. (3–175) can be obtained from Fig. 3-18 by using Mason's gain formula.

It is evident that the cascade decomposition scheme is suitable only if the numerator and the denominator of the transfer function are in factored form.

(3) *Parallel Decomposition*

If only the denominator of a transfer function is in factored form, then it is possible to represent the latter as a sum of partial fractioned terms. Now consider that a transfer function has only simply real poles at

$-p_1$ and $-p_2$, and it is factored by partial fraction expansion into the following form:

$$\frac{C(s)}{R(s)} = \frac{K_1}{s + p_1} + \frac{K_2}{s + p_2} \qquad (3\text{-}179)$$

Then the state transition signal flow graph of the system can be portrayed by the parallel combination of the flow graph representation of each of the first-order terms on the right-hand side of Eq. (3-179). When the transfer function has multiple order poles, the same procedure can be applied. When the transfer function has complex conjugate poles, it is necessary to represent the poles in the quadratic form: $(s^2 + as + b)$. The complete flow graph is shown in Fig. 3-19.

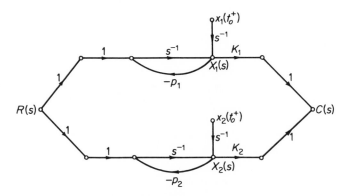

FIG. 3-19. State transition signal flow graph of the transfer function of Eq. (3-167) by parallel decomposition.

The state equations of the system are now written as

$$\begin{bmatrix} \dfrac{dx_1(t)}{dt} \\ \dfrac{dx_2(t)}{dt} \end{bmatrix} = \begin{bmatrix} -p_1 & 0 \\ 0 & -p_2 \end{bmatrix} \begin{bmatrix} x_1(t) \\ x_2(t) \end{bmatrix} + \begin{bmatrix} 1 \\ 1 \end{bmatrix} r(t) \qquad (3\text{-}180)$$

and the output equation is

$$c(t) = [K_1 \quad K_2] \begin{bmatrix} x_1(t) \\ x_2(t) \end{bmatrix} \qquad (3\text{-}181)$$

One of the advantages of this method of decomposition is that for transfer functions with simple poles, the resulting **A** matrix is always a diagonal matrix. Therefore, parallel decomposition can be used to diagonalize the **A** matrix, which is useful in the study of the *controllability* and *observability* of feedback control systems (Sec. 11.2).

Decomposition of Discrete-data Transfer Functions

The three schemes of decomposition can be applied to transfer functions of discrete-data systems without modification. Therefore, the method needs no elaboration. As an illustrative example, the three state transition signal flow graphs for the transfer function

$$G(z) = \frac{C(z)}{R(z)} = \frac{z + 2}{z^2 + 5z + 3} = \frac{z + 2}{(z + 4.3)(z + 0.7)} \qquad (3\text{-}182)$$

are shown in Fig. 3-20.

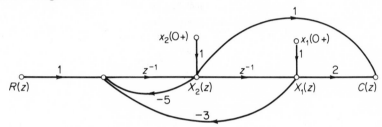

(a) $\dfrac{C(z)}{R(z)} = \dfrac{z + 2}{z^2 + 5z + 3}$ (direct decomposition)

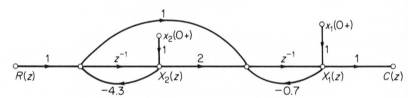

(b) $\dfrac{C(z)}{R(z)} = \left(\dfrac{z + 2}{z + 4.3}\right)\left(\dfrac{1}{z + 0.7}\right)$ (cascade decomposition)

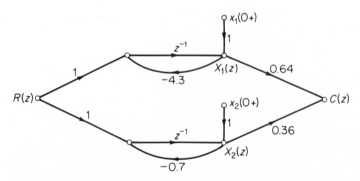

(c) $\dfrac{C(z)}{R(z)} = \dfrac{0.64}{z + 4.3} + \dfrac{0.36}{z + 0.7}$ (parallel decomposition)

FIG. 3-20. Three different state transition signal flow graphs of the transfer function $G(s) = \dfrac{z + 2}{z^2 + 5z + 3}$.

3.11 State Transition Signal Flow Graphs of Feedback Control Systems

In the last section the relationship between a transfer function and its state transition signal flow graph was discussed. Now we shall investigate a more practical problem, which is the construction of the state transition signal flow graph of a system which usually involves an interconnection of transfer functions. We realize that once the state transition signal flow graph of the over-all system is obtained, the questions concerning how the state variables should be defined as well as the state equations are readily answered.

When a feedback control system with continuous data has only one input and one output, the problem of constructing its state transition signal flow graph is straightforward. Our effort, however, will be concentrated on systems with multiple inputs and outputs, which include the single input and output systems as special cases, and discrete-data systems. The discrete-data control systems need special attention, since in practice, they contain continuous as well as discrete data.

Multivariable Systems

When a system has only one input and one output, the order of the system is equal to the highest power of s in the transfer function (after all common factors in the numerator and the denominator are cancelled out). The number of state variables is also equal to the order of the system. However, for a multivariable system, the relationship between the transfer function matrix and the order of the system is not so straightforward. In this case, it is necessary to determine the minimum number of integrators (or delay units) in a state transition signal flow graph which portrays the multivariable system. The number of state variables, or the order of the system, is then equal to this minimum number of integrators (delay units).

The problem of finding the minimum number of integrators for a multivariable system is illustrated simply by the system with two outputs and one input shown in Fig. 3-21. The transfer matrix equation of the system is written as

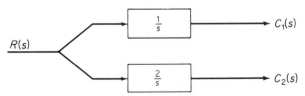

FIG. 3-21. A multivariable system with one input and two outputs.

$$\mathbf{C}(s) = \begin{bmatrix} C_1(s) \\ C_2(s) \end{bmatrix} = \begin{bmatrix} G_{11}(s) \\ G_{21}(s) \end{bmatrix} R(s) = \begin{bmatrix} \dfrac{1}{s} \\ \dfrac{2}{s} \end{bmatrix} R(s) \qquad (3\text{--}183)$$

At first glance, it seems that we need two integrators in the state transition signal flow graph, as shown in Fig. 3-22a. However, it is easy to see that in this case we can realize the transfer relation by use of only one integrator,

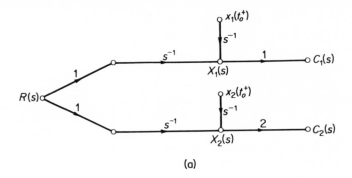

(a)

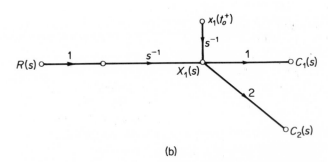

(b)

FIG. 3-22. (a) A state transition signal flow graph of the system in Fig. 3–21 using two integrators (non-minimum); (b) A state transition signal flow graph of the system in Fig. 3–21 using only one integrator (minimum).

as shown by the graph of Fig. 3-22b. Therefore, the system is of the first order, and only one state variable is necessary. The two channels of the system in this case share the same integrator.

In general, of course, practical multivariable systems often have configurations and transfer functions more complicated than that of Fig. 3-21. Therefore, the inspection method used in this simple example will not always be successful.

A general method of determining the minimum order of a multivariable system makes use of the partial fraction expansion of the transfer function matrix $G(s)$. Assume that $G(s)$ is a rational transfer function matrix whose elements have a finite number of simple* poles at $s = \lambda_i$, $i = 1, 2, \ldots, m$ in the finite s-plane. Let the partial fraction expansion of $G(s)$ be

$$G(s) = \sum_{i=1}^{m} \frac{K_i}{s - \lambda_i} + D \tag{3-184}$$

where

$$K_i = \lim_{s \to \lambda_i} (s - \lambda_i) G(s) \tag{3-185}$$

and

$$D = \lim_{s \to \infty} G(s) \tag{3-186}$$

Let the rank† of the ith pole, r_i, be defined as the rank of the matrix K_i, Then the minimum order of the system $G(s)$ is given by

$$n = \sum_{i=1}^{m} r_i \tag{3-187}$$

As a simple illustrative example of the applications of Eqs. (3-184) through (3-187), let us consider the $G(s)$ given by Eq. (3-183). Since $G(s)$ has only one pole at $s = 0$, it is written as

$$G(s) = \frac{1}{s} \begin{bmatrix} 1 \\ 2 \end{bmatrix} = \frac{1}{s} K_1 \tag{3-188}$$

Therefore,

$$K_1 = \begin{bmatrix} 1 \\ 2 \end{bmatrix}$$

which has a rank of *one*, since the maximum order of a nonzero determinant that can be formed for K_1 is one. This verifies our earlier findings that it requires only one integrator to realize the multivariable system of Fig. 3-21.

Example 3-6. Consider the multivariable system shown in Fig. 3-23. The transfer function matrix of the system is given by

$$G(s) = \begin{bmatrix} \dfrac{s + 2}{(s + 1)^2} & \dfrac{1}{s + 1} \\ \dfrac{1}{s(s + 1)} & \dfrac{1}{s + 1} \end{bmatrix} \tag{3-189}$$

Performing partial fraction expansion on $G(s)$, we have

$$G(s) = \begin{bmatrix} \dfrac{1}{s + 1} + \dfrac{1}{(s + 1)^2} & \dfrac{1}{s + 1} \\ \dfrac{1}{s} - \dfrac{1}{s + 1} & \dfrac{1}{s + 1} \end{bmatrix} \tag{3-190}$$

*The method also applies to $G(s)$, whose elements have multiple order poles.

†The rank of a matrix is the maximum order of a nonzero determinant that can be formed by using the elements of the matrix.

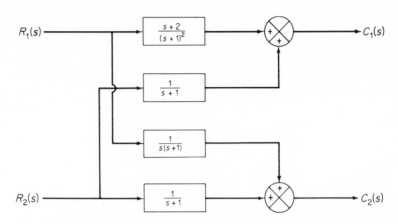

FIG. 3-23. A multivariable control system for Example 3–6.

Therefore,

$$\mathbf{G}(s) = \frac{1}{s+1}\begin{bmatrix} 1 & 1 \\ -1 & 1 \end{bmatrix} + \frac{1}{(s+1)^2}\begin{bmatrix} 1 & 0 \\ 0 & 0 \end{bmatrix} + \frac{1}{s}\begin{bmatrix} 0 & 0 \\ 1 & 0 \end{bmatrix} \qquad (3\text{-}191)$$

The ranks of the coefficient matrices $\mathbf{K}_1$, $\mathbf{K}_2$, and $\mathbf{K}_3$ are identified as follows:

$$\mathbf{K}_1 = \begin{bmatrix} 1 & 1 \\ -1 & 1 \end{bmatrix} \qquad \text{rank } r_1 = 2$$

$$\mathbf{K}_2 = \begin{bmatrix} 1 & 0 \\ 0 & 0 \end{bmatrix} \qquad \text{rank } r_2 = 1$$

$$\mathbf{K}_3 = \begin{bmatrix} 0 & 0 \\ 1 & 1 \end{bmatrix} \qquad \text{rank } r_3 = 1$$

From Eq. (3–187), the order of the system is

$$n = r_1 + r_2 + r_3 = 4 \qquad (3\text{-}192)$$

In other words, the state transition signal flow graph of the multivariable system should contain only four integrators, and the minimum number of state variables required to characterize the dynamic behavior of the system is four. The complete state transition signal flow graph of the system is now shown in Fig. 3-24.

In feedback control system studies, accurate determination of the order of a multivariable system is important not just because a minimum number of integrators will result in the simplest state transition flow graph configuration, but also for stability and design reasons. In stability analysis the number of characteristic equation roots should be equal to the order of the system. In the optimal design of multivariable control systems, it is essential sometimes that the minimum number of state variables be deter-

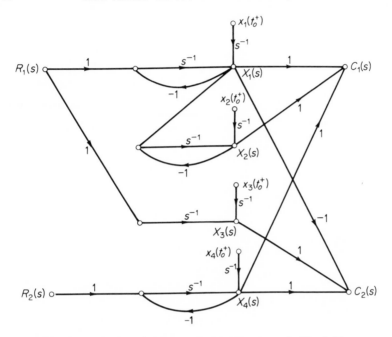

FIG. 3-24. State transition flow graph of the system in Fig. 3–23.

mined before one attempts to drive the states to their desired equilibrium points.

Discrete-data Control Systems

Because discrete-data control systems often contain continuous as well as discrete signals, the construction of the state transition signal flow graphs of this class of systems requires special consideration.

Let us consider the feedback control system which has a sampler and zero-order hold in the forward path, as shown in Fig. 3-25. The transfer function $G(s)$ describes the characteristics of the linear continuous-data portion of the system. A continuous-data state transition signal flow graph can be drawn for $G(s)$ with $H(s)$ as the input node and $C(s)$ as the output node. The output of the zero-order hold is constant between two consecutive sampling instants, and is described by

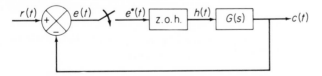

FIG. 3-25. A discrete-data feedback control system.

$$h(t) = e(kT) \qquad \text{for } kT \leq t < (k+1)T \tag{3-193}$$

Therefore,

$$H(s) = \mathscr{L}[h(t)] = \frac{e(kT)}{s} \qquad \text{for } kT \leq t < (k+1)T \tag{3-194}$$

Also,

$$e(kT) = r(kT) - c(kT) \tag{3-195}$$

The output of the system, $c(t)$, is related to the state variables through the output equation, which is usually of the form

$$c(kT) = \mathbf{D}\mathbf{x}(kT) \tag{3-196}$$

for $t = kT$. Therefore, Eq. (3-195) becomes

$$e(kT) = r(kT) - \mathbf{D}\mathbf{x}(kT) \tag{3-197}$$

$\mathbf{D}$ is a constant coefficient matrix.

The state transition signal flow graph of the discrete-data system is now

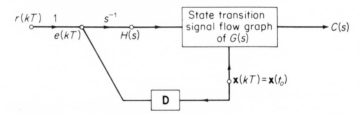

FIG. 3-26. State transition signal flow graph of the discrete-data control system shown in Fig. 3-25.

drawn as shown in Fig. 3-26. The state transition equation of the system can be written by applying Mason's gain formula to Fig. 3-26 in the usual manner.

Example 3-7. Consider that for the discrete-data control system of Fig. 3-25,

$$G(s) = \frac{1}{s(s+1)} \tag{3-198}$$

and $T = 1$ sec. The state transition signal flow graph for $G(s)$ is shown in Fig. 3-27a. The sample-and-hold operation is described by Eq. (3-194). The output equation is simply

$$c(kT) = x_1(kT) \tag{3-199}$$

Now using Fig. 3-27a, Eqs. (3-194), (3-195), and (3-199), we construct the state transition signal flow graph of the entire system for the time interval $kT \leq t \leq (k+1)T$ as shown in Fig. 3-27b.

The transformed state transition equation of the system is written by applying Mason's gain formula to Fig. 3-27b. We have

$$\begin{bmatrix} X_1(s) \\ X_2(s) \end{bmatrix} = \begin{bmatrix} \dfrac{1}{s} - \dfrac{1}{s^2(s+1)} & \dfrac{1}{s(s+1)} \\ \dfrac{-1}{s(s+1)} & \dfrac{1}{s+1} \end{bmatrix} \begin{bmatrix} x_1(kT) \\ x_2(kT) \end{bmatrix} + \begin{bmatrix} \dfrac{1}{s^2(s+1)} \\ \dfrac{1}{s(s+1)} \end{bmatrix} r(kT) \quad (3\text{-}200)$$

Taking the inverse Laplace transform on both sides of Eq. (3–200), we have

$$\begin{bmatrix} x_1(t) \\ x_2(t) \end{bmatrix} = \begin{bmatrix} 1 - [t - kT - 1 + e^{-(t-kT)}] & [1 - e^{-(t-kT)}] \\ -[1 - e^{-(t-kT)}] & e^{-(t-kT)} \end{bmatrix} \begin{bmatrix} x_1(kT) \\ x_2(kT) \end{bmatrix}$$
$$+ \begin{bmatrix} t - kT - 1 + e^{-(t-kT)} \\ 1 - e^{-(t-kT)} \end{bmatrix} r(kT) \qquad (3\text{-}201)^*$$

for $kT \le t \le (k+1)T$.

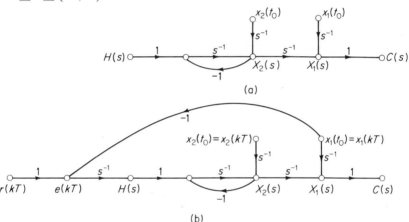

(a)

(b)

FIG. 3-27. State transition signal flow graph of the system shown in Fig. 3–25 with $G(s) = \dfrac{1}{s(s+1)}$.

If we are interested in the responses only at the sampling instants, we let $t = (k+1)T$. Then, Eq. (3–201) becomes

$$\begin{bmatrix} x_1(k+1)T \\ x_2(k+1)T \end{bmatrix} = \begin{bmatrix} 0.632 & 0.632 \\ -0.632 & 0.368 \end{bmatrix} \begin{bmatrix} x_1(kT) \\ x_2(kT) \end{bmatrix} + \begin{bmatrix} 0.368 \\ 0.632 \end{bmatrix} r(kT) \qquad (3\text{-}202)$$

It is interesting to note that Eq. (3–202) is of the form of Eq. (3–69), which is

$$\mathbf{x}[(k+1)T] = \mathbf{\Phi}(T)\mathbf{x}(kT) + \mathbf{\Theta}(T)r(kT) \qquad (3\text{-}203)$$

The solution of Eq. (3–202) can be obtained by use of Eq. (3–75) once $\mathbf{x}(0)$ and $r(t)$ are specified. Another method of solving Eq. (3–202) is the use of the z-transformation as described in Sec. 3.6. The output of the system at the sampling instants is obtained from

*Since the initial time is $t_0 = kT$, the inverse Laplace transform of $1/s^2$ is $(t - t_0)u(t - t_0) = (t - kT)u(t - kT)$, and that of $1/(s + 1)$ is $e^{-(t-kT)}u(t - kT)$.

$$c(kT) = x_1(kT) \qquad (3\text{-}204)$$

However, the use of Eq. (3–75) and the z-transform method of solving Eq. (3–203) can all be tedious, since in the first method successive multiplication of the matrix $\Phi(T)$ is required, and in the second, matrix inverse and matrix multiplication are involved. Just as in the continuous-data case, the state transition signal flow graph can again be called upon to give a

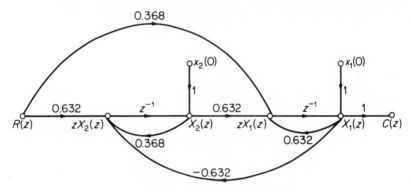

FIG. 3-28. State transition signal flow graph of Eq. (3–202).

simple solution of Eq. (3–202). The discrete state transition signal flow graph of Eq. (3–202) is drawn as shown in Fig. 3–28. Applying Mason's gain formula to Fig. 3-28, we get

$$\begin{bmatrix} X_1(z) \\ X_2(z) \end{bmatrix} = \frac{1}{\Delta} \begin{bmatrix} (1 - 0.368z^{-1}) & 0.632z^{-1} \\ -(0.632)^2 z^{-1} & (1 - 0.632z^{-1}) \end{bmatrix} \begin{bmatrix} x_1(0) \\ x_2(0) \end{bmatrix}$$

$$+ \frac{1}{\Delta} \begin{bmatrix} 0.368(1 - 0.368z^{-1})z^{-1} + (0.632)^2 z^{-2} \\ 0.632z^{-1}(1 - 0.632z^{-1}) - 0.368(0.632)z^{-2} \end{bmatrix} R(z) \qquad (3\text{-}205)$$

where

$$\Delta = 1 - 0.368z^{-1} - 0.632z^{-1} + (0.632)^2 z^{-2} + 0.368(0.632)z^{-2}$$
$$= 1 - z^{-1} + 0.632z^{-2} \qquad (3\text{-}206)$$

After simplification, Eq. (3–205) reads

$$\begin{bmatrix} X_1(z) \\ X_2(z) \end{bmatrix} = \frac{1}{z^2 - z + 0.632} \begin{bmatrix} z(z - 0.368) & 0.632z \\ -0.4z & z(z - 0.632) \end{bmatrix} \begin{bmatrix} x_1(0) \\ x_2(0) \end{bmatrix}$$

$$+ \frac{1}{z^2 - z + 0.632} \begin{bmatrix} 0.368z + 0.264 \\ 0.632(z - 1) \end{bmatrix} R(z) \qquad (3\text{-}207)$$

The solution of $\mathbf{x}(kT)$ in terms of $\mathbf{x}(0)$ and the input is obtained by taking the inverse z-transform of Eq. (3–207).

It is worth noting that the state transition method also provides solution to the system's responses in between sampling instants. This is an advantage of the method over the z-transform method. Equation (3–202) implies that the transition of state takes place from $t = kT$ directly to $t = (k + 1)T$, for $k = 0, 1, 2, \ldots$. If we are interested in the response between sampling instants, we let $t = (k + \Delta)T$ in Eq. (3–201), where $0 < \Delta \leq 1$. Then Eq. (3–201) becomes

$$\begin{bmatrix} x_1[(k + \Delta)T] \\ x_2[(k + \Delta)T] \end{bmatrix} = \begin{bmatrix} 2 - \Delta T - e^{-\Delta T} & 1 - e^{-\Delta T} \\ -(1 - e^{-\Delta T}) & e^{-\Delta T} \end{bmatrix} \begin{bmatrix} x_1(kT) \\ x_2(kT) \end{bmatrix}$$
$$+ \begin{bmatrix} \Delta T - 1 + e^{-\Delta T} \\ 1 - e^{-\Delta T} \end{bmatrix} r(kT) \qquad (3\text{–}208)$$

Now using $t_0 = (k + \Delta)T$ as the initial state, we obtain the state at $t = (k + 1)T$ from Eq. (3–201) after replacing $x(kT)$ by $x[(k + \Delta)T]$ as the initial state, and $r(kT)$ by $r[(k + \Delta)T]$. Therefore,

$$\begin{bmatrix} x_1[(k + 1)T] \\ x_2[(k + 1)T] \end{bmatrix} = \begin{bmatrix} 2 - (1 - \Delta)T - e^{-(1-\Delta)T} & 1 - e^{-(1-\Delta)T} \\ -[1 - e^{-(1-\Delta)T}] & e^{-(1-\Delta)T} \end{bmatrix} \begin{bmatrix} x_1[(k + \Delta)T] \\ x_2[(k + \Delta)T] \end{bmatrix}$$
$$+ \begin{bmatrix} (1 - \Delta)T - 1 + e^{-(1-\Delta)T} \\ 1 - e^{-(1-\Delta)T} \end{bmatrix} r[(k + \Delta)T] \qquad (3\text{–}209)$$

In general, Eqs. (3–208) and (3–209) can be written as

$$\mathbf{x}[(k + \Delta)T] = \mathbf{\Phi}(\Delta T)\mathbf{x}(kT) + \mathbf{\Theta}(\Delta T)r(kT) \qquad (3\text{–}210)$$

and

$$\mathbf{x}[(k + 1)T] = \mathbf{\Phi}[(1 - \Delta)T]\mathbf{x}[(k + \Delta)T] + \mathbf{\Theta}[(1 - \Delta)T]r[(k + \Delta)T] \qquad (3\text{–}211)$$

respectively. By varying Δ between zero and unity, the response of the system at any time between sampling instants can be obtained by using Eq. (3–208).

Example 3-8. A discrete-data control system with a digital controller is shown in Fig. 3-29. The transfer function of the digital controller is

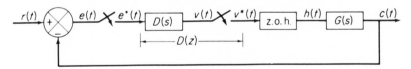

FIG. 3-29. A discrete-data control system with a digital controller.

$$D(z) = \frac{V(z)}{E(z)} = \frac{a_0 z + a_1}{z + b_1} \qquad (3\text{–}212)$$

and the transfer function of the linear continuous plant is

$$G(s) = \frac{K}{s(s + 1)} \qquad (3\text{–}213)$$

In this case, since the system contains two different types of transfer functions in $D(z)$ and $G(s)$, we must first obtain the difference equations for $D(z)$ so that a state transition signal flow graph can be drawn for the entire system. The discrete state transition signal flow graph of $D(z)$ is shown in Fig. 3-30. From Fig. 3-30, the state equation and the output equation for the digital controller are obtained as

$$x_3[(k + 1)T] = e(kT) - b_1 x_3(kT) \tag{3-214}$$

$$v(kT) = (a_1 - a_0 b_1)x_3(kT) + a_0 e(kT) \tag{3-215}$$

We construct the state transition signal flow graph of the entire system using Eqs. (3–214) and (3–215), and the state transition flow graph of the

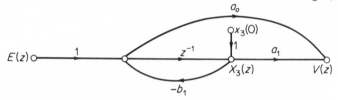

FIG. 3-30. State transition signal flow graph for $D(z) = \dfrac{a_0 z + a_1}{z + b_1}$.

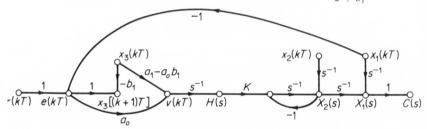

FIG. 3-31. State transition signal flow graph of the discrete-data control system shown in Fig. 3–29; $kT \le t \le (k + 1)T$.

zero-order hold and $G(s)$. The complete flow graph is shown in Fig. 3-31. Notice that the system has three state variables: two continuous state variables in $x_1(t)$ and $x_2(t)$, and one discrete state variable in $x_3(kT)$.

We obtain the state transition equations of the system from Fig. 3-31, using Mason's gain formula.

$$X_1(s) = \left[\frac{1}{s} - \frac{a_0 K}{s^2(s + 1)}\right] x_1(kT) + \frac{1}{s(s + 1)} x_2(kT) + \frac{K(a_1 - a_0 b_1)}{s^2(s + 1)} x_3(kT)$$

$$+ \frac{a_0 K}{s^2(s + 1)} r(kT) \tag{3-216}$$

$$X_2(s) = -\frac{a_0 K}{s(s + 1)} x_1(kT) + \frac{1}{s + 1} x_2(kT) + \frac{K(a_1 - a_0 b_1)}{s(s + 1)} x_3(kT)$$

$$+ \frac{a_0 K}{s(s + 1)} r(kT) \tag{3-217}$$

$$x_3[(k + 1)T] = -x_1(kT) - b_1 x_3(kT) + r(kT) \tag{3-218}$$

Taking the inverse Laplace transform of Eqs. (3–216) and (3–217), and letting $t = (k + 1)T$, we write the state transition equations in matrix form as

$$
\begin{bmatrix} x_1[(k+1)T] \\ x_2[(k+1)T] \\ x_3[(k+1)T] \end{bmatrix} = \begin{bmatrix} 1-a_0K(T-1+e^{-T}) & 1-e^{-T} & K(a_1-a_0b_1)(T-1+e^{-T}) \\ -a_0K(1-e^{-T}) & e^{-T} & K(a_1-a_0b_1)(1-e^{-T}) \\ -1 & 0 & -b_1 \end{bmatrix}
$$

$$
\times \begin{bmatrix} x_1(kT) \\ x_2(kT) \\ x_3(kT) \end{bmatrix} + \begin{bmatrix} a_0K(T-1+e^{-T}) \\ a_0K(1-e^{-T}) \\ 1 \end{bmatrix} r(KT) \qquad (3\text{-}219)
$$

which can be solved by using Eq. (3–75), the z-transform method, or the state transition signal flow graph method.

REFERENCES

1. B. C. Kuo, *Linear Networks and Systems*, McGraw-Hill Book Company, New York, N. Y., 1967.

2. L. A. Zadeh, "An Introduction to State Space Techniques," Workshop on Techniques for Control Systems, *Proceedings*, Joint Automatic Control Conference, Boulder, Colorado, 1962.

3. R. J. Schwarz and B. Friedland, *Linear Systems*, McGraw-Hill Book Company, New York, N. Y., 1965.

4. B. C. Kuo, "State Transition Flow Graphs of Continuous and Sampled Dynamic Systems," *WESCON Convention Records*, **18.1**, August, 1962.

5. C. L. Johnson, *Analog Computer Techniques*, 2nd ed., McGraw-Hill Book Company, New York, 1963.

PROBLEMS

3-1. Write state equations for the networks shown in Fig. 3P-1.

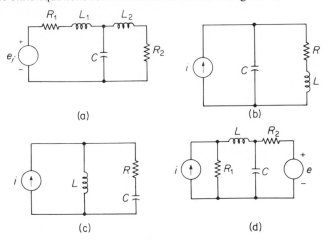

(a)   (b)

(c)   (d)

FIG. 3P-1.

3-2. Write state equations for the following differential equations:

(a) $\dfrac{d^2 c(t)}{dt^2} + 2.5 \dfrac{dc(t)}{dt} + c(t) = r(t)$

(b) $\dfrac{d^3 c(t)}{dt^3} + 6 \dfrac{dc(t)}{dt} + 5c(t) = r(t)$

(c) $3 \dfrac{d^2 c(t)}{dt^2} + 3 \dfrac{dc(t)}{dt} + c(t) = 2 \dfrac{dr(t)}{dt}$

3-3. Write the dynamic equations (state equations and output equation) in matrix-vector form for the following differential equations:

(a) $4 \dfrac{d^2 c(t)}{dt^2} + \dfrac{dc(t)}{dt} + 2c(t) = 0.5r(t)$

(b) $\dfrac{d^2 c(t)}{dt^2} + 2 \dfrac{dc(t)}{dt} + c(t) + \displaystyle\int_0^t c(\tau)d\tau = r(t)$

3-4. The state equations of a linear system are expressed as

$$\begin{bmatrix} \dfrac{dx_1(t)}{dt} \\[2ex] \dfrac{dx_2(t)}{dt} \end{bmatrix} = \begin{bmatrix} 0 & 0 \\ -1 & -2 \end{bmatrix} \begin{bmatrix} x_1(t) \\ x_2(t) \end{bmatrix} + \begin{bmatrix} 1 \\ 1 \end{bmatrix} r(t)$$

Find the state transition matrix $\boldsymbol{\Phi}(t)$.

3-5. The state equations of a linear system are expressed as

$$\begin{bmatrix} \dfrac{dx_1(t)}{dt} \\[2ex] \dfrac{dx_2(t)}{dt} \end{bmatrix} = \begin{bmatrix} -2 & 0 \\ 0 & -2 \end{bmatrix} \begin{bmatrix} x_1(t) \\ x_2(t) \end{bmatrix} + \begin{bmatrix} 10 \\ 1 \end{bmatrix} r(t)$$

Find the state transition matrix $\boldsymbol{\Phi}(t)$.

3-6. Find the state transition equations for the system in Problem 3-4 for $t \geq 0$. It is assumed that $\mathbf{x}(0^+)$ and $r(t)$ for $t \geq 0$ are given.

3-7. Find the state transition equations for the system in Problem 3-5 for $t \geq t_0$. It is assumed that $\mathbf{x}(t_0^+)$ and $r(t)$ for $t \geq t_0$ are given.

3-8. The difference equation of a linear discrete-data system is given by

$$c[(k + 2)T] + 0.5c[(k + 1)T] + c(kT) = 1$$

(a) Write the state equations of the system.
(b) The initial conditions are given as $c(0) = 1$ and $c(T) = 0$. Find $c(nT)$ for $n = 2, 3, \ldots, 10$ by means of recursion.

3-9. Given the state equations

$$x_1(k + 1) = x_2(k)$$
$$x_2(k + 1) = -x_1(k) + 2x_2(k) + r(k)$$

Find the state transition matrix $\boldsymbol{\Phi}(k)$.

3-10. A linear system is characterized by the following differential equation:

$$\frac{d^2c(t)}{dt^2} + 2\frac{dc(t)}{dt} + c(t) = r(t)$$

(a) Find the state transition matrix $\Phi(t)$.

(b) With $c(0) = 1$, $dc(0)/dt = 0$, and $r(t) = u(t)$ (unit step function), find the state transition equations for the system.

(c) Find the characteristic equation of the system. What are the roots of the characteristic equation?

3-11. Draw state transition signal flow graphs for the following transfer functions by means of direct decomposition:

(a) $G(s) = \dfrac{10}{s^3 + 5s^2 + 4s + 10}$

(b) $G(s) = \dfrac{6(s + 1)}{s(s + 2)(s + 3)}$

3-12. Draw state transition signal flow graphs for the following systems by means of parallel decomposition:

(a) $G(s) = \dfrac{6(s + 1)}{s(s + 2)(s + 3)}$

(b) $\dfrac{d^2c(t)}{dt^2} + 6\dfrac{dc(t)}{dt} + 5c(t) = 2\dfrac{dr(t)}{dt} + r(t)$

3-13. Draw state transition signal flow graphs for the systems in Problem 3-12 by means of cascade decomposition.

3-14. Draw a state diagram for the system which is described by the following integro-differential equation:

$$\frac{d^2c(t)}{dt^2} + 1.5\frac{dc(t)}{dt} + 2c(t) + \int_0^t c(\tau)\,d\tau = r(t)$$

3-15. The block diagram of a feedback control system is shown in Fig. 3P-15.

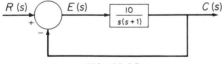

FIG. 3P-15.

(a) Write the dynamic equations for the system in vector-matrix form.

(b) Find the state transition equations for the system. Express the equations in matrix form. The initial states are represented by $\mathbf{x}(t_0^+)$, and the input $r(t)$ is a unit step function $u(t - t_0)$, which is applied at $t = t_0$.

3-16. A linear system is described by the following transfer function:

$$G(s) = \frac{(s + 1)}{(s + 2)^2(s + 5)}$$

Draw state transition signal flow graphs using the three methods of decomposition. Make sure that the flow graphs contain a minimum number of integrators.

3-17. The state transition signal flow graph of a linear system is shown in Fig. 3P-17.

(a) Write the dynamic equations for the system.

(b) Find the transfer function $C(s)/R(s)$.

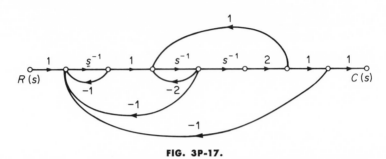

FIG. 3P-17.

3-18. A discrete-data control system is described by the difference equation

$$c[(k + 2)T] + 5c[(k + 1)T] + 2c(kT) = 2T$$

(a) Draw a state transition signal flow graph for the system.

(b) Write the dynamic equation for the system in matrix form.

3-19. A discrete-data system is characterized by the transfer function

$$\frac{C(z)}{R(z)} = \frac{Kz}{(z - 1)(z^2 - z + 3)}$$

(a) Draw a state transition signal flow graph for the system.

(b) Write the dynamic equations of the system.

3-20. A multivariable control system is described by the following matrix transfer equation:

$$\mathbf{C}(s) = \mathbf{G}(s)\mathbf{R}(s)$$

where

$$\mathbf{G}(s) = \begin{bmatrix} \dfrac{1}{s^2} & \dfrac{1}{s^2(s + 1)} \\ \dfrac{2}{s(s + 2)} & \dfrac{1}{s} \end{bmatrix}$$

(a) Draw a state transition signal flow graph with minimum order for the system.

(b) Write the state equations in matrix form.

3-21. The transfer function matrix of a multivariable system is

$$\mathbf{G}(s) = \begin{bmatrix} \dfrac{s + 2}{(s + 1)^2} & \dfrac{1}{s + 1} \\ \dfrac{a}{s(s + 1)} & \dfrac{1}{s + 1} \end{bmatrix}$$

Find the non-zero value of a so that the state transition signal flow graph of the system contains only three integrators.

3-22. (a) Draw a state transition signal flow graph for the discrete-data control system shown in Fig. 3P-22.

(b) Write the state transition equations for the system in terms of $\mathbf{x}(0^+)$, and $r(t) = u(t)$, a unit step function.

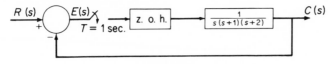

FIG. 3P-22.

4

Equations and Transfer Functions
of Control System Elements

4.1 Introduction

The methods of characterizing linear systems discussed in the preceding chapters are applied in this chapter to elements commonly found in control systems. In general, these elements may be classified as electrical, mechanical, electromechanical, hydraulic, pneumatic, and others. Our emphasis will be on the state variables and the state equations, since it has been pointed out that these give a more versatile and more complete way of representing physical systems. Also, emphasis will be placed on the demonstration of the method of arriving at the state equations and transfer functions of linear systems, rather than a complete coverage of the control system components.

4.2 Equations of Electrical Networks

The classical way of writing network equations of an electrical network includes the loop method and the node method which are formulated from the two laws of Kirchhoff.

Since the loop and node analyses are well covered in standard texts[1,2] on network analysis, and it is assumed that the reader is already familiar with the subject, they are not repeated here.

The subject of the state equations of electrical networks is also covered in recent texts.[3,4] However, we shall treat the subject briefly in this section, since the same technique is carried over to the state analysis of control systems.

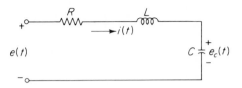

FIG. 4-1. An RLC network.

Consider the simple RLC series network shown in Fig. 4-1. It is a simple matter to write the loop equation of the network:

$$e(t) = L\frac{d^2q(t)}{dt^2} + R\frac{dq(t)}{dt} + \frac{1}{C}q(t) \tag{4-1}$$

where

$$q(t) = \int_0^t i(\tau)\,d\tau \tag{4-2}$$

It is shown in Sec. 3.2 that the second-order differential equation in Eq. (4-1) can be replaced by two first-order differential equations called the state equations. It is convenient to define the state variables as

$$x_1(t) = \frac{q(t)}{C} = e_C(t) \tag{4-3}$$

where $e_C(t)$ is the voltage across the capacitor, and

$$x_2(t) = \frac{dq(t)}{dt} = i(t) = C\frac{dx_1(t)}{dt} \tag{4-4}$$

Substituting Eqs. (4-3) and (4-4) into Eq. (4-1) yields

$$e(t) = L\frac{dx_2(t)}{dt} + Rx_2(t) + x_1(t) \tag{4-5}$$

Thus, the state equations of the network are

$$\frac{dx_1(t)}{dt} = \frac{1}{C}x_2(t) \tag{4-6}$$

$$\frac{dx_2(t)}{dt} = \frac{-1}{L}x_1(t) - \frac{R}{L}x_2(t) + \frac{e(t)}{L} \tag{4-7}$$

A more direct way of arriving at the state equations is to assign the current in the inductor L and the voltage across the capacitor C directly as the state variables. Then, the state equations are written by equating the current in C and the voltage across L in terms of the state variables and the input source. This way, the state equations are written by inspection from the network. Therefore,

$$\text{Current in } C: \quad C\frac{de_C(t)}{dt} = i(t) \tag{4-8}$$

$$\text{Voltage across } L: \quad L\frac{di(t)}{dt} = -e_C(t) - Ri(t) + e(t) \tag{4-9}$$

Since $x_1(t) = e_C(t)$ and $x_2(t) = i(t)$, it is apparent that these state equations are identical to those of Eqs. (4-6) and (4-7).

In general, it is appropriate to assign the voltages across the capacitors and the currents in the inductors as state variables in an electric network, although there are exceptions[4,5,6] which call for slight modifications of this rule.

The basic laws used in writing state equations for electric networks are still the Kirchhoff's laws. The state equations of Eqs. (4-8) and (4-9) are arrived at by inspection. The inspection method, of course, is not always reliable, especially in complicated networks. However, a general method using the theory of linear graphs of network analysis is available and is described in the literature.[4,5,6]

Example 4-1. As another example of writing the state equations of an electric network, consider the network shown in Fig. 4-2. According to the foregoing discussion, the voltage across the capacitor C and the currents

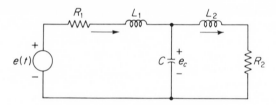

FIG. 4-2. A network with Example 4-1.

in the inductors, i_1 and i_2, are assigned as state variables as shown in Fig. 4-2.

The state equations of the network are obtained by writing the *voltages* across the *inductors* and the *currents* in the *capacitor* in terms of the three state variables. The state equations are

$$L_1 \frac{di_1(t)}{dt} = -R_1 i_1(t) - e_C(t) + e(t) \tag{4-10}$$

$$L_2 \frac{di_2(t)}{dt} = -R_2 i_2(t) + e_C(t) \tag{4-11}$$

$$C \frac{de_C(t)}{dt} = i_1(t) - i_2(t) \tag{4-12}$$

Rearranging the constant coefficients, we write the state equations in the following matrix form:

$$\begin{bmatrix} \dfrac{di_1(t)}{dt} \\ \dfrac{di_2(t)}{dt} \\ \dfrac{de_C(t)}{dt} \end{bmatrix} = \begin{bmatrix} -\dfrac{R_1}{L_1} & 0 & -\dfrac{1}{L_1} \\ 0 & -\dfrac{R_2}{L_2} & \dfrac{1}{L_2} \\ \dfrac{1}{C} & -\dfrac{1}{C} & 0 \end{bmatrix} \begin{bmatrix} i_1(t) \\ i_2(t) \\ e_C(t) \end{bmatrix} + \dfrac{1}{L_1}\begin{bmatrix} 1 \\ 0 \\ 0 \end{bmatrix} e(t) \tag{4-13}$$

4.3 Equations of Mechanical Systems

Most feedback control systems contain mechanical as well as electrical components. From a mathematical viewpoint, there is very little difference between electrical and mechanical elements. In fact, one can show that given an electrical device, there is usually an analogous mechanical counterpart, and vice versa. The analogy, of course, is a mathematical one; that is, two systems are analogous to each other if they are described mathematically by similar equations.

The equations governing the motions of mechanical systems are often directly or indirectly formulated from Newton's law of motion. The law states that the algebraic sum of forces (or torques) acting on a body in a given direction is equal to the mass (inertia) of the body times its acceleration (angular acceleration) in the same direction. Strangely enough, this statement sounds just like Kirchhoff's voltage law, which says that the sum of the voltage rises in a given loop is equal to the sum of the voltage drops. They are indeed analogous.

The motion of mechanical elements can be described as translational, rotational, or a combination of both. These different types of motion and the mechanical elements involved will be discussed in the following sections.

(1) Mechanical Elements of Translational Motion

The motion of translation is defined as a motion along a straight line. The variables which are used to describe translational motion are acceleration, velocity, and displacement. The following elements are usually involved in translational motion:

(a) *Mass M*. Mass is considered to be an element which stores the kinetic energy of translational motion. It is analogous to inductance of electrical systems. If W is the weight of a given body, then M is given by

$$M = W/g$$

where g is the acceleration of the body due to gravity (sometimes also called the acceleration of free-fall). Figure 4-3a illustrates the situation where a force $f(t)$ is acting on a body with mass M in the y-direction.* The displace-

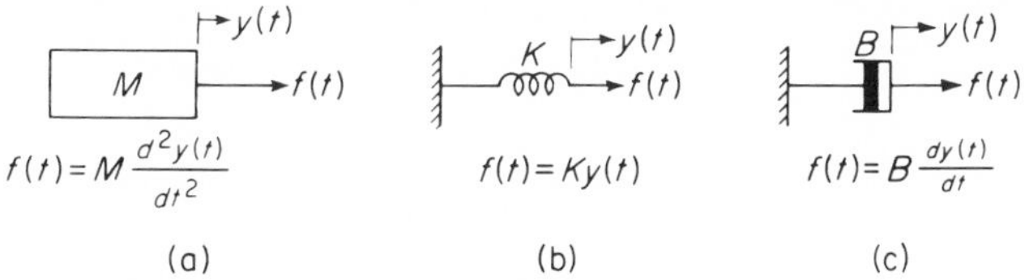

$$f(t) = M \frac{d^2 y(t)}{dt^2}$$

(a)

$$f(t) = Ky(t)$$

(b)

$$f(t) = B \frac{dy(t)}{dt}$$

(c)

FIG. 4-3. Symbolic representations of linear elements in mechanical systems. (a) mass, (b) spring, (c) friction (dashpot).

*The notation y is used here because x has been reserved for state variables.

ment $y(t)$ is measured with the $+y$ direction as positive reference. The force-displacement equation according to Newton's second law of motion, is

$$f(t) = M\frac{d^2y(t)}{dt^2} = M\frac{dv(t)}{dt} \qquad (4\text{-}14)$$

where v is velocity. An analogous equation in electric system is

$$e(t) = L\frac{d^2q(t)}{dt^2} = L\frac{di(t)}{dt} \qquad (4\text{-}15)$$

where $q(t)$ is electric charge.

It is interesting to note that Eq. (4-15) is also the state equation for an inductor. Thus, Eq. (4-14) is regarded as the state equation of the force applied on a mass.

(b) *Linear Spring.* A mechanical spring is considered to be an element which stores potential energy. It is analogous to the capacitance in electric systems. In practice, of course, all springs are nonlinear to some extent. But if the deformation of a spring is kept small, it is justifiable to approximate its behavior by a linear relationship,

$$f(t) = Ky(t) \qquad (4\text{-}16)$$

where K is a constant. In other words, the force acting on the spring is directly proportional to the displacement (deformation) exhibited by the spring. The proportional constant K is called the *spring constant*, or simply *stiffness*.

We notice that the force equation for a linear spring is analogous to the voltage equation for a capacitor; or

$$e_c(t) = \frac{1}{C}q(t) \qquad (4\text{-}17)$$

However, in order to be expressed in state equation form, Eq. (4-16) must be rewritten as

$$\frac{1}{K}\frac{df(t)}{dt} = \frac{dy(t)}{dt} = v(t) \qquad (4\text{-}18)$$

which apparently is analogous to the state equation of a capacitor

$$C\frac{de_c(t)}{dt} = i(t) \qquad (4\text{-}19)$$

The model representation of the linear spring is shown in Fig. 4-3b.

(c) *Friction.* Whenever there are motions or tendency of motions between physical bodies, frictional forces exist. Friction between mechanical elements is just like resistance in electric systems. It simply cannot be avoided. However, friction is not entirely undesirable in physical systems; on the contrary, we often need friction to check or restrict the response of a "lively" system from going wild. From the viewpoint of control, a system without friction of any kind would definitely have stability problems, and frictional force would have to be introduced to improve its behavior. A familiar example can be cited in automobile brakes and the use of sand and snow tires to improve traction when driving a car on an icy road.

While the Ohm's law which assumes linear property in electrical resistances is found to be quite valid in most practical situations, the friction encountered by physical systems is usually nonlinear. Further, the nature of the frictional force between two given surfaces often depends on such factors as the surface condition, the pressure between the surfaces, their relative velocity, and others, so that an exact mathematical description of the force is very difficult. However, for all practical purposes, the following expression has been used extensively as a mathematical description of frictional force:

$$f_r(t) = F_c\left(\frac{v}{|v|}\right) \pm (F_s)_{v=0} + Bv(t) + B_1v^2(t) + B_2v^3(t) + \cdots \quad (4\text{--}20)$$

where F_c, F_s, B, B_1, and B_2 are constants yet to be defined, and v is linear velocity.

The first term on the right-hand side of Eq. (4–20) is called the *Coulomb friction*, with F_c denoting the *Coulomb friction coefficient*. Coulomb friction is a force which has a constant amplitude with respect to the change in velocity, but the sign of the force changes with the reversal of the direction of v. The pictorial representation of the force-velocity relation of Coulomb friction is shown in Fig. 4-4a.

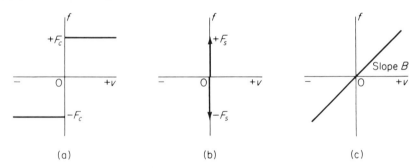

(a)   (b)   (c)

FIG. 4-4. Linear and nonlinear frictional forces. (a) Coulomb friction, (b) static friction, (c) viscous friction (linear).

The second term in Eq. (4–20) is defined as the *static frictional force*, which exists only when the body is stationary but has a tendency of moving. In other words, static friction is a force which tends to prevent motion from beginning, a phenomenon often observed and experienced in our daily lives. The sign of static friction, therefore, depends also on the direction of motion or the initial direction of velocity. The force-velocity relation of static friction is illustrated in Fig. 4-4b. Notice that once motion begins, the static frictional force vanishes, and other frictions take over.

The remaining terms on the right-hand side of Eq. (4–20) are best regarded as a series approximation of nonlinear friction. In fact, every term except Bv in Eq. (4–20) is a nonlinear relationship. If we neglect all but this linear term, Eq. (4–20) becomes

$$f_F(t) = Bv(t) = B\frac{dy(t)}{dt} \tag{4-21}$$

which is the linear friction, or *viscous friction*. The constant B is referred to as the *viscous friction coefficient*. A symbolic notation of viscous friction is the dashpot element shown in Fig. 4-3c. Figure 4-3c gives the functional relation between viscous frictional force and velocity.

The units used in translational motion are summarized in Table 4-1. The symbols and the equations are given in Table 4-2.

Table 4-1

UNITS OF TRANSLATIONAL MOTION

Elements		Units		
		CGS	MKS	English
Active elements	Force F	dyne	newton	pound	ounce
	Velocity v	cm/sec	meter/sec	ft/sec	in./sec
Passive elements	Mass M	gram	kilogram	pound	ounce
	Stiffness K	dyne/cm	newton/m	pound/ft	ounce/in.
	Viscous friction f	$\dfrac{dyne}{cm/sec}$	$\dfrac{newton}{m/sec}$	$\dfrac{pound}{ft/sec}$	$\dfrac{ounce}{in./sec}$

Table 4-2

SYMBOLS AND EQUATIONS OF TRANSLATIONAL MOTION

	Elements	Symbols	Force equation	State equation
Active elements	Force	$\rightarrow f(t)$	—	—
	Velocity	$\rightarrow v(t)$	—	—
Passive elements	Mass M		$f(t) = M\dfrac{dv(t)}{dt}$	$\dfrac{dv(t)}{dt} = \dfrac{f(t)}{M}$
	Stiffness K		$f(t) = Ky(t)$	$\dfrac{df(t)}{dt} = Kv(t)$
	Viscous friction B		$f(t) = Bv(t)$	—

(2) Mechanical Elements of Rotational Motion

The rotational motion of a body may be defined as motion around a fixed axis. The variables generally used to describe the motion of rotation are angular acceleration α, angular velocity ω, and angular displacement θ. We shall not dwell with the details of the mathematical descriptions of rota-

Table 4-3

UNITS OF ROTATIONAL MOTION

		Units		
	Elements	CGS	MKS	English
Active elements	Torque T	dyne-cm	newton-m	pound-ft	ounce-in.
	Angular velocity	rad/sec	rad/sec	rad/sec	rad/sec
Passive elements	Moment of inertia J	gram-cm^2	Kg-m^2	slug-ft^2	oz-in.^{2} = 2.59·10^{-3} oz. in.-sec^2
	Stiffness S	$\dfrac{\text{gram-cm}}{\text{rad}}$	$\dfrac{\text{newton-m}}{\text{rad}}$	$\dfrac{\text{pound-ft}}{\text{rad}}$	$\dfrac{\text{ounce-in.}}{\text{rad}}$
	Friction B	$\dfrac{\text{gram-cm}}{\text{rad/sec}}$	$\dfrac{\text{newton-m}}{\text{rad/sec}}$	$\dfrac{\text{pound-ft}}{\text{rad/sec}}$	$\dfrac{\text{ounce-in.}}{\text{rad/sec}}$

Table 4-4

SYMBOLS AND EQUATIONS OF ROTATIONAL MOTION

	Elements	Symbols	Torque equation	State equation
Active elements	Torque T	$T(t)$	—	—
	Angular vel.	$\omega(t)$	—	—
Passive elements	Moment of inertia M		$T(t) = J\dfrac{d\omega(t)}{dt}$	$\dfrac{d\omega(t)}{dt} = \dfrac{T(t)}{J}$
	Stiffness S		$T(t) = S\theta(t)$	$\dfrac{dT(t)}{dt} = S\omega(t)$
	Viscous friction B		$T(t) = B\omega(t)$	—
	Gear train		$\dfrac{T_1}{T_2} = \dfrac{N_1}{N_2} = \dfrac{\theta_2}{\theta_1}$	—

tional elements, since they are similar to the translational case. The units, symbols, and equations for rotational motion are summarized in Table 4-3 and Table 4-4.

The linear analysis of any mechanical system essentially involves first representing the system by a model containing interconnecting linear elements, and then the system equations are written in much the same way as those of linear electric networks.

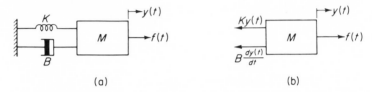

FIG. 4-5. (a) A mass-spring-friction system. (b) Free-body diagram.

Let us consider the mechanical system with mass, linear spring, and viscous friction in Fig. 4-5a. A systematic way of analyzing this type of system is to draw a free-body diagram as shown in Fig. 4-5b. The force equation of the system is then written by applying Newton's law of motion to the free-body diagram. The force equation thus obtained is

$$f(t) = M\frac{d^2y(t)}{dt^2} + B\frac{dy(t)}{dt} + Ky(t) \qquad (4\text{-}22)$$

This second-order differential equation can be resolved into two first-order state equations. With $x_1 = y$ and $x_2 = dx_1/dt$ assigned as the state variables, the state equations are easily written as

$$\frac{dx_1(t)}{dt} = x_2(t) \qquad (4\text{-}23)$$

$$\frac{dx_2(t)}{dt} = -\frac{K}{M}x_1(t) - \frac{B}{M}x_2(t) + \frac{1}{M}f(t). \qquad (4\text{-}24)$$

It is not difficult to see that this mechanical system is analogous to a series R-L-C electric circuit. With this analogy, it is possible to formulate the state equations directly from the mechanical system using a different set of state variables. If we consider that mass is analogous to inductance, and the spring constant K is analogous to the inverse of capacitance, $1/C$, it is logical to call $f(t)$ (analogous to current in L) and $f_K(t)$ (analogous to voltage across C), which is the force acting on the spring, state variables. Then, the state equations of the system are

Force on mass: $$M\frac{dv(t)}{dt} = f(t) - f_K(t) - Bv(t) \qquad (4\text{-}25)$$

Velocity of spring: $$\frac{1}{K}\frac{df_K(t)}{dt} = v(t) \qquad (4\text{-}26)$$

This simple illustration supports our earlier statement that the choice of the state variables in a given system can be somewhat arbitrary. However, if the problem is to solve for the displacement and the velocity of the system, Eqs. (4–23) and (4–24) would be preferable.

Example 4-2. As a second example of writing equations for mechanical systems, consider the system shown in Fig. 4-6a. Since the spring is deformed when it is subjected to the force $f(t)$, two displacements, y_1 and y_2, must be

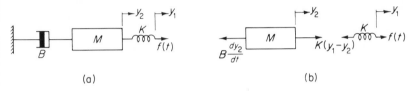

(a)   (b)

FIG. 4-6. Mechanical system in Example 4–2. (a) Mass-spring-friction system, (b) free-body diagrams.

assigned to the end points of the spring. The free-body diagrams of the system are drawn in Fig. 4-6b. From these free-body diagrams the differential equations of the system are written as

$$f(t) = K[y_1(t) - y_2(t)] \tag{4-27}$$

$$K[y_1(t) - y_2(t)] = M\frac{d^2y_2(t)}{dt^2} + B\frac{dy_2(t)}{dt} \tag{4-28}$$

How do we formulate the state equations of this system? Using the same method as illustrated in the previous example, we assign the velocity v of the mass as a state variable, and the force f_K on the spring as another, so we have

$$M\frac{dv(t)}{dt} = -Bv(t) + f_K(t) \tag{4-29}$$

and

$$f_K(t) = f(t) \tag{4-30}$$

One may wonder at this point if the two equations in Eqs. (4-29) and (4-30) are correct, since it seems that only (4-29) is a state equation and we do have two state variables in v and f_K. Why do we need only one state equation here, whereas Eqs. (4–27) and (4–28) clearly are two independent equations, and the latter is of the second order? The situation is clarified if we refer to the analogous electric network of the system shown in Fig. 4-7.

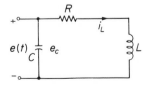

FIG. 4-7. An electric network analogous to the system in Fig. 4–6.

It is evident that although the network has two reactive elements in L and C, and thus there should be two state variables, the capacitance becomes a redundant element, since e_c is equal to the applied voltage $e(t)$. However, given the system as shown in Fig. 4-6, the state equations in Eqs. (4–29) and (4–30) can provide only the solution to the velocity of M once $f(t)$ is given. If we need to find the displacement y_1 at the point where $f(t)$ is applied, we have to use the relation

$$y_1(t) = \frac{f_K(t)}{K} + y_2(t) = \frac{f_K(t)}{K} + \int_{0^+}^{t} v(\tau)\, d\tau + y_2(0^+) \qquad (4\text{–}31)$$

where $y_2(0^+)$ is the initial displacement of the mass M.

Example 4-3. In this example, the equations for the mechanical system in Fig. 4-8a are to be written. The free-body diagrams for the two masses are shown in Fig. 4-8b, with the positive directions of the displacements y_1

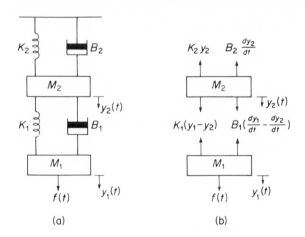

(a)   (b)

FIG. 4-8. Mechanical system in Example 4–3.

and y_2 as indicated. The Newton's force equations for the system are written directly from the free-body diagram. The two force equations are

$$f(t) = M_1 \frac{d^2 y_1(t)}{dt^2} + B_1 \left[\frac{dy_1(t)}{dt} - \frac{dy_2(t)}{dt} \right] + K_1[y_1(t) - y_2(t)] \qquad (4\text{–}32)$$

$$0 = -B_1 \left[\frac{dy_1(t)}{dt} - \frac{dy_2(t)}{dt} \right]$$
$$\quad - K_1[y_1(t) - y_2(t)] + M_2 \frac{d^2 y_2(t)}{dt^2} + B_2 \frac{dy_2(t)}{dt} + K_2 y_2(t) \qquad (4\text{–}33)$$

We may now convert these two second-order simultaneous differential equations into four state equations by defining the following state variables:

$$x_1 = y_1 \tag{4-34}$$

$$x_2 = y_2 \tag{4-35}$$

$$x_3 = \frac{dx_1}{dt} = \frac{dy_1}{dt} \tag{4-36}$$

$$x_4 = \frac{dx_2}{dt} = \frac{dy_2}{dt} \tag{4-37}$$

Equations (4–36) and (4–37) form the first two state equations; the other two are obtained by rearranging the terms in (4–32) and (4–33). The four state equations thus obtained are

$$\frac{dx_1}{dt} = x_3 \tag{4-38}$$

$$\frac{dx_2}{dt} = x_4 \tag{4-39}$$

$$\frac{dx_3}{dt} = -\frac{K_1}{M_1}(x_1 - x_2) - \frac{B_1}{M_1}(x_3 - x_4) + \frac{1}{M_1}f(t) \tag{4-40}$$

$$\frac{dx_4}{dt} = \frac{K_1}{M_2}x_1 - \frac{(K_1 + K_2)}{M_2}x_2 + \frac{B_1}{M_2}x_3 - \frac{1}{M_2}(B_1 + B_2)x_4 \tag{4-41}$$

A set of equations can also be obtained directly from the mechanical system. The state variables are assigned as $v_1 = dy_1/dt$, $v_2 = dy_2/dt$, and the forces on the two springs, f_{K1} and f_{K2}, respectively. Then, if we write the forces acting on the masses and the velocities of the springs as functions of the four state variables and the external force, the state equations are

Force on M_1: $$M_1\frac{dv_1}{dt} = -B_1v_1 + B_1v_2 - f_{K1} + f(t) \tag{4-42}$$

Force on M_2: $$M_2\frac{dv_2}{dt} = B_1v_1 - (B_1 + B_2)v_2 + f_{K1} - f_{K2} \tag{4-43}$$

Velocity of K_1: $$\frac{df_{K1}}{dt} = K_1(v_1 - v_2) \tag{4-44}$$

Velocity of K_2: $$\frac{df_{K2}}{dt} = K_2v_2 \tag{4-45}$$

It is easy to see that Eqs. (4–42) and (4–43) are really the same as Eqs. (4–32) and (4–33), respectively.

Example 4-4. The rotational system shown in Fig. 4-9a consists of a disk mounted on a shaft; the other end of the shaft is fixed. The moment of inertia of the disk is J, and the friction on the disk is given by the viscous friction coefficient B. The stiffness of the shaft is S.

When a torque $T(t)$ is applied to the disk as shown, it is easy to see that this system is a counterpart of the translational system of Fig. 4-5. The free-body diagram of the system is drawn in Fig. 4-9b.

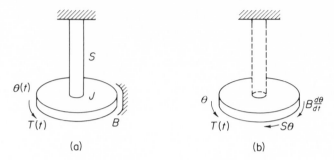

FIG. 4-9. Rotational system in Example 4-4.

In this case, the state variables of the system are defined as the angular displacement θ and the angular velocity ω. Thus,

$$x_1(t) = \theta(t) \tag{4-46}$$

$$\frac{dx_1(t)}{dt} = x_2(t) \tag{4-47}$$

The first state equation is simply Eq. (4-47). The second state equation is obtained by writing $dx_2(t)/dt$, which is the angular acceleration of the disk, as a function of x_1, x_2, and T. Thus,

$$\frac{dx_2(t)}{dt} = \frac{1}{J} T(t) - \frac{S}{J} x_1(t) - \frac{B}{J} x_2(t) \tag{4-48}$$

(3) Gear Trains

Gear trains are used in control systems to attain torque magnification and speed reduction. Like the transformers used in electrical networks for the optimum matching of impedance and power levels, gear trains in me-

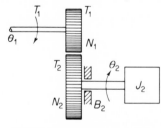

FIG. 4-10. A gear train system.

chanical systems are also regarded as matching devices used to attain maximum power transfer. Two gears are shown coupled together in Fig. 4-10. The gear with N_1 (number of) teeth is called the *primary gear* (analogous to the primary windings of an electric transformer), and the gear with N_2 teeth is called the *secondary gear*.

The relationships between torque T, angular displacement θ, and the teeth number N, of a gear train are derived from the following facts:

(1) The number of teeth on the surface of the gears is proportional to the radii of the gears; i.e., $r_1 N_2 = r_2 N_1$ (r = radius of gear).

(2) The linear distance traveled along the surface of each gear is the same; therefore, $\theta_1 r_1 = \theta_2 r_2$.

(3) The work done by one gear is equal to that of the other; $T_1\theta_1 = T_2\theta_2$. From the relations given above, we have

$$\frac{T_1}{T_2} = \frac{\theta_2}{\theta_1} = \frac{N_1}{N_2} \tag{4-49}$$

Notice that this expression closely resembles the voltage-current-turns ratio relation of an ideal transformer in electrical networks. An ideal transformer is simply an idealized element used to describe certain relationships between a set of variables in electrical systems. An ideal transformer does not exist in its strictest sense physically. Similarly, Eq. (4-49) must also have been derived under an idealized situation. In practice, all gear trains have some amount of backlash between the coupled gear teeth, and when two gear teeth are in contact there certainly will be friction. Keeping the backlash small will inevitably increase friction and wear out the gear teeth quickly, but excessive amount of backlash is known to have an adverse effect on the stability of a servo system.

Once the linear relations between the gear train variables are defined, the equations of a mechanical system with gear trains can be written in the same way as described before. Referring to Fig. 4-10, we find that the torque equation for the secondary side of the gear train is

$$T_2 = J_2\frac{d^2\theta_2}{dt^2} + B_2\frac{d\theta_2}{dt} \tag{4-50}$$

where T_2 is the torque developed at the secondary gear. The inertia of the gears and shafts are assumed to be negligible.

By the use of Eq. (4-49), it is possible to write Eq. (4-50) as

$$T_1 = J_2\left(\frac{N_1}{N_2}\right)^2\frac{d^2\theta_1}{dt^2} + B_2\left(\frac{N_1}{N_2}\right)^2\frac{d\theta_1}{dt} \tag{4-51}$$

Equation (4-51) indicates clearly that the original system can be represented by the equivalent system shown in Fig. 4-11, with the system equation given by

$$T_1 = J_1\frac{d^2\theta_1}{dt^2} + B_1\frac{d\theta_1}{dt} \tag{4-52}$$

where

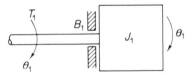

FIG. 4-11. Equivalent system of Fig. 4-10.

$$J_1 = J_2(N_1/N_2)^2 \tag{4-53}$$

and

$$B_1 = B_2(N_1/N_2)^2 \tag{4-54}$$

are regarded as the equivalent inertia and friction referred to the primary shaft.

The concept of equivalent inertia, friction, and torque just described can also be extended to a multiple-gear train system, as shown in Fig. 4-12.

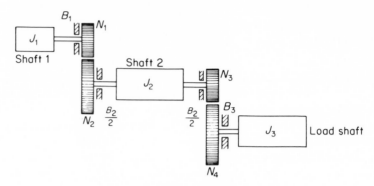

FIG. 4-12. Multiple-gear train system.

The inertia J_3 and friction B_3 at the load shaft are referred to shaft 2, and the equivalent quantities are

$$J_{2eq} = J_2 + J_3(N_3/N_4)^2 \qquad (4\text{-}55)$$

$$B_{2eq} = B_2 + B_3(N_3/N_4)^2 \qquad (4\text{-}56)$$

The equivalent inertia and friction at shaft 2 are now referred to shaft 1, resulting in

$$J_{1eq} = J_1 + J_{2eq}(N_1/N_2)^2 = J_1 + J_2(N_1/N_2)^2 + J_3(N_1 N_3/N_2 N_4)^2 \qquad (4\text{-}57)$$

$$B_{1eq} = B_1 + B_{2eq}(N_1/N_2)^2 = B_1 + B_2(N_1/N_2)^2 + B_3(N_1 N_3/N_2 N_4)^2 \qquad (4\text{-}58)$$

Similarly, the inertia and friction at shaft 1 can be referred to the load shaft. Thus

$$J_{3eq} = J_3 + J_1(N_2 N_4/N_1 N_3)^2 + J_2(N_4/N_3)^2 \qquad (4\text{-}59)$$

$$B_{3eq} = B_3 + B_1(N_2 N_4/N_1 N_3)^2 + B_2(N_4/N_3)^2 \qquad (4\text{-}60)$$

From these examples, we can conclude that the equivalent inertia or friction of a system referred to a common shaft is found by multiplying each inertia or friction by the square of the total gear ratio between the inertia or friction and the common shaft.

The following example illustrates the writing of the equations of a typical gear train system.

Example 4-5. Consider the mechanical system shown in Fig. 4-13, in which a load is driven by a motor through a gear train. The motor has moment of inertia J_m; the viscous friction coefficient at the motor bearing is denoted by B_m; the torque developed by the motor is T_m. The torsional spring constants of the motor shaft and the load shaft are S_m and S_L, respectively. The moments of inertia of the gears are assumed to be J_1 and J_2, respectively.

The free-body diagrams of the gear train system and the associated

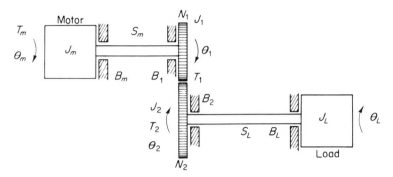

FIG. 4-13. Motor-load system with gear train.

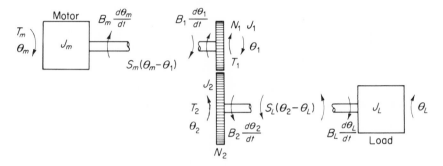

FIG. 4-14. Free-body diagrams and torques of motor-load-gear-train system in Fig. 4–13.

torque expressions are given in Fig. 4-14. The following torque equations are written directly from the free-body diagram:

$$T_m = J_m \frac{d^2\theta_m}{dt^2} + B_m \frac{d\theta_m}{dt} + S_m(\theta_m - \theta_1) \qquad (4\text{–}61)$$

$$S_m(\theta_m - \theta_1) = J_1 \frac{d^2\theta_1}{dt^2} + B_1 \frac{d\theta_1}{dt} + T_1 \qquad (4\text{–}62)$$

$$T_2 = J_2 \frac{d^2\theta_2}{dt^2} + B_2 \frac{d\theta_2}{dt} + S_L(\theta_2 - \theta_L) \qquad (4\text{–}63)$$

$$S_L(\theta_2 - \theta_L) = J_L \frac{d^2\theta_L}{dt^2} + B_L \frac{d\theta_L}{dt} \qquad (4\text{–}64)$$

and $T_1/T_2 = N_1/N_2$, $\theta_1/\theta_2 = N_2/N_1$.

Now referring the inertias and frictions from the load side to the motor side through the gear ratio relationship, we find that the torque equations become

$$T_m = J_m \frac{d^2\theta_m}{dt^2} + B_m \frac{d\theta_m}{dt} + S_m(\theta_m - \theta_1) \qquad (4\text{–}65)$$

$$S_m(\theta_m - \theta_1) = (J_1 + n^2 J_2)\frac{d^2\theta_1}{dt^2} + (B_1 + n^2 B_2)\frac{d\theta_1}{dt} + n^2 S_L\left(\theta_1 - \frac{\theta_L}{n}\right) \quad (4\text{-}66)$$

$$n^2 S_L\left(\theta_1 - \frac{\theta_L}{n}\right) = nJ_L\frac{d^2\theta_L}{dt^2} + nB_L\frac{d\theta_L}{dt} \quad (4\text{-}67)$$

where $n = N_1/N_2$.

If we consider the following elements as being analogous to each other, the torque equations indicate that an electric analog of the system can be constructed as shown in Fig. 4-15.

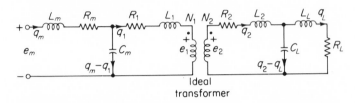

FIG. 4-15. An electric analog of the mechanical system in Fig. 4–13.

Torque T	Voltage e
Angular displacement θ	Electric charge q
Angular velocity ω	Electric current i
Inertia J	Inductance L
Viscous friction B	Resistance R
Stiffness S	Inverse of capacitance $1/C$
Ideal gear train $N_1/N_2 = n$	Ideal transformer $N_1/N_2 = n$

Figure 4-16 depicts the equivalent circuit of the electric analog with all the elements and variables in the secondary referred to the primary side. Notice that in referring all the elements to the primary side, resistances

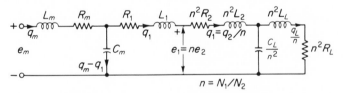

FIG. 4-16. Simplified version of Fig. 4–15 with all secondary elements referred to the primary side of the transformer.

and reactances are multiplied by the turns ratio squared, $n^2 = (N_1/N_2)^2$, and the electric charges q_2 and q_L are divided by n.

The state equations of the system can be written in a straightforward manner; this will be left as an exercise for the reader.

4.4 Equations of Electromechanical Systems

Many control systems utilize electromechanical elements which convert mechanical and electrical energies from one form to the other. In this section we shall show how the state equations of these elements are written. The signal flow graph and transfer function representations are also considered.

D-C Servo Motors[7,8]

A motor is known to be a device which converts electrical energy into mechanical energy. In control systems applications, motors are often used as powering devices which drive the controlled elements to the desired objectives.

Most of the d-c motors in control applications have separately excited fields. The control signal can be applied to either the field windings terminals or the armature terminals of the motor. When the field is energized by the control signal, the motor is said to be *field-controlled;* if the armature is energized by the signal, the motor is *armature-controlled.*

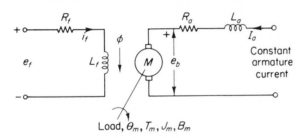

FIG. 4-17. Schematic diagram of a field-controlled motor.

The schematic diagram of a field-controlled d-c motor is shown in Fig. 4-17. For linear analysis, the following assumptions are made:

(1) A constant current I_a is fed into the armature.

(2) The air gap flux $\phi(t)$ is proportional to the field current $i_f(t)$; i.e.,

$$\phi(t) = K_f i_f(t) \qquad (4\text{--}68)$$

where K_f is a constant.

(3) The torque developed by the motor, $T_m(t)$, is proportional to the air gap flux and the armature current. Thus,

$$T_m(t) = K'_m I_a \phi(t) \qquad (4\text{--}69)^*$$

Substituting $\phi(t)$ from Eq. (4–68) into Eq. (4–69) gives

*This explains why it is necessary to assume that the armature current I_a is constant.

$$T_m(t) = K_m' I_a K_f i_f(t) = K_m K_f i_f(t) \tag{4-70}$$

where

$$K_m = K_m' I_a \tag{4-71}$$

The state equation of the field circuit is

$$L_f \frac{di_f(t)}{dt} = -R_f i_f(t) + e_f(t) \tag{4-72}$$

where $e_f(t)$ is the control signal.

This state equation may be regarded as a cause-and-effect relationship; that is, $e_f(t)$ causes the armature current $i_f(t)$. The current $i_f(t)$ now, together with I_a, develops the motor torque according to Eq. (4–70). The state equation for the mechanical elements is

$$J_m \frac{d\omega_m(t)}{dt} = -B_m \omega_m(t) + T_m(t) \tag{4-73}$$

where J_m and B_m are the inertia and the viscous friction of the motor shaft. $\omega_m(t)$ is the motor velocity, and is assigned as a state variable. Therefore, the motor system has two state variables in $i_f(t)$ and $\omega_m(t)$.

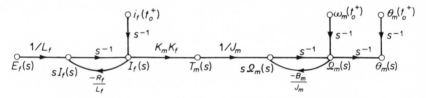

FIG. 4-18. State transition signal flow graph of a field-controlled d-c motor.

The state transition signal flow graph of the d-c motor is drawn in Fig. 4-18, Eqs. (4-70), (4-72), and (4-73) being used.

In the figure, the motor displacement $\theta_m(t)$ is also defined as a state variable. Thus, a total of three integrators is necessary. Strictly, another state equation relating $\omega_m(t)$ and $\theta_m(t)$ is necessary.

The transfer function between $E_f(s)$ and $\Theta_m(s)$ is obtained by applying Mason's formula to the flow graph between the two nodes, and assuming zero initial states. The transfer function is

$$\frac{\Theta_m(s)}{E_f(s)} = \frac{(K_m K_f / J_m L_f) s^{-3}}{1 + \left(\dfrac{R_f}{L_f} + \dfrac{B_m}{J_m}\right) s^{-1} + \dfrac{R_f B_m}{L_f J_m} s^{-2}}$$

$$= \frac{K_m K_f}{s(J_m s + B_m)(L_f s + R_f)} \tag{4-74}$$

or

$$\frac{\Theta_m(s)}{E_f(s)} = \frac{K_m K_f}{R_f B_m s(1 + T_m s)(1 + T_f s)} \tag{4-75}$$

where

$$T_m = J_m/B_m = \text{motor (mechanical) time constant} \qquad (4\text{-}76)$$

$$T_f = L_f/R_f = \text{field (electrical) time constant} \qquad (4\text{-}77)$$

The transformed state transition equations of the system are determined by applying Mason's gain formula to the state transition flow graph with E_f, $i_f(t_0^+)$, $\omega_m(t_0^+)$ and $\theta_m(t_0^+)$ all acting as input nodes. Thus, the transformed state transition equations for $t \geq t_0$ are

$$\Theta_m(s) = \frac{1}{s}\theta_m(t_0^+) + \frac{J_m(L_f s + R_f)}{\Delta}\omega_m(t_0^+) + \frac{L_f K_m K_f}{\Delta}i_f(t_0^+) + \frac{K_m K_f}{\Delta}E_f(s)$$

$$(4\text{-}78)$$

$$\Omega_m(s) = \frac{sJ_m(L_f s + R_f)}{\Delta}\omega_m(t_0^+) + \frac{L_f K_m K_f}{\Delta}i_f(t_0^+) + \frac{K_m K_f s}{\Delta}E_f(s) \qquad (4\text{-}79)$$

$$I_f(s) = \frac{L_f}{L_f s + R_f}i_f(t_0^+) + \frac{1}{L_f s + R_f}E_f(s) \qquad (4\text{-}80)$$

where $\Delta = s(J_m s + B_m)(L_f s + R_f)$. It is easy to see that $\Delta = 0$ is the characteristic equation of the system.

The time-domain state transition equations are obtained by taking the inverse Laplace transforms of Eqs. (4–78), (4–79), and (4–80).

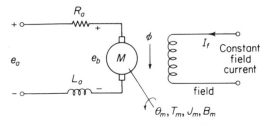

FIG. 4-19. Schematic diagram of an armature-controlled d-c motor.

The schematic diagram of an armature-controlled d-c motor is shown in Fig. 4-19. In this type of application, the armature of the motor is energized by the control signal, and the field current is held constant.

The following assumptions are made in linear analysis:

(1) The air gap flux is proportional to the field current; i.e.,

$$\phi(t) = K_f I_f = \text{constant} = \phi \qquad (4\text{-}81)$$

(2) The torque developed by the motor is proportional to the air gap flux and the armature current. Thus,

$$T_m(t) = K'_m \phi i_a(t) \qquad (4\text{-}82)$$

Substituting Eq. (4–81) into Eq. (4–82) gives

$$T_m(t) = K'_m K_f I_f i_a(t) = K_i i_a(t) \qquad (4\text{-}83)$$

(3) The back electromotive-force (emf) voltage is proportional to the
motor speed. That is,

$$\text{Back emf voltage } e_b(t) = K_b \omega_m(t) \tag{4-84}$$

Starting with the armature circuit, the state equation with $i_a(t)$ as the state
variable is

$$L_a \frac{di_a(t)}{dt} = -R_a i_a(t) + e_a(t) - e_b(t) \tag{4-85}$$

where $e_a(t)$ is the control signal.

The state equations for the mechanical elements are

$$J_m \frac{d\omega_m(t)}{dt} = -B_m \omega_m(t) + T_m(t) \tag{4-86}$$

and

$$\frac{d\theta_m(t)}{dt} = \omega_m(t) \tag{4-87}$$

The state transition signal flow graph is now constructed in Fig. 4-20,
Eqs. (4–83), (4–84), (4–85), (4–86), and (4–87) being used.

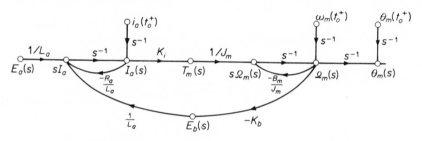

FIG. 4-20. State transition signal flow graph of an armature-controlled d-c motor.

The state transition signal flow graph of Fig. 4-20 shows that there is
an important difference between the field-controlled and the armature-
controlled d-c motors. When Figs. 4-19 and 4-20 are compared, it is clear
that the field-controlled motor acts as an open-loop system, whereas the
armature-controlled motor has a "built-in" feedback loop caused by the
back emf effect. Physically, the back emf voltage represents the feedback of
a negative signal which is proportional to the speed of the motor.

The transfer function of the motor is obtained by applying Mason's
formula to Fig. 4-20, and assuming zero initial states.

$$\frac{\Theta_m(s)}{E_a(s)} = \frac{\dfrac{K_i}{L_a J_m} s^{-3}}{1 + \left(\dfrac{R_a}{L_a} + \dfrac{B_m}{J_m}\right) s^{-1} + \left(\dfrac{K_b K_i}{L_a J_m} + \dfrac{R_a B_m}{L_a J_m}\right) s^{-2}}$$

$$= \frac{K_i}{L_a J_m s^3 + (R_a J_m + B_m L_a)s^2 + (K_b K_i + R_a B_m)s} \tag{4-88}$$

It is observed in Eq. (4–88) that the back emf represents an added term to the resistance and friction term. Therefore, qualitatively, it can be stated that the back emf voltage has the effect of an "electrical friction" in an armature-controlled motor. This "built-in" friction usually improves the stability and damping of the control system in which the motor is an element.

The state transition equations of the armature-controlled d-c motor can be written in the same way as demonstrated for the field-controlled case.

A-C Servomotor[9, 10]

For low power applications, a-c motors are preferred, because they are lightweight, rugged, and there are no brush contacts to maintain. Most of the a-c motors used in control systems are of the two-phase induction type. Unlike the motors used for other general purposes, the output power of the a-c servomotor usually varies from a fraction of a watt up to only a few hundred watts. The frequency of the motor is normally either 60 cycles, 400 cycles, or 1000 cycles.

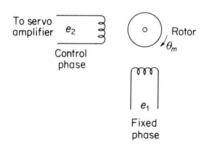

FIG. 4-21. Schematic diagram of a two-phase induction motor.

A schematic diagram of a two-phase induction motor is shown in Fig. 4-21. The motor consists of a stator with two distributed windings displaced 90 electrical degrees apart. Under normal operating conditions in control applications, a fixed voltage from a constant-voltage source is applied to one phase called the *fixed phase;* the other phase, which is called the *control phase*, is energized by a voltage which is at 90 degrees out of phase with respect to the voltage of the fixed phase. The control phase voltage is usually supplied from a servo amplifier, and it has a variable magnitude and polarity. The direction of rotation of the motor reverses if the control phase signal changes sign.

The torque-speed relation of a two-phase induction motor is extremely nonlinear. However, for linear analysis, some assumptions and approximations are necessary. It is generally considered an acceptable practice to approximate the torque-speed relation of a two-phase induction motor by the

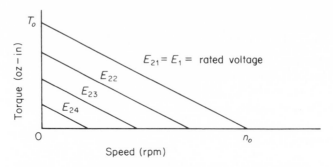

FIG. 4-22. Completely linearized torque-speed characteristics of a two-phase induction motor.

linear characteristics shown in Fig. 4-22. These curves are straight lines parallel to the line at rated control voltage ($E_2 = E_1$ = rated voltage), and they are equally spaced for equal increments of the control voltage.

The state equations of the motor are determined as follows: Let k be the blocked rotor torque at rated voltage per unit control voltage; i.e.,

$$k = \frac{\text{blocked rotor torque } E_2 = E_1}{\text{rated control voltage } E_1} = \frac{T_0}{T_1} \tag{4-89}$$

Let m be a negative number representing the slope of the linearized torque-speed curve shown in Fig. 4-22. Then

$$m = -\frac{\text{blocked rotor torque}}{\text{no load speed}} = -\frac{T_0}{n_0} \tag{4-90}$$

For any torque T_m, the family of straight lines in Fig. 4-22 are represented by the equation

$$T_m(t) = m\omega_m(t) + ke_2(t) \tag{4-91}$$

where $\omega_m(t)$ is the speed of the motor.

Now if we designate $\omega_m(t)$ as a state variable, one of the state equations is

$$J_m \frac{d\omega_m(t)}{dt} = -B_m\omega_m(t) + T_m(t) \tag{4-92}$$

where J_m and B_m denote the inertia and friction of the motor, respectively. Substituting Eq. (4-91) into Eq. (4-92), and recognizing that θ_m is also a state variable, we find that the state equations of the motor are

$$\frac{d\theta_m(t)}{dt} = \omega_m(t) \tag{4-93}$$

$$\frac{d\omega_m(t)}{dt} = \frac{1}{J_m}(m - B_m)\omega_m + \frac{k}{J_m}e_2(t) \tag{4-94}$$

The state transition signal flow graph of the system is shown in Fig. 4-23. The transfer function is determined from Fig. 4-23 in the usual manner.

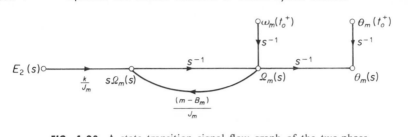

FIG. 4-23. A state transition signal flow graph of the two-phase induction motor.

$$\frac{\text{Motor displacement}}{\text{Control phase voltage}} = \frac{\Theta_m(s)}{E_2(s)} = \frac{(k/J_m)s^{-2}}{1 - \frac{m - B_m}{J_m}s^{-1}}$$

$$= \frac{k}{(B_m - m)s\left(1 + \frac{J_m}{B_m - m}s\right)} \qquad (4\text{-}95)$$

or

$$\frac{\Theta_m(s)}{E_2(s)} = \frac{K_m}{s(1 + \tau_m s)} \qquad (4\text{-}96)$$

where

$$K_m = \frac{k}{B_m - m} = \text{motor gain constant} \qquad (4\text{-}97)$$

$$\tau_m = \frac{J_m}{B_m - m} = \text{motor time constant} \qquad (4\text{-}98)$$

Since m is a negative number, the equations above show that the effect of the slope of the torque-speed curve is to add more friction to the motor, which improves the damping of the motor. The added damping effect is sometimes called the "internal electric damping" of a two-phase motor. It is analogous to the back emf effect of a d-c motor. However, if m is a positive number, for $m > B_m$, negative damping occurs and it can be shown that the motor becomes unstable.

A-C Tachometers[8]

The a-c tachometer is an electromechanical device which is very similar to a two-phase induction motor. A schematic diagram of an a-c tachometer is shown in Fig. 4-24. A sinusoidal voltage of rated value is applied to the reference winding setting up a flux in the tachometer. The control winding is placed at a 90 deg angle mechanically with respect to the reference winding, so that when the rotor shaft is stationary the output voltage at the control winding is zero. When the rotor shaft is rotated, the output voltage is proportional to the rotor velocity. The polarity of the voltage is dependent on the direction of rotation. Thus, the state equation of the a-c tachometer is

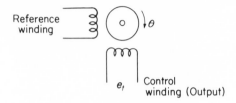

FIG. 4-24. Schematic diagram of an a-c tachometer.

$$K_t \frac{d\theta(t)}{dt} = e_t(t) \qquad (4\text{-}99)$$

where $e_t(t)$ is the output voltage of the control winding; $\theta(t)$, the rotor shaft position, is the state variable. K_t is the *tachometer constant* in volt/rad/sec or volt/rpm.

The transfer function of the a-c tachometer is simply

$$\frac{E_t(s)}{\Theta(s)} = K_t s \qquad (4\text{-}100)$$

4.5 Closed-loop Systems

In this section we shall illustrate the writing of the equations of closed-loop control systems. The systems equations will include cause-and-effect equations and state equations.

Consider the feedback control system shown in Fig. 4-25. The objective

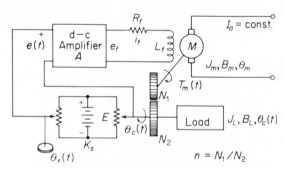

FIG. 4-25. A closed-loop control system.

of the system is to control the position of a load according to the positoin of the reference shaft. In this case, the controlled position of the load, $\theta_c(t)$, is the output, and the reference shaft, $\theta_r(t)$, is the input.

The two potentiometers connected in parallel as shown act as an *error sensing device*, or an *error detector*. The error detector converts the input and the output positions into proportional electric signals; the signals are, in turn, compared, and the difference voltage $e(t)$ is produced at the terminals of the device.

The d-c amplifier has a gain of A, and its output drives the field circuit of the d-c motor. The motor will rotate in such a direction as to reduce the error between θ_r and θ_c.

The following equations are written by following around the closed loop of the system:

$$\theta_e(t) = \theta_r(t) - \theta_c(t) \tag{4-101}$$

Error detector:

$$e(t) = K_s \theta_e(t) \tag{4-102}$$

Amplifier:

$$e_f(t) = Ae(t) \tag{4-103}$$

State equation of motor field:

$$\frac{di_f(t)}{dt} = \frac{-R_f}{L_f} i_f(t) + \frac{1}{L_f} e_f(t) \tag{4-104}$$

Motor torque:

$$T_m(t) = K_m K_f i_f(t) \tag{4-105}$$

State equation of motor load:

$$\frac{d\omega_m(t)}{dt} = -\frac{B_{me}}{J_{me}} \omega_m(t) + \frac{T_m(t)}{J_{me}} \tag{4-106}$$

Motor displacement:

$$\frac{d\theta_m(t)}{dt} = \omega_m(t) \tag{4-107}$$

Output displacement:

$$\theta_c(t) = \frac{N_1}{N_2} \theta_m(t) = n\theta_m(t) \tag{4-108}$$

In Eq. (4–102), K_s denotes the sensitivity of the error detector in volt/rad, or volt/degree. In Eq. (4–106) B_{me} and J_{me} are values of the equivalent friction and inertia measured on the motor side; i.e.,

$$J_{me} = J_m + n^2 J_L \tag{4-109}$$

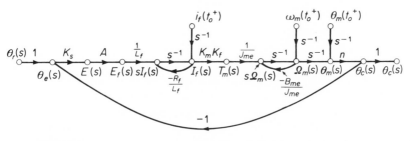

FIG. 4-26. A state transition signal flow graph of the system in Fig. 4-25.

$$B_{me} = B_m + n^2 B_L \qquad (4\text{-}110)$$

A state transition signal flow graph is now constructed for the control system as shown in Fig. 4-26. The open-loop transfer function of the system is obtained from the graph by opening the feedback path with a gain of -1.

$$G(s) = \frac{\Theta_c(s)}{\Theta_e(s)} = \frac{\dfrac{AK_sK_mK_fn}{L_fJ_{me}}s^{-3}}{1 + \dfrac{R_f}{L_f}s^{-1} + \dfrac{B_{me}}{J_{me}}s^{-1} + \dfrac{R_fB_{me}}{L_fJ_{me}}s^{-2}}$$

$$= \frac{AK_sK_mK_fn}{s(L_fs + R_f)(J_{me}s + B_{me})} \qquad (4\text{-}111)$$

The closed-loop transfer function of the system is

$$M(s) = \frac{\Theta_c(s)}{\Theta_r(s)} = \frac{AK_sK_mK_fn}{s(L_fs + R_f)(J_{me}s + B_{me}) + AK_sK_mK_fn} \qquad (4\text{-}112)$$

Notice that in this case, the closed-loop system can be represented by the block diagram shown in Fig. 2-8, with $G(s)$ given by Eq. (4–111) and $H(s)$ as unity. Therefore, the closed-loop transfer function of Eq. (4-112) can be determined by substituting $G(s)$ from Eq. (4–111) into Eq. (2–38).

It is interesting at this point to check if the output of system is capable of following a specific input. Consider that the reference shaft is suddenly rotated in any direction by R degrees; it is desired to know if the output shaft also rotates the same amount in the same direction when steady state is reached. This problem can be solved simply by use of the final-value theorem of Laplace transform theory in Eq. (1–47).

The input signal described above can be represented by a step function of magnitude R. Thus,

$$\Theta_r(s) = \frac{R}{s} \qquad (4\text{-}113)$$

Substituting Eq. (4–113) into Eq. (4–112) and applying the final-value theorem gives

$$\lim_{t\to\infty} \theta_c(t) = \lim_{s\to 0} s\Theta_c(s) = \lim_{s\to 0} \frac{RAK_sK_mK_fn}{s(L_fs + R_f)(J_{me}s + B_{me}) + AK_sK_mK_fn} = R \qquad (4\text{-}114)$$

Therefore, the system is capable of following a step function input with zero error. However, it must be reminded that the final-value theorem is applied with the assumption that the output $\theta_c(t)$ will not increase without bound as time approaches infinity. In other words, the system must be *stable* before the final-value theorem can validly be applied. We shall show later that the stability of the system depends on the location of the poles of the closed-loop transfer function. Thus, in this case, it is apparent that the stability of the system depends upon the system's parameters. If the system is unstable, the result given by Eq. (4–114) is completely meaningless.

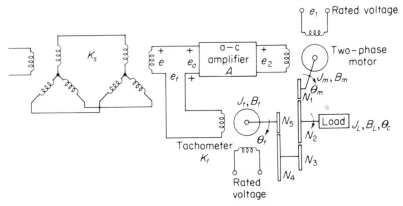

FIG. 4-27. An a-c control system with tachometer.

As another illustrative example, consider the control system shown in Fig. 4-27. To provide additional damping to the system, a tachometer is placed in the feedback path. The error detector consists of a pair of synchros connected as shown. The inertias and the frictions considered for the motor, tachometer, and the load are indicated as shown in Fig. 4-27. It is convenient to refer all these elements to the motor side. Thus,

$$J_{me} = J_m + \left(\frac{N_1}{N_2}\right)^2 J_L + \left(\frac{N_1}{N_2}\frac{N_2}{N_3}\frac{N_4}{N_5}\right)^2 J_t \tag{4-115}$$

$$B_{me} = B_m + \left(\frac{N_1}{N_2}\right)^2 B_L + \left(\frac{N_1}{N_2}\frac{N_2}{N_3}\frac{N_4}{N_5}\right)^2 B_t \tag{4-116}$$

The transfer function of the two-phase motor is written as

$$\frac{\Theta_m(s)}{E_2(s)} = \frac{K_m}{s(1 + \tau_m s)} \tag{4-117}$$

where, from Eqs. (4–97) and (4–98),

$$K_m = \frac{k}{B_{me} - m} \tag{4-118}$$

$$\tau_m = \frac{J_{me}}{B_{me} - m} \tag{4-119}$$

The transfer function in Eq. (4–117) can be decomposed into two state equations of the form of Eqs. (4–93) and (4–94).

The equations of the closed-loop system are written as

$$\theta_e(t) = \theta_r(t) - \theta_t(t) \tag{4-120}$$

$$e(t) = K_s \theta_e(t) \tag{4-121}$$

$$e_a(t) = e(t) - e_t(t) \tag{4-122}$$

$$e_2(t) = A e_a(t) \tag{4-123}$$

$$\frac{d\omega_m(t)}{dt} = -\frac{1}{\tau_m}\omega_m(t) + \frac{K_m}{\tau_m}e_2(t) \tag{4-124}$$

$$\frac{d\theta_m(t)}{dt} = \omega_m(t) \tag{4-125}$$

$$\theta_c(t) = \frac{N_1}{N_2}\theta_m(t) \tag{4-126}$$

$$\omega_t(t) = \left(\frac{N_1}{N_3}\frac{N_4}{N_5}\right)\omega_m(t) \tag{4-127}$$

$$e_t(t) = K_t\frac{d\theta_t(t)}{dt} = K_t\omega_t(t) \tag{4-128}$$

Based on these equations, the state transition signal flow graph of the system is drawn as shown in Fig. 4-28. If only the frequency domain analysis

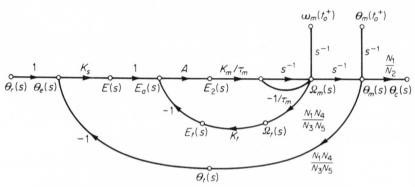

FIG. 4-28. A state transition signal flow graph for the system in Fig. 4–27.

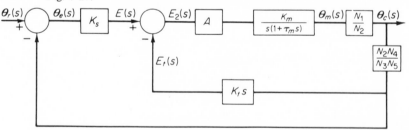

FIG. 4-29. A block diagram of the control system in Fig. 4–27.

is to be performed on the system, it is sufficient to draw the block diagram as shown in Fig. 4-29.

Although the block diagram seems simpler than the state transition flow graph, it does not contain as much information as the latter. The transfer function is obtained from the block diagram.

$$\frac{\Theta_c(s)}{\Theta_r(s)} = \frac{K_s A K_m n_1}{\tau_m s^2 + (1 + A K_m K_t n_2)s + K_s A K_m n_2} \tag{4-129}$$

where $n_1 = N_1/N_2$ and $n_2 = (N_2 N_4/N_3 N_5)$. The state transition signal flow graph contains information on both the transfer function and the state transition equations. Thus, from Fig. 4-28, the following transformed state transition equations are written in matrix form:

$$
\begin{bmatrix} \Theta_m(s) \\ \Omega_m(s) \end{bmatrix}
$$

$$
= \begin{bmatrix} \dfrac{s^{-1}\left(1 + \dfrac{s^{-1}}{\tau_m} + \dfrac{K_m K_t A N_1 N_4 s^{-1}}{\tau_m N_3 N_5}\right)}{\Delta} & \dfrac{s^{-2}}{\Delta} \\[4mm] -\dfrac{\dfrac{K_s A K_m N_1 N_4}{\tau_m N_3 N_5} s^{-2}}{\Delta} & \dfrac{s^{-1}}{\Delta} \end{bmatrix} \begin{bmatrix} \theta_m(t_0^+) \\ \omega_m(t_0^+) \end{bmatrix} + \begin{bmatrix} \dfrac{K_s A K_m}{\tau_m} s^{-2} \\[4mm] \dfrac{K_s A K_m}{\tau_m} s^{-1} \\ \Delta \end{bmatrix} \Theta_r(s)
$$

$$(4\text{--}130)$$

where

$$\Delta = 1 + \frac{1}{\tau_m} s^{-1} + \frac{A K_m K_t N_1 N_4}{\tau_m N_3 N_5} s^{-1} + \frac{K_s K_m A N_1 N_4}{\tau_m N_3 N_5} s^{-2} \qquad (4\text{--}131)$$

The state transition equations for $t \geq t_0$ are obtained by taking the inverse Laplace transform on both sides of Eq. (4–130).

4.6 Systems with Transportation Lags

Thus far we have considered only systems whose transfer functions are quotients of algebraic polynomials. These systems are characterized by the fact that the output starts to respond immediately after the application of the input. In some control systems, especially in systems with hydraulic, pneumatic, or mechanical transmissions, pure time lags may be encountered such that the output will not begin to respond to a transient input until after a given time interval. Because of the time lag effect, the transfer functions of these systems are no longer quotients of polynomials; they usually consist of the term e^{-Ts}, where T denotes the time lag or transportation lag.

In terms of state variables, a system with time lag can no longer be adequately described by the matrix state equation of Eq. (3–28). A general state description of a system containing time lags is given by the following matrix *differential-difference equation*:

$$\frac{d\mathbf{x}(t)}{dt} = \sum_{i=1}^{p} A_i \mathbf{x}(t - T_i) + \sum_{j=1}^{q} B_j \mathbf{r}(t - T_j) \qquad (4\text{--}132)$$

where T_i and T_j are fixed time lags. Equation (4–132) represents a general situation where time delays exist in both the inputs as well as the state variables.

Figure 4-30 depicts examples in which transportation lags are observed. Figure 4-30a outlines an arrangement in which two different fluids are to be

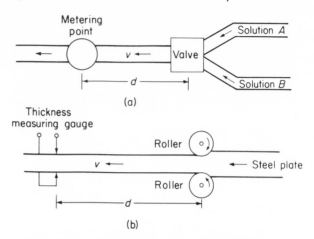

FIG. 4-30. Physical systems with transportation lags.

mixed in appropriate proportions. In order to make sure that a homogeneous solution is measured, the metering point is located at some distance from the mixing point. Thus, transportation lag exists between the mixing point and the place where the change in concentration is detected. If the rate of flow of the mixed solution is v inches per second, and d is the distance between the mixing and the metering points, the time lag is given by

$$T = d/v \text{ (sec)} \tag{4-133}$$

If it is assumed that the concentration at the mixing point is $c(t)$ and that it is reproduced without change T seconds later at the metering point, the measured quantity is

$$b(t) = c(t - T) \tag{4-134}$$

The Laplace transform of Eq. (4-134) is

$$B(s) = e^{-Ts}C(s) \tag{4-135}$$

or

$$\frac{B(s)}{C(s)} = e^{-Ts} \tag{4-136}$$

The arrangement shown in Fig. 4-30b may be thought of as a thickness control of the rolling of steel plates. As in the above case, the transfer function between the thickness at the roller and the measuring point is also given by Eq. (4-136).

Other examples of transportation lags are found in human beings as control systems where action and reaction are always accompanied by time delays. The operation of the sampler and hold device of a sampled-data system closely resembles a pure time delay; it sometimes can be approximated by a single time lag term, e^{-sT}.

The block diagram of a typical control which has a transportation lag

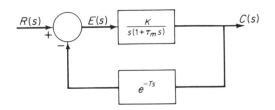

FIG. 4-31. Block diagram of a feedback control system with transportation lag.

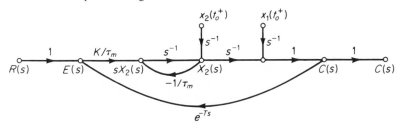

FIG. 4-32. State transition signal flow graph of the control system in Fig. 4–31.

is shown in Fig. 4-31. The system can be regarded as one which controls the rolling of steel plates as in Fig. 4-30b. The closed-loop transfer function of the system can be determined in the usual manner, and is

$$\frac{C(s)}{R(s)} = \frac{Ke^{-Ts}}{s(1 + \tau_m s) + Ke^{-Ts}} \tag{4-137}$$

The state transition signal flow graph of the system is shown in Fig. 4-32. The state equations of the system in matrix form are obtained as follows:

$$\begin{bmatrix} \dfrac{dx_1(t)}{dt} \\[3mm] \dfrac{dx_2(t)}{dt} \end{bmatrix} = \begin{bmatrix} 0 & 1 \\[2mm] 0 & -\dfrac{1}{\tau_m} \end{bmatrix} \begin{bmatrix} x_1(t) \\[2mm] x(t_2) \end{bmatrix} + \begin{bmatrix} 0 \\[2mm] \dfrac{K}{\tau_m} \end{bmatrix} e(t) \tag{4-138}$$

But since $e(t) = r(t) - x_1(t - T)$, Eq. (4–138) becomes

$$\begin{bmatrix} \dfrac{dx_1(t)}{dt} \\[3mm] \dfrac{dx_2(t)}{dt} \end{bmatrix} = \begin{bmatrix} 0 & 1 \\[2mm] 0 & -\dfrac{1}{\tau_m} \end{bmatrix} \begin{bmatrix} x_1(t) \\[2mm] x_2(t) \end{bmatrix} + \begin{bmatrix} 0 & 0 \\[2mm] -\dfrac{K}{\tau_m} & 0 \end{bmatrix} \begin{bmatrix} x_1(t - T) \\[2mm] x_2(t - T) \end{bmatrix} + \begin{bmatrix} 0 \\[2mm] \dfrac{K}{\tau_m} \end{bmatrix} r(t) \tag{4-139}$$

which fits the description of Eq. (4–132).

REFERENCES

1. B. Friedland, O. Wing, and R. Ash, *Principles of Linear Networks*, McGraw-Hill Book Company, New York, N. Y., 1961.

2. M. E. Van Valkenburg, *Network Analysis*, 2nd ed., Prentice-Hall, Inc., Englewood Cliffs, N. J., 1964.

3. R. J. Schwarz and B. Friedland, *Linear Systems*, McGraw-Hill Book Company, New York, N. Y., 1965.

4. B. C. Kuo, *Linear Networks and Systems Analysis*, McGraw-Hill Book Company, New York, N. Y., 1967.

5. T. Bashkow, "The A Matrix, A New Network Description," *IRE Trans. on Circuit Theory*, Vol. **CT-4**, pp. 117–119, September, 1957.

6. P. R. Bryant, "The Explicit Form of Bashkow's A Matrix," *IRE Trans. on Circuit Theory*, Vol. **CT-9**, no. 3, pp. 303–306, 1962.

7. R. A. Bruns and R. M. Saunders, *Analysis of Feedback Control Systems*, McGraw-Hill Book Company, New York, N. Y., 1955.

8. J. E. Gibson and F. B. Tuteur, *Control System Components*, McGraw-Hill Book Company, New York, N. Y., 1958.

9. W. A. Stein and G. J. Thaler, "Effect of Nonlinearity in a 2-Phase Servomotor," *AIEE Trans.*, Vol. **73**, part II, 1954, pp. 518–521.

10. B. C. Kuo, "Studying the Two-Phase Servomotor," *Instrument Society of America Journal*, Vol. **7**, no. 4, April, 1960, pp. 64–65.

PROBLEMS

4-1. Write the force equations for the mechanical systems shown in Fig. 4P-1.

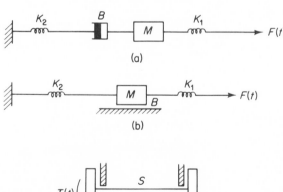

(a)

(b)

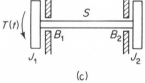

(c)

FIG. 4P-1.

4-2. Write state equations for the mechanical systems shown in Fig. 4P-2.

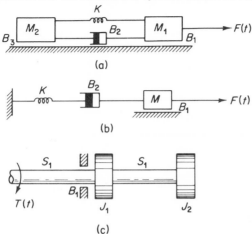

(a)

(b)

(c)

FIG. 4P-2.

4-3. For the system of Fig. 4P-3, determine the transfer function $E_o(s)/T_m(s)$. The potentiometer rotates through 10 turns and the voltage applied across the potentiometer terminals is E volts.

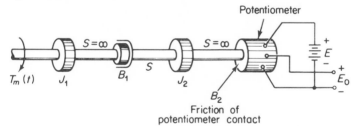

Potentiometer

Friction of
potentiometer contact

FIG. 4P-3.

4-4. Write the differential equations of the gear train system shown in Fig. 4P-4. The moments of inertia of the gears and shafts are J_1, J_2, and J_3. $T(t)$ is the

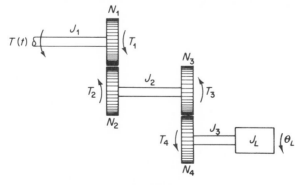

FIG. 4P-4.

applied torque. N denotes the number of gear teeth. Assume $S = \infty$ for all shafts (rigid shafts).

4-5. Write the transfer functions $Y_2(s)/F(s)$ for the mechanical systems of Fig. 4P-1 a and b, where $Y_2(s)$ is the Laplace transform of the displacement of M.

4-6. The spring of the mechanical system shown in Fig. 4P-6 is non-Hookean (nonlinear). The restoring force of the spring is described by

$$F_s = Kx^2$$

where K is a constant and x is linear displacement. Determine the displacement of the mass as a function of time when the applied force is a unit step function, $f(t) = u(t)$. Assume zero initial conditions.

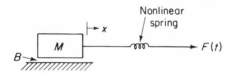

FIG. 4P-6.

4-7. A simple positional servo system is shown in Fig. 4P-7. The air gap flux ϕ of the motor is assumed to be proportional to the field current by the constant K_f; the motor torque is proportional to the field flux and the armature current $(T_m = K'_m \phi I_a)$. The sensitivity of the potentiometer-error detector is $K_s(v/\text{rad})$.

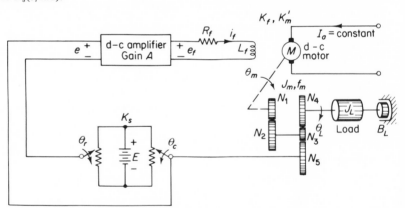

FIG. 4P-7.

(a) Construct a signal flow graph of the servo system using nodes to represent variables $\theta_r, E_e, E_f, T_m, \theta_m, \theta_L,$ and θ_c.

(b) Draw a block diagram of the system with blocks representing the error detector, the amplifier, the motor, and the gear trains.

(c) Evaluate expressions of the open-loop transfer function $\Theta_L(s)/E_e(s)$ and the closed-loop transfer function $\Theta_L(s)/\Theta_r(s)$.

4-8. A simple positional servo system is shown in Fig. 4P-8. The transfer function of the demodulator is given as K_d a-c v/d-c v. The sensitivity of the synchro error detector is K_s in v/rad; e_b is the back emf of the d-c motor.

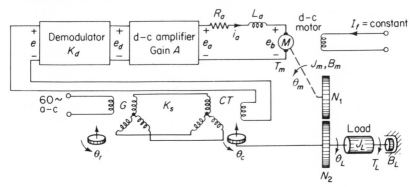

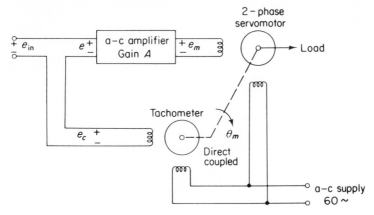

FIG. 4P-8.

(a) Write the cause-and-effect and state equations for the system.

(b) Draw a state transition signal flow graph for the system. Neglect the external torque disturbance T_L shown on the diagram.

(c) Find the open-loop transfer function $\Theta_c(s)/\Theta_e(s)$ and the closed-loop transfer function $\Theta_c(s)/\Theta_r(s)$, where $\Theta_e(s) = \Theta_r(s) - \Theta_c(s)$.

(d) An external torque disturbance is applied to the load as shown in Fig. 4P-8. Modify the signal flow graph constructed in part (b) to include this effect. Evaluate the transfer function $\Theta_c(s)/T_L(s)$ when $\Theta_r(s) = 0$.

4-9. An a-c tachometer is used as a component in an integrator of a certain computer, as shown in Fig. 4P-9. The transfer function of the tachometer may be represented by K_t in v/rad/sec. The motor is assumed to be ideal with a torque constant of K_m(lb-ft/v). The total inertia of the motor load and tachometer is J, and the viscous friction is B.

FIG. 4P-9.

(a) Construct a signal flow graph for the system, using nodes to represent e_{in}, e, e_c, and θ_m. Evaluate $\Theta_m(s)/E_{in}(s)$.

(b) Draw a block diagram of the system, using three blocks to represent the amplifier, the motor load, and the tachometer, respectively.

4-10. A two-phase servomotor has the torque-speed characteristics shown in Fig. 4P-10. In the low-speed range, these characteristics may be closely approximated by a series of parallel straight lines whose intersections with the vertical axis are proportional to the magnitude of the control phase voltage e_2 when

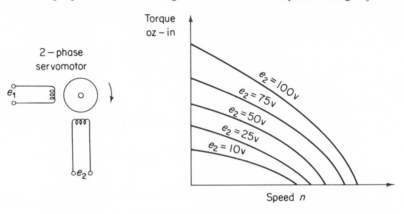

FIG. 4P-10.

the voltage e_1 is held constant. The motor develops a blocked-rotor torque of 5 oz-in. when e_2 is at rated 75 volts. An extension of the linear portion of the torque-speed curve for $e_2 = 75\,v$ intersects the horizontal axis at 4500 rpm. The inertia of the motor is 0.1 oz-in.^{2} The viscous friction of the motor may be neglected.

(a) Draw the linearized torque-speed curves for the motor with values of e_2 equal to 10, 25, 50, 75, and 100 v.

(b) Write an algebraic equation for the motor developed torque in terms of e_2 and motor angular velocity.

(c) Determine the transfer function $\Theta_m(s)/E_2(s)$ of the motor.

5

General
Feedback Theory

5.1 What Is Feedback?

The concept of feedback[1,2] plays an important role in control system engineering. In order to understand and appreciate the significance of feedback, it is important to define the term. Although it appears to have a very simple meaning, and despite the fact that it is often used in our daily language, a precise definition is surprisingly difficult. The existence of feedback in physical systems is often obscure and difficult to demonstrat . In Chapter 1, we gave several simple illustrations of feedback control systems: in each system, a specific variable is to be controlled; control is brought about by making a comparison of the actual value of this variable with its desired value and utilizing the difference to reduce the error observed. When feedback is deliberately introduced for the purpose of control, its existence and function are easily identified. The reduction of system error is merely one of the many effects that feedback may have upon a system. We shall show in the following sections that feedback also affects such system properties as stability, bandwidth, over-all gain, impedance level, nonlinearity and distortion effects, and transient response, etc. In order to understand the effect of feedback on all these parameters, it is essential that we examine this elusive and sometimes paradoxical phenomenon with a very broad mind. As a matter of fact, some of the physical systems which we identify as inherently nonfeedback systems may turn out to have feedback if we look at them in a certain manner. An example is readily found by referring to the passive ladder network shown in Fig. 2-28a. Certainly we do not recognize that the network possesses any physical feedback; at least, there is no visual feedback path. But, referring to the signal flow graph of the network shown in Fig. 2-28b, we can identify three feedback loops, each representing a *closed sequence of cause-and-effect relation* between certain currents and voltages. From a general point of view, the last statement may be used to define adequately the existence of feedback in physical systems. We can state that whenever a closed sequence of cause-and-effect relationships exists among variables of a system, feedback is said to exist. This viewpoint will inevitably admit feedback in a large number of systems which we ordinarily would identify as nonfeedback systems. But with the availability of signal flow graphs and the mathematics of feedback theory, this general definition of feedback enables numerous systems, with or without physical feedback, to be studied through the use of feedback theory once the existence of feedback in the above-mentioned sense is established.

5.2 The Effect of Feedback

This section and the following sections are devoted to a general analysis of feedback systems and the meaning of feedback. The principal object of the analysis is the development of a general feedback theory through the use of familiar electronic amplifier circuits.

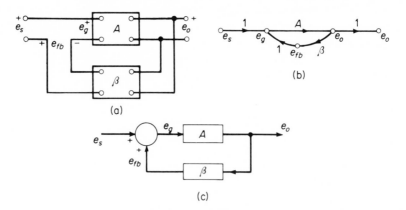

FIG. 5-1. Single-loop feedback system. (a) Simplified schematic diagram representation; (b) Signal flow graph representation; (c) Block diagram representation.

Three common ways of representing a single-loop feedback system are shown in Fig. 5-1. The over-all transfer function, or gain, of the system portrayed is given by

$$M = \frac{e_0}{e_s} = \frac{A}{1 - A\beta} \tag{5-1}$$

where A and β denote the transfer functions of the forward and feedback paths, respectively, and are frequency-dependent quantities in general.*

Effect of Feedback on Over-all Gain

As seen from Eq. (5-1) and Fig. 5-1, without the feedback path, the transfer function of the system would be given by $M = A$. Therefore:

Feedback reduces the gain of a feedback system by the factor $1 - A\beta$.

The statement just made is true when A and β are pure numbers. But A and β may be functions of frequency, so that the magnitude of $1 - A\beta$ may be greater than unity in one frequency range but less than one in another. Therefore, feedback could increase the gain of a feedback amplifier in one frequency range, but decrease the gain in another.

Effect of Feedback on Sensitivity[1]

Sensitivity is normally used to express the ratio of the percentage variation in some specific system quantities such as gain, impedance, etc., to the percentage variation in one of the system parameters. The sensitivity function is defined as

$$S_K^M = \frac{d \ln M}{d \ln k} = \frac{dM/M}{dk/k} = \frac{\text{Percentage change in } M \text{ (due to change in } k)}{\text{Percentage change in } k}$$

$$(5\text{-}2)$$

where M is a transfer function and k is a specified parameter.

Let us consider the signal flow graph configuration of Fig. 5-1b. First, when the feedback path is open, the sensitivity of the over-all gain M to the variation of forward path gain A is apparently equal to unity. This result is expected, since without feedback $M = A$ and $S_A^M = 1$. With the feedback loop closed, the sensitivity of over-all gain with respect to $k = A$ is given by

$$S_A^M = \frac{d \ln M}{d \ln k} = \frac{dM}{dk} \frac{k}{M} = \frac{1}{1 - A\beta} \qquad (5\text{-}3)$$

The sensitivity can be made arbitrarily small by increasing $A\beta$. In the ideal case, $A\beta \to \infty$, and $S_A^M \to 0$.

When the feedback element β is considered to be variable, $k = \beta$.

$$S_\beta^M = \frac{dM}{d\beta} \frac{\beta}{M} = \frac{A\beta}{1 - A\beta} \qquad (5\text{-}4)$$

The possibility of reducing the sensitivity does not exist (unless $A = 0$); as $A\beta$ grows larger, sensitivity S approaches unity.

*It should be noted that the notations of feedback amplifiers are used here. If we let $A = G$ and $\beta = -H$, then Eq. (5-1) is identical with the notation used for single-loop feedback control systems. The difference in sign between H and β stems from the fact that negative feedback concept is assumed in control systems (feedback signal is subtracted from the input), whereas in feedback amplifiers, positive feedback is assumed, with the feedback signal being added to the input signal.

In view of the preceding discussion, we can make the following conclusions in regard to the effect of feedback on sensitivity:

(1) Feedback, when used properly, may reduce sensitivity with respect to change in system parameter.

(2) Feedback does not affect variations of parameters in the feedback path.

(3) Feedback does not affect variations of parameters in a path with no feedback path around it (open-loop system).

(4) Feedback reduces sensitivity with respect to a parameter located in the forward path of a loop. The larger the loop gain $A\beta$, the more effective feedback is in reducing sensitivity.

Effect of Feedback on Distortion

Feedback may be used to reduce the effects of certain types of extraneous signals which occur in amplifiers and control systems. "Extraneous signal" is intended here to include many types of unwanted effects either from external or internal sources of a system. Examples of extraneous signals are thermal noise voltage in amplifier circuits, synchro noise of servo systems, wind gust exerted on antenna of radar systems, or harmonic components resulting from nonlinear characteristics of system components.

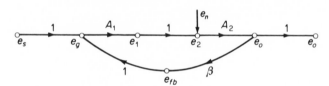

FIG. 5-2. Signal flow graph of feedback system with extraneous signal in the forward path.

The effect of feedback on extraneous signals depends greatly upon where the signal is introduced into the system. Let us refer to the signal flow graph shown in Fig. 5-2. In this graph, e_n represents a noise signal which is considered to be introduced at an arbitrary point in the forward path. In the absence of feedback, that is, for β equals zero, the output signal is

$$e_o = A_1 A_2 e_s + A_2 e_n = e_{os} + e_{on} \qquad (5\text{--}5)$$

where e_{os} represents the signal component of the output, and e_{on} is the noise component. The output signal-to-noise ratio with no feedback is

$$\frac{\text{Output due to signal}}{\text{Output due to noise}} = \left| \frac{e_{os}}{e_{on}} \right| = \left| \frac{A_1 A_2 e_s}{A_2 e_n} \right| = \left| \frac{A_1 e_s}{e_n} \right| \qquad (5\text{--}6)$$

Evidently, in order to increase the signal-to-noise ratio, we should increase the magnitude of A_1 or e_s relative to that of e_n. Varying the magnitude of A_2 would have no effect whatsoever on the ratio.

With the presence of feedback, the system output signal is given by

$$e_{o\,\text{fb}} = \frac{A_1 A_2}{1 - A_1 A_2 \beta} e_s + \frac{A_2}{1 - A_1 A_2 \beta} e_n$$

$$= e_{os\,\text{fb}} + e_{on\,\text{fb}} \tag{5-7}$$

Comparing Eq. (5–7) with Eq. (5–5), we see that the noise component in the output signal, $e_{on\,\text{fb}}$, is reduced by the factor $(1 - A_1 A_2 \beta)$, but the signal component, $e_{os\,\text{fb}}$, is also reduced by the same amount.

Therefore, the signal-to-noise ratio is

$$\left| \frac{e_{os\,\text{fb}}}{e_{on\,\text{fb}}} \right| = \left| \frac{A_1 A_2 e_s / (1 - A_1 A_2 \beta)}{A_2 / (1 - A_1 A_2 \beta)} \right| = \left| \frac{A_1 e_s}{e_n} \right| \tag{5-8}$$

and is the same as that without feedback. In this case, feedback has no direct effect on the output signal-to-noise ratio. However, the application of feedback suggests a possibility of improving the signal-noise ratio. Let us assume that with feedback incorporated, we increase the magnitude of A_1 to A_1', and e_s to e_s' with other factors unchanged, so that the output due to signal alone is at the same level as that when feedback is absent. In other words, we set

$$\left| e_{os\,\text{fb}} \right| = \left| \frac{A_1' A_2 e_s'}{1 - A_1' A_2 \beta} \right| = \left| A_1 A_2 e_s \right| \tag{5-9}$$

But when A_1 becomes larger, the output due to noise becomes

$$\left| e_{on\,\text{fb}} \right| = \left| \frac{A_2 e_n}{1 - A_1' A_2 \beta} \right| \tag{5-10}$$

which is smaller than e_{on} when feedback is absent. The signal-to-noise ratio is now

$$\left| \frac{e_{os\,\text{fb}}}{e_{on\,\text{fb}}} \right| = \left| \frac{e_s A_1}{e_n} (1 - A_1' A_2 \beta) \right| \tag{5-11}$$

Through the comparison of this ratio with that of Eq. (5–6), it is apparent that the signal-to-noise ratio with feedback is increased by a factor of $(1 - A_1' A_2 \beta)$. If, however, e_s and A_1 could not be increased, then feedback would be of no avail in improving the output signal-noise ratio.

Let us now investigate the situation when the noise signal is originated at the output of a system. This may be due to ripples in the power supply

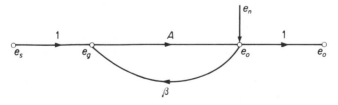

FIG. 5-3. Signal flow graph of feedback system with extraneous signal in the output.

voltage of the output stage of an amplifier, or disturbance exerted on the load of a servo system. A signal flow graph illustrating this situation is depicted in Fig. 5-3.

It can be shown that, in this case, feedback does not affect the output signal-to-noise ratio. But, as in the previous case, if e_s and A can be increased (to e_s' and A', respectively) with respect to e_n, the signal-noise ratio may be increased by a factor of $(1 - A'\beta)$.

When extraneous signal e_n appears at the same point as the input signal e_s, it is as if the input were $e_n + e_s$. It is easy to see that feedback will have no effect and will not provide improvement of the signal-to-noise ratio. The extraneous signal in the input may be due to synchro noise or transducer noise in servo systems, or to hum voltage in an input transformer of an electrical amplifier.

Effect of Feedback on Bandwidth

Bandwidth is the characteristic of the frequency response which is most often specified in the design of amplifiers and feedback control systems. The definition of bandwidth is depicted on typical frequency responses of amplifiers and servo systems in Fig. 5-4. The bandwidth is significant because

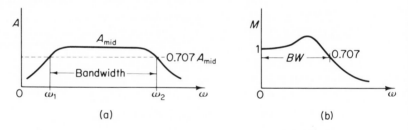

(a)   (b)

FIG. 5-4. (a) Typical frequency response of an RC-coupled amplifier; (b) Typical frequency response of a feedback control system.

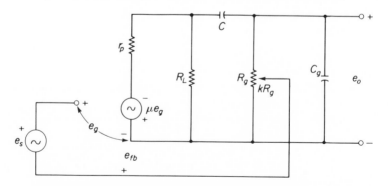

FIG. 5-5. Single-stage RC-coupled amplifier with negative feedback.

it measures the ability of the amplifier or servo system to reproduce the input signal, and the noise rejection characteristics. The effect of feedback on bandwidth is illustrated here by considering the single stage R-C coupled amplifier with potentiometer feedback, as shown in Fig. 5-5.

If R_g is much greater than R_L (this is usually true), for sinusoidal quantities, the gain of the amplifier without feedback ($k = 0$) is given by

$$A = \left(\frac{-\mu R_L}{r_p + R_L}\right)\left(\frac{j\omega R_g C}{1 + j\omega R_g C}\right)\left(\frac{1}{1 + j\omega R_e C_g}\right) \tag{5-12}$$

where

$$R_e = \frac{r_p R_L}{r_p + R_L} \tag{5-13}$$

If we assume that a middle frequency range exists, the reactance of the coupling capacitor C is so small that it virtually constitutes a short circuit, and the reactance of the shunt capacitance C_g is so large as to form an open circuit. The amplifier gains at mid-frequency, low frequency, and high frequency ranges are given, respectively, by

$$A_{\text{mid}} = -\frac{\mu R_L}{r_p + R_L} \tag{5-14}$$

$$A_{\text{low}} = A_{\text{mid}}\left(\frac{j\omega R_g C}{1 + j\omega R_g C}\right) \tag{5-15}$$

$$A_{\text{hi}} = A_{\text{mid}}\left(\frac{1}{1 + j\omega R_e C_g}\right) \tag{5-16}$$

When the frequency is equal to $1/R_g C$ (rad/sec), from Eq. (5–15), the magnitude of the low frequency gain is found to be equal to $0.707 A_{\text{mid}}$. Hence, the lower half power frequency of the amplifier without feedback is $1/R_g C$. Similarly, from Eq. (5–16), it is clear that the upper half power frequency is equal to $1/R_e C_g$.

Now consider that feedback is in effect, ($k \neq 0$). The gain at mid-band is given by

$$A_{\text{mid fb}} = \frac{A_{\text{mid}}}{1 - kA_{\text{mid}}} \tag{5-17}$$

since the feedback amplifier is of the single-loop configuration shown in Fig. 5-1. The gain at the low frequency range is obtained in the same manner:

$$A_{\text{low fb}} = \frac{A_{\text{low}}}{1 - kA_{\text{low}}} \tag{5-18}$$

Substituting Eq. (5–15) into Eq. (5–18) and simplifying, we have

$$A_{\text{low fb}} = \frac{A_{\text{mid}} j\omega R_g C}{1 + j\omega R_g C(1 - kA_{\text{mid}})} \tag{5-19}$$

By the use of Eq. (5–17), the last equation is written as

$$A_{\text{low fb}} = A_{\text{mid fb}} \frac{j\omega R_g C(1 - kA_{\text{mid}})}{1 + j\omega R_g C(1 - kA_{\text{mid}})} \tag{5-20}$$

Equation (5-20) is of the same form as Eq. (5-15); therefore, the lower half power frequency of the amplifier with feedback is $1/R_g C(1 - kA_{\text{mid}})$. Hence, the lower half power frequency of the feedback amplifier is reduced by the factor $(1 - kA_{\text{mid}})$.

The gain with feedback at the high frequency end is

$$A_{\text{hi fb}} = \frac{A_{\text{hi}}}{1 - kA_{\text{hi}}} \tag{5-21}$$

Substituting Eq. (5-16) into Eq. (5-21) and simplifying, we have

$$A_{\text{hi fb}} = A_{\text{mid fb}} \frac{1}{1 + \dfrac{j\omega R_e C_g}{1 - kA_{\text{mid}}}} \tag{5-22}$$

which is of the same form as Eq. (5-16). Therefore, the upper half power frequency of the feedback amplifier is equal to $(1 - kA_{\text{mid}})/R_e C_g$, and is increased by the factor $(1 - kA_{\text{mid}})$ over that of the amplifier without feedback. Typical frequency responses of the single-stage amplifier with and

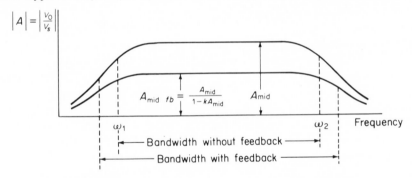

FIG. 5-6. Effect of feedback on bandwidth of single-stage RC-coupled amplifier.

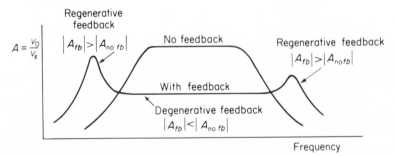

FIG. 5-7. Effect of feedback on bandwidth of three-stage RC-coupled amplifier (feedback around all three stages).

without feedback are depicted in Fig. 5-6. The bandwidth of the feedback amplifier is increased by the factor $(1 - kA_{\mathrm{mid}})^2$, while the mid-band gain is reduced by the factor $(1 - kA_{\mathrm{mid}})$. In this case, the feedback is described as *degenerative** over the complete frequency range, since the gain with feedback is always less than the gain without feedback. Figure 5-7 depicts the effect of feedback on the frequency response if feedback is applied across three stages of cascaded R-C coupled amplifiers. In the low and high frequency regions, the gain with feedback is greater than that of no feedback, and the feedback is described as *regenerative* at these frequencies.

Effect of Feedback on Impedance

One of the important effects of feedback is its influence on the impedance that the system presents to any external system or circuit connected to it. For instance, in electronic amplifiers, the input impedance faced by the source of signal voltage, or the output impedance faced by the load are important, since they affect the efficiency of power transfer from the source to the amplifier, and from the amplifier to the load. In servo systems, by analogy, we can regard the torque-to-velocity ratio of the system output as the output impedance faced by the load. In general, feedback may increase or decrease the impedance seen between any two open terminals of a system, depending on the type of feedback associated with the terminals. Generally speaking, shunt feedback will decrease impedance, and series feedback will increase impedance. First we shall define the meanings of series and shunt feedback.

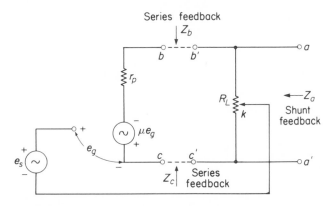

FIG. 5-8. Illustration of series and shunt feedback by means of a feedback amplifier.

Let us consider the simple feedback amplifier circuit shown in Fig. 5-8. We are primarily interested in the types of feedback into the terminals a–a', b–b', and c–c', and the effect of feedback on the impedance into these terminals.

*Feedback is defined as degenerative if $|A_{fb}| < |A_{no\ fb}|$; otherwise, it is regenerative.

With reference to any pair of terminals, if the feedback signal is in series with the terminals, feedback is described as series feedback. If the feedback signal is parallel with the terminals in question, shunt feedback is said to exist. In the present case, for terminals a–a', the feedback is of the shunt type, and for the terminals b–b' and c–c', we have series feedback. Therefore, the same circuit is said to have either shunt or series feedback, depending upon the point at which feedback is measured.

The impedances into the three pairs of terminals are now to be evaluated for the amplifier with and without feedback. Let Z_a be the impedance into terminals a–a' with e_s replaced by a short circuit (this is also the output impedance) and without feedback ($k = 0$), and $Z_{a\,\text{fb}}$, with feedback. Then

$$Z_a = \frac{r_p R_L}{r_p + R_L} \tag{5–23}$$

The output impedance with feedback is

$$Z_{a\,\text{fb}} = \frac{r_p R_L}{r_p + R_L + \mu k R_L} \tag{5–24}$$

which can also be written as

$$Z_{a\,\text{fb}} = \frac{r_p R_L/(r_p + R_L)}{1 + k \dfrac{\mu R_L}{r_p + R_L}} = \frac{Z_a}{1 - Ak} \tag{5–25}$$

where A is the gain of the amplifier without feedback ($k = 0$) and is given by

$$A = -\frac{\mu R_L}{r_p + R_L} \tag{5–26}$$

Thus, the impedance into shunt feedback terminals is reduced by a factor $(1 - Ak)$.

The impedance at terminals b–b' is evaluated by considering that a voltage generator with voltage e is inserted between b–b', and the impedance is equal to the ratio of e to the current i that flows through the generator (e_s is shorted). Without feedback ($k = 0$),

$$Z_b = r_p + R_L \tag{5–27}$$

When feedback is in effect, the following loop equations are written for the circuit:

$$e = (r_p + R_L)i - \mu e_g \tag{5–28}$$

$$e_g = -kiR_L \tag{5–29}$$

From the last two equations, the impedance at terminals b–b' is obtained as

$$Z_{b\,\text{fb}} = e/i = r_p + R_L + k\mu R_L \tag{5–30}$$

or

$$Z_{b\,\text{fb}} = (r_p + R_L)\left(1 + k \frac{\mu R_L}{r_p + R_L}\right) = Z_b(1 - kA) \tag{5–31}$$

Therefore, the impedance into series feedback terminals is increased by the factor $(1 - Ak)$.

In the same manner, we can show that the impedance at terminals c–c' with no feedback is

$$Z_c = \frac{r_p + R_L}{(1 + \mu)} \tag{5-32}$$

and when feedback is incorporated,

$$
\begin{aligned}
Z_{c\,n} &= \frac{r_p + R_L + k\mu R_L}{(1 + \mu)} \\
&= \frac{(r_p + R_L)(1 + Ak)}{(1 + \mu)}
\end{aligned}
\tag{5-33}
$$

It should be mentioned that it may be difficult to determine the type of feedback in a complex system. Quite often, it may be a combination of both shunt and series feedback, and then the increase or decrease of impedance due to feedback may depend entirely upon the values of the system parameters used.

Effect of Feedback on Transient Response

The effect of feedback on the transient response of linear systems is investigated by means of two simple illustrations. Consider the single stage feedback amplifier shown in Fig. 5-9. When there is no feedback ($k = 0$), the transfer function or gain of the amplifier is of the form:

$$\frac{E_0}{E_s} = \frac{A}{1 + sT} \tag{5-34}$$

where

$$A = -\frac{\mu R_L}{r_p + R_L} \tag{5-35}$$

and

$$T = \frac{r_p R_L C}{r_p + R_L} \tag{5-36}$$

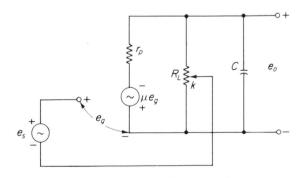

FIG. 5-9. Single-stage feedback amplifier.

The inverse Laplace transform of C/R is the impulse response of the system; hence

$$g(t) = \mathscr{L}^{-1}\left(\frac{E_0}{E_s}\right) = \frac{A}{T}\,e^{-t/T} \tag{5-37}$$

Since the time constant T is always positive, the impulse response of the amplifier without feedback is an exponential decay, and the amplifier is said to be always *stable*.

When $k \neq 0$, the closed-loop transfer function of the amplifier is

$$\frac{E_0}{E_s}(s) = \frac{A}{Ts + (1 - Ak)} = \frac{A}{T\left(s + \dfrac{1 - Ak}{T}\right)} \tag{5-38}$$

and the inverse Laplace transform is

$$g(t) = \frac{A}{T}e^{-(1-Ak)t/T} = \frac{A}{T}e^{-t/T_0} \tag{5-39}$$

where

$$T_0 = \frac{T}{1 - Ak} \tag{5-40}$$

is the time constant of the closed-loop system. From Eq. (5-40), T_0 may be positive or negative, depending on the value of Ak. If Ak is negative (positive feedback), T_0 is positive, and the impulse response in Eq. (5-39) is an exponential decay; but if Ak is positive (negative feedback), and greater than unity, T_0 becomes negative, the impulse response will increase without bound,

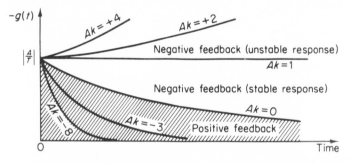

FIG. 5-10. Time responses showing the effect of feedback.

and the response (or the system) is said to be *unstable*. Figure 5-10 shows how the impulse response varies with different values for Ak.

It is of interest to study the variation of the poles of $E_0(s)/E_s(s)$ when the value of Ak is varied. The denominator of $E_0(s)/E_s(s)$ when it is set equal to zero is called the *characteristic equation* of the system. Without feedback, the characteristic equation of the system is simply

$$1 + sT = 0 \tag{5-41}$$

which has a root at $s = -1/T$ in the s-plane. When feedback is applied, the characteristic equation of the feedback amplifier is given by

$$s + (1 - Ak)/T = 0 \qquad (5\text{--}42)$$

and the root is at $-(1 - Ak)/T$, which varies when Ak takes on different values. The locus of the root when Ak is varied is depicted in Fig. 5-11. When Ak is positive and greater than one, the root moves into the right

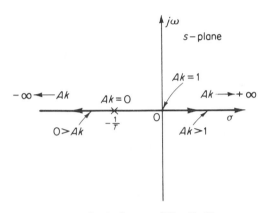

FIG. 5-11. Loci of roots of Eq. (5–42).

half of the s-plane, the impulse response diverges, and the system is unstable. In general, the relation between the location of the characteristic equation roots and the system transient response is apparent, since the roots with positive real parts will give rise to exponential time functions which increase with time, and those in the left half of the s-plane correspond to exponential-decay time functions.

As a second example, consider that two stages of the amplifier shown in Fig. 5-9 are connected in cascade and feedback is applied across the over-all circuit. Without feedback ($k = 0$), the transfer function of the two-stage amplifier is simply

$$\frac{E_0}{E_s} = \frac{A^2}{(1 + sT)^2} \qquad (5\text{--}43)$$

where A and T are as given in Eqs. (5–35) and (5–36). The inverse Laplace transform of $E_0(s)/E_s(s)$ is obtained from the Laplace transform table in Appendix A. Thus

$$g(t) = \mathscr{L}^{-1}\left(\frac{E_0}{E_s}\right) = \frac{A^2}{T^2} t e^{-t/T} \qquad (5\text{--}44)$$

Without feedback, the amplifier is stable since, with $k = 0$, $g(t)$ approaches zero as time approaches infinity. A sketch of the impulse response $g(t)$ is shown in Fig. 5-12.

When feedback is applied, the over-all transfer function of the amplifier is

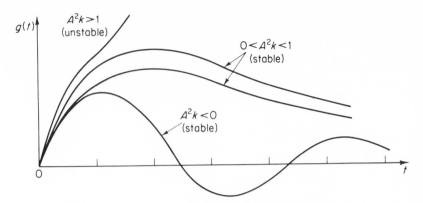

FIG. 5-12. Time responses showing the effect of feedback.

$$\frac{E_0}{E_s}(s) = \frac{A^2/(1 + sT)^2}{1 - A^2k/(1 + sT)^2} = \frac{A^2}{T^2s^2 + 2Ts + (1 - A^2k)} \qquad (5\text{--}45)$$

The characteristic equation of the amplifier with feedback, obtained by setting the denominator of Eq. (5–45) equal to zero, is

$$T^2s^2 + 2Ts + (1 - A^2k) = 0 \qquad (5\text{--}46)$$

Since Eq. (5–46) is a quadratic equation of s, its two roots will be located in the left half of the s-plane so long as the coefficients of the equation are all of the same sign; otherwise, at least one of the roots will be found in the right half of the s-plane. The two roots of the characteristic equation are given by

$$s_{1,2} = -\frac{1}{T} \pm \frac{1}{2}\sqrt{\frac{4A^2k}{T^2}} \qquad (5\text{--}47)$$

Figure 5-13 shows how the roots vary with different values for A^2k. When

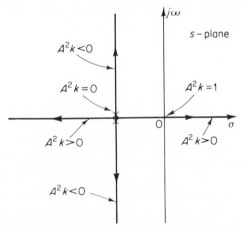

FIG. 5-13. Loci of roots of Eq. (5–47)

A^2k is positive (negative feedback), the two roots are real; the over-all transfer function in Eq. (5–45) can be written as

$$\frac{E_0}{E_s}(s) = \frac{A^2}{T^2} \frac{1}{(s + a)(s + b)} \tag{5-48}$$

where

$$a = \frac{1}{T}(1 + A\sqrt{k}) \tag{5-49}$$

$$b = \frac{1}{T}(1 - A\sqrt{k}) \tag{5-50}$$

The impulse response of the system is the inverse Laplace transform of E_0/E_s in Eq. (5–48). Therefore,

$$g(t) = \frac{A}{2T\sqrt{k}}(e^{-bt} - e^{-at}) \tag{5-51}$$

For $0 < A^2k < 1$, the impulse response is convergent, since a and b are all positive constants. For A^2k greater than unity, b is negative and the impulse response is divergent. The stable and unstable responses are depicted in Fig. 5-12.

When A^2k is negative, the roots s_1 and s_2 in Eq. (5–47) are complex. In this case, the inverse Laplace transform of Eq. (5–45) is obtained from the transform table:

$$g(t) = \frac{A}{T} \frac{1}{\sqrt{k}} e^{-t/T} \sin\left(\frac{A\sqrt{k}}{T}\right)t \tag{5-52}$$

which is of the form of a damped sinusoid. The frequency of the damped oscillation is $A\sqrt{k}/T$ rad/sec.

From the two illustrative examples just given, it is seen that the impulse responses of the amplifiers without feedback are always convergent (stable). But when negative feedback is applied, if the loop gain exceeds unity, the feedback amplifier will become unstable. Therefore, although negative feedback generally gives improved characteristics for sensitivity, distortion, and others mentioned previously, it does have an adverse effect on system stability.

5.3 Mathematical Definition of Feedback[1, 3]

The reason that the existence and effects of feedback have been so vividly illustrated by the examples in the preceding section is that we have considered only simple system configurations which can be represented by the single-loop diagram of Fig. 5-1. Since the forward path A and the feedback path β are readily identified in these simple systems, the effect of feedback on system characteristics is evaluated without much difficulty. However, not all systems have apparent feedback structures; the A and β paths are not apparent in systems with complex configurations (such as a multiple-loop system). Therefore, it is necessary to derive a set of mathematical definitions for feedback which will be general enough to be used on systems of any complexity.

In general, a qualitative measure of feedback with reference to a given element of a system is given by the quantities termed the "return ratio" and the "return difference."[1] The definitions of these terms can be made general enough by considering the signal flow graph shown in Fig. 5-14a.

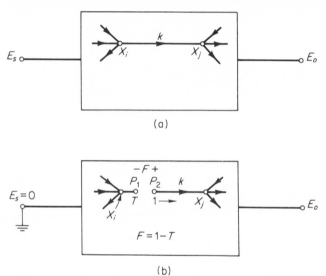

(a)

(b)

FIG. 5-14. (a) Signal flow graph for any arbitrary system; k is an element that appears as a gain in only one branch; (b) Signal flow graph with the input end of the branch containing k opened.

The signal flow graph is drawn in a very general sense; only the input and the output nodes are shown (of course, it may be extended to systems with several input and output nodes). We assume that the element k appears as the transmittance or gain of a branch between two nodes, for example, x_i and x_j (k does not appear anywhere else in the flow graph). The return ratio and return difference are defined as follows:

(1) The branch with transmittance k is broken at the beginning of the branch. Effectively, we have introduced two new nodes, P_1 and P_2, at either side of the break (see Fig. 5-14b). That is, $E_s = 0$.

(2) The input node is grounded; that is, $E_s = 0$.

(3) A signal of unity strength is transmitted from node P_2, and the signal returning to node P_1 is measured. The returned signal at P_1 is obtained by considering P_2 to be the input node and P_1 to be the output node and applying Mason's signal flow graph formula.

(4) The ratio of the returned to the transmitted signal is the return ratio for the element k, and is denoted by T_k.

(5) The return difference for the element k, denoted by F_k, is the difference between the transmitted and the returned signal, or

$$F_k = 1 - T_k \tag{5–53}$$

A general expression can be derived for the return difference by use of Mason's formula. Let Δ be the determinant of the flow graph shown in Fig. 5-14a, i.e., when the branch containing k is not broken. Since k is considered to appear as a gain factor only in one branch, we can factor out k and all the terms that are associated with k from Δ, so that Δ is written

$$\Delta = \Delta^0 + k \sum_q M_q \Delta_q^0 \tag{5–54}$$

where Δ^0 represents the terms in Δ that do not contain k, or simply

$$\Delta^0 = \Delta \mid_{k=0} \tag{5–55}$$

and M_q = gain of the qth forward path between node i and node j with the k-branch opened (Fig. 5-14b).

Δ_q^0 = determinant of the part of the flow graph not touching the qth forward path between node i and node j when the k-branch is opened (Fig. 5-14b).

It should be noted here that the requirement that k appear only in one branch is necessary only from the point of view of interpreting F physically. Mathematically, Eq. (5–54) is true if k appears in more than one branch provided that it appears as first-order gain factors. This condition also carries over to the validity of the formula of F which will be given in Eq. (5–58).

According to the definition of return ratio, T_k is obtained by applying Mason's formula to the signal flow graph of Fig. 5-14b between node P_2 (input) and node P_1 (output). We have

$$T_k = \frac{-k \sum_q M_q \Delta_q^0}{\Delta^0} \tag{5–56}$$

The return difference is obtained from Eq. (5–53):

$$F_k = 1 - \frac{-k \sum_q M_q \Delta_q^0}{\Delta^0} = \frac{\Delta^0 + k \sum_q M_q \Delta_q^0}{\Delta^0} \tag{5–57}$$

Hence

$$F_k = \frac{\Delta}{\Delta^0} \tag{5–58}$$

Therefore, the return difference for an element k in a system is equal to the ratio of the values assumed by the signal flow graph determinant when the specified element has its normal value and when the element vanishes. Equation (5–58) expresses F_k in terms of the determinant of the system flow graph, which can normally be evaluated by inspection. The formula for

F thus represents one of the most convenient working formulas for the analytic treatment of feedback.

Let us now illustrate the usefulness of F_k by means of the single-loop structure shown in Fig. 5–15. In the system, A is considered to be the specific

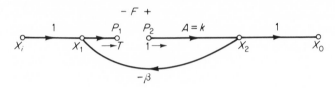

FIG. 5-15. Single loop feedback structure illustrating the return difference.

element for which feedback will be measured. The branch containing A is broken at the input end and a unit signal is sent into node P_2; the returned signal at node P_1 is $A\beta$. Hence

$$T_A = A\beta \tag{5-59}$$

In this simple structure the return ratio is shown to be equal to the loop gain. The return difference for A is

$$F_A = 1 - T_A = 1 - A\beta \tag{5-60}$$

This is the factor by which the sensitivity, impedance, bandwidth, and over-all gain are increased or decreased on account of the presence of feedback in the simple systems shown in the last section. Therefore, for simple cases at least, the return difference is a direct measure of feedback.

The calculation of the return difference for a practical system is given in the following examples.

Example 5-1. Consider the simple amplifier circuit shown in Fig. 5-16a. The return difference for the amplification factor μ of the tube is to be determined. The network equations for the construction of a signal flow graph are

$$E_g = E_s - IR_k \tag{5-61}$$

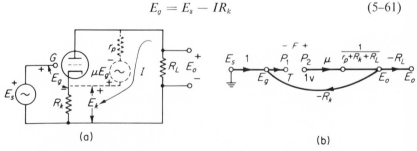

(a)   (b)

FIG. 5-16. (a) Amplifier circuit; (b) Signal flow graph for the evaluation of F_μ.

$$I = \frac{\mu E_g}{r_p + R_k + R_L} \tag{5-62}$$

$$E_0 = -IR_L \tag{5-63}$$

The signal flow graph with the element μ appearing as a gain factor in only one branch is depicted in Fig. 5-16b. In this case, it appears that the easiest way to find F_k is to use Eq. (5-58). The determinant of the flow graph is obtained by inspection.

$$\Delta = 1 + \frac{\mu R_k}{r_p + R_k + R_L} \tag{5-64}$$

and

$$\Delta^0 = \Delta \mid_{\mu=0} = 1 \tag{5-65}$$

Hence

$$F_\mu = \frac{\Delta}{\Delta_0} = \frac{r_p + R_L + (1 + \mu)R_k}{r_p + R_k + R_L} \tag{5-66}$$

The same solution can also be arrived at by following the definitions of T_μ and F_μ. As shown in Fig. 5-16b, the input node is grounded ($E_s = 0$) and the input end of the μ branch is broken; a signal of unity strength is transmitted from node P_2. (In this case, since the input node of μ is E_g, the transmitted signal is 1 volt.) The returned signal at P_1, or the return ratio, is

$$T_\mu = -\frac{\mu R_k}{r_p + R_k + R_L} \tag{5-67}$$

which apparently will lead to the same result for F_μ as appeared in Eq. (5-66).

Example 5-2. As a second example, the return difference for the cathode resistor R_k in the circuit used in the last example is to be determined. The signal flow graph depicted in Fig. 5-16b cannot be used in this case, since R_k does not appear as a gain factor in one branch. We may rewrite the system equations as

$$E_g = E_s - E_k \tag{5-68}$$

$$I = \frac{\mu E_g - E_k}{r_p + R_L} \tag{5-69}$$

$$E_k = IR_k \tag{5-70}$$

$$E_0 = -IR_L \tag{5-71}$$

The signal flow graph representing the last four equations is now drawn in Fig. 5-17, and R_k appears only in one branch. Hence

$$F_{R_k} = \frac{\Delta}{\Delta^0} = \frac{1 + \dfrac{R_k}{r_p + R_L} + \dfrac{\mu R_k}{r_p + R_L}}{1} = \frac{r_p + R_L + (1 + \mu)R_k}{r_p + R_L} \tag{5-72}$$

From the return ratio concept, a signal of one ampere is transmitted into

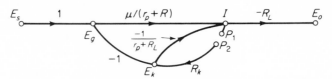

FIG. 5-17. A signal flow graph of the circuit in Fig. 5–16, with R_k isolated in one branch.

node P_2 (since the node represents current I), and the return current I at node P_1 is measured. The return ratio is

$$T_{R_k} = -\frac{R_k}{r_p + R_L} - \frac{\mu R_k}{r_p + R_L} \qquad (5\text{-}73)$$

Physical Interpretation of Return Difference and Return Ratio

We have illustrated in the last two examples how the return differences for an active element (μ of a tube) and a passive element (cathode resistor) are determined. We may then ask the question: What is the physical meaning of "return difference of the μ of a tube" or "return difference of R_k"? The concept of return difference and return ratio in terms of the signal flow graph is clear, but it seems that an interpretation of F and T in terms of the physical elements is still desirable.

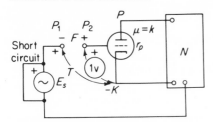

FIG. 5-18. Circuit for physical interpretation of F_μ.

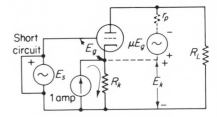

FIG. 5-19. Circuit for physical interpretation of F_{R_k}.

The physical interpretation of T_μ may be illustrated by referring to Fig. 5-18. The vacuum tube in which we are interested is isolated from the rest of the network. The grid lead of the tube is broken at P_1 and P_2, and a voltage of one volt is applied across the grid-cathode terminals P_2K. The voltage returning to P_1 and measured across P_1K is termed the return voltage. Since the transmitted signal is one volt, the return voltage is also equal to the return ratio T_μ. The return difference for μ is obtained readily by taking the difference between the transmitted and the returned voltages.

The return difference for a passive element has the following significance. With reference to Fig. 5-19, a current of one ampere is injected into R_k; this is equivalent to placing across R_k a generator of R_k volts with the polarities as shown. The return current I is measured and is numerically equal to T_{R_k}. In the circuit, E_s is zero; E_g equals $- R_k$ volts; the return current is

$$I = -\frac{(1 + \mu)R_k}{r_p + R_L} = T_{R_k} \tag{5-74}$$

which agrees with the result given by Eq. (5-73). Notice that, since the voltage across R_k is considered a source, R_k itself is not used in the loop impedance.

In a similar manner the physical interpretation of T for a transistor is shown in Fig. 5-20.

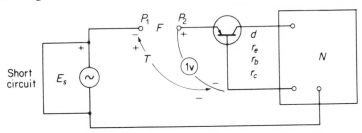

FIG. 5-20. Physical interpretation of T and F for a transistor circuit.

Example 5-3. We shall use this example to illustrate the evaluation of the return ratio and return difference for a transistor circuit. Shown in Fig. 5-21a is a simple transistor amplifier whose equivalent circuit is shown in Fig. 5-21b.

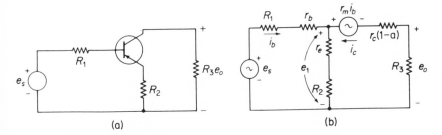

FIG. 5-21. A transistor amplifier circuit and its equivalent circuit.

The network equations using branch currents and node voltages as indicated on the circuit diagram are

$$i_b = \frac{1}{R_1 + r_b}(e_s - e_1) \tag{5-75}$$

$$e_1 = (r_e + R_2)(i_b + i_c) \tag{5-76}$$

$$i_c = \frac{1}{r_c(1 - a)}(-e_1 + r_m i_b + e_0) \tag{5-77}$$

$$e_0 = -R_3 i_c \tag{5-78}$$

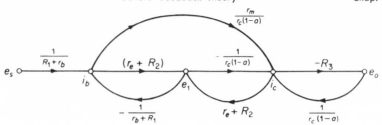

FIG. 5-22. A signal flow graph of the transistor amplifier circuit in Fig. 5-21.

The signal flow graph based on these four equations is now drawn in Fig. 5-22.

The determinant of the signal flow graph is now obtained in the usual manner.

$$\Delta = \frac{r_c(1-a)(R_1+r_b) + (r_e+R_2)r_c(1-a) + (R_1+r_b)(R_2+r_e+R_3) + (r_e+R_2)(R_3+r_m)}{r_c(1-a)(R_1+r_b)}$$

$$\Delta = \frac{r_c(1-a)(R_1+r_b+r_e+R_2) + (R_1+r_b)(R_2+r_e+R_3) + (r_e+R_2)(R_3+r_m)}{r_c(1-a)(R_1+r_b)} \quad (5\text{-}79)$$

Let us now define

$$\Delta^0 = \Delta|_{r_m=0} \quad (5\text{-}80)$$

Then, the return difference for r_m is

$$F_{r_m} = \frac{\Delta}{\Delta^0} = \frac{r_c(1-a)(R_1+r_b+r_e+R_2) + (R_1+r_b)(R_2+r_e+R_3) + (r_e+R_2)(R_3+r_m)}{r_c(1-a)(R_1+r_b+r_e+R_2) + (R_1+r_b)(R_2+r_e+R_3) + (r_e+R_2)R_3} \quad (5\text{-}81)$$

In a similar manner, we can evaluate the return difference for any other circuit parameter such as r_e, R_1, R_2, a, etc.

In the signal flow graph of Fig. 5-22, since r_m appears only in one branch as a branch gain, it is again possible to obtain T_{r_m} and F_{r_m} by breaking up the input end of the branch containing r_m, and to proceed to send a signal of unity strength through and to measure the returned signal.

5.4 The Sensitivity Function[1]

The simple illustrations given in Sec. 5.3 clearly indicate that system sensitivity is quantitatively measured by the return difference. A general relation between sensitivity and return difference can be established from the general signal flow graph of Fig. 5-14. The sensitivity of the over-all gain with respect to a given parameter k has been defined in Eq. (5-2):

$$S_k^M = \frac{d \ln M}{d \ln k} \tag{5-82}$$

where

$$M = \frac{\sum_m M_m \Delta_m}{\Delta} \quad \text{(Mason's formula)} \tag{5-83}$$

is the over-all gain of the system. Substitution of Eq. (5–83) into Eq. (5–82) yields

$$S_k^M = \frac{d\left(\dfrac{\ln \sum_m M_m \Delta_m}{\ln \Delta}\right)}{d \ln k} \tag{5-84}$$

or

$$S_k^M = \frac{d \ln \left(\sum_m M_m \Delta_m\right)}{d \ln k} - \frac{d \ln \Delta}{d \ln k} \tag{5-85}$$

Equation (5–85) can be written

$$S_k^M = \frac{d \sum_m M_m \Delta_m}{dk} \frac{k}{\sum_m M_m \Delta_m} - \frac{d\Delta}{dk} \frac{k}{\Delta} \tag{5-86}$$

In this analysis we assume that the specific element k appears only as a first-order gain factor in a number of branches (again, as described in the last section, it is not necessary that k appear only in one branch); then $d\Delta/dk$ represents the value of Δ with only the terms containing k retained. Using the notation defined in Eq. (5–54), we have

$$\frac{d\Delta}{dk} = \sum_q M_q \Delta_q^0 \tag{5-87}$$

where M_q and Δ_q^0 have been defined previously. Hence, from Eq. (5–54),

$$k\frac{d\Delta}{dk} = k \sum_q M_q \Delta_q^0 = \Delta - \Delta^0 \tag{5-88}$$

For similar reasons, we can write

$$k\frac{d\left(\sum_m M_m \Delta_m\right)}{dk} = \sum_m M_m \Delta_m - \left(\sum_m M_m \Delta_m\right)^0 \tag{5-89}$$

where

$$\left(\sum_m M_m \Delta_m\right)^0 = \sum_m M_m \Delta_m \Big|_{k=0} \tag{5-90}$$

Substituting Eqs. (5–88) and (5–89) into Eq. (5–86), we have

$$S_k^M = \frac{\sum_m M_m \Delta_m - \left(\sum_m M_m \Delta_m\right)^0}{\sum_m M_m \Delta_m} - \frac{\Delta - \Delta^0}{\Delta} \tag{5-91}$$

Simplifying gives

$$S_k^M = \frac{\Delta^0}{\Delta} - \frac{\left(\sum_m M_m \Delta_m\right)^0}{\sum_m M_m \Delta_m} \tag{5-92}$$

or

$$S_k^M = \frac{\Delta^0}{\Delta}\left(1 - \frac{\left(\sum_m M_m \Delta_m\right)^0/\Delta^0}{\sum_m M_m \Delta_m/\Delta}\right) \tag{5-93}$$

Therefore, the sensitivity for the over-all gain with respect to k is

$$S_k^M = \frac{1}{F_k}\left(1 - \frac{M^0}{M}\right) \tag{5-94}$$

and

$$M_0 = M\,|\,_{k=0} \tag{5-95}$$

is sometimes termed the *direct transmission* between the input and output of the system; M^0 is the over-all gain when all the branches containing k are broken. When the direct transmission is zero, Eq. (5–94) becomes

$$S_k^M = \frac{1}{F_k} \tag{5-96}$$

and the sensitivity is inversely proportional to the return difference.

As an example of the calculation of sensitivity, the sensitivity functions of the over-all gain, with respect to μ and R_k in the circuit of Fig. 5-16a, are determined as follows: With reference to the flow graph in Fig. 5-16b, when μ vanishes, the direct transmission M^0 is zero (there is no transmission between V_s and V_0 when P_1 and P_2 are broken). Therefore,

$$S_\mu^M = \frac{1}{F_\mu} = \frac{r_p + R_k + R_L}{r_p + R_L + (1 + \mu)R_k} \tag{5-97}$$

In order to determine $S_{R_k}^M$, we refer to the flow graph in Fig. 5-17. The over-all gain of the flow graph is

$$M = \frac{-\mu R_L}{r_p + R_L + (1 + \mu)R_k} \tag{5-98}$$

In this case, the direct transmission is not zero; it is

$$M^0 = M\,|\,_{R_k=0} = \frac{-\mu R_L}{r_p + R_L} \tag{5-99}$$

Thus,

$$S_{R_k}^M = \frac{1}{F_{R_k}}\left(1 - \frac{M^0}{M}\right) = \frac{-(1 + \mu)R_k}{r_p + R_L + (1 + \mu)R_k} \tag{5-100}$$

5.5 Impedance and Admittance Functions

It has been shown that feedback has definite effects on impedances seen by looking into a system at various points. For this reason, it is a common practice to introduce feedback into certain types of systems for the purpose of controlling impedances.

In a very general way, the impedance function (or the admittance function) can be regarded as a cause-and-effect relation between two specific variables. If we bear the cause-and-effect concept in mind, the understanding of the significance of impedance and admittance functions and the means of controlling them will be greatly enhanced. The definition of driving point and transfer impedances and admittances based on the cause-and-effect

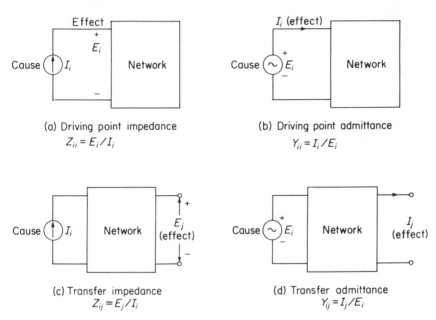

(a) Driving point impedance
$Z_{ii} = E_i / I_i$

(b) Driving point admittance
$Y_{ii} = I_i / E_i$

(c) Transfer impedance
$Z_{ij} = E_j / I_i$

(d) Transfer admittance
$Y_{ij} = I_j / E_i$

FIG. 5-23. Cause-and-effect concept of impedance and admittance functions.

relation are illustrated in Fig. 5-23. For example, in Fig. 5-23a the driving point impedance of the network between input terminals is defined as the cause-and-effect relation between the current source, which acts as the cause, and the voltage appearing across the terminals, which is regarded as the effect (with all other external sources replaced by their internal impedances). Thus

$$\text{Driving point impedance } Z_{ii} = \frac{E_i \text{ (effect)}}{I_i \text{ (cause)}} \tag{5-101}$$

The other impedance and admittance functions, depicted in Fig. 5-23b, c, and d, are defined in similar fashions.

It is important to note that the cause-and-effect view of impedance and admittance functions is exactly analogous to the foundation of signal flow graphs, a fact which suggests that the signal flow graph method can be used for the evaluation of impedance and admittance functions. For example, to determine the driving point impedance Z_{ii} of Fig. 5-23a, I_i is denoted as the input node and E_i as the output node of the network signal flow graph, and Z_{ii} is readily determined by applying Mason's formula.

One of the important considerations in the design of control systems is the minimization of the effect of the external disturbances which may occur at various points of a system. The term disturbance is used here to include any extraneous effect, such as the variation of load impedance of an amplifier, gusts of wind against a radar antenna, and others, which usually have harmful effects on the performance of a control system. In general, if the effect ratio-disturbance (cause) is dimensionally an impedance or an admittance, the minimization of the effect/cause ratio may be realized by controlling the impedance or admittance level at the point (or points) of interest. For example, changes in load impedance at the output of an electronic amplifier usually cause the amplifier output voltage to vary. In this case, the variation in the load current represents disturbance (cause), and the effect is the corresponding variation in the output voltage; thus, the output impedance of the amplifier is a direct measure of the disturbance effect and should be kept small. Gusts of wind against a radar antenna are disturbances in the forms of torques, and they can cause large oscillations in the antenna position. In such a case, the output velocity (effect) to disturbance (cause) ratio may be regarded as the mechanical output admittance of the system and should be kept small. In general, the effect of disturbance and noise signal in any signal system can be evaluated either as driving point or as transfer immittances,* depending upon the location of the cause and effects.

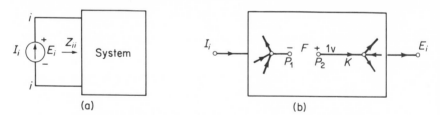

FIG. 5-24. (a) Driving point impedance of a system; (b) Signal flow graph for system in (a).

Consider that the impedance into a pair of terminals designated as i-i' of the system shown in Fig. 5-24a is desired (with all external signal sources replaced by their internal impedances). A signal flow graph may be constructed for the system with I_i as the input node and E_i the resultant voltage between the two terminals, as the output node. A general flow graph configuration is shown in Fig. 5-24b.

The driving point impedance seen into terminals i-i' is readily obtained from the signal flow graph of Fig. 5-24b by means of Mason's formula; that is,

*The term *immittance* is used to represent impedance or admittance.

$$Z_{ii} = \frac{\sum_m M_m \Delta_m}{\Delta} \qquad (5\text{-}102)$$

where the equation represents the gain between nodes I_i and V_i. In general, the same method can be applied to the determination of transfer impedance or admittances. It is possible to express the impedance (or admittance) functions in terms of the feedback properties of the system; namely, the return difference. Equation (5-102) is written

$$Z_{ii} = \frac{\sum_m M_m \Delta_m}{\Delta} \frac{\Delta^0}{\Delta^0} \frac{\left(\sum_m M_m \Delta_m\right)^0}{\left(\sum_m M_m \Delta_m\right)^0} \qquad (5\text{-}103)$$

Rearranging, we have

$$Z_{ii} = \frac{\left(\sum_m M_m \Delta_m\right)^0}{\Delta^0} \frac{\sum_m M_m \Delta_m}{\left(\sum_m M_m \Delta_m\right)^0} \frac{\Delta^0}{\Delta} \qquad (5\text{-}104)$$

The first term in the last equation is identified as the direct transmission between I_i and E_i, that is, the transmission when the element k is equal to zero. Hence

$$Z_{ii}^0 \text{ (direct transmission)} = (Z_{ii})_{k=0} = \frac{\left(\sum_m M_m \Delta_m\right)^0}{\Delta^0} \qquad (5\text{-}105)$$

The last term of Eq. (5-104) is simply the inverse of the return difference for k, where k can be any element of the system, passive or active. Therefore, Eq. (5-104) can be written

$$Z_{ii} = Z_{ii}^0 \frac{1}{F_k} \frac{\sum_m M_m \Delta_m}{\left(\sum_m M_m \Delta_m\right)^0} \qquad (5\text{-}106)$$

Equation (5-106) is similar to the following expression given by Bode:[1]

$$Z = Z(0)\frac{F_k(0)}{F_k(\infty)} \qquad (5\text{-}107)$$

where $F_k(\infty)$ denotes the return difference for k with the terminals $i\text{-}i'$ open (the normal F_k in this case), and $F_k(0)$ denotes the return difference for k with the terminals $i\text{-}i'$ shorted; $F_k(0)$ is given the name *null return difference*. The corresponding Z's in Eqs. (5-106) and (5-107) have the same meaning; therefore,

$$F(0) = \frac{\sum_m M_m \Delta_m}{\left(\sum_m M_m \Delta_m\right)^0} \qquad (5\text{-}108)$$

To prove this equation, let us refer to the signal flow graph in Fig. 5-24b. The terminals at P_1 and P_2 are opened in front of the element k (again, there may be more than one branch having k as a multiplying factor as far as the validity of Eqs. (5-106) and (5-108) is concerned). The null return difference $F_k(0)$ is defined as the return difference for the element k when the terminals

i-i' are shorted; that is, E_i is zero. It should be noted, however, that, unlike the process of evaluating F_k [or $F_k(\infty)$], the input I_i is not set to zero; it is, rather, set at a specific value, so that the zero E_i condition is realized. In terms of the signal flow graph shown in Fig. 5-24b, the desired value for I_i is determined as follows: A unit signal is transmitted from node P_2; this and the signal I_i should contribute to zero E_i. Therefore,

$$\frac{\sum M_{P_2 E_i} \Delta_{P_2 E_i} + I_i (\sum M_m \Delta_m)^0}{\Delta^0} = 0 \tag{5-109}$$

where the first term represents the unit signal times the transmission between nodes P_2 and E_i, and the second term is the product of I_i and the direct transmission between I_i and E_i. From Eq. (5-109), we have

$$I_i = \frac{-\sum M_{P_2 E_i} \Delta_{P_2 E_i}}{(\sum M_m \Delta_m)^0} \tag{5-110}$$

According to the definition of the null return difference, the null return ratio for k is equal to the signal which appears at node P_1 when a unit signal is transmitted from P_2 with the simultaneous application of I_i, whose value is given by Eq. (5-110). The null return ratio is

$$T_k(0) = \frac{I_i \sum M_{I_i P_1} \Delta_{I_i P_1} - k(d\Delta/dk)}{\Delta^0} \tag{5-111}$$

where the first term on the right side denotes the product of I_i and the transmission between I_i and P_1, and the second term is the transmission from node P_2 to P_1. Substituting Eqs. (5-88) and (5-110) into Eq. (5-111) and simplifying, we write the null return difference

$$F_k(0) = 1 - T_k(0) = \frac{\sum M_{I_i P_1} \Delta_{I_i P_1} \sum M_{P_2 E_i} \Delta_{P_2 E_i} + \Delta(\sum M_m \Delta_m)^0}{(M_m \Delta_m)^0 \Delta^0} \tag{5-112}$$

But the over-all transmission of the signal flow graph of Fig. 5-24b can be written as

$$\frac{\sum M_m \Delta_m}{\Delta} = \frac{\sum M_{I_i P_1} \Delta_{I_i P_1}}{\Delta} \times \frac{\sum M_{P_2 E_i} \Delta_{P_2 E_i}}{\Delta^0} + \frac{(\sum M_m \Delta_m)^0}{\Delta^0} \tag{5-113}$$

Hence, Eq. (5-112) reads

$$F_k(0) = \frac{\sum M_m \Delta_m}{(\sum M_m \Delta_m)^0} \tag{5-114}$$

Similarly, the admittance seen looking into any pair of terminals of a system (with all external sources replaced by their internal admittances) is calculated by using the voltage between the terminals as the input, and the current as the output. In terms of the admittance functions, Eq. (5-107) is written as

$$Y = Y(0) \frac{F_k(0)}{F_k(\infty)} \tag{5-115}$$

,where $Y(0)$ = admittance seen looking into the terminals when $k = 0$.

$F_k(0)$ = return difference for k when the terminals are open (zero admittance); equal to the normal F_k.

$F_k(\infty)$ = return difference for k when the terminals are shorted (infinite admittance); equal to the null return difference.

The feedback amplifier circuit shown in Fig. 5-8 is used here to illustrate the calculation of the impedance into terminals a–a' (output impedance). The amplification factor (μ) of the tube is taken as the reference element k.

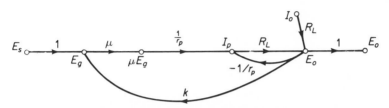

FIG. 5-25. Signal flow graph for feedback amplifier in Fig. 5-8.

The signal flow graph of the system is drawn in Fig. 5-25; the current I_0 is introduced for the purpose of computing the output impedance. Applying Mason's formula directly to the flow graph with I_0 as the input and E_0 as the output (E_s is shorted), we find that the output impedance of the amplifier is

$$Z_a(Z_{\text{out}}) = \frac{r_p R_L}{r_p + R_L(1 + \mu k)} \tag{5-116}$$

This result can also be obtained by use of Eq. (5-107). The impedance seen between a–a' when μ is zero is

$$Z(0) = \frac{r_p R_L}{r_p + R_L} \tag{5-117}$$

The return difference for μ when the terminals a–a' are open is

$$F(\infty) = \frac{\Delta}{\Delta^0} = \frac{r_p + R_L(1 + \mu k)}{r_p + R_L} \tag{5-118}$$

The return difference for μ when the terminals a–a' are shorted is

$$F(0) = 1 \tag{5-119}$$

since there is no feedback with output terminals shorted. Thus,

$$Z_a(Z_{\text{out}}) = Z(0)\frac{F_k(0)}{F_k(\infty)} = \frac{r_p R_L}{r_p + R_L(1 + \mu k)} \tag{5-120}$$

which agrees with the result given by Eq. (5-116).

REFERENCES

1. H. W. Bode, *Network Analysis and Feedback Amplifier Design*, D. Van Nostrand Company, Inc., New York, N. Y., 1945.

2. H. W. Bode, "Feedback—The History of an Idea," *Proc. of the Symposium on Active Networks and Feedback Systems*, Polytechnic Institute of Brooklyn, pp. 1–17, 1960.

3. W. A. Lynch and J. G. Truxal, *Principles of Electronic Instrumentation*, McGraw-Hill Book Company, New York, N. Y., 1962.

PROBLEMS

5-1. In Fig. 5P-1:
  (a) Find the return difference F_k for $k = \mu$.
  (b) Find the return difference F_k for $k = R_k$.
  (c) Show that $F_\mu = F_{g_m}$.

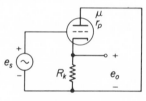

FIG. 5P-1.

5-2. Determine the relationship between $F_{k\,\text{mesh}}$ and $F_{k\,\text{node}}$ for $k = $ bilateral passive element; $F_{k\,\text{mesh}}$ represents return difference for k, evaluated by mesh method, and $F_{k\,\text{node}}$ is F_k obtained by node method.

5-3. Determine the return difference for R_4 (F_{R_4}) in Fig. 5P-3 by use of the signal flow graph method. Check the result by means of the physical meaning of F_k.

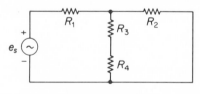

FIG. 5P-3.

5-4. For the circuit shown in Fig. 5P-4, determine the sensitivity function S_k^M, where $M = e_0/e_s$ and $k = X_c/R_2 = 1/\omega C R_2$. Give the significance of this sensitivity function. Assume $R_2 \gg R_1$.

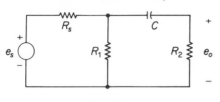

FIG. 5P-4.

5-5. For the amplifier circuit shown in Fig. 5P-1, determine

$$S_\mu^M, S_{R_k}^M, \text{ and } S_{r_p}^M$$

where

$$M = e_0/e_s.$$

Use signal flow graph technique.

5-6. The network shown in Fig. 5P-6 has an external source at the kth node. Y_L is an admittance located at the nth node.

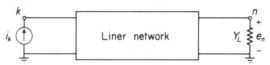

FIG. 5P-6.

Prove that $\dfrac{e_n(Y_L = 0)}{e_n(Y_L = Y_L)} = F$ (return difference for Y_L)

Δ = determinant of network.

5-7. A feedback amplifier has several tubes and several feedback loops. The impedance seen in a given mesh is to be determined in terms of the passive impedance seen into the mesh. "Passive" means that there are no active elements in the entire circuit. Derive a relation similar to the relationship given by Eq. (5-107) in the text.

5-8. With reference to Fig. 5P-8,

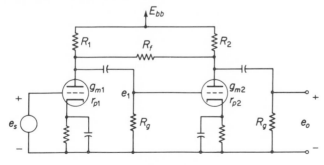

FIG. 5P-8.

(a) Draw the current source mid-band incremental equivalent circuit. Does the amplifier have positive or negative feedback?

(b) Construct a signal flow graph for the amplifier.

(c) Evaluate the following quantities:

$M = e_0/e_s$, $F_{g_{m1}}$, $F_{g_{m2}}$, $S_{g_{m2}}^{M}$ (when g_{m2} is very large)

6

Time Domain Analysis
of Feedback Control Systems

6.1 Introduction

In most control systems, since time is used as an independent variable, it is usually of interest to evaluate the time domain response of the systems. Often a reference input signal is applied to a system, and the behavior of the system is studied as a function of time. If the purpose of the control system is to have the output variable follow the input as closely as possible, it is important to compare the input and the output variables at all times.

The time response of a control system is usually divided into two parts: the *transient response*, and the *steady-state response*. If $c(t)$ is a time response, then, in general,

$$c(t) = c_t(t) + c_{ss}(t) \qquad (6-1)$$

where $c_t(t)$ denotes the transient portion and $c_{ss}(t)$ is the steady-state portion of the response. However, the definition of steady state has not been standardized. In circuit analysis, it is sometimes useful to define steady state as being a constant. In control systems applications, however, when a response has reached its steady state it can still be a function of time. In control systems the steady-state response is simply the response when time reaches infinity. Therefore, a sine wave is considered as a steady state because its behavior does not alter at $t = \infty$.

Transient is defined as the part of the response which goes to zero as time becomes large. Therefore, $c_t(t)$ has the property

$$\lim_{t \to \infty} c_t(t) = 0 \qquad (6-2)$$

In feedback control systems, since inertia and friction are unavoidable, the output response cannot follow a sudden change in the input instantaneously, and a transient is usually observed.

The steady-state response, when compared with the input, gives an indication of the accuracy of the system. If the output steady-state response does not agree with the input exactly, the system is said to have a *steady-state error*.

6.2 Typical Test Input Signals for the Transient Analysis of Feedback Control Systems

In practice, the input excitation to a feedback control system is not known ahead of time. In most cases, the actual inputs vary in random fashions with respect to time. For instance, in a radar tracking system, the position and speed of the target to be tracked may vary in any unpredictable manner, so they cannot be expressed mathematically by any simple equation. However, for the purpose of analysis and design, it is necessary to assume some basic types of input functions so that the performance of a system can be analyzed with at least these test signals. In a design problem, performance criteria are derived with respect to these test signals, and linear systems are designed to meet the criteria.

When the system performance is analyzed in the frequency domain, a sinusoidal input with variable frequency is used. When the input frequency is swept from zero to beyond the significant range of the system characteristics, curves in terms of the amplitude ratio and phase shift between input and output are drawn as functions of frequency. It is possible to predict the time domain behavior of the system from its frequency domain characteristics.

In the time domain analysis, the following test signals are often used:

(1) *Step Displacement Input*

This is the instantaneous change in the reference input variable; e.g., a sudden rotation of an input shaft. The mathematical representation of a step function is

$$r(t) = R \qquad t > 0$$
$$r(t) = 0 \qquad t < 0$$

$$(6\text{--}3)$$

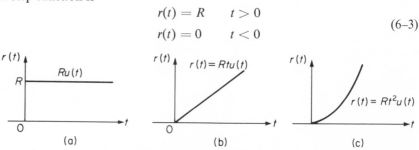

FIG. 6-1. Simple test signals.

where R is a constant. Or

$$r(t) = Ru(t) \tag{6-4}$$

where $u(t)$ is the unit-step function. The function $r(t)$ is not defined at $t = 0$. The step function is shown in Fig. 6-1a.

(2) *Step Velocity Input* (*Ramp Function*)

In this case, the reference input variable is considered to have a constant change in position with respect to time. Mathematically, a ramp function is represented by

$$r(t) = Rt \qquad t > 0$$
$$r(t) = 0 \qquad t < 0 \tag{6-5}$$

or simply

$$r(t) = Rtu(t) \tag{6-6}$$

The ramp function is shown in Fig. 6-1b.

(3) *Acceleration Input* (*Parabolic Function*)

The mathematical representation of an acceleration input is

$$r(t) = Rt^2 \qquad t > 0$$
$$r(t) = 0 \qquad t < 0 \tag{6-7}$$

or simply

$$r(t) = Rt^2 u(t) \tag{6-8}$$

The graphical representation of an acceleration function is shown in Fig. 6-1c.

6.3 Time Domain Performance Characteristics of Feedback Control Systems

(1) *Steady State Performance*

It was mentioned previously that the steady-state error is a measure of the system accuracy when a specific type of input is applied to a feedback control system. In a physical system, because of friction and other related factors, the steady-state output response of a system seldom agrees exactly with the reference input. The steady-state performance of a feedback control system is generally judged by evaluating the steady-state error due to the three typical test signals given above. A detailed study of the steady-state error of feedback control systems will be given in Sec. 6.9.

(2) *Transient Performance*

The transient performance of a feedback control system is normally analyzed by using a unit-step function as the reference input. A typical step

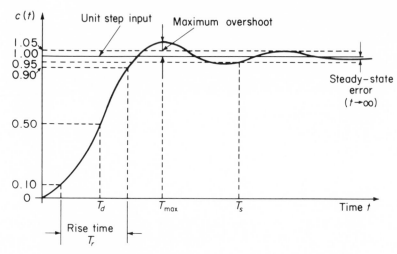

FIG. 6-2. Response to unit step input showing time-domain specifications of feedback control systems.

response is shown in Fig. 6-2. The response is usually characterized by the following quantities:

(a) *Overshoot.* The overshoot is an indication of the largest error between input and output during the transient state. It is also recognized as a measure of the relative stability of a system. The overshoot is often represented as a percentage of the final value; that is,

$$\text{Per cent overshoot} = \frac{\text{Maximum overshoot}}{\text{Final desired value}} \times 100 \qquad (6\text{-}9)$$

(b) *Time delay.* The time delay T_d is normally defined as the time required for the response to reach 50 per cent of the final value.

(c) *Rise time.* The rise time T_r is defined as the time required for the response to rise from 10 per cent to 90 per cent of its final value. Sometimes an equivalent measure is to represent the rise time as the reciprocal of the slope of the response at the instant the response is equal to 50 per cent of its final value.

(d) *Settling time.* The settling time T_s is defined as the time required for the response to decrease to and stay within a specified percentage of its final value. A frequently used figure is 5 per cent.

There are other important quantities, such as the damping ratio, the damping factor, and the undamped natural frequency, which cannot be represented on the time response shown in Fig. 6-2. The significance of these quantities will be discussed in the next section.

6.4 Characteristic Equations of Feedback Control Systems

The characteristic equation of a linear system has been defined in Sec. 3.6 in terms of the system's differential equation, transfer function, and state equations. In this section we shall point out the importance of the characteristic equation of a feedback control system.

Consider that the closed-loop transfer function of a feedback control system is

$$M(s) = \frac{C(s)}{R(s)} = \frac{G(s)}{1 + G(s)H(s)} \qquad (6-10)$$

According to the definition given in Sec. 3.6, the characteristic equation of the feedback control system is obtained by equating the denominator of Eq. (6–10) to zero; that is,

$$1 + G(s)H(s) = 0 \qquad (6-11)$$

Notice that Eq. (6–11) usually is not the characteristic equation, since its left-hand side is a quotient of two polynomials. However, with reference to Eq. (6–11) it is sufficient to say that equating the numerator polynomial of $1 + G(s)H(s)$ to zero gives the characteristic equation.

Consider that a feedback control system (without time lag) is described by the following closed-loop transfer function:

$$M(s) = \frac{C(s)}{R(s)} = \frac{K(s + z_1)(s + z_2) \ldots (s + z_m)}{(s + p_1)(s + p_2) \ldots (s + p_n)} \qquad (6-12)$$

where $-z_1, -z_2, \ldots, -z_m$ are the zeros, and $-p_1, -p_2, \ldots, -p_n$ are the poles of the transfer function; the $-p$'s are also the roots of the characteristic equation. If the transfer function $M(s)$ is a rational function of s, the poles and zeros of $M(s)$ must be real numbers or complex numbers in conjugate pairs. Therefore, Eq. (6–12) can be written as

$$M(s) = \frac{K(s + z_1)(s + z_2) \ldots (s + z_m)}{\displaystyle\prod_{i=1}^{k} (s + \sigma_i) \prod_{j=1}^{q} (s^2 + 2\alpha_j s + \omega_{nj}^2)} \qquad (6-13)*$$

where $(s + \sigma_i)$ represents the k real poles and $(s^2 + 2\alpha_j s + \omega_{nj}^2)$ corresponds to complex conjugate poles.

The response of the system to an input signal $r(t)$ is

$$c(t) = \mathscr{L}^{-1}[C(s)] = \mathscr{L}^{-1}[R(s)M(s)] \qquad (6-14)$$

If $r(t)$ is a unit step function and $M(s)$ is given by Eq. (6–13),

*The Π sign represents product.

$$c(t) = \mathcal{L}^{-1} \left[\frac{K \prod_{j=1}^{m} (s + z_j)}{s \prod_{i=1}^{k} (s + \sigma_i) \prod_{j=1}^{q} (s^2 + 2\alpha_j s + \omega_{nj}^2)} \right] \qquad (6\text{-}15)$$

When expanded by partial fraction expansion, Eq. (6-15) becomes

$$c(t) = \mathcal{L}^{-1} \left[\frac{A}{s} + \sum_{i=1}^{k} \frac{B_i}{(s + \sigma_i)} + \sum_{j=1}^{q} \frac{C_j s + D_j}{s^2 + 2\alpha_j s + \omega_{nj}^2} \right] \qquad (6\text{-}16)$$

where A, B_i, C_j, and D_j are constants which depend on the poles and zeros of $M(s)$. It is assumed that $M(s)$ does not have repeated poles.

From the Laplace transform table, the following transform pairs are identified:

$$\mathcal{L}^{-1} \left[\frac{A}{s} \right] = Au(t) \qquad (6\text{-}17)$$

$$\mathcal{L}^{-1} \left[\frac{1}{s + \sigma_i} \right] = e^{-\sigma_i t} \qquad (6\text{-}18)$$

$$\mathcal{L}^{-1} \left[\frac{as + 1}{s^2 + 2\alpha_j s + \omega_{nj}^2} \right] = E_j e^{-\alpha_j t} \sin (\sqrt{\omega_{nj}^2 - \alpha_j^2}\, t + \phi_j) \qquad (6\text{-}19)$$

where

$$\phi_j = \tan^{-1} \frac{a\sqrt{\omega_n^2 - \alpha_j^2}}{1 - a\alpha_j} \qquad (6\text{-}20)$$

$$E_j = \sqrt{\frac{1 - 2a\alpha_j + a^2 \omega_{nj}^2}{\omega_{nj}^2 - \alpha_j^2}} \qquad (6\text{-}21)$$

Therefore, the output response is

$$c(t) = Au(t) + \sum_{i=1}^{k} B_i e^{-\sigma_i t} + \sum_{j=1}^{q} D_j E_j\, e^{-\alpha_j t} \sin (\sqrt{\omega_{nj}^2 - \alpha_j^2}\, t + \phi_j) \qquad (6\text{-}22)$$

The first term on the right-hand side of Eq. (6-22) is due to the step function input. If σ_i and α_j are all positive real numbers, the exponential terms in Eq. (6-22) will decrease with the increase of time. Then all terms appearing under the summation symbol represent the transient response, and the first term, $Au(t)$, is the steady-state response. However, if any one of the σ_i or α_j coefficients is negative, the output response will increase without bound and the system is said to be unstable. With reference to Eq. (6-13), it is clear that $-\sigma_i$ and $-\alpha_j$ can be referred to as the real parts of the poles of the transfer function $M(s)$, or of the roots of the characteristic equation. Therefore, this demonstrates that the roots of the characteristic equation play an important role on the form of the transient response. It is apparent that if any one of the real roots is positive, i.e., located in the right half of the s-plane, its corresponding exponential term in the transient response will increase monotonically with time; the system is said to be unstable. Similarly, a pair of complex conjugate roots with positive real parts will correspond to a sinusoidal oscillation with increasing amplitude. Hence, we can conclude that for a stable response, the roots of the characteristic equation should not be found in the right half of the s-plane. Roots which are on the imaginary axis correspond to systems with sustained constant amplitude oscillations. The effect on the shape of the exponential and damped sinusoidal responses by various root locations in the s-plane is shown in Fig. 6-3.

From the responses given in Fig. 6-3, it is seen that stable responses

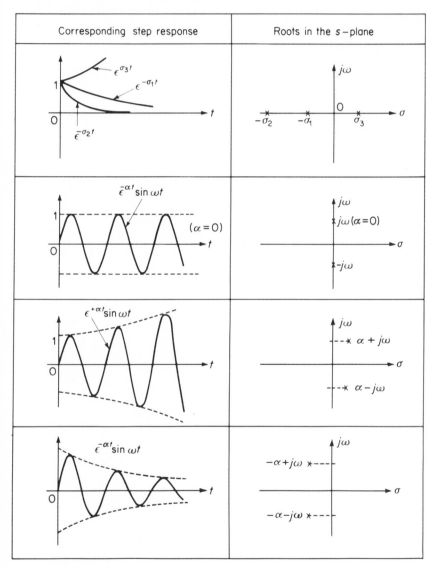

FIG. 6-3. Response comparison for various root locations in the s-plane.

which correspond to roots close to the imaginary axis die out more slowly than do those which correspond to roots that are far away from the imaginary axis. The time required for the decay of the transient response is measured by the horizontal distance from the root to the $j\omega$ axis. The smaller the distance, the more slowly the transient dies out. The roots which are closest to the $j\omega$ axis are sometimes called the *dominant roots* of the characteristic equation, because all other roots will cause transients to decay more rapidly. In feedback control systems, usually the dominant roots are in complex conjugate pairs.

Consider the equation

$$s^2 + 2\alpha s + (\alpha^2 + \omega^2) = 0 \tag{6-23}$$

Normally, it is convenient to write the last equation in the form

$$s^2 + 2\delta\omega_n s + \omega_n^2 = 0 \tag{6-24}$$

The two roots of Eq. (6–24) are

$$s_1, s_2 = -\delta\omega_n \pm j\omega_n\sqrt{1 - \delta^2} = -\alpha \pm j\omega \tag{6-25}$$

where δ = damping ratio.

ω_n = undamped natural frequency = frequency of oscillation when damping is zero ($\delta = 0$), $\omega_n = \sqrt{\alpha^2 + \omega^2}$.

$\alpha = \delta\omega_n$ = damping constant (actual damping).

$\omega = \omega_n\sqrt{1 - \delta^2}$ = conditional frequency.*

In terms of the damping ratio, the roots of the characteristic equation are real if $\delta \geq 1$.

For

$\delta < 1 \quad s_1, s_2 = -\delta\omega_n \pm j\omega_n\sqrt{1 - \delta^2}$ (underdamped case)

$\delta = 1 \quad s_1, s_2 = -\omega_n$ (critical damped case)

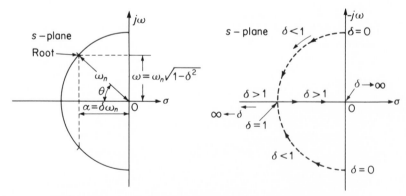

FIG. 6-4. Locus of roots of Eq. (6–24) when the damping ratio is varied from 0 to ∞ (ω_n is held constant).

*Although ω is frequently called the actual frequency of the damped sinusoid, strictly speaking, it is not a true frequency, since a damped sinusoid is not a periodic function.

$$\delta > 1 \qquad s_1, s_2 = -\delta\omega_n \pm \omega_n\sqrt{\delta^2 - 1} \qquad \text{(overdamped case)}$$

$$\delta = 0 \qquad s_1, s_2 = \pm j\omega_n \qquad \text{(undamped case)}$$

If ω_n is held constant and is varied from 0 to ∞, the location of the roots of the characteristic equation will move away from the imaginary axis along a circular path of radius ω_n; the roots will meet at the point $s = -\alpha = -\omega_n$ when $\delta = 1$, and then separate and travel along the real axis toward zero and infinity. This is illustrated in Fig. 6-4.

For complex roots, ω_n is the radial distance from the roots to the origin ($\omega_n = \sqrt{(\alpha^2 + \omega^2)}$). The damping ratio is equal to the cosine of the angle between the radial line to the roots and the negative real axis; i.e.,

$$\delta = \cos\theta \qquad (6-26)$$

6.5 Transient Response of a Second-order System

Consider a feedback control system with the closed-loop transfer function

$$\frac{C(s)}{R(s)} = \frac{\omega_n^2}{s^2 + 2\delta\omega_n s + \omega_n^2} \qquad (6-27)$$

For a unit step function input, the output response of the system is

$$c(t) = \mathscr{L}^{-1}\left[\frac{\omega_n^2}{s(s^2 + 2\delta\omega_n s + \omega_n^2)}\right] \qquad (6-28)$$

The inverse Laplace transform of the last equation is found in the Laplace transform table.

$$c(t) = 1 + \frac{e^{-\delta\omega_n t}}{\sqrt{1 - \delta^2}} \sin\left[\omega_n\sqrt{1 - \delta^2}\, t - \tan^{-1}\frac{\sqrt{1 - \delta^2}}{-\delta}\right] \qquad (6-29)$$

$$(t \geq 0)$$

In Fig. 6-5 is plotted the variation of the output response of the system for various values of damping ratio δ as a function of the normalized time $\omega_n t$. It is seen that the response becomes more oscillatory as δ decreases in value. When $\delta \geq 1$, there is no overshoot in the response; the output response never exceeds the reference input. The exact relation between the damping ratio and the amount of overshoot can be obtained by taking the derivative of Eq. (6-29) and setting it equal to zero. Thus,

$$\frac{dc(t)}{dt} = -\frac{\delta\omega_n e^{-\delta\omega_n t}}{\sqrt{1 - \delta^2}} \sin(\omega t - \phi) + \frac{e^{-\delta\omega_n t}}{\sqrt{1 - \delta^2}} \omega_n\sqrt{1 - \delta^2} \cos(\omega t - \phi) \qquad (6-30)$$

$$(t \geq 0)$$

where

$$\phi = \tan^{-1}\frac{\sqrt{1 - \delta^2}}{-\delta} \qquad (6-31)$$

Equation (6-30) can also be simplified to

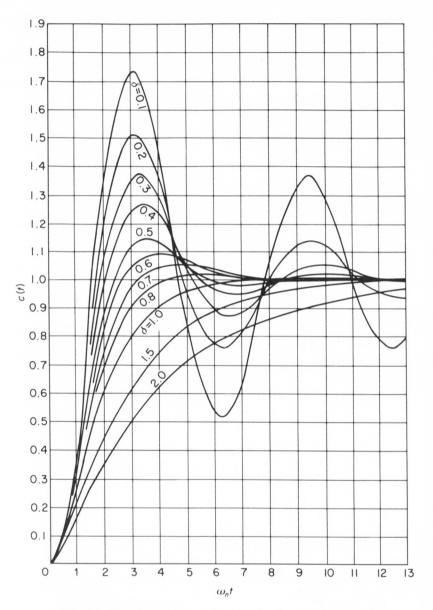

FIG. 6-5. Transient response of a second-order system to a unit step displacement input.

$$\frac{dc(t)}{dt} = \frac{\omega_n}{\sqrt{1 - \delta^2}} e^{-\delta\omega_n t} \sin \omega_n \sqrt{1 - \delta^2} t \qquad (t \geq 0) \qquad (6\text{-}32)$$

Therefore, when $dc(t)/dt = 0$, Eq. (6-32) gives $t = \infty$ and

$$\omega_n \sqrt{1 - \delta^2}\, t = n\pi \qquad (n = 0, 1, 2, \ldots) \qquad (6\text{-}33)$$

or

$$t = \frac{n\pi}{\omega_n \sqrt{1 - \delta^2}} \qquad (6\text{-}34)$$

The first maximum value of the output response $c(t)$ occurs at $n = 1$; hence,

$$t_{\max} = \frac{\pi}{\omega_n \sqrt{1 - \delta^2}} \qquad (6\text{-}35)$$

In general, for all odd values of n, that is, $n = 1, 3, 5, \ldots$, Eq. (6-34) gives the times at which the overshoots occur; for all even values of n, it gives the times at which the undershoots occur (Fig. 6-6). It is interesting

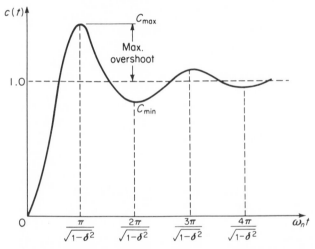

FIG. 6-6. Step response illustrating that the maxima and minima occur at periodic intervals.

to note that, although the maxima and the minima of the response occur at periodic intervals, the damped sinusoid is not a periodic function. The magnitudes of the overshoots and the undershoots can be obtained by substituting Eq. (6-34) into Eq. (6-29). Hence,

$$c(t)\big|_{\max \text{ or } \min} = 1 + \frac{e^{-n\pi\delta/\sqrt{1-\delta^2}}}{\sqrt{1 - \delta^2}} \sin \left(n\pi - \tan^{-1} \frac{\sqrt{1 - \delta^2}}{-\delta} \right) \qquad (6\text{-}36)$$

for $n = 1, 2, 3, \ldots$, or

$$c(t)\big|_{\max \text{ or } \min} = 1 + (-1)^{n-1} e^{-n\pi\delta/\sqrt{1-\delta^2}} \qquad . \qquad (6\text{-}37)$$

The maximum overshoot is obtained by letting $n = 1$ in the last equation.

$$\text{Maximum overshoot} = c_{\max} - 1 = e^{-\pi\delta/\sqrt{1-\delta^2}} \tag{6-38}$$

and

$$\text{Per cent overshoot} = 100\,e^{-\pi\delta/\sqrt{1-\delta^2}} \tag{6-39}$$

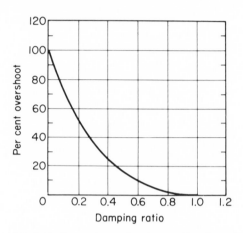

FIG. 6-7. Per cent overshoot as a function of damping ratio for the step displacement response of a second-order system.

Therefore, for a second-order system, the overshoot of the step response is only a function of the damping ratio. The relationship between per cent overshoot and damping ratio for a second-order system is depicted in Fig. 6-7.

6.6 State Transition Equations of a Second-order System

Since the starting point of the derivation of the time response in the last section is the transfer function, the solution is obtained with the assumption of zero initial conditions. We shall show in this section that the state variable method provides a more versatile and more complete solution in the time domain.

Using the method described in Sec. 3.8, we decompose the closed-loop transfer function of Eq. (6-27) into the following state equations:

$$\frac{dx_1(t)}{dt} = x_2(t) \tag{6-40}$$

$$\frac{dx_2(t)}{dt} = -\omega_n^2 x_1(t) - 2\delta\omega_n x_2(t) + r(t) \tag{6-41}$$

The output equation is

$$c(t) = \omega_n^2 x_1(t) \qquad (6\text{--}42)$$

The state transition signal flow graph of the system is shown in Fig. 6-8. Applying Mason's gain formula to Fig. 6-8, we write the transformed state transition equations as

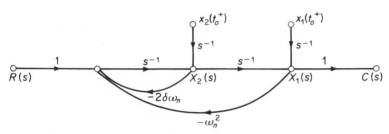

FIG. 6-8. State transition signal flow graph of a second-order feedback control system.

$$\begin{bmatrix} X_1(s) \\ X_2(s) \end{bmatrix} = \frac{1}{\Delta} \begin{bmatrix} s + 2\delta\omega_n & 1 \\ -\omega_n^2 & s \end{bmatrix} \begin{bmatrix} x_1(t_0^+) \\ x_2(t_0^+) \end{bmatrix} + \frac{1}{\Delta} \begin{bmatrix} 1 \\ s \end{bmatrix} R(s) \qquad (6\text{--}43)$$

where

$$\Delta = s^2 + 2\delta\omega_n s + \omega_n^2 \qquad (6\text{--}44)$$

The inverse Laplace transform of Eq. (6–43) is obtained with the help of the Laplace transform table. The state transition equation for $t \geq t_0^+$ and a unit step input $u(t - t_0^+)$ is

$$\begin{bmatrix} x_1(t) \\ x_2(t) \end{bmatrix} = \begin{bmatrix} \dfrac{1}{\sqrt{1 - \delta^2}} e^{-\delta\omega_n(t - t_0^+)} \sin\left[\omega_n\sqrt{1 - \delta^2}(t - t_0^+) + \phi_1\right] \\[2ex] \dfrac{-\omega_n}{\sqrt{1 - \delta^2}} e^{-\delta\omega_n(t - t_0^+)} \sin \omega_n\sqrt{1 - \delta^2}(t - t_0^+) \end{bmatrix}$$

$$\begin{bmatrix} \dfrac{1}{\omega_n\sqrt{1 - \delta^2}} e^{-\delta\omega_n(t - t_0^+)} \sin \omega_n\sqrt{1 - \delta^2}(t - t_0^+) \\[2ex] \dfrac{1}{\sqrt{1 - \delta^2}} e^{-\delta\omega_n(t - t_0^+)} \sin\left[\omega_n\sqrt{1 - \delta^2}(t - t_0^+) + \phi_2\right] \end{bmatrix} \begin{bmatrix} x_1(t_0^+) \\ x_2(t_0^+) \end{bmatrix}$$

$$+ \begin{bmatrix} \dfrac{1}{\omega_n^2}\left\{1 + \dfrac{1}{\sqrt{1 - \delta^2}} e^{-\delta\omega_n(t - t_0^+)} \sin\left[\omega_n\sqrt{1 - \delta^2}(t - t_0^+) - \phi_2\right]\right\} \\[2ex] \dfrac{1}{\omega_n\sqrt{1 - \delta^2}} e^{-\delta\omega_n(t - t_0^+)} \sin \omega_n\sqrt{1 - \delta^2}(t - t_0^+) \end{bmatrix} \qquad (t \geq t_0)$$

$$(6\text{--}45)$$

where

$$\phi_1 = \tan^{-1} \frac{\sqrt{1 - \delta^2}}{\delta} \qquad (6\text{--}46)$$

$$\phi_2 = \tan^{-1} \frac{\sqrt{1 - \delta^2}}{-\delta} \qquad (6\text{--}47)$$

It is easy to see that these state transition equations also include the zero-initial-condition solutions of Eqs. (6–29) and (6–32).

The output response of the second-order system with a unit step function input is

$$c(t) = \omega_n^2 x_1(t)$$

$$= \frac{\omega_n^2}{\sqrt{1 - \delta^2}} e^{-\delta\omega_n(t - t_0^+)} \sin \left[\omega_n\sqrt{1 - \delta^2} \, (t - t_0^+) + \phi_1 \right] x_1(t_0^+)$$

$$+ \frac{\omega_n}{\sqrt{1 - \delta^2}} e^{-\delta\omega_n(t - t_0^+)} \sin \omega_n\sqrt{1 - \delta^2} \, (t - t_0^+) x_2(t_0^+)$$

$$+ 1 + \frac{1}{\sqrt{1 - \delta^2}} e^{-\delta\omega_n(t - t_0^+)} \sin \left[\omega_n\sqrt{1 - \delta^2} \, (t - t_0^+) - \phi_2 \right] \quad (6\text{–}48)$$

$$(t \geq t_0)$$

6.7 Time Response of a Positional Servomechanism

Consider the simple servomechanism shown in Fig. 6-9a. The system is to position a mechanical load with viscous friction and inertia. A potentiometric error-detector with sensitivity K_s is used to measure the discrepancy between the reference and the controlled shaft. The actuating signal is

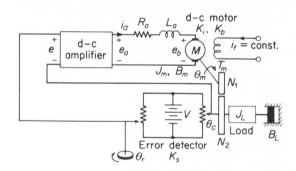

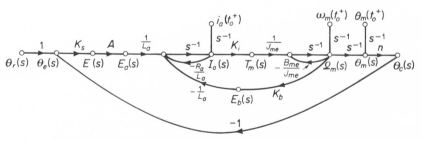

FIG. 6-9. (a) A d-c positional servomechanism, (b) State transition signal flow of the system in (a).

amplified by a d-c amplifier, whose output is connected across the armature of a d-c motor.

The constants of the system are given as follows:

Sensitivity of error detector	$K_s = 1/57.3$ volt/deg $= 1$ volt/rad
Gain of the d-c amplifier	A (variable)
Resistance in the armature of motor	$R_a = 5$ ohms
Inductance in the armature of motor	$L_a =$ negligible
Inertia of motor	$J_m = 10^{-3}$ lb-ft/rad/sec^2
Friction of motor	$B_m =$ negligible
Friction of load	$B_L = 0.1$ lb-ft/rad/sec
Inertia of load	$J_L = 0.1$ lb-ft/rad/sec^2
Gear ratio	$n = N_1/N_2 = 1/10$
Motor constant	$K_i = 0.5$ lb-ft/amp

The first step in the analysis is to write the cause-and-effect and the state equations for each component of the system.

(1) Error detector

$$\theta_e(t) = \theta_r(t) - \theta_c(t) \tag{6-49}$$

$$e(t) = K_s \theta_e(t) \tag{6-50}$$

(2) D-c amplifier

$$e_a(t) = A e(t) \tag{6-51}$$

(3) D-c motor (armature-controlled)

$$L_a \frac{di_a(t)}{dt} = -R_a i_a(t) + e_a(t) - e_b(t) \tag{6-52}$$

$$e_b(t) = K_b \omega_m(t) \tag{6-53}$$

$$J_{me} \frac{d\omega_m(t)}{dt} = -B_{me} \omega_m(t) + T_m(t) \tag{6-54}$$

$$T_m(t) = K_i i_a(t) \tag{6-55}$$

and

$$J_{me} = J_m + n^2 J_L = 10^{-3} + \tfrac{1}{100}0.1 = 2 \cdot 10^{-3} \text{ lb-ft/rad/sec}^2 \tag{6-56}$$

$$B_{me} = B_m + n^2 B_L = 10^{-3} \text{ lb-ft/rad/sec} \tag{6-57}$$

(4) Output

$$\frac{d\theta_m(t)}{dt} = \omega_m(t) \tag{6-58}$$

$$\theta_c(t) = n\theta_m(t) \tag{6-59}$$

The back emf constant K_b is not given originally, but a definite relation exists between K_b and K_i. In the English unit system, K_i is given in lb-ft/amp and the unit of the back emf constant is volt/rad/sec. With these units, K_b and K_i differ only by a constant ratio. The mechanical power developed in the motor armature is

$$p(t) = e_b(t)i_a(t) \text{ watts}$$

$$= \frac{1}{746} e_b(t)i_a(t) \qquad \text{hp} \tag{6-60}$$

Since $e_b(t)$ is related to $\omega_m(t)$ by Eq. (6-53), and $i_a(t)$ and $T_m(t)$ are related according to Eq. (6-55), Eq. (6-60) becomes

$$p(t) = \frac{K_b}{746K_i} T_m(t)\omega_m(t) \qquad \text{hp} \tag{6-61}$$

Also,

$$p(t) = \frac{1}{550} T_m(t)\omega_m(t) \qquad \text{hp} \tag{6-62}$$

Hence, equating Eq. (6-61) to Eq. (6-62) gives

$$p(t) = \frac{K_b}{746K_i} T_m(t)\omega_m(t) = \frac{1}{550} T_m(t)\omega_m(t) \tag{6-63}$$

from which

$$K_i = \frac{550}{746} K_b = 0.737 K_b \tag{6-64}$$

or

$$K_b = 1.36K_i \tag{6-65}$$

In this problem, $K_i = 0.5$ lb-ft/amp; thus, $K_b = 1.36K_i = 0.68$ volt/rad/sec.

The state transition signal flow graph of the over-all system is now constructed as shown in Fig. 6-9b.

When the initial conditions are assumed to be zero, the open-loop transfer function of the system is obtained from Fig. 6-9b.

$$\frac{\Theta_c(s)}{\Theta_e(s)} = \frac{K_s A K_i n}{R_a B_{me}s(1 + \tau_a s)(1 + \tau_{me} s) + K_b K_i s} \tag{6-66}$$

where

$$\tau_a = L_a/R_a \quad \text{and} \quad \tau_{me} = J_{me}/B_{me} = 2 \sec$$

The closed-loop transfer function of the system is

$$\frac{\Theta_c(s)}{\Theta_r(s)} = \frac{K_s A K_i n}{R_a B_{me}s(1 + \tau_a s)(1 + \tau_{me} s) + K_b K_i s + K_s A K_i n} \tag{6-67}$$

The state transition equations of the system can be obtained from the state transition signal flow graph in much the same way as described in the last section. However, the main objective of this problem is to demonstrate the behavior of the time response of the positional control system with respect to the system parameter, and it is sufficient to assume that all the initial states of the system are zero.

Since L_a is negligible, $\tau_a = 0$, the closed-loop transfer function in Eq. (6-67) is simplified to

$$\frac{\Theta_c(s)}{\Theta_r(s)} = \frac{K_s A K_i n}{R_a J_{me}s^2 + (K_b K_i + R_a B_{me})s + K_s A K_i n} \tag{6-68}$$

The last equation is of the second order; thus, it can be written in the standard form of Eq. (6–27). The undamped natural frequency of the system is

$$\omega_n = \pm\sqrt{\frac{K_s A K_i n}{R_a J_{me}}} \qquad (6\text{–}69)$$

The damping ratio is

$$\delta = \frac{K_b K_i + R_a B_{me}}{2 R_a J_{me} \omega_n} = \frac{K_b K_i + R_a B_{me}}{2\sqrt{K_s A K_i R_a J_{me} n}} \qquad (6\text{–}70)$$

When the values of the system parameters are substituted into Eq. (6–68), we have

$$\frac{\Theta_c(s)}{\Theta_r(s)} = \frac{5A}{s^2 + 34.5s + 5A} \qquad (6\text{–}71)$$

Suppose that the gain of the d-c amplifier is arbitrarily set at 200. The natural undamped frequency and the damping ratio are, respectively,

$$\omega_n = \pm\sqrt{1000} = \pm 31.6 \text{ rad/sec} \qquad (6\text{–}72)$$

$$\delta = 0.546 \qquad (6\text{–}73)$$

The characteristic equation of the system is

$$s^2 + 34.5s + 1000 = 0 \qquad (6\text{–}74)$$

whose roots are

$$s_1, s_2 = -17.25 \pm j\,26.5 \qquad (6\text{–}75)$$

For the unit step displacement input, $\theta_r(t) = 1$ rad, the output response of the system under zero initial state condition is

$$\theta_c(t) = \mathscr{L}^{-1}\left[\frac{1000}{s(s^2 + 34.5s + 1000)}\right] \qquad (6\text{–}76)$$

Or

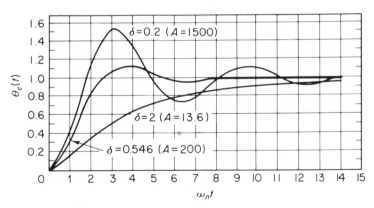

FIG. 6-10. Transient response of the servo system given in Fig. 6–8 when the input is a unit-step displacement.

$$\theta_c(t) = 1 + 1.2e^{-0.516\omega_n t} \sin(0.837\omega_n t + \pi + \tan^{-1} 1.53)$$
$$= 1 + 1.2e^{-17.25t} \sin(26.4t + 236.8°) \qquad (6\text{-}77)$$

The output response of the system is plotted in Fig. 6-10 as a function of the normalized time $\omega_n t$.

It is interesting to see how the time response changes when the gain A is varied. Note that in Eq. (6-69) and in Eq. (6-70), an increase in the gain A will increase the undamped natural frequency ω_n but will decrease the damping ratio. For $A = 1500$, the damping ratio δ is 0.2, and $\omega_n = 86.2$ rad/sec. The output response to a unit step displacement input in this case is shown in Fig. 6-10. The response oscillates violently back and forth about the final steady-state value. The overshoot is very large, although the rise time T_r is apparently reduced. The settling time T_s is also shortened by increasing the gain.* On the other hand, for low values of gain, for example, $A = 13.5$, the damping ratio and the natural undamped frequency are $\delta = 2.0$ and $\omega_n = 8.62$ rad/sec, respectively. The output step response corresponding to $A = 13.5$ is overdamped. Table 6-1 gives the comparison of the transient behavior of the servo system for the three different values of gain A.

The velocity of the controlled shaft is obtained by taking the first derivative of $\theta_c(t)$ with respect to $\omega_n t$.

$$\frac{d\theta_c(t)}{d\omega_n t} = \frac{\delta}{\sqrt{1 - \delta^2}} e^{-\delta\omega_n t} \sin(\omega_n\sqrt{1 - \delta^2}\,t + \phi)$$
$$- e^{-\delta\omega_n t} \cos(\omega_n\sqrt{1 - \delta^2}\,t + \phi) \qquad (6\text{-}78)$$

which is simplified to

$$\frac{d\theta_c(t)}{d\omega_n t} = \frac{1}{\sqrt{1 - \delta^2}} e^{-\delta\omega_n t} \sin \omega_n\sqrt{1 - \delta^2}\,t \qquad (6\text{-}79)$$

Table 6-1

COMPARISON OF TRANSIENT RESPONSE OF A SECOND-ORDER SERVO SYSTEM
WHEN THE GAIN VARIES

Gain A	Damping ratio δ	Undamped frequency ω_n	Maximum overshoot	Per cent overshoot	Delay time T_d	Rise time T_r	Settling time T_s	Time at max. overshoot $t_{\max}$
13.5	2.0	8.62	0	0	0.348	1.043	1.51	—
200	0.546	31.6	0.141	14.1	0.041	0.057	0.168	0.119
1500	0.2	86.2	0.52	52	0.012	0.014	0.15	0.037

*In Fig. 6-10, the response for $A = 1500$ seems to take a longer time to reach the steady state then that for $A = 200$. This is not true, however, since the responses are plotted as a function of the normalized time $\omega_n t$; for $A = 1500$, $\omega_n = 86.2$ rad/sec, as compared to $\omega_n = 31.6$ rad/sec for $A = 200$.

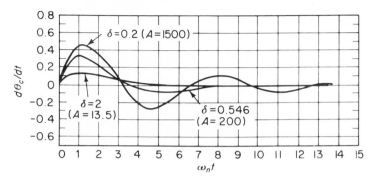

FIG. 6-11. Output velocity of servo system given in Fig. 6–8 when the input is a unit-step displacement.

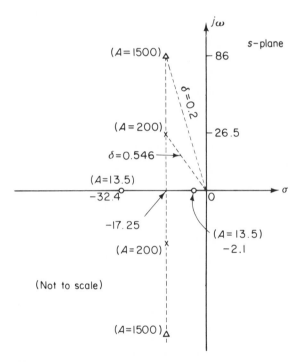

FIG. 6-12. Roots of the characteristic equation of the servo system given in Fig. 6–8 for $A = 13.5, 200, 1500$ respectively.

The output velocity of the system for $A = 13.6$, 200, and 1500 are plotted in Fig. 6-11 as functions of $\omega_n t$.

In Fig. 6-12 is shown the variation of the location of the roots of the system characteristic equation as a function of amplifier gain A. For values of A between zero and 59.5, the two roots of the characteristic equation are real and lie on the negative real axis in the s-plane, and the system response is overdamped. For values of A greater than 59.5, the roots are complex conjugate; the real parts of the roots are equal to -17.25 and are not affected by the change in values of A. Thus, as the value of A approaches infinity, the damping factor α is always equal to 17.25 sec^{-1}. It is also apparent that a second-order system is always stable for all finite positive values of gain.

Response to Ramp Input

When a unit ramp function input $\theta_r(t) = tu(t)$ is applied to the servo system shown in Fig. 6-8, the output response becomes

$$\theta_c(t) = \mathscr{L}^{-1}\left[\frac{\omega_n^2}{s^2(s^2 + 2\delta\omega_n s + \omega_n^2)}\right] \tag{6-80}$$

and from the Laplace transform table, we have

$$\theta_c(t) = t - \frac{2\delta}{\omega_n} + \frac{1}{\omega_n\sqrt{1 - \delta^2}}\, e^{-\delta\omega_n t} \sin(\omega_n\sqrt{1 - \delta^2}\, t - \phi) \tag{6-81}$$

where

$$\phi = 2\tan^{-1}\frac{\sqrt{1 - \delta^2}}{-\delta} \tag{6-82}$$

When $A = 200$, Eq. (6-81) becomes

$$\theta_c(t) = t - \frac{1.092}{\omega_n} + \frac{1.2}{\omega_n}\, e^{-0.546\omega_n t} \sin(0.837\omega_n t + 113.6°) \tag{6-83}$$

In the last equation, note that when t approaches infinity, the steady-state response of the system is

$$\lim_{t \to \infty}\theta_c(t) = \theta_{c_{ss}} = t - \frac{1.092}{\omega_n}\Big|_{t \to \infty} \tag{6-84}$$

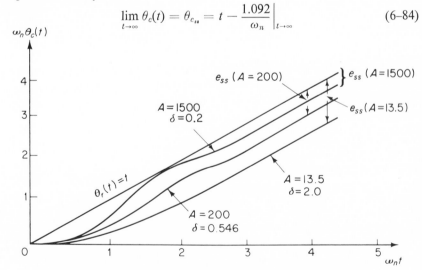

FIG. 6-13. Output displacement of the servo system shown in Fig. 6-8 when the input is a unit-ramp function.

It is apparent that the output response at steady state does not agree with the unit ramp input. The steady-state error, which is defined as

$$\theta_r(t) - \theta_{c_{ss}} \qquad (6\text{--}85)$$

is a displacement lag of $1.092/\omega_n$ rad in this case. Figure 6-13 shows the output responses $\theta_c(t)$ when the input is a unit ramp function, for A equals 13.5, 200, and 1500. The steady-state error is decreased as the gain is increased. However, if we choose to improve the steady-state accuracy of the servo system by increasing the forward gain, the transient response of the system will, in general, become more oscillatory, or it may sometimes even become unstable. This phenomenon is rather characteristic of all servo systems.

Transient Response of a Third-order System

It was shown in the last section that if the motor armature inductance L_a is neglected, the control system is of the second order; it can be shown that a second-order system is always stable for all positive values of A. Suppose we now let $L_a = 0.1$ henry in the system in Fig. 6-8 and keep the other parameters unchanged. The armature constant τ_a is now 0.02 sec. The closed-loop transfer function given by Eq. (6–67) is now

$$\frac{\Theta_c(s)}{\Theta_r(s)} = \frac{250A}{5 \cdot 10^{-3} s(1 + 0.02s)(1 + 2s) + 0.34s + 0.05A} \qquad (6\text{--}86)$$

or

$$\frac{\Theta_c(s)}{\Theta_r(s)} = \frac{250A}{s^3 + 50.5s^2 + 1725s + 250A} \qquad (6\text{--}87)$$

The characteristic equation of the system is

$$s^3 + 50.5s^2 + 1725s + 250A = 0 \qquad (6\text{--}88)$$

The system is now of the third order, and we are confronted with the task of solving a third-order characteristic equation.

If we let $A = 13.5$, the characteristic equation has a real root of $s = -2.08$ and two complex roots at $-24.2 \pm j32.2$. The closed-loop transfer function can now be written as

$$\frac{\Theta_c(s)}{\Theta_r(s)} = \frac{1}{(1 + 0.48s)(1 + 0.0298s + 0.000616s^2)} \qquad (6\text{--}89)$$

For a unit step displacement input, the Laplace transform of the output is

$$\Theta_c(s) = \frac{1}{s(1 + 0.48s)(1 + 0.298s + 0.000616s^2)} \qquad (6\text{--}90)$$

The inverse Laplace transform of the last equation is

$$\theta_c(t) = 1 - 1.06e^{-2.08t} + 0.0667e^{-24.2t} \sin(32.2t + 1.88\text{rad}) \qquad (6\text{--}91)$$

$$(t \geq 0)$$

In Eq. (6–91), since the time constant of the pure exponential term is

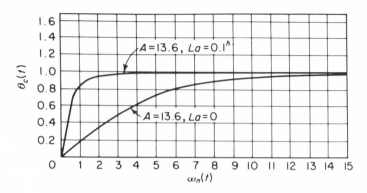

FIG. 6-14. Step responses of the servo system in Fig. 6-9.

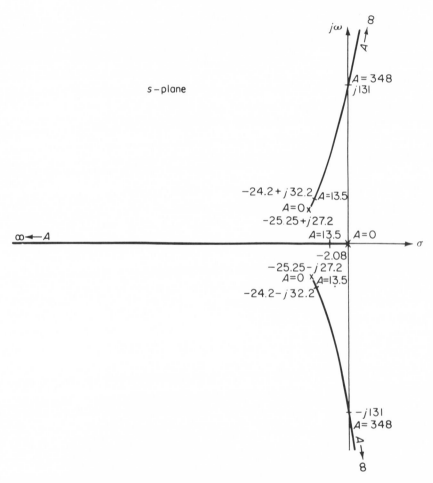

FIG. 6-15. Root loci of the characteristic equation of Eq. (6-88) when A varies between zero and infinity.

more than ten times greater than that of the damped sinusoid term, the transient response of $\theta_c(t)$ is predominantly governed by the pole of $\Theta_c(s)/\Theta_r(s)$ at $s = -2.08$. The oscillatory mode due to the complex conjugate poles at $-24.2 \pm j32.2$ decreases very rapidly. The step response of $\theta_c(t)$ for $L_a = 0.1$ henry is shown in Fig. 6-14. When compared with the step response of the system with $L_a = 0$, the step response of the third-order system is seen to have a faster rise time. Obviously, we should expect this result, since adding inductance to a system is the same as adding inertia, which makes the response of the system more lively.

It can be shown that when A is equal to 348, the two complex roots are located on the imaginary axis of the s-plane. The response corresponding to these imaginary roots of the characteristic equation is an undamped sinusoid. The frequency of oscillation is 131 rad/sec. This response is later defined as a marginal case of instability of linear systems. The loci of the three characteristic equation roots when A is varied from zero to infinity are sketched in Fig. 6-15. It is seen that for all values of A greater than 348, the step response of the system will increase with time without bound, since the two complex roots will be located in the right-hand half of the s-plane.

From the preceding examples we have learned the important fact that a second-order system is always stable so long as the loop gain is finite and positive, but a third-(or higher-)order system may become unstable if the loop gain exceeds a certain marginal value.

6.8 Effects of Derivative and Integral Controls on the Transient Performance of Feedback Control Systems

The discussions of the transient response of servomechanisms given so far in this chapter cover only systems of the proportional type; a proportional-type feedback control system is one which develops a correcting effort proportional to the magnitude of the actuating signal. The example given in the previous section shows one limitation, or disadvantage, of a proportional-type system; a compromise is often necessary in selecting a proper forward gain A so that the size of the steady-state error and the maximum overshoot of the output response are within acceptable tolerances. A compromise, however, cannot always be reached, since, in most practical cases, the system corresponding to the gain selected to realize a maximum acceptable steady-state error may have excessive overshoot in its time response, or may even be unstable.

It is logical, then, to consider some other types of control which may improve the transient or steady-state behavior of an ordinary proportional type system. In general, the following three basic principles are adapted to modify the performance of feedback control systems:

(1) Derivative control.

(2) Integral control.

(3) Rate-feedback control.

It will be shown that it is impossible to improve both the transient and the steady-state performance by means of one of the above schemes. The derivative control, for instance, will improve the overshoot of a given system, but will not affect a constant steady-state error. On the other hand, a system with integral control will have better steady-state accuracy than will the proportional type, but it will be less stable in general.

The Effect of Derivative Control on Transient Response

Figure 6-16(a) shows the typical step response of a proportional-type servomechanism; the corresponding error signal $e(t)$ and the time rate of change of $e(t)$ are shown in Fig. 6-16(b) and Fig. 6-16(c), respectively. Let us first consider that the system has only a proportional-type control and that high overshoot in the step response is observed. The large overshoot is entirely due to the excessive amount of positive torque developed by the motor in the time interval $0 < t < t_1$, during which the error signal is positive. For the time interval $t_1 < t < t_3$, the error signal is negative, and the motor torque is reversed in direction; this negative torque acts as a retarding torque, bringing the overshooting output back. When $t = t_3$, the torque is positive again, tending to reduce the undershoot in the response caused by the negative torque in the interval $t_2 < t < t_3$. The process is repeated, and for a stable system, a steady state is finally reached.

Considering the explanation given above, we can say that the contributing factors to a high overshoot are as follows: (1) The positive correcting torque in the interval $0 < t < t_1$ is too large, and (2) the retarding torque in the interval $t_1 < t < t_2$ is inadequate. A logical approach to the reduction of the high overshoot in the output response is to decrease the amount of positive correcting torque and to increase the retarding torque. Similarly, in the time interval $t_2 < t < t_4$, the negative corrective torque would be reduced and the retarding torque, which is now in the positive direction, should be increased in order to improve the undershoot. The derivative control is a scheme designed to give precisely this kind of effect. Now consider that the proportional-type servomechanism is modified so that the torque developed by the motor is proportional to the signal $e(t) + \tau_d \, de/dt$, where τ_d is a constant. In other words, in addition to the error signal, a signal which is proportional to the time rate of change of the error is also applied to the motor. The block diagram of a basic second-order system with derivative control is shown in Fig. 6-17. In Fig. 6-16, it is seen that for $0 < t < t_1$, the time derivative of $e(t)$ is negative; this will reduce the original positive torque due to $e(t)$ alone. For $t_1 < t < t_2$, both $e(t)$ and $de(t)/dt$ are negative, which means that the negative retarding torque devel-

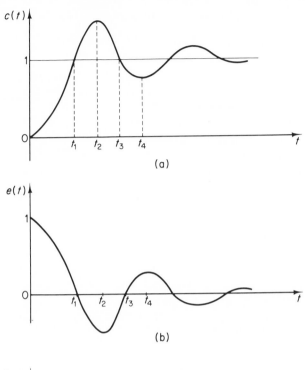

FIG. 6-16. Wave forms of $c(t)$, $e(t)$ and de/dt showing the effect of derivative control. (a) Step response; (b) Error signal; (c) Time rate of change of error signal.

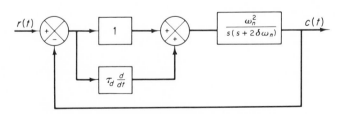

FIG. 6-17. Feedback control system with derivative control.

oped will be greater than that of the proportional case. Therefore, all these effects will result in a smaller overshoot (however, usually at the expense of a longer delay time). It is easy to see that $e(t)$ and $de(t)/dt$ have opposite signs in the time interval $t_2 < t < t_3$; therefore, the negative torque which originally contributes to the undershoot is also reduced.

The derivative control is essentially an anticipatory type of control. Normally, if the slope of $e(t)$ or $c(t)$ is large in linear systems, a high overshoot will occur in the very near future. The derivative control measures the instantaneous slope of $e(t)$, predicts the large overshoot ahead of time, and makes proper correcting effort before the overshoot occurs.

It is apparent that the derivative control affects the steady-state error of a system only if the steady-state error varies with time. If the steady-state error of a system is constant with respect to time, the derivative control has no effect on this error. But if the steady-state error increases with time, a torque is again developed proportional to de/dt, which reduces the magnitude of the error. Steady-state error of a feedback control system will be discussed in more detail in the following sections.

The effect of derivative control on time response of a feedback control system can also be evaluated by analytical means. The open-loop transfer function of the system with derivative control shown in Fig. 6-17 is

$$G(s) = \frac{C(s)}{E(s)} = \frac{(1 + \tau_d s)\omega_n^2}{s(s + 2\delta\omega_n)} \qquad (6\text{-}92)$$

from which the closed-loop transfer function is determined as

$$\frac{C(s)}{R(s)} = \frac{(1 + \tau_d s)\omega_n^2}{s^2 + (2\delta\omega_n + \tau_d\omega_n^2)s + \omega_n^2} \qquad (6\text{-}93)$$

The characteristic equation of the system is

$$s^2 + (2\delta\omega_n + \tau_d\omega_n^2)s + \omega_n^2 = 0 \qquad (6\text{-}94)$$

The form of the last equation is similar to that of the characteristic equation of the proportional-type system, except that the coefficient of the s term is increased by the quantity $\tau_d\omega_n^2$. This actually means that the damping of the system is increased. For instance, in the system given in the previous section, if the derivative control is applied, the open-loop transfer function is

$$G(s) = \frac{C(s)}{E(s)} = \frac{5A(1 + \tau_d s)}{s^2 + 34.5s} \qquad (6\text{-}95)$$

Let us take the case in which $A = 1500$, and arbitrarily choose a τ_d of 0.01 sec. The characteristic equation of the system with derivative control is now

$$s^2 + 109.5s + 7500 = 0 \qquad (6\text{-}96)$$

from which the damping ratio of the system is obtained as 0.634, and $\omega_n = 86.2$ rad/sec; the maximum overshoot is 7.6 per cent. It is apparent that the transient performance of the system is vastly improved by the derivative control, since the original system has a damping ratio of 0.2 and the overshoot is 52 per cent. Therefore, this illustration verifies that this type of derivative control improves the damping of the time response.

Effect of Integral Control on the Transient Response

In order to eliminate a positional error completely, a logical approach is to introduce a signal to the servomotor which is proportional to the time integral of the error. As long as there is an error signal, there will always be a torque developed by the motor in a direction to correct this error. Figure 6-18 shows the block diagram of a feedback control system with integral control.

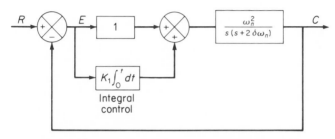

FIG. 6-18. Feedback control system with integral control.

The signal supplied to the motor consists of two components: one proportional to the instantaneous error, the other, to the time integral of the error. The open-loop transfer function of the system is

$$\frac{C(s)}{E(s)} = \frac{\omega_n^2(1 + K_1/s)}{s(s + 2\delta\omega_n)} = \frac{\omega_n^2(s + K_1)}{s^2(s + 2\delta\omega_n)} \tag{6-97}$$

It is clear that the integral control has converted the second-order system into a third-order one. For reasons which will become apparent in future discussions, the higher the system order, the more the system tends to become unstable. An inherent property of a second-order system is that it is always stable for finite positive values of open-loop gain. We have shown that for a third-order system, the roots of the characteristic equation may be found in the right half of the s-plane if the gain is high.

Consider the servo system shown in Fig. 6-9; the open-loop transfer function of the system when the integral control is applied is

$$\frac{C(s)}{E(s)} = \frac{5A(s + K_1)}{s^2(s + 34.5)} \tag{6-98}$$

The closed-loop transfer function is

$$\frac{C(s)}{R(s)} = \frac{5A(s + K_1)}{s^3 + 34.5s^2 + 5As + 5AK_1} \tag{6-99}$$

For $A = 1500$, the characteristic equation is

$$s^3 + 34.5s^2 + 7500s + 7500K_1 = 0 \qquad (6\text{--}100)$$

The roots of the characteristic equation depend on the value of K_1; if K_1 is very small, the transient response behaves very close to that of the original system; if the value of K_1 is large, for example, $K_1 = 47$, the roots of the characteristic equation are at -44.5, $5 + j89$, and $5 - j89$ in the s-plane. Since the complex roots have positive real parts, for $K_1 = 47$ the system is unstable for all values of A greater than zero.

It will be shown that the integral control does give improved steady-state performance to the servo system. From Eqs. (6–98) and (6–99), the transform of the error is written

$$E(s) = \frac{s^2(s + 34.5)}{s^3 + 34.5s^2 + 5As + 5AK_1} R(s) \qquad (6\text{--}101)$$

If it is assumed that the system is stable, the steady-state error of the system is obtained by applying the final-value theorem of the Laplace transform to Eq. (6–101).

$$e_{ss}(t) = \lim_{t \to \infty} e(t) = \lim_{s \to 0} sE(s) \qquad (6\text{--}102)$$

Substituting Eq. (6–101) into Eq. (6–102), we see that when the reference input is either a step or a ramp function, the steady-state error of the system is zero; for a parabolic function input, the e_{ss} is a constant. Recall that, in the original system, the steady-state error is a constant [see Eq. (6–84)] when the input is a ramp function, and will increase with time if the input is proportional to t^2.

The effect of the derivative and the integral control on the transient response of a feedback control system can also be studied by plotting the root loci of the characteristic equation when the open-loop gain is varied from zero to infinity. When the derivative control is applied to a second-order system, the open-loop transfer function is given by Eq. (6–95). We see that the derivative control has added a zero at $s = -1/\tau_d$ to the open-loop transfer function. The characteristic equation is now

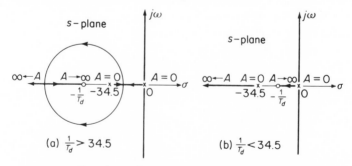

(a) $\dfrac{1}{\tau_d} > 34.5$ (b) $\dfrac{1}{\tau_d} < 34.5$

FIG. 6-19. Root locus diagrams of characteristic equation of servo system with derivative control, $s^2 + (34.5 + 5A T_d)s + 5A = 0$.

$$s^2 + (34.5 + 5A_d)s + 5A = 0 \qquad (6\text{-}103)$$

The loci of the two roots of Eq. (6-103), when A is varied from zero to infinity, are depicted in Fig. 6-19 for two different values of τ_d ($\tau_d < 34.5$ and $\tau_d > 34.5$). From these locus diagrams, the effect of the derivative control on the damping of the transient response is apparent. In Fig. 6-19a, the effect of adding the zero at $-1/\tau_d$ is to cause the original loci to bend toward the left, and for large values of A the output response is overdamped. It can be verified that the loci of the complex roots in Fig. 6-19a form a circle with the center at $-1/\tau_d$. In Fig. 6-19b, when a more derivative signal is applied ($\tau_d > 34.5$), the loci lie only on the negative real axis of the s-plane, and the system output response does not oscillate at all for all positive values of A.

From the open-loop transfer function given by Eq. (6-98), the effect of the integral control is to add a zero at $-K_1$ and a pole at the origin in the s-plane. The characteristic equation of the system is now

$$s^3 + 34.5s^2 + 5As + 5AK_1 = 0 \qquad (6\text{-}104)$$

It can be shown that the last equation will have roots only in the left half of the s-plane if the following condition is met:

$$0 < K_1 < 34.5 \qquad (6\text{-}105)$$

In other words, if the value of K_1 exceeds 34.5, the closed-loop system with integral control will be unstable for all positive values of A, since two of the three roots will have positive real parts. The root loci of Eq. (6-104) as a function A are sketched in Fig. 6-20 for two different values of K_1. It is clear that the addition of the integral dipole (pole-zero combination) moves the loci toward the right in the s-plane.

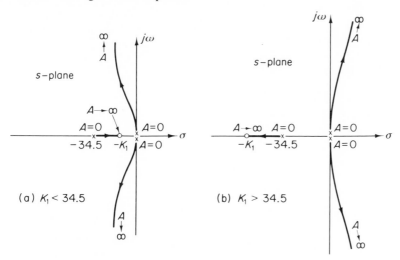

FIG. 6-20. Root locus diagrams of characteristic equation of servo system with integral control, $s^3 + 34.5s^2 + 5As + 5AK_1 = 0$.

Rate-feedback (Tachometer) Control

The philosophy of using the derivative of the actuating signal to improve the damping of a system can also be extended to the output signal. The same effect can be obtained by feeding back the derivative of the output signal and comparing it with the reference input. Figure 6-21 shows the block diagram of a simple second-order system with a secondary path feeding

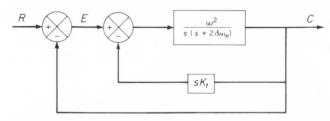

FIG. 6-21. Feedback control system with tachometer feedback.

back the output velocity of the system. The closed-loop transfer function of the system is given by

$$\frac{C(s)}{R(s)} = \frac{\omega_n^2}{s^2 + (2\delta\omega_n + K_t\omega_n^2)s + \omega_n^2} \qquad (6\text{-}106)$$

and the characteristic equation is

$$s^2 + (2\delta\omega_n + K_t\omega_n^2)s + \omega_n^2 = 0 \qquad (6\text{-}107)$$

Comparing this equation with Eq. (6–94), we see that they are of the same form. As a matter of fact, if τ_d in Eq. (6–94) were replaced by K_t, they would be identical. Therefore, we can conclude that the rate-feedback (or tachometer feedback) also improves the damping of the time response of a control system.

Although for the same damping ratio, the amount of overshoot for a second-order system will be the same for derivative control and rate-feedback, the two step responses are not the same. In general, because of the added zero in the open-loop transfer function, the rise time of the derivative controlled system will be faster.

6.9 Steady-state Response of Feedback Control Systems — Steady-state Error[1]

In the previous section, only the transient response of feedback control systems was discussed. In the analysis and design of feedback control systems, the steady-state response is also of great importance. For instance, for a positional servomechanism, it is desirable to have the final position of the output in exact correspondence with the reference position; in a velocity control system, it is essential that the controlled velocity be as close as possible to the reference value. But in actual practice, because of physical imperfections of system components, friction, and other inherent properties of feedback, there is usually a deviation between the actual output variable and the desired quantity in the steady state.

If the reference input $r(t)$ and the controlled output $c(t)$ are dimensionally the same (a voltage controlling a voltage, a position controlling a position, etc.) and are at the same level or of the same magnitude (unity-feedback systems), the error function is simply

$$e(t) = r(t) - c(t) \qquad (6\text{--}108)$$

However, sometimes it may be impossible or inconvenient to provide a reference input which is at the same level or even of the same dimension as the controlled variable. For instance, it may be necessary to use a low voltage source for the control of the output of a high voltage power source; in a velocity servomechanism (perfect integrator), a voltage source or position input may be used to control the velocity of the output shaft. In such cases,

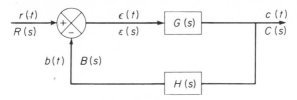

FIG. 6-22. Non-unity-feedback control system.

a nonunity element, H, is usually incorporated in the feedback path, and the error defined in Eq. (6–108) becomes meaningless. In other words, error cannot be defined simply as the difference between reference input and controlled output; the input and the output signals must be of the same dimension and at the same level before subtraction. For a nonunity-feedback system, the error of the system is measured by use of the actuating signal ϵ (see Fig. 6-22); that is,

$$\epsilon(t) = r(t) - b(t) \qquad (6\text{--}109)$$

or, in terms of the Laplace transformed variables,

$$\epsilon(s) = R(s) - B(s) = R(s) - H(s)C(s) \qquad (6\text{--}110)$$

For example, if a 10 volt reference is used to regulate a 100 volt voltage supply, H is a constant and is equal to 0.1. When the output voltage is exactly 100 volts, the actuating signal is

$$\epsilon(t) = 10 - 0.1 \times 100 = 0 \qquad (6\text{--}111)$$

The steady-state error of a feedback control system is defined as the error (or actuating signal, in general) when the steady state is reached; that is,

$$\text{Steady-state error} = e_{ss} = \lim_{t \to \infty} e(t) \tag{6-112}$$

or

$$\epsilon_{ss} = \lim_{t \to \infty} \epsilon(t) \tag{6-113}$$

Before we proceed, it is necessary to investigate the factors which have direct influence on the steady-state error of a feedback control system. In the simple servomechanism analyzed in Sec. 6.7, for $L_a = 0$, the system is of the second order; when a unit step displacement input is applied to the system, the output response given by Eq. (6–77) shows that it is in exact correspondence with the reference input when the steady state is reached. In other words, there is no steady-state error in the system response. However, for the same system, if a unit ramp function is applied as reference input, Eqs. (6–83) and (6–84) show that the output displacement will lag behind the input by $1.092/\omega_n$ rad when the steady state is reached. It can also be shown that if a parabolic function is applied as input, the steady-state error will increase linearly with time. Therefore, from this simple example, we have learned that the steady-state error of a given system depends upon the type of input applied. Furthermore, the steady-state error also depends to a great extent upon the nature and characteristics of the system itself. Since we have little or no control over the input signal of a control system, we could reduce the steady-state error by increasing the forward path gain or by altering the characteristic of the system, but the system may become less stable or even unstable.

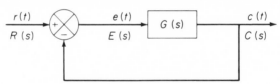

FIG. 6-23. Unity-feedback control system.

For the sake of simplicity, the following discussion is given with reference to systems with unity feedback, but the extension to nonunity-feedback system is quite straightforward. Consider the feedback control system shown in Fig. 6-23. The Laplace transformed error function is given by

$$E(s) = \frac{R(s)}{1 + G(s)} \tag{6-114}$$

By the use of the final-value theorem, the steady-state error of the system is written

$$e_{ss} = \lim_{t \to \infty} e(t) = \lim_{s \to 0} sE(s) \tag{6-115}*$$

*For a nonunity feedback system, the actuating signal is given by

$$\epsilon(s) = \frac{R(s)}{1 + G(s)H(s)}$$

and then simply by replacing $E(s)$ by $\epsilon(s)$ in Eq. (6-115).

where $sE(s)$ is to have no poles which lie on the imaginary axis and in the right half of the s-plane. Substituting Eq. (6–114) into Eq. (6–115), we have

$$e_{ss} = \lim_{s \to 0} \frac{sR(s)}{1 + G(s)} \tag{6-116}$$

which shows that the steady-state error depends on the reference input $R(s)$ and the system transfer function $G(s)$.

The computation of the steady-state error is simplified if some basic facts and relationships among the types of inputs, systems, and the steady-state error are established. We shall consider only the three basic types of test inputs (step, ramp, acceleration) at present.

(1) *Steady-state Error of Systems with Step Displacement Input* (*the Positional Error Constant* K_p)

If the reference input to the feedback system of Fig. 6-23 is a step displacement of magnitude R, the Laplace transform of $r(t)$ is R/s. Equation (6–116) now becomes

$$e_{ss} = \lim_{s \to 0} \frac{sR(s)}{1 + G(s)} = \lim_{s \to 0} \frac{R}{1 + G(s)} = \frac{R}{1 + \lim_{s \to 0} G(s)} \tag{6-117}$$

If we let

$$K_p = \lim_{s \to 0} G(s) \tag{6-118}$$

where K_p is defined as the *positional error constant*, Eq. (6–117) is written as

$$e_{ss} = \frac{R}{1 + K_p} \tag{6-119}$$

Since R is the amplitude of the step displacement input, and also is the desired magnitude of the steady-state output response, we can write Eq. (6–119) as

$$K_p = \frac{R - e_{ss}}{e_{ss}} \tag{6-120}$$

or, positional error constant

$$K_p = \frac{\text{desired output} - \text{allowable } e_{ss}}{\text{allowable steady-state error}} \tag{6-121}$$

Equation (6–121) indicates that, whenever the desired output positional response and its allowable steady-state error are specified for a servo system, the corresponding K_p of the system is determined; with the use of Eq. (6–118), the desired behavior of $G(s)$ at $s = 0$ is fixed.

(2) *Steady-state Error of Systems with Step Velocity Input* (*Velocity Error Constant* K_v)

If the input to the feedback control system of Fig. 6-23 is

$$r(t) = Rtu(t) \tag{6-122}$$

where R is in displacement/sec, the Laplace transform of $r(t)$ is $R(s) = R/s^2$. Substituting $R(s)$ into Eq. (6–116), we have

$$e_{ss} = \lim_{s \to 0} \frac{R}{s + sG(s)} = \frac{R}{\lim\limits_{s \to 0} sG(s)} \qquad (6\text{–}123)$$

If we let

$$K_v = \lim_{s \to 0} sG(s) = \text{velocity error constant} \qquad (6\text{–}124)$$

Eq. (6–123) reads

$$e_{ss} = R/K_v \qquad (6\text{–}125)$$

or

$$K_v = \frac{R}{e_{ss}} = \frac{\text{desired output velocity}}{\text{steady-state error}} (\text{sec}^{-1}) \qquad (6\text{–}126)$$

The steady-state error represented by Eq. (6–125) is usually called the *velocity error*. It should be kept in mind that the velocity error is not an error in velocity; it is, rather, the error in displacement due to a ramp-type input, $r(t) = Rtu(t)$. Figure 6-24 further clarifies this point by showing a typical ramp input with the output response lagging behind it by an error in displacement when the system has reached its steady state.

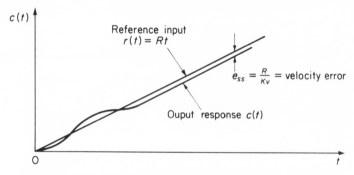

FIG. 6-24. Output response of feedback control system with ramp input.

(3) *Steady-state Error of Systems with Acceleration Input* (*the Acceleration Error Constant K_a*)

If an acceleration input $r(t) = Rt^2u(t)/2$ is applied to the system of Fig. 6-23, the Laplace transform of $r(t)$ is R/s^3, where R is in displacement/sec²; Eq. (6–116) now becomes

$$e_{ss} = \lim_{s \to 0} \frac{R}{s^2 + s^2G(s)} = \frac{R}{\lim\limits_{s \to 0} s^2 G(s)} = \frac{R}{K_a} \qquad (6\text{–}127)$$

where

$$K_a = \lim_{s \to 0} s^2 G(s) = \text{acceleration error constant} \qquad (6\text{–}128)$$

or

$$K_a = \frac{R}{e_{ss}} = \frac{\text{desired output acceleration}}{\text{steady-state error}} \, (\text{sec}^{-2}) \qquad (6\text{-}129)$$

As in the two previous cases, the steady-state error given by Eq. (6–127) is called the *acceleration error*, which is the error in displacement due to an acceleration-type input. Figure 6-25 illustrates a typical acceleration error in the steady-state output response when the input is of the acceleration type.

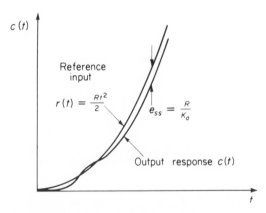

FIG. 6-25. Output response of feedback control system with acceleration input.

From the foregoing discussions, it is clear that when the reference input to a unity-feedback control system is of the step displacement, ramp, or acceleration type, the steady-state error due to each input depends upon the error constants K_p, K_v, and K_a, respectively. The error constants are summarized as follows:

(1) Positional error constant $K_p = \lim_{s \to 0} G(s)$ (6–130)

(2) Velocity error constant $K_v = \lim_{s \to 0} sG(s)$ (6–131)

(3) Acceleration error constant $K_a = \lim_{s \to 0} s^2 G(s)$ (6–132)

The Classification of G(s)

The values of the error constants for a given system with unity-feedback apparently depend upon the type of $G(s)$. In order to classify the open-loop transfer function $G(s)$, in general, we may write

$$G(s) = \frac{K(1 + T_1 s)(1 + T_2 s) \dots (1 + T_m s)}{s^j (1 + T_a s)(1 + T_b s) \dots (1 + T_n s)} \qquad (6\text{-}133)$$

where K is the forward gain and the T's are constants of the system. The poles at the origin, s^j, where $j = 0, 1, 2, 3, \ldots$, may be used to determine the type of the system, since, in Eqs. (6–130) through (6–132), the behavior of $G(s)$ at $s = 0$ determines the error constants, and at $s = 0$, $G(s)$ approaches K/s^j. Thus, a type 0 system is one for which $j = 0$; a type 1 system, $j = 1$; etc. For instance,

$$G(s) = \frac{K(1 + 0.5s)}{s(1 + s)(1 + 2s)} \qquad (6\text{–}134)$$

represents a type 1 system, since $j = 1$. In simple words, the value of j in Eq. (6–133) completely determines the type of the feedback control system. The values of m, n, and T bear no importance in the system type and do not affect the values of the error constants.

Once the type of a system is determined by inspection, the error constants of the system are determined readily from Eqs. (6–130) through (6–132). The error constants are then used to calculate the steady-state error when the reference input is specified as one of the three basic types mentioned earlier.

For a specific type of feedback control system, the error constants can be infinite, zero, or finite in value. For instance, for a type 0 system, $G(s)$ is of the form

$$G(s) = \frac{K(1 + T_1 s)(1 + T_2 s) \ldots (1 + T_m s)}{(1 + T_a s)(1 + T_b s) \ldots (1 + T_n s)} \qquad (6\text{–}135)$$

Hence, $K_p = K$, $K_v = 0$, and $K_a = 0$. This means that the steady-state error of the system due to a step displacement input of $r(t) = Ru(t)$ will be $R/(K + 1)$; the steady-state error due to a ramp input, $r(t) = Rtu(t)$, will be equal to $R/K_v = \infty$; the steady-state error due to an acceleration input is also infinite. A steady-state error of infinite magnitude simply means that the error increases with time. It can be shown by actually solving the

Table 6-2

THE STEADY-STATE ERROR

Type of system	K_p	K_v	K_a	Step displacement input $e_{ss} = \dfrac{R}{1 + K_p}$	Velocity input $e_{ss} = \dfrac{R}{K_v}$	Acceleration input $e_{ss} = \dfrac{R}{K_a}$
0	K	0	0	Position error $e_{ss} = \dfrac{R}{1 + K}$	Velocity error $e_{ss}(t) = A + Bt$ $= \infty$	Acceleration error $e_{ss}(t) = C + Dt + Et^2$ $= \infty$
1	∞	K	0	$e_{ss} = 0$	$e_{ss} = R/K$	$e_{ss}(t) = D + Et$ $= \infty$
2	∞	∞	K	$e_{ss} = 0$	$e_{ss} = 0$	$e_{ss} = R/K$
3	∞	∞	∞	$e_{ss} = 0$	$e_{ss} = 0$	$e_{ss} = 0$

(A, B, C, D, and E are constants.)

system differential equation that the steady-state error of the above system with ramp input increases as the first order of t, and that the steady-state error with an acceleration input will increase as the second order of t; i.e., t^2.

The error constants for other types of feedback control systems are computed in the same manner. The relations among the error constants, types of system, and the input types are summarized in Table 6–2. The chief disadvantage of the definition of the error constants is that only one of the constants has a finite value which is not zero for a particular system. Another drawback is that, in cases in which the steady-state error is a function of time, the error constants give only an answer of infinity and do not provide any indication of how the error varies with time.

However, the applications of the error constants are not limited only to systems with inputs classified as one of the three basic types of test signals. For linear systems, the concept can easily be extended to systems with inputs that can be represented by a polynomial, for example, $r(t) = (1 + 2t + t^2/2)u(t)$. The steady-state error in this case is simply $e_{ss} = 1/K_p + 2/K_v + 1/K_a$ — a superposition of the errors due to each input signal component acting alone.

6.10 The Generalized Definition of Error Coefficients (the Error Series)[1]

In this section, the error constant concept is generalized to include inputs of almost any arbitrary function of time. Equation (6–114) states that

$$E(s) = \frac{R(s)}{1 + G(s)} \tag{6–136}$$

where $E(s)$ represents the error of a unity-feedback control system. From the theory of the convolution integral discussed in Sec. 2.3, the error $e(t)$ may be written as

$$e(t) = \int_{-\infty}^{t} w_e(\tau) r(t - \tau) \, d\tau \tag{6–137}$$

where $w_e(\tau)$ is the inverse Laplace transform of $W_e(s) = 1/[1 + G(s)]$, and τ is a dummy time variable. If the first n derivatives of $r(t)$ exist for all values of τ, the function $r(t - \tau)$ can be expanded into a Taylor series; that is,

$$r(t - \tau) = r(t) - \tau r'(t) + \frac{\tau^2}{2!} r''(t) - \frac{\tau^3}{3!} r'''(t) + \dots \tag{6–138}$$

where the primes denote time derivatives.

Since $r(t)$ is zero for negative time, the limit of the convolution integral may be taken from 0 to t; substituting Eq. (6–138) into Eq. (6–137), we have

$$e(t) = \int_{0}^{t} w_e(\tau) \left[r(t) - \tau r'(t) + \frac{\tau^2}{2!} r''(t) - \frac{\tau^3}{3!} r'''(t) + \dots \right] d\tau$$

$$= r(t) \int_{0}^{t} w_e(\tau) \, d\tau - r'(t) \int_{0}^{t} \tau w_e(\tau) \, d\tau + r''(t) \int_{0}^{t} \frac{\tau^2}{2!} w_e(\tau) \, d\tau + \cdots \tag{6–139}$$

The steady-state error is obtained by taking the limit of $e(t)$ as t approaches infinity; that is,

$$e_{ss} = \lim_{t \to \infty} e(t) = \lim_{t \to \infty} \int_0^t w_e(\tau) r(t - \tau)\, d\tau = \int_0^\infty w_e(\tau) r_s(t - \tau)\, d\tau$$

$$= r_s(t) \int_0^\infty w_e(\tau)\, d\tau - r_s'(t) \int_0^\infty \tau w_e(\tau)\, d\tau + r_s''(t) \int_0^\infty \frac{\tau^2}{2!} w_e(\tau)\, d\tau - \cdots$$

$$(6\text{--}140)$$

where $r_s(t)$ denotes the limit of $r(t)$ as t approaches infinity; i.e., the steady-state part of $r(t)$.

If we define

$$C_0 = \int_0^\infty w_e(\tau)\, d\tau \tag{6--141}$$

$$C_1 = -\int_0^\infty \tau w_e(\tau)\, d\tau \tag{6--142}$$

$$C_2 = \int_0^\infty \tau^2 w_e(\tau)\, d\tau \tag{6--143}$$

.

.

$$C_n = (-1)^n \int_0^\infty \tau^n w_e(\tau)\, d\tau \tag{6--144}$$

Eq. (6–140) can be written

$$e_{ss} = \lim_{t \to \infty} e(t) = C_0 r_s(t) + C_1 r_s'(t) + \frac{C_2}{2!} r_s''(t) + \cdots + \frac{C_n}{n!} r_s^{(n)}(t) + \cdots$$

$$(6\text{--}145)$$

where the coefficients, $C_0, C_1, C_2, \ldots, C_n, \ldots$ are defined as the *generalized error coefficients*. In Eq. (6–145), the steady-state error is shown to be dependent on the generalized error coefficients, the steady-state part of the input, $r_s(t)$, and all the higher derivatives of $r_s(t)$. The error coefficients may readily be evaluated from the system transfer function $G(s)$ for a unity-feedback system; for a nonunity feedback system, $G(s)H(s)$ should be used.

Consider the equation

$$W_e(s) = \int_0^\infty w_e(\tau) e^{-\tau s}\, d\tau \tag{6--146}$$

which is the Laplace transform of $w_e(\tau)$. Taking the limit of Eq. (6–146) as s approaches zero, we have

$$\lim_{s \to 0} C_0 e^{-\tau s} = C_0 = \lim_{s \to 0} W_e(s) \tag{6--147}$$

Taking the derivative of $W_e(s)$ with respect to s yields

$$\frac{dW_e(s)}{ds} = -\int_0^\infty \tau w_e(\tau) e^{-\tau s}\, d\tau = C_1 e^{-\tau s} \tag{6--148}$$

from which we have

$$C_1 = \lim_{s \to 0} \frac{d W_e(s)}{ds} \qquad (6\text{-}149)$$

The rest of the error coefficients are obtained by successive differentiation of Eq. (6-148); therefore,

$$C_2 = \lim_{s \to 0} \frac{d^2 W_e(s)}{ds^2} \qquad (6\text{-}150)$$

$$C_3 = \lim_{s \to 0} \frac{d^3 W_e(s)}{ds^3} \qquad (6\text{-}151)$$

.

.

$$C_n = \lim_{s \to 0} \frac{d^n W_e(s)}{ds^n} \qquad (6\text{-}152)$$

The advantages of using the generalized error coefficients are summarized as follows:

(1) The generalized error coefficients provide a simple way of determining the nature of the response of a feedback control system to almost any arbitrary input.

(2) The generalized error coefficients lead to the calculation of the complete steady-state response without actually solving the system differential equation.

Example 6-1. In this example, the steady-state error of a unity-feedback control system will be computed by use of the generalized error coefficients. Consider a unity-feedback control system with the open-loop transfer function given as

$$G(s) = \frac{K}{s + 1} \qquad (6\text{-}153)$$

The error constants are

$$K_p = K, \qquad K_v = 0, \quad \text{and} \quad K_a = 0$$

Therefore, when the reference input to the system is a unit step displacement, the steady-state error in the output is $1/(1 + K)$; when the input is either a velocity or an acceleration function, the steady-state error is infinite in magnitude, since it increases with time. It is clear that the classic error constants fail to indicate the manner in which the error function increases with time. Ordinarily, if the steady-state response of this system due to a velocity or an acceleration input is desired, the system differential equation must be solved. We shall show in the following that the steady-state output response can actually be obtained from the error series.

For this system,

$$W_e(s) = \frac{1}{1 + G(s)} = \frac{s + 1}{s + K + 1} \qquad (6\text{-}154)$$

Thus

$$C_0 = \lim_{s \to 0} W_e(s) = \frac{1}{1+K} \qquad (6\text{--}155)$$

$$C_1 = \frac{K}{(1+K)^2} \qquad (6\text{--}156)$$

$$C_2 = \frac{-2K}{(1+K)^3} \qquad (6\text{--}157)$$

With the substitution of the error coefficients into Eq. (6–145), the error series is

$$e_{ss}(t) = \frac{1}{1+K} r_s(t) + \frac{K}{(1+K)^2} r'_s(t) + \frac{-K}{(1+K)^3} r''_s(t) + \cdots \qquad (6\text{--}158)$$

(1) When the input signal is a unit step displacement, the steady-state error given by Eq. (6–158) is

$$e_{ss} = \frac{1}{1+K} \qquad (6\text{--}159)$$

which agrees with the result given by the classical error constant.

(2) When the input signal is a unit step velocity, $r_s(t) = tu(t)$. Then, $r'_s(t) = 1$, $r''_s(t) = 0$, $r'''_s(t)$ and all higher derivatives are zero. The system steady-state error is given by

$$e_{ss}(t) = \frac{1}{1+K} t + \frac{K}{(1+K)^2} \qquad (6\text{--}160)$$

which consists of $K/(1+K)^2$ units of positional error, and $1/(1+K)$ units of error which increase linearly with time.

(3) For an acceleration input, $r(t) = (t^2/2)u(t)$, $r'(t) = tu(t)$, $r''(t) = u(t)$, and all other higher derivatives are zero. The steady-state error is

$$e_{ss}(t) = \frac{1}{1+K} \frac{t^2}{2} + \frac{K}{(1+K)^2} t - \frac{K}{(1+K)^3} \qquad (6\text{--}161)$$

Now the error is proportional to t and t^2.

(4) When the input signal is represented by a polynomial of t, for example,

$$r(t) = \left(a_0 + a_1 t + \frac{a_2 t^2}{2} \right) u(t) \qquad (6\text{--}162)$$

where a_0, a_1, and a_2 are constants,

$$r'(t) = (a_1 + a_2 t)u(t) \qquad (6\text{--}163)$$

$$r''(t) = a_2 u(t) \qquad (6\text{--}164)$$

the error series is written

$$e_{ss}(t) = \frac{1}{1+K} r_s(t) + \frac{1}{(1+K)^2} r'_s(t) + \frac{-K}{(1+K)^3} r''_s(t) \qquad (6\text{--}165)$$

Substituting the steady-state inputs into Eq. (6–165), we have

$$e_{ss}(t) = \left[\frac{1}{1+K} a_0 + \frac{K}{(1+K)^2} a_1 - \frac{K}{(1+K)^3} a_2 \right]$$
$$+ \left[\frac{a_1}{1+K} + \frac{a_2 K}{(1+K)^2} \right] t + \frac{a_2}{2(1+K)} t^2 \qquad (6\text{–}166)$$

6.11 Time Response of Discrete-data Control Systems[2]

Since a great majority of the discrete-data control systems in practice have outputs which are continuous functions of time, the interpretation of the time responses of this class of system is the same as those of strictly continuous-data systems. Therefore, the time response of a discrete-data control system is still described by such terms as overshoot, rise time, delay time, settling time, etc. However, when the z-transform method or the state transition equation at $t = kT$ is used, the responses of the system are described only at the sampling instants. Therefore, the maximum overshoot and the other criteria measured with respect to the discrete data characteristics may provide only an approximation to the actual values.

In this section, we shall discuss various methods of evaluating the time response of a discrete-data control system, the interpretation of the pole-zero configuration and transient response relationship in the s-plane and the z-plane, and finally, the steady-state error analysis of discrete-data control systems.

The Evaluation of the Time Response of a Second-order Discrete-data Control System

A typical second-order control system with sample-and-hold is shown in Fig. 6-26. We shall evaluate the unit-step response of the system, using the z-transform method and the state transition method.

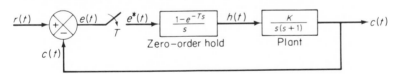

FIG. 6-26. A second-order discrete-data control system with sample-and-hold.

From Eq. (2–101), the z-transform of the output is given by

$$C(z) = \frac{G_{h0}G(z)}{1 + G_{h0}G(z)} R(z) \qquad (6\text{–}167)$$

where $G_{h0}G(z)$ denotes the z-transform of the zero-order hold and $G(s)$; that is,

$$G_{h0}G(z) = \mathscr{Z} \left[\frac{1 - e^{-Ts}}{s} G(s) \right] \qquad (6\text{–}168)$$

Therefore,

$$G_{h0}G(z) = \mathscr{L}\left[\frac{1 - e^{-Ts}}{s}\frac{K}{s(s + 1)}\right]$$

$$= (1 - z^{-1})\mathscr{L}\left[\frac{K}{s^2(s + 1)}\right] \qquad (6\text{-}169)$$

or

$$G_{h0}G(z) = K(1 - z^{-1})\mathscr{L}\left(\frac{1}{s^2} - \frac{1}{s} + \frac{1}{s + 1}\right) \qquad (6\text{-}170)$$

From the z-transform table, Eq. (6-171) is written as

$$G_{h0}G(z) = K(1 - z^{-1})\left[\frac{Tz}{(z - 1)^2} - \frac{z}{z - 1} + \frac{z}{z - e^{-T}}\right] \qquad (6\text{-}171)$$

For $T = 1$ sec, Eq. (6-171) is simplified to

$$G_{h0}G(z) = \frac{K(0.368z + 0.264)}{(z - 1)(z - 0.368)} \qquad (6\text{-}172)$$

For a unit step function input,

$$R(z) = \frac{z}{z - 1} \qquad (6\text{-}173)$$

Substituting Eqs. (6-172) and (6-173) into Eq. (6-167) and simplifying, we obtain the z-transform of the output response as

$$C(z) = \frac{Kz(0.368z + 0.264)}{(z - 1)[z^2 + (0.368K - 1.368)z + 0.368 + 0.264K]} \qquad (6\text{-}174)$$

Let us first set $K = 1$, so that Eq. (6-174) becomes

$$C(z) = \frac{z(0.368z + 0.264)}{(z - 1)(z^2 - z + 0.632)} \qquad (6\text{-}175)$$

Now dividing the numerator of $C(z)$ by its denominator continuously, we have

$$C(z) = 0.368z^{-1} + 1.00z^{-2} + 1.40z^{-3} + 1.40z^{-4} + 1.15z^{-5} + 0.90z^{-6}$$
$$+ 0.80z^{-7} + 0.86z^{-8} + 0.97z^{-9} + 1.05z^{-10} + 1.06z^{-11} + 1.01z^{-12}$$
$$+ 0.96z^{-13} + \cdots \qquad (6\text{-}176)$$

Since, by definition,

$$C(z) = \sum_{k=0}^{\infty} c(kT)z^{-k} \qquad (6\text{-}177)$$

the coefficients of the power series expansion in z^{-1} of $C(z)$ represent the values of $c(t)$ at the sampling instants.

The expansion of $C(z)$ in Eq. (6-176) indicates that the maximum overshoot in the step response is 40 per cent. However, this value is really the maximum of $c^*(t)$ and not necessarily that of $c(t)$. In general, the maximum overshoot of $c(t)$ will be somewhat greater than that indicated by the values of $c(kT)$ measured at the sampling instants. If the power series expansion

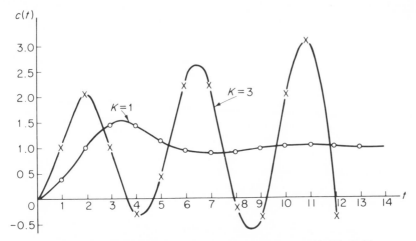

FIG. 6-27. Output responses of the discrete-data system in Fig. 6–26 when the input is a unit step function.

of $C(z)$ in Eq. (6–176) were to be carried on indefinitely, the final value of $c^*(t)$ would approach unity, which is the desired steady-state response. The entire step response of the system with $k = 1$ is shown in Fig. 6-27.

Now let us increase the value of K to 3; then Eq. (6–174) gives

$$C(z) = \frac{3z(0.368z + 0.264)}{(z - 1)(z^2 - 0.264z + 1.16)} \qquad (6\text{–}178)$$

which is expanded into the following series in z^{-1}:

$$C(z) = 1.1z^{-1} + 2.19z^{-2} + 1.19z^{-3} + 0.33z^{-4} + 0.42z^{-5} + 2.38z^{-6}$$
$$+ 2.15z^{-7} - 0.19z^{-8} - 0.54z^{-9} + 2.08z^{-10} + 3.18z^{-11} + 0.43z^{-12}$$
$$+ \cdots \qquad (6\text{–}179)$$

When the series is carried out indefinitely, we can show that the coefficients of the series increase without bound, which means that the system is unstable. We recall a well-known fact for a second-order system with continuous data—that the system is always stable so long as K is finite and positive. However, this illustrative example has shown that a second-order control system with sampling and hold can be unstable if the loop gain of the system is excessive. It will be shown later that the critical value of K for stability for this system is 2.43.

A closed form solution for $c(kT)$ can be obtained by using the inversion formula of the z-transform. Therefore,

$$c(kT) = \frac{1}{2\pi j} \oint_\Gamma C(z) z^{k-1}\, dz \qquad (6\text{–}180)$$

Substituting Eq. (6–175) into Eq. (6–180), we have

$$c(kT) = \frac{1}{2\pi j} \oint_\Gamma \frac{z(0.368z + 0.264)}{(z - 1)(z^2 - z + 0.632)} z^{k-1} \, dz$$

$$= \frac{1}{2\pi j} \oint_\Gamma \frac{0.368z(z - z_1)}{(z - 1)(z - p_1)(z - \bar{p}_1)} z^{k-1} \, dz \qquad (6\text{-}181)$$

where Γ is a circle centered at the origin of the z-plane which encloses all the poles of $C(z)z^{k-1}$. When the residue theorem is applied, Eq. (6–181) gives

$$c(kT) = 1 + 2\left|\frac{0.368(p_1 - z_1)}{(p_1 - 1)(p_1 - \bar{p}_1)}\right| |p_1|^k \cos(k\phi_1 + \theta_1) \qquad (6\text{-}182)$$

where

$$p_1 = 0.5 + j0.618$$
$$\bar{p}_1 = 0.5 - j0.618$$
$$z_1 = -0.717$$
$$\phi_1 = \tan^{-1}(0.618/0.5) = 51° \text{ or } 0.888 \text{ rad}$$

$$\theta_1 = \arg(p_1 - z_1) - \arg(p_1 - 1) - \frac{\pi}{2} = -193° \text{ or } -3.32 \text{ rad}$$

Therefore, the output sequence is

$$c(kT) = 1 + 1.02(0.8)^k \cos(0.888k - 3.32) \qquad (6\text{-}183)$$

When $k \to \infty$, $(0.8)^k$ approaches zero; thus,

$$\lim_{k \to \infty} c(kT) = 1 \qquad (6\text{-}184)$$

which is the final value of the output.

Similarly, a closed form solution of the inverse z-transform of $C(z)$ in Eq. (6–178) can be obtained in the same manner. It is interesting to point out that the poles of $C(z)/R(z)$ in this case are at $p_1 = 0.132 + j1.07$ and $\bar{p}_1 = 0.132 - j1.07$. Therefore, $|p_1| = 1.077$, and $|1.077|^k$ will become infinite when k approaches infinity. This verifies the fact that when $K = 3$, the system is unstable. Equation (6–181) also points out the fact that, in general, if $|p_1|$ exceeds unity, meaning that the poles of $C(z)/R(z)$ are outside the unit-circle in the z-plane, the system will be unstable.

As an alternative, the system of Fig. 6-26 can be analyzed by using the state transition method. Using the method discussed in Sec. 3.11, we draw the state transition signal flow graph of the system as shown in Fig. 6-28.

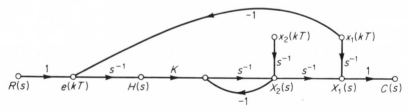

FIG. 6-28. State transition signal flow graph of the discrete-data control system in Fig. 6–26 for $kT \leq t \leq (k + 1)T$.

From this signal flow graph, the state transition equation of the system for $kT \leq t \leq (k+1)T$ is obtained as

$$\begin{bmatrix} x_1(t) \\ x_2(t) \end{bmatrix} = \begin{bmatrix} 1 - K[t - kT - 1 + e^{-(t-kT)}] & [1 - e^{-(t-kT)}] \\ -K[1 - e^{-(t-kT)}] & e^{-(t-kT)} \end{bmatrix} \begin{bmatrix} x_1(kT) \\ x_2(kT) \end{bmatrix}$$
$$+ \begin{bmatrix} K[t - kT - 1 + e^{-(t-kT)}] \\ K[1 - e^{-(t-kT)}] \end{bmatrix} r(kT) \tag{6-185}$$

For a unit step function input, $r(kT) = 1$ for all $k \geq 0$. Setting $t = (k+1)T$ and $T = 1$ sec in Eq. (6–185), we get

$$\begin{bmatrix} x_1[(k+1)T] \\ x_2[(k+1)T] \end{bmatrix} = \begin{bmatrix} 1 - 0.368K & 0.632 \\ -0.632K & 0.368 \end{bmatrix} \begin{bmatrix} x_1(kT) \\ x_2(kT) \end{bmatrix} + \begin{bmatrix} 0.368K \\ 0.632K \end{bmatrix} \tag{6-186}$$

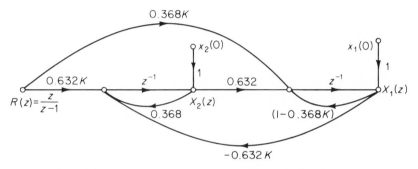

FIG. 6-29. Discrete state transition signal flow graph for the solution of Eq. (6–186).

The state transition signal flow graph of Eq. (6–186) is drawn in Fig. 6-29. From this flow graph, the following result is obtained by use of Mason's gain formula:

$$\begin{bmatrix} X_1(z) \\ X_2(z) \end{bmatrix} = \frac{1}{\Delta} \begin{bmatrix} z(z - 0.368) & 0.632z \\ -0.632Kz & z[z - (1 - 0.368K)] \end{bmatrix} \begin{bmatrix} x_1(0) \\ x_2(0) \end{bmatrix}$$
$$+ \frac{1}{\Delta} \begin{bmatrix} 0.368Kz + 0.264K \\ 0.632Kz(z - 1) \end{bmatrix} \frac{z}{z - 1} \tag{6-187}$$

where

$$\Delta = z^2 + (0.368K - 1.368)z + (0.368 + 0.264K) \tag{6-188}$$

For $K = 1$, $x_1(0) = 0$, and $x_2(0) = 0$, Eq. (6–187) gives

$$\begin{bmatrix} X_1(z) \\ X_2(z) \end{bmatrix} = \begin{bmatrix} \dfrac{z(0.368z + 0.264)}{(z - 1)(z^2 - z + 0.632)} \\[2ex] \dfrac{0.632z^2}{z^2 - z + 0.632} \end{bmatrix} \tag{6-189}$$

In this case, since $C(z) = X_1(z)$, it is easy to see that Eq. (6–189) gives the same result for $C(z)$ as Eq. (6–175). However, the state transition method has the advantage that Eq. (6–187) gives the solution of the system response when the initial conditions are not zero. The time sequences for $x_1(kT)$ and $x_2(kT)$ are obtained from Eq. (6–187) by taking the inverse z-transforms.

Interpretation of Time Response from the z-plane

In the study of continuous-data control systems it was shown that the transient response depends upon the location of the poles and zeros of the closed-loop transfer function in the s-plane. For instance, complex conjugate poles in the left half of the s-plane give rise to damped sinusoidal responses; poles on the negative real axis correspond to monotonically decaying responses; and complex conjugate poles on the imaginary axis will give rise to undamped sinusoidal oscillations. All poles in the right half of the s-plane correspond to unstable response. For a discrete-data control system similar relations exist between the pole-zero location of the closed loop transfer function in the z-plane and the time sequence $c(kT)$. However, since the z-transform may be regarded as a transformation from s to z, we shall first study the relationship between the s-plane and the z-plane.

The z-transform relation is given by

$$z = e^{Ts} \qquad (6\text{–}190)$$

Therefore, the imaginary axis of the s-plane $s = j\omega$ corresponds to

$$z = e^{j\omega T} \qquad (6\text{–}191)$$

which describes a circle with unit radius with center at the origin in the z-plane. The circle is usually referred to as the *unit circle*, and the mapping is illustrated as shown in Fig. 6-30. The region in the left half of the s-plane corresponds to the region inside the unit circle, and the right half of the

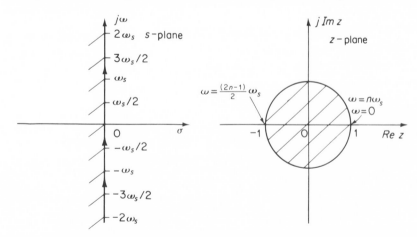

FIG. 6-30. Mapping of the imaginary axis of the s-plane onto the z-plane.

s-plane corresponds to the region outside the s-plane. Therefore, this simple mapping relationship verifies our earlier finding that the criterion for stability for a discrete-data system is that all the roots of the characteristic equation in z must be found inside the unit circle in the z-plane.

When $\omega = n\omega_s$ for $n = 0, \pm 1, \pm 2, \ldots$, $z = e^{jn\omega_s T} = e^{j2\pi n} = 1$; and when $\omega = \pm \omega_s/2, \pm 3\omega_s/2, \pm 5\omega_s/2, \ldots$, $z = -1$.

The real axis in the s-plane corresponds to

$$z = e^{Ts} = e^{T\sigma} \qquad (6\text{--}192)$$

which occupies the positive real axis of the z-plane. The negative real axis of the s-plane corresponds to $Re\,(z) \leq 1$, and the positive real axis of the s-plane corresponds to the real axis portion outside the unit circle in the z-plane. In fact, horizontal lines displaced at $\omega = \pm n\omega_s$, $n = \pm 1, \pm 2, \ldots$ in the s-plane all correspond to the positive portion of the real axis in the z-plane. Similarly, the horizontal lines that are displaced at $\omega = \pm \omega_s/2$, $\pm 3\omega_s/2, \ldots$ in the x-plane all correspond to the negative portion of the real axis in the z-plane. These mapping relationships are illustrated as shown in Fig. 6-31.

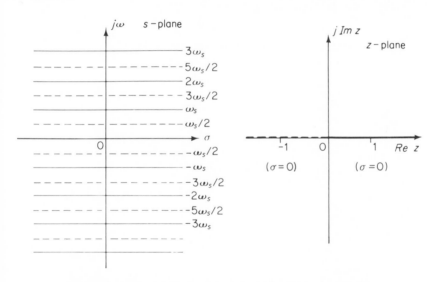

FIG. 6-31. Periodic strips in the s-plane. All solid horizontal lines in the s-plane correspond to the positive real axis and dotted lines correspond to the negative real axis in the z-plane.

The following mappings of trajectories are useful in interpreting the time response of discrete-data systems.

(1) *Constant Damping Loci*

For a constant damping factor σ_1 in the s-plane, the corresponding z-

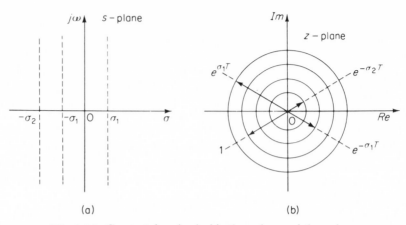

FIG. 6-32. Constant damping loci in the s-plane and the z-plane.

plane locus is a circle of radius $z = e^{\sigma_1 T}$ which is centered at the origin in the z-plane (Fig. 6-32).

(2) *The Constant Frequency Loci*

For any constant frequency ω_1 in the s-plane, the corresponding z-plane locus is a straight line emanating from the origin at an angle of $\theta = \omega_1 T$ measured from the positive real axis (Fig. 6–33).

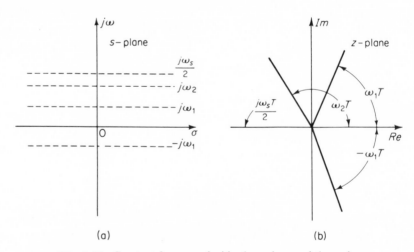

FIG. 6-33. Constant frequency loci in the s-plane and the z-plane.

(3) *The Constant Damping Ratio Loci*

For a constant damping ratio δ, the constant δ line in the s-plane, which is shown in Fig. 6-34a, is represented by

$$s = -\omega \tan \beta + j\omega \qquad (6\text{–}193)$$

Then

$$z = e^{Ts} = e^{(-\omega \tan\beta + j\omega)T}$$

$$= e^{-(2\pi/\omega_s)\omega\tan\beta} \Big\lfloor \frac{2\pi}{\omega_s}\omega \tag{6-194}$$

The constant δ path corresponding to Eq. (6-194) in the z-plane when $\beta = $ constant is a logarithmic spiral, except for $\beta = 0$ deg and 90 deg. The region shown shaded in Fig. 6-34a corresponds to the interior of the shaded region in Fig. 6-34b. In Fig. 6-35, the constant δ paths for $\beta = 30$ deg are shown in both the s-plane and the z-plane. Each half revolution of the logarithmic spiral corresponds to the passage of the δ path in the s-plane through a change of $j\omega_s/2$ along the $j\omega$ axis.

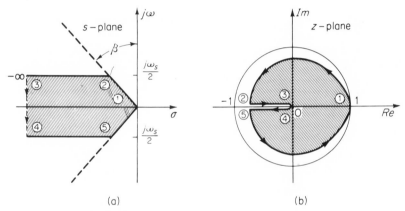

FIG. 6-34. Constant damping ratio loci in the s-plane and the z-plane.

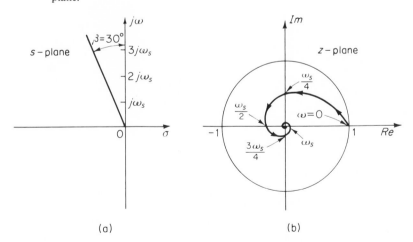

FIG. 6-35. Constant damping δ path for $\beta = 30°$ in the s-plane and the z-plane.

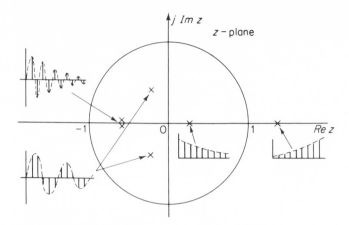

FIG. 6-36. Time responses corresponding various pole locations of $C(z)/R(z)$ in the z-plane.

Once the relationship between the s-plane and the z-plane is clarified, it is possible to relate the location of the poles of $C(z)$ to the time response behavior of $c^*(t)$. Figure 6-36 illustrates several cases of corresponding time responses and pole locations of $C(z)/R(z)$.

Steady-state Error in Discrete-data Control Systems

Since the input and output signals of most discrete-data control systems are continuous functions of time, strictly, the steady-state error of such systems is defined in the same way as that of continuous-data control systems; that is,

$$\text{Steady-state error} = e_{ss} = \lim_{t \to \infty} e(t) = \lim_{t \to \infty} [r(t) - c(t)] \qquad (6\text{-}195)$$

However, since the study of discrete-data systems relies to a great deal on the z-transform and the discrete state transition methods, which characterize the response only at the sampling instants, it is convenient to define a discrete steady-state error:

$$e_{ss}^* = \lim_{t \to \infty} e^*(t) = \lim_{k \to \infty} e(kT) = \lim_{k \to \infty} [r(kT) - c(kT)] \qquad (6\text{-}196)$$

Applying the final-value theorem of the z-transformation to Eq. (6–196), we have

$$e_{ss}^* = \lim_{k \to \infty} e(kT) = \lim_{z \to 1} (1 - z^{-1}) E(z) \qquad (6\text{-}197)$$

if $(1 - z^{-1}) E(z)$ does not have any pole on or outside the unit circle in the z-plane. Using the same approach as described in Sec. 6.9, we can define a set of *error constants* for discrete-data control systems. For instance, when the input signal to a discrete-data control system with unity feedback is a step function $r(t) = Ru(t)$,

$$R(z) = \frac{Rz}{z - 1} \qquad (6\text{-}198)$$

Then,

$$e_{ss}^* = \lim_{z \to 1} (1 - z^{-1}) E(z) = \lim_{z \to 1} (1 - z^{-1}) \frac{R(z)}{1 + G(z)}$$

$$= \frac{R}{1 + \lim_{z \to 1} G(z)} \qquad (6\text{-}199)$$

Now we define a positional error constant

$$K_p = \lim_{z \to 1} G(z) \qquad (6\text{-}200)$$

Equation (6-199) becomes

$$e_{ss}^* = \frac{R}{1 + K_p} \qquad (6\text{-}201)$$

Similarly, for a ramp input, it can be shown that the steady-state error is given by

$$e_{ss}^* = \frac{R}{K_v} \qquad (6\text{-}202)$$

where K_v is the velocity error constant and is given by

$$K_v = \frac{1}{T} \lim_{z \to 1} [(z - 1) G(z)] \qquad (6\text{-}203)$$

For an acceleration input, $r(t) = Rt^2 u(t)/2$, the acceleration error constant is defined as

$$K_a = \frac{1}{T^2} \lim_{z \to 1} (z - 1)^2 G(z) \qquad (6\text{-}204)$$

The steady-state error is related to R and K_a by

$$e_{ss}^* = \frac{R}{K_a} \qquad (6\text{-}205)$$

REFERENCES

1. J. G. Truxal, *Automatic Feedback Control System Synthesis*, McGraw-Hill Book Company, New York, N. Y., 1955.

2. B. C. Kuo, *Analysis and Synthesis of Sampled-data Control Systems*, Prentice-Hall, Inc., Englewood Cliffs, N. J., 1963.

PROBLEMS

6-1. A pair of complex conjugate poles in the s-plane is required to meet the various specifications given below. For each specifications, sketch the region in the s-plane in which the poles may be located.

(a) $\delta \geq 0.707$, $\omega_n \geq 2$ rad/sec (positive damping, stable)

(b) $0 \leq \delta \leq 0.707$ conditional frequency $\omega \leq 2$ rad/sec (positive damping)

(c) $\delta \leq 0.5$, $2 \leq \omega_n \leq 4$ rad/sec (positive damping)

(d) $0.5 \leq \delta \leq 0.707$, $\omega_n \leq 2$ rad/sec (positive and negative damping)

6-2. The open-loop transfer function of a servo system with unity feedback is given by

$$G(s) = \frac{C(s)}{E(s)} = \frac{1}{s(s^2 + 5s + 6)}$$

(a) When the input to the system is a unit step function, find the time required for the output response to settle down to 1 per cent of its final value.

(b) With the input still a unit step function, calculate the initial value of $c(t)$, and the first three initial derivatives of $c(t)$; i.e., $c'(0^+)$, $c''(0^+)$, $c'''(0^+)$.

6-3. The open-loop transfer function of a unity-feedback control system is given by

$$G(s) = \frac{A}{s(1 + Ts)}$$

(a) By what factor should the amplifier gain A be multiplied so that the damping ratio is increased from a value of 0.2 to 0.6?

(b) By what factor should the amplifier gain A be multiplied so that the overshoot of the unit step response is reduced from 80 per cent to 20 per cent?

6-4. The open-loop transfer function of a servo system with unity feedback is given by

$$G(s) = \frac{1}{s(1 + 0.5s)(1 + 0.2s)}$$

Determine the damping ratio and undamped natural frequency of the oscillatory roots. What is the per cent overshoot of the response to a unit step function input?

6-5. The block diagram of a simple servo system is shown in Fig. 6P-5.

(a) For $K = 10$, determine the values of a and b to give an overshoot of 16 per cent, and a time constant of 0.1 sec of the system response to

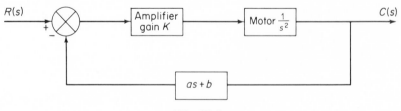

FIG. 6P-5.

a unit step input. Time constant is defined here as the inverse of the damping factor.

(b) If the value of K is decreased slightly, how does it affect the damping ratio of the system?

(c) Plot several points on the loci of roots of the system characteristic equation as K is varied from 0 to infinity.

6-6. The parameters of the positioning servo system shown in Fig. 6P-6 are given below:

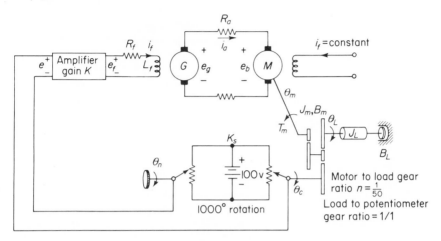

FIG. 6P-6.

J_L = Load inertia   1 ft-lb/rad/sec²
B_L = Load viscous friction   0.00143 ft-lb/rad/sec
J_m = Motor inertia $8 \cdot 10^{-4}$ ft-lb/rad/sec²
B_m = Motor viscous friction   negligible
R_f = Generator field resistance   50 ohms
L_f = Generator field inductance   5 henries
R_a = Total armature resistance of generator & motor   48.8 ohms
K_i = Motor torque constant   0.812 ft-lb/amp
K_g = Generator constant   200 v/amp
L_a = Total armature inductance of generator & motor   negligible

(a) For an amplifier gain of $K = 100$, find the roots of the characteristic equation of the system. Locate these roots in the s-plane.

(b) For $K = 100$, evaluate the output response $\theta_L(t)$ when $\theta_r(t)$ is a unit step displacement input. Sketch the waveform of $\theta_L(t)$.

(c) Repeat parts (a) and (b) for $K = 60.7$.

(d) Repeat parts (a) and (b) for $K = 50$. How does the steady-state response of $\theta_L(t)$ compare with the reference input $\theta_r(t)$?

6-7. The following parameters are given for the servo system shown in Fig. 4P-8.

K_s = Sensitivity of error detector   1 volt/rad
J_L = Load inertia   0.05 ft-lb/rad/sec²
B_L = Load viscous friction   0.005 ft-lb/rad/sec
J_m = Motor inertia   0.05 ft-lb/rad/sec²
B_i = Motor viscous friction   negligible
K_i = Motor torque constant   1 ft-lb/amp

L_a = Motor armature inductance   negligible
R_a = Motor armature resistance   10 ohms
K_d = Gain of demodulator   1 v/v
Gear ratio $n = N_1/N_2$ 1 : 1

(a) Write the characteristic equation of the system and determine the value of the d-c amplifier gain A for a critically damped system.

(b) For a unit ramp function input $\theta_r(t) = tu(t)$, what should be the minimum value of A so that the steady-state value of the response $\theta_L(t)$ will follow the reference input with a positional error not exceeding 0.0186 radian? With this gain setting, evaluate the output response $\theta_L(t)$.

6-8. In the feedback control system shown in Fig. 6P-8, the sensitivity of the synchro error detector is 1 v/deg. After the entire system is set up, the transfer function of the two-phase motor is determined experimentally as

$$\frac{\Theta_m(s)}{E_2(s)} = \frac{K_m}{s(1 + T_m s)}$$

where $K_m = 10\ v/sec$, and $T_m = 0.1$ sec.

$2\ rad/sec/volt$

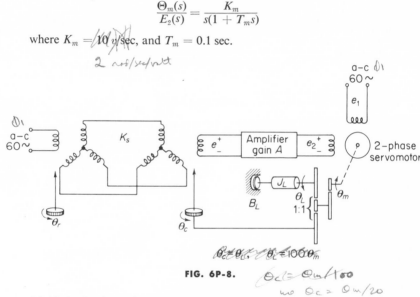

a-c
60 ~

$\theta_c = \theta_L,\ \theta_L = 100\ \theta_m$

FIG. 6P-8. $\theta_{cL} = \theta_m/100$

$\omega_0\ \ \theta_c = \theta_m/20$

(a) If the load on the output shaft is to be driven in its steady state at a constant speed of 30 rpm, what is the maximum value of gain A of the amplifier in order that the deviation between output and input positions will not exceed 3 deg when the steady state is reached?

(b) The gain of the amplifier is given by $A = 35$. Determine the damping ratio δ and the undamped natural frequency of the system.

(c) The amplifier is modified to differentiate the error signal so that the output of the amplifier is written as

$$e_2(t) = Ae(t) + AT_d\frac{de(t)}{dt}$$

where $A = 35$. Determine the value of T_d so that the damping ratio is 40 per cent. Repeat part (a) with the modified amplifier.

6-9. Determine the position, velocity, and acceleration error constants for the following feedback control systems (with unity feedback); the open-loop transfer functions are given by:

(a) $G(s) = \dfrac{50}{(1 + 0.1s)(1 + 2s)}$

(b) $G(s) = \dfrac{K}{s(1 + 0.1s)(1 + 0.5s)}$

(c) $G(s) = \dfrac{K}{s(s^2 + 4s + 200)}$

(d) $G(s) = \dfrac{K(1 + 2s)(1 + 4s)}{s^2(s^2 + 2s + 10)}$

6-10. For the systems of Problem 6-9, determine the steady-state errors for a unit step input, a unit ramp input t, and an aceleration input $t^2/2$.

6-11. A control system is being designed to keep the antenna of a tracking radar pointed at a flying target. The system must be able to follow a target traveling a straight-line course with speed up to 600 mph with a maximum permissible error of 0.01 deg. The shortest distance from antenna to target is 1000 ft. Determine the value of the velocity error constant K_v in order to satisfy these requirements.

6-12. Determine the error constants K_p, K_v, and K_a of the system in Problem 6-7 when $A = 186$. Evaluate the steady-state error between the output and the reference input when $\theta_r(t) = u(t)$, $tu(t)$, and $t^2u(t)/2$, respectively. Repeat the problem when the amplifier is introduced with a 180 deg phase shift ($A = -186$).

6-13. The open-loop transfer function of a control system with unity feedback is

$$G(s) = \frac{500}{s(1 + 0.1s)}$$

Evaluate the error series for the system. Determine the steady-state error of the system when the following inputs are applied:

(a) $r(t) = t^2 u(t)/2$

(b) $r(t) = 1 + 2t + t^2$ $(t > 0)$

Show that the steady-state error obtained from the error series is equal to the inverse Laplace transform of $E(s)$ with the terms generated by the poles of $E(s)/R(s)$ discarded.

6-14. In Problem 6-13, if a sinusoidal input $r(t) = \sin \omega t$ is applied to the system at $t = 0$, determine the steady-state error of the system by use of the error series for $\omega = 5$ rad/sec. What are the limitations in the error series when $r(t)$ is sinusoidal?

6-15. In the control system of Fig. 6P-5, write the error series for the system. Determine the steady-state error when the input is $r(t) = (1 + 2t + t^2)u(t)$.

6-16. Assume that the control system being designed in Problem 6-13 has an open-loop transfer function

$$G(s) = \frac{K}{s(1 + Ts)}$$

and $H(s) = 1$. The specifications are the same as those given in Problem 6-13. By use of the error series, determine the values of K and T which will satisfy the specifications.

6-17. For the discrete-data control system shown in Fig. 6P-17, given

$$G(s) = \frac{1}{s^2(s + 5)}, \qquad H(s) = 1$$

and $T = 1$ sec. The input is a unit step function applied at $t = 0$. Assuming zero initial conditions,

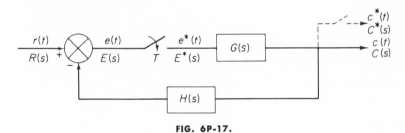

FIG. 6P-17.

(a) Obtain the z-transform of the output
(b) Obtain the output response at the sampling instants
(c) Determine the final value of the output response.

6-18. Write the discrete state equations for the system in Problem 6-17 in the form of

$$x[(k + 1)T] = \Phi(T)x(kT) + \Theta(T)r(kT)$$

Find $X(z)$, where $r(t)$ is a unit step function.

6-19. For the discrete-data control system shown in Fig. 6P-17,

$$G(s) = \frac{1}{s(s + 1)(s + 2)}$$

and $T = 1$ sec. The input signal is a unit step function.
(a) Draw a state transition signal flow graph for the system.
(b) Write the discrete state equations in the form of

$$x[(k + 1)T] = \Phi(T)x(kT) + \Theta(T)r(kT)$$

6-20. Determine the error constants of the discrete-data control system in Problem 6-17.

6-21. Determine the error constants of the discrete-data control system in Problem 6-19.

7

Stability of Linear Control Systems

7.1 Introduction

It has been shown in the previous chapter that the transient response of a feedback control system is controlled by the locations of the roots of the characteristic equation in the s-plane. Basically, the design of feedback control systems can be regarded as a problem of arranging the location of the characteristic equation roots in such a way that the corresponding system will perform according to the prescribed specifications. Among the many usual performance specifications, the most important requirement is that the system must be stable at all times. Intuitively, the term *stability* is used to distinguish two classes of systems: *useful* and *useless*. From a practical sense, a stable system may be a useful one, whereas an unstable system is useless, although there are a few exceptional cases.

In essence, the analysis of linear control systems is centered on stability studies. First, the system is tested to determine its *absolute stability;* that is, stable or unstable. If the system is found to be stable, then it is necessary to find out how stable it is, and the degree of stability is a measure of *relative stability*. Parameters such as overshoot and damping ratio used in relation to the transient response in the last chapter provide indications of the relative stability of a linear system in the time domain. However, in this chapter, we are concerned only with the absolute stability of linear time-invariant systems, which is simply a *yes* or *no* proposition.

From the examples worked out in the last chapter, the relation between the transient response and the characteristic equation roots can be summarized as follows:

(1) When all the roots of the characteristic equation are found in the left half of the s-plane, the responses due to the initial conditions will decrease to zero as time approaches infinity.

(2) If one or more pairs of simple roots are located on the imaginary axis, but with no roots in the right half of the s-plane, the responses will be undamped sinusoidal oscillations.

(3) If one or more roots are found in the right half of the s-plane, the responses will increase in magnitude as time increases.

Usually, in linear system theory, the last two categories are defined as *unstable* conditions.

The stability of a linear time-invariant system can be defined in a number of ways. Strictly, in linear systems, stability is independent of the input excitations. However, a well-known definition of stability is as follows: *A system is said to be stable if its output is bounded for any bounded input.*

In other words, let $c(t)$ be the output and $r(t)$ the input of a linear system. Then, if

$$|r(t)| \leq N < \infty \quad \text{for} \quad t \geq t_0 \tag{7-1}$$

$$|c(t)| \leq M < \infty \quad \text{for} \quad t \geq t_0 \tag{7-2}$$

However, there are a few exceptions to the foregoing definition. A differentiator gives rise to an impulse response at $t = t_0$ when it is subjected to a unit step function input $u(t - t_0)$. In this case the input is bounded, but the output is not, since an inpulse is known to have an infinite amplitude. Also, when $u(t - t_0)$ is applied to an integrator, the output is a ramp function $(t - t_0) u(t - t_0)$ which is not bounded for $t > t_0$. However, since a differentiator and an integrator are all useful systems, they are defined as stable systems.

The definition of stability given above may lead to several different ways of interpreting the stability criterion of linear time-invariant systems. These are discussed in the following sections.

7.2 Stability Defined According to Impulse Response

The definition on stability given in the last section leads to an important requirement on the impulse response of a stable system.

Given a linear system with input $r(t)$, output $c(t)$, then

$$c(t) = \int_0^\infty r(t - \tau) g(\tau) \, d\tau \tag{7-3}$$

where $g(\tau)$ is the impulse response of the system.

Taking the absolute value on both sides of Eq. (7-3) gives

$$|c(t)| = \left| \int_0^\infty r(t - \tau) g(\tau) \, d\tau \right| \tag{7-4}$$

From the knowledge that the absolute value of an integral is no greater than the integral of the absolute value of the integrand, Eq. (7-4) is written as

$$|c(t)| \leq \int_0^\infty |r(t-\tau)||g(\tau)| \, d\tau \qquad (7\text{-}5)$$

Now if $r(t)$ is a bounded signal, then from Eq. (7-1),

$$|c(t)| \leq \int_0^\infty N|g(\tau)| \, d\tau = N \int_0^\infty |g(\tau)| \, d\tau \qquad (7\text{-}6)$$

Therefore, if $c(t)$ is to be a bounded output,

$$N \int_0^\infty |g(\tau)| \, d\tau \leq M < \infty \qquad (7\text{-}7)$$

or

$$\int_0^\infty |g(\tau)| \, d\tau \leq P < \infty \qquad (7\text{-}8)$$

A physical interpretation of Eq. (7-8) is that the area under the absolute-value curve of the impulse response $g(t)$, evaluated from $t = 0$ to $t = \infty$, must be finite.

We shall now show that the requirement on the impulse response for stability can be linked to the restrictions on the characteristic equation roots.

By definition, the transfer function $G(s)$ of the system and the impulse response $g(t)$ are related through the Laplace transform integral,

$$G(s) = \int_0^\infty g(t)e^{-st} \, dt \qquad (7\text{-}9)$$

Taking the absolute value on both sides of the last expression gives

$$|G(s)| \leq \int_0^\infty |g(t)||e^{-st}| \, dt \qquad (7\text{-}10)$$

The roots of the characteristic equation are the poles of $G(s)$, and when s takes on these values, $|G(s)| = \infty$. Also, $s = \sigma + j\omega$; the absolute value of e^{-st} is $|e^{-\sigma t}|$. Equation (7-10) becomes

$$\infty \leq \int_0^\infty |g(t)||e^{-\sigma t}| \, dt \qquad (7\text{-}11)$$

If one or more roots of the characteristic equation are in the right half and on the imaginary axis of the s-plane, $\sigma \geq 0$, and thus $|e^{-\sigma t}| \leq N = 1$. Thus, Eq. (7-11) is written as

$$\infty \leq \int_0^\infty N|g(t)| \, dt = \int_0^\infty |g(t)| \, dt \qquad (7\text{-}12)$$

for Re $(s) = \sigma \geq 0$.

Since Eq. (7-12) contradicts the stability criterion given in Eq. (7-8), we conclude that for the system to be stable, *the roots of the characteristic equation must all lie inside the left half of the s-plane.* Another way of stating this stability criterion is that *the roots of the characteristic equation must all have negative real parts.*

7.3 Stability from the Viewpoint of State Variables[1]

The stability condition of a linear time-invariant system can also be established from the state variable approach. Since stability is independent of the input, the condition that $x(t) = 0$, where $x(t)$ is the state vector, can be regarded as the *equilibrium state* of the system. Now consider that the system is subjected to a disturbance of finite amplitude at $t = t_0$ so that the initial state is given by $x(t_0) \neq 0$. If the system under zero input condition returns to its equilibrium state as t approaches infinity, it is said to be stable; otherwise, it is unstable. For linear systems the magnitude of the initial state is unimportant so long as it is finite. For nonlinear systems, however, different initial states may lead to entirely different stability conditions.

In view of the foregoing discussion, the stability condition from the viewpoint of the state variable can be stated as:

A system is said to be stable if for any finite initial state $x(t_0)$, *there is a positive number* M(*which depends on* $x(t_0)$) *such that*

and

$$(1)\quad \|x(t)\| < M \quad \text{for all}\quad t \geq t_0 \tag{7-13}$$

$$(2)\quad \lim_{t \to \infty} \|x(t)\| = 0 \tag{7-14}$$

where $\|x(t)\|$ represents the *norm** of the state vector $x(t)$, or

$$\|x(t)\| = \left[\sum_{i=1}^{n} x_i(t)^2 \right]^{1/2} \tag{7-15}$$

The condition stated in Eq. (7-13) implies that the transition of state for any $t > t_0$ as represented by the norm of the vector $x(t)$ must be bounded. Equation (7-14) states that the system must reach its equilibrium point as t approaches infinity.

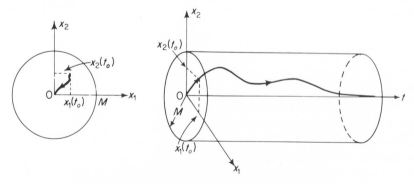

FIG. 7-1. Stability concept illustrated in the state space.

*The norm of a vector is a generalization of the idea of length. $\|x\|$ is always a real number.

The stability criterion is illustrated by the second-order case shown in Fig. 7-1. The trajectory represents the transition of $\mathbf{x}(t)$ for $t > t_0$ from a finite initial state $\mathbf{x}(t_0)$. As shown on the figure, $\mathbf{x}(t_0)$ is represented by a point which is the tip of the vector obtained from the vector sum $x_1(t_0)$ and $x_2(t_0)$. A cylinder with radius M forms the upper bound for the trajectory points for all $t > t_0$, and as t approaches infinity, the system reaches its equilibrium point $\mathbf{x}(t) = \mathbf{0}$.

Now we shall show that the definition of stability of linear systems given above leads to the same conclusion on the restrictions of the roots of the characteristic equation.

For zero-input conditions, the state transition equation of the system is

$$\mathbf{x}(t) = \mathbf{\Phi}(t - t_0)\,\mathbf{x}(t_0) \quad (t \geq t_0) \tag{7-16}$$

where $\mathbf{\Phi}(t - t_0)$ is the state transition matrix.

Taking the norm on both sides of Eq. (7-16) gives

$$\|\mathbf{x}(t)\| = \|\mathbf{\Phi}(t - t_0)\,\mathbf{x}(t_0)\| \tag{7-17}$$

An important property of the norm of a vector is

$$\|\mathbf{x}(t)\| \leq \|\mathbf{\Phi}(t - t_0)\|\,\|\mathbf{x}(t_0)\| \tag{7-18}*$$

Then the condition in Eq. (7-13) requires that $\|\mathbf{\Phi}(t - t_0)\|\,\|\mathbf{x}(t_0)\|$ is finite. Thus, if $\|\mathbf{x}(t_0)\|$ is finite as postulated, $\|\mathbf{\Phi}(t - t_0)\|$ must also be finite for $t > t_0$. Similarly, Eq. (7-14) leads to the condition that

$$\lim_{t \to \infty} \|\mathbf{\Phi}(t - t_0)\| = \mathbf{0} \tag{7-19}$$

In Eq. (3-45) the state transition matrix is written as

$$\mathbf{\Phi}(t) = \mathscr{L}^{-1}[(s\mathbf{I} - \mathbf{A})^{-1}] \quad t \geq 0 \tag{7-20}$$

or

$$\mathbf{\Phi}(t) = \mathscr{L}^{-1}\frac{[\Delta_{ij}]'}{|s\mathbf{I} - \mathbf{A}|} \tag{7-21}$$

where $[\Delta_{ij}]'$ is defined in Eq. (3-106).

Since $|s\mathbf{I} - \mathbf{A}| = 0$ is the characteristic equation of the system, Eq. (7-21) implies that the time response of $\mathbf{\Phi}(t)$ is controlled by the roots of the characteristic equation. Thus, the condition in Eq. (7-19) requires that the roots of the characteristic equation must all have negative real parts.

The discussions conducted in the preceding sections indicate that the stability of linear systems can be tested by locating the roots of the characteristic equation in the s-plane. The regions of stability and instability in the s-plane are illustrated in Fig. 7-2. The imaginary axis, except the origin, is included in the unstable region.

As a concluding remark, it must be pointed out that the stability of nonlinear systems is a complex subject. Since the input condition and the initial

---

*This property is analogous to the relation between magnitudes of vectors: If $|\mathbf{A}| = |\mathbf{B}\,\mathbf{C}|$, then $|\mathbf{A}| \leq |\mathbf{B}|\,|\mathbf{C}|$.

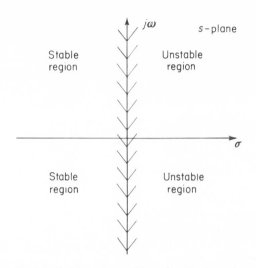

FIG. 7-2. Stable and unstable regions in the s-plane.

state all affect the stability of a nonlinear system, it is necessary to define a variety of definitions of stability.

7.4 Methods of Determining Stability of Linear Control Systems

Although stability of linear systems is defined with respect to the impulse response, the state transition matrix, or the roots of the characteristic equation, in practice, these criteria are difficult to implement. For instance, the impulse response is obtained by taking the inverse Laplace transform of the transfer function, which is not always a simple task; a similar process is required to evaluate $\Phi(t)$. The solving of the roots of a high-order polynomial is usually quite involved. Therefore, the stability analysis of a control system is seldom carried out by working with the impulse response or the transition matrix, or even by finding the exact location of the roots of the characteristic equation.

The methods outlined below are often used for the stability studies of linear control systems.

(1) Routh-Hurwitz Criterion.[2] This is an algebraic method which gives answer to the absolute stability of the system. The criterion tests whether any roots of the characteristic equation lie in the right half of the s-plane.

(2) Nyquist Criterion.[3] This is a graphical method which gives information on the difference between the number of poles and zeros of the closed-loop transfer function that are in the right half s-plane by observing the behavior of the Nyquist plot of the loop transfer function.

(3) The Root Locus Plot.[4] The root locus diagram indicates graphically the location of roots of the characteristic equation when the open-loop gain K of the system is varied.

(4) Bode Diagram. The Bode plot of the loop transfer function $G(s)$ $H(s)$ may be used to determine the stability of the closed-loop system in the same sense as the Nyquist criterion. However, the result is conclusive only if the transfer function is of the minimum phase type.

(5) Lyapunov's Stability Criterion.[5] This stability criterion is formulated on the basis of the state equation. The stability of the system is determined by checking on the properties of the *Lyapunov's function* of the system.

The first four methods are valid strictly only for linear control systems, although in isolated cases the Nyquist criterion and the root locus method can be extended to certain nonlinear systems. The Lyapunov's method was originally intended for nonlinear systems, although it is also valid for linear systems.

7.5 Routh-Hurwitz Criterion

It is established that the problem of determining the stability of a linear system is one of finding the roots of the characteristic equation. However, for polynomials of the third order or higher, the task of finding the roots is very tedious and time-consuming. Hence, it is desirable that an alternate method be used, so that the system stability can be determined without actually solving for the roots of the characteristic equation.

Suppose that the characteristic equation of a linear system is written in the general form:

$$F(s) = a_0 s^n + a_1 s^{n-1} + a_2 s^{n-2} + \cdots + a_{n-1} s + a_n = 0 \qquad (7\text{-}22)$$

where all the coefficients are real numbers.

In order that there be no roots of the last equation with positive real parts, it is necessary but not sufficient that*

*From the basic laws of algebra, the following relations are true for the polynomial given in Eq. (7-22):

$$\frac{a_1}{a_0} = -\sum \text{ all roots}$$

$$\frac{a_2}{a_0} = \sum \text{ products of the roots taken two at a time}$$

$$\frac{a_3}{a_0} = -\sum \text{ products of the roots taken three at a time}$$

$$\vdots$$

$$\frac{a_n}{a_0} = (-1)^n \text{ products of all roots}$$

All the ratios must be positive and nonzero unless at least one of the roots has a positive real part.

(1) All the coefficients of the polynomial have the same sign.

(2) None of the coefficients vanish.

The two necessary conditions given above can be checked by inspection. However, they are not sufficient; it is quite possible that a polynomial with all its coefficients positive and nonzero will have roots in the right half of the s-plane. The necessary and sufficient condition that all the roots of an nth order polynomial lie in the left half of the s-plane is that the polynomial's *Hurwitz determinants* $D_k(k = 1,2,3, \ldots, n)$ must be all positive.

The Hurwitz determinants of Eq. (7-22) are given by

$$D_1 = a_1 \qquad D_2 = \begin{vmatrix} a_1 & a_3 \\ a_0 & a_2 \end{vmatrix} \qquad D_3 = \begin{vmatrix} a_1 & a_3 & a_5 \\ a_0 & a_2 & a_4 \\ 0 & a_1 & a_3 \end{vmatrix}$$

$$\ldots \qquad D_n = \begin{vmatrix} a_1 & a_3 & a_5 & \ldots & a_{2n-1} \\ a_0 & a_2 & a_4 & \ldots & a_{2n-2} \\ 0 & a_1 & a_3 & \ldots & a_{2n-3} \\ 0 & a_0 & a_2 & \ldots & a_{2n-4} \\ 0 & 0 & a_1 & \ldots & a_{2n-5} \\ & & \cdot & & \\ & & \cdot & & \\ & & \cdot & & \\ 0 & 0 & 0 & \ldots & a_n \end{vmatrix} \qquad (7\text{-}23)$$

where the coefficients with indexes larger than n or with negative indexes are replaced by zeros.

Routh-Hurwitz's criterion is stated as follows: *The necessary and sufficient condition that all the roots of the polynomial $F(s) = 0$ of Eq. (7-22) lie in the left half of the s-plane is that $a_0 > 0$, $D_1 > 0$, $D_2 > 0$, \ldots, $D_n > 0$, where D_1, D_2, D_3, \ldots, D_n are defined in Eq. (7-23).*

At first glance, the application of the criterion may seem to be formidable for high-order polynomials because of the labor involved in evaluating the Hurwitz determinants. However, the rule can be applied without actually working with the high-order determinants given in Eq. (7-23) by following the steps given below.

The first step in the simplification of the Routh-Hurwitz criterion is to arrange the polynomial coefficients into two rows. The first row consists of the first, third, fifth coefficients, etc., and the second row consists of the second, fourth, sixth coefficients, etc., as shown in the following tabulation:

$$a_0 \quad a_2 \quad a_4 \quad a_6 \quad a_8 \quad \ldots$$

$$a_1 \quad a_3 \quad a_5 \quad a_7 \quad a_9 \quad \ldots$$

The next step is to form the following array of numbers obtained by the indicated operations. The example is shown for a sixth-order system.

s^6	a_0	a_2	a_4	a_6
s^5	a_1	a_3	a_5	0
s^4	$\dfrac{a_1a_2 - a_3a_0}{a_1} = A$	$\dfrac{a_1a_4 - a_0a_5}{a_1} = B$	$\dfrac{a_1a_6 - a_0 \times 0}{a_1} = a_6$	0
s^3	$\dfrac{Aa_3 - a_1B}{A} = C$	$\dfrac{Aa_5 - a_1a_6}{A} = D$	$\dfrac{A \times 0 - a_1 \times 0}{A} = 0$	0
s^2	$\dfrac{CB - AD}{C} = E$	$\dfrac{Ca_6 - A \times 0}{C} = a_6$	$\dfrac{C \times 0 - A \times 0}{C} = 0$	0
s^1	$\dfrac{ED - Ca_6}{E} = F$	0	0	0
s^0	$\dfrac{Fa_6 - E \times 0}{F} = a_6$	0	0	0

The last step is to investigate the signs of the numbers in the first column in the last tabulation. *The roots of the polynomial are all in the left half of the s-plane if all the elements of the first column are of the same sign. If there are changes of signs in the elements of the first column, the number of sign changes indicates the number of roots with positive real parts.* The reason for this statement is apparent, since the relations between the elements in the first column and the Hurwitz determinants are given as follows:

$$s^6 \quad a_0 = a_0$$
$$s^5 \quad a_1 = D_1$$
$$s^4 \quad A = D_2/D_1$$
$$s^3 \quad C = D_3/D_2$$
$$s^2 \quad E = D_4/D_3$$
$$s^1 \quad F = D_5/D_4$$
$$s^0 \quad a_6 = D_6/D_5$$

Example 7-1. Consider the polynomial

$$(s - 2)(s + 1)(s - 3) = s^3 - 4s^2 - 5s + 6 = 0 \qquad (7\text{-}24)$$

The polynomial given in the last equation has negative coefficients; thus, from the necessary condition, we know without applying Routh's test that there are roots with positive real parts. But for the purpose of illustrating Routh-Hurwitz's criterion, the Routh's tabulation is formed as follows:

	s^3	1	-5
Change in sign	s^2	-4	6
	s^1	$\dfrac{(-4)(-5) - 6}{-4} = -3.5$	0
Change in sign	s^0	$\dfrac{(-3.5)(6) - (-4)(0)}{-3.5} = 6$	

Since there are two sign changes in the first column, the polynomial has two roots located in the right half of the s-plane. This checks with the known result, since it is known that the two unstable roots are $s = 2$ and $s = 3$.

Example 7-2. Consider the polynomial

$$2s^4 + s^3 + 3s^2 + 5s + 10 = 0 \tag{7-25}$$

Since the polynomial has no missing terms, and the coefficients are of the same sign, it satisfies the necessary condition of stability. However, it is still necessary to check the sufficient condition. The Routh's tabulation is

$$
\begin{array}{c|ccc}
s^4 & 2 & 3 & 10 \\
s^3 & 1 & 5 & 0 \\
s^2 & \dfrac{(1)(3) - (2)(5)}{1} = -7 & 10 & 0 \\
s^1 & \dfrac{(-7)(5) - (1)(10)}{-7} = 6.43 & 0 & 0 \\
s^0 & 10 & &
\end{array}
$$

Change in sign (at s^2)

Change in sign (at s^1)

Since there are two changes in sign in the first column, the polynomial has two roots with positive real parts.

Special Cases

Occasionally, in applying Routh-Hurwitz's criterion, the following kinds of difficulties may occur:

(1) The first element in any one row of the Routh's tabulation is zero, but the other elements are not.

(2) The elements in one row of the Routh's tabulation are all zero. These two cases will be discussed separately as follows:

(1) When the first element in any row of the Routh's tabulation is zero, but the other elements are not: If a zero appears in the first position of a row, the elements in the next row become infinite, and Routh's test breaks down. To restore the missing power of s, simply multiply the polynomial by the factor $(s + a)$ where a is any positive real number,* and carry on the usual Routh's test.

Example 7-3. Consider the equation

$$(s - 1)^2 (s + 2) = s^3 - 3s + 2 = 0 \tag{7-26}$$

Since the coefficient of the s^2 term is zero, we know from the necessary condition that there must be at least one root of the polynomial which is located in the right half of the s-plane. The Routh's tabulation of the coefficients is given below.

*Although a negative real number is also allowed, it contributes a root in the right half of the plane, and this root should be taken into account when one is interpreting the Routh's tabulation.

$$s^3 \quad 1 \quad -3$$
$$s^2 \quad 0 \quad 2$$
$$s^1 \quad \infty$$
$$s^0$$

Because of the zero in the first element of the second row, the first element of the third row is infinite. To correct this situation, simply multiply the polynomial in Eq. (7-26) by the factor $(s + a)$. If the constant a is arbitrarily chosen as 3 (for reasons which will become apparent later, the value of a is not chosen as 1 or 2), we have

$$(s - 1)^2(s + 2)(s + 3) = s^4 + 3s^3 - 3s^2 - 7s + 6 = 0 \qquad (7\text{--}27)$$

The Routh's tabulation of the last equation is

s^4	1	-3	6
s^3	3	-7	0
Change in sign $\quad s^2$	$\dfrac{-9 + 7}{3} = \dfrac{-2}{3}$	6	
Change in sign $\quad s^1$	$\dfrac{\left(\dfrac{-2}{3}\right)(-7) - 18}{\left(\dfrac{-2}{3}\right)} = 20$	0	
s^0	6		

Since there are two changes in sign in the first column of the Routh's tabulation, two roots of the equation are in the right half of the s-plane.

As an alternative to the remedy of the situation described above, we can replace the zero element in the Routh's tabulation by an arbitrary small positive number ϵ, and then proceed with the Routh's test. For instance, for the equation given in Eq. (7-26), if we replace the zero element in the second row of the Routh's tabulation, and proceed with the tabulation, we have

s^3	1	-3
s^2	ϵ	2
s^1	$\dfrac{-3\epsilon - 2}{\epsilon}$	0
s^0	2	

Now since $(-3\epsilon - 2)/\epsilon$ approaches $-2/\epsilon$, which is a negative number, the first column of the last tabulation has two changes in sign. This agrees with the result obtained earlier.

(2) When all the elements in one row of the Routh's tabulation are zero: This condition indicates that there are pairs of real roots with opposite signs, pairs of conjugate roots on the imaginary axis, or both; or conjugate roots

forming a quadrate in the s-plane. The equation corresponding to the coefficients just above the row of zeros is called the *auxiliary equation*. *The order of the auxiliary equation is always even, and it indicates the number of root pairs that are equal in magnitude but opposite in sign.* For example, if the auxiliary equation is of the second order, there are two equal and opposite roots. For a fourth-order auxiliary equation, there must be two pairs of equal and opposite roots. All these roots with equal magnitude can be obtained by solving the auxiliary equation. Again, Routh's test breaks down; in this case, because of the row of zeros. To correct this situation, simply take the first derivative of the auxiliary equation with respect to s, replace the row of zeros with the coefficients of the resultant equation obtained by taking the derivative of the auxiliary equation, and carry on with the Routh's test.

Example 7-4. Consider the same equation used in Example 7-3, $s^3 - 3s + 2 = 0$. In multiplying this equation by a factor $(s + a)$, logically, the first number that comes into one's mind would be $a = 1$. Thus,

$$(s - 1)^2(s + 2)(s + 1) = s^4 + s^3 - 3s^2 - s + 2 = 0 \qquad (7\text{-}28)$$

The Routh tabulation of this equation is

$$
\begin{array}{cccc}
s^4 & 1 & -3 & 2 \\[4pt]
s^3 & 1 & -1 & \\[4pt]
s^2 & \dfrac{-3+1}{1} = -2 & 2 & \text{(coefficients of the auxiliary equation)} \\[6pt]
s^1 & \dfrac{2-2}{-2} = 0 & 0 &
\end{array}
$$

Since the s^1 row contains all zeros, Routh's test breaks down. The multiplication of the factor $(s + 1)$ to the original equation, which has a root at $s = 1$, has made the new polynomial fit the special case (2). The auxiliary equation is obtained by using the elements contained in the s^2 row as the coefficients of the equation. Thus,

$$A(s) = -2s^2 + 2 = 0 \qquad (7\text{-}29)$$

and

$$\frac{dA(s)}{ds} = -4s \qquad (7\text{-}30)$$

Now the row of zeros in the Routh's tabulation are replaced by the coefficients of the last equation; the Routh's tabulation reads as follows:

$$
\begin{array}{rccc}
& s^4 & 1 & -3 & 2 \\[4pt]
\text{Change in sign} & s^3 & 1 & -1 & \\[4pt]
& s^2 & -2 & 2 & \\[4pt]
& s^1 & -4 & 0 & \left(\text{coefficients of } \dfrac{dA(s)}{ds}\right) \\[6pt]
\text{Change in sign} & s^0 & 2 & 0 &
\end{array}
$$

Since there are two changes in sign in the elements in the first column of the new Routh's tabulation, two roots of the equation have positive real parts. By solving the roots of the auxiliary equation in Eq. (7–29) we have

$$s^2 = 1, \quad \text{or} \quad s = \pm 1.$$

Example 7-5. Consider the equation

$$(s + 2)(s - 2)(s + j)(s - j)(s^2 + s + 1) = s^6 + s^5 - 2s^4 - 3s^3 - 7s^2$$
$$-4s - 4 = 0 \tag{7–31}$$

It is known that the last equation has two pairs of equal roots with opposite signs at $s = \pm 2$ and $s = \pm j$. The Routh's tabulation is

s^6	1	-2	-7	-4
s^5	1	-3	-4	
s^4	$\dfrac{-2+3}{1} = 1$	$\dfrac{-7+4}{1} = -3$	-4	
s^3	0	0	0	

The auxiliary equation is

$$A(s) = s^4 - 3s^2 - 4 = 0 \tag{7–32}$$

which indicates that there are two pairs of equal roots with opposite signs. The first derivative of the auxiliary equation with respect to s is

$$\frac{dA(s)}{ds} = 4s^3 - 6s \tag{7–33}$$

from which the coefficients 4 and -6 are substituted into the row of zeros in the Routh's tabulation. The new Routh's tabulation is

	s^6	1	-2	-7	-4
	s^5	1	-3	-4	
	s^4	1	-3	-4	
	s^3	4	-6	0	$\leftarrow$ Coefficients of $\dfrac{dA(s)}{ds}$
Change in sign	s^2	$\dfrac{-12+6}{4} = -1.5$	-4	0	
	s^1	$\dfrac{-9+16}{-1.5} = -16.7$	0		
	s^0	-4	0		

Since there is only one change in sign in the first column of the new Routh's tabulation, the polynomial has one root with a positive real part. This result obviously checks with the given polynomial roots. The two pairs of equal roots are obtained by solving the auxiliary equation given in Eq. (7–32). The roots are $s = \pm 2$ and $s = \pm j$.

A frequent use of Routh's criterion is to determine the condition of stability of a linear feedback control system. For instance, the servo system with integral control shown in Fig. 6-18 has the characteristic equation

$$s^3 + 34.5s^2 + 7500s + 7500K_1 = 0 \qquad (7\text{-}34)$$

The Routh's criterion is to be applied to the last equation to determine the range of value of K_1 for which the closed-loop system is stable. The Routh's tabulation of Eq. (7-34) is

$$
\begin{array}{ccc}
s^3 & 1 & 7500 \\
s^2 & 34.5 & 7500K_1 \\
s^1 & (258{,}750 - 7500K_1)/34.5 & 0 \\
s^0 & 7500K_1 &
\end{array}
$$

For the system to be stable, all the coefficients in the first column of the Routh's tabulation must be positive. The conditions are

$$(258{,}750 - 7500K_1)/34.5 > 0 \qquad (7\text{-}35)$$

and

$$7500K_1 > 0 \qquad (7\text{-}36)$$

From the condition in Eq. (7-35) we have

$$K_1 < 34.5 \qquad (7\text{-}37)$$

and from the condition in Eq. (7-36) we have

$$K_1 > 0 \qquad (7\text{-}38)$$

Hence, the condition for stability is that K_1 must satisfy the relation

$$0 < K_1 < 34.5 \qquad (7\text{-}39)$$

Example 7-6. Consider the characteristic equation of a certain closed-loop system,

$$s^3 + 3Ks^2 + (K + 2)s + 4 = 0 \qquad (7\text{-}40)$$

The Routh's tabulation is

$$
\begin{array}{ccc}
s^3 & 1 & (K + 2) \\
s^2 & 3K & 4 \\
s^1 & \dfrac{3K(K + 2) - 4}{3K} & 0 \\
s^0 & 4 &
\end{array}
$$

From the s^2 row, the condition of stability is

$$K > 0$$

and from the s^1 row, we have

$$3K^2 + 6K - 4 > 0$$

from which

$$K < -2.528 \text{ or } K > 0.528$$

When the conditions $K > 0$ and $K > 0.528$ are compared, apparently the latter limitation is the most stringent one. Hence, for the closed-loop system to be stable the value of K must be greater than 0.528.

It should be reiterated that the Routh-Hurwitz criterion is valid only if the characteristic equation is algebraic and that all the coefficients are real. If any one of the coefficients of the characteristic equation is a complex number, or if the equation contains exponential functions of s, such as in the case of a system with time delays, the Routh-Hurwitz criterion breaks down completely.

Another limitation of the Routh-Hurwitz criterion is that it offers information only on the absolute stability of the system. If a control system is found to be stable by the Routh's test, one still does not know how good the system is—in other words, how closely the roots of the characteristic equation are located to the imaginary axis of the s-plane. On the other hand, if the system is unstable, the Routh's test gives no indication on how the system can be stabilized. For information of the relative stability of a control system, one must turn to the Nyquist criterion or the root locus method.

7.6 The Nyquist Criterion

Thus far, two methods of determining the location of the roots of the characteristic equation have been indicated:

(1) The roots are actually determined by solving the characteristic equation.

(2) The location of the roots with respect to the imaginary axis of the s-plane is determined by means of the Routh-Hurwitz criterion.

Although the application of the Routh-Hurwitz criterion is quite straightforward, the only information that the criterion can furnish is the absolute stability of the system.

The Nyquist criterion possesses the following features which make it particularly desirable for the stability analysis of feedback control systems:

(1) It provides the same amount of information on the absolute stability of a feedback system as the Routh-Hurwitz criterion.

(2) In addition to the absolute system stability, the Nyquist criterion also indicates the degree of stability of a stable system, and gives information on how the system stability may be improved, if necessary.

(3) The Nyquist locus gives information concerning the frequency response of the system.

Consider the feedback control system shown in Fig. 7–3. The closed-loop transfer function of the system is

$$\frac{C(s)}{R(s)} = \frac{G(s)}{1 + G(s)H(s)} \qquad (7\text{–}41)$$

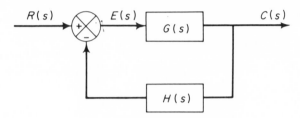

FIG. 7-3. Feedback control system.

Let the denominator of Eq. (7–41) be represented by $F(s)$; that is,

$$F(s) = 1 + G(s)H(s) \qquad (7\text{-}42)$$

The zeros of $F(s)$ are the roots of the characteristic equation of the system. In this chapter the functions $G(s)$ and $H(s)$ are assumed to be rational functions. In other words, $G(s)H(s)$ is a quotient of two polynomials with constant coefficients. Thus, in general, $F(s)$ can be written as

$$F(s) = 1 + G(s)H(s) = \frac{(s + z_1)(s + z_2) \dots (z + z_m)}{s^j(s + p_1)(s + p_2) \dots (s + p_n)} \qquad (7\text{-}43)$$

The zeros of $F(s)$ at $-z_1, -z_2, -z_3, \dots, -z_m$ are the roots of the characteristic equation; they are either real, imaginary, or in complex conjugate pairs. For a stable closed-loop system, it is required that none of these roots has a positive real part; there is no particular restriction on the location of the poles of $F(s)$, which are at $s = 0, -p_1, -p_2, \dots, -p_n$. It is important to note that the poles of $F(s)$ are the same as those of $G(s)H(s)$. If any one of the poles of $G(s)H(s)$ lies in the right half of the s-plane, the open-loop system* is said to be unstable; however, the closed-loop system can still be stable if all the zeros of $F(s)$ are found in the left half of the s-plane. This is a very important feature of a feedback control system. In previous chapters, it was made clear that a high forward gain K generally reduces the steady-state error of a system; consequently, it is a common practice to use high gain in multiple-loop systems. Although this practice may result in an unstable inner-loop system, the entire closed-loop system can be made stable by proper design.

This section can be summarized as follows:

(1) Identification of the poles and zeros:

(a) The loop-gain zeros $=$ The zeros of $G(s)H(s)$
(b) The loop-gain poles $=$ The poles of $G(s)H(s)$
(c) The closed-loop poles $=$ The poles of $C(s)/R(s)$
$ = $ The zero of $F(s) = 1 + G(s)H(s)$
$ = $ The roots of the characteristic equation

(2) The poles of $F(s)$ are the same as the poles of the loop gain.

*The open-loop system here refers to the loop transfer function $G(s)H(s)$.

(3) For a stable feedback control system, there is no restriction on the location of the poles and zeros of the loop gain, but the closed-loop poles must all be located in the left half of the s-plane.

"Encircled" Versus "Enclosed"

Before starting on the discussion of the Nyquist criterion, it is important to distinguish between two terms—*encircled* and *enclosed*—which will be used frequently with the Nyquist criterion.

(1) *Encircled*

A point is said to be encircled by a closed path if it is found inside the path. For example, the point A shown in Fig. 7-4a is encircled by the closed path Γ, since A is found inside the closed path. The direction of encirclement is

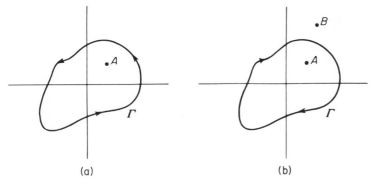

(a)   (b)

FIG. 7-4. Encircled points and regions. (a) Point A is encircled by Γ in the counterclockwise direction; (b) point A is encircled by Γ in the clockwise direction.

also indicated by the arrow on the path. The point A shown in Fig. 7-4b is encircled by the locus Γ in a clockwise direction, whereas that of Fig. 7-4a is encircled by Γ in a counterclockwise direction. In Fig. 7-4b the point B is not encircled by the closed path Γ.

When applying all the points inside the closed path, we can say that the region inside the closed path Γ is encircled by the path in the indicated direction.

(2) *Enclosed*

A point or region is said to be enclosed by a closed path if it is found to lie to the left of the path when the path is traversed in a prescribed direction. For instance, the shaded regions shown in Fig. 7-5a and Fig. 7-5b are considered to be enclosed by the Γ locus. In other words, the point A in Fig. 7-5a is enclosed by Γ, but the point A in Fig. 7-5b is not. However, the point B and the region outside the path in Fig. 7-5b are enclosed.

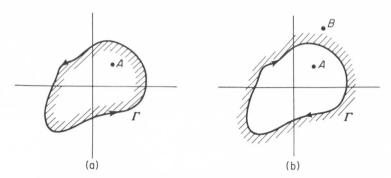

FIG. 7-5. Enclosed points and regions. (a) Point A is enclosed by Γ; (b) point A is not enclosed but B is enclosed by the locus Γ.

The Principle of the Argument

The Nyquist criterion was originated from the principle of the argument in complex variable theories. Let $F(s)$ be a single-valued rational function which is analytic everywhere in a specified region except at a finite number of points in the s-plane. For each point of analyticity in the specified region in the s-plane, there is a corresponding point in the $F(s)$-plane. Suppose that a continuous closed path Γ_s is arbitrarily chosen in the s-plane, as shown in Fig. 7-6; if all the points on Γ_s are in the specified region in which $F(s)$ is analytic,

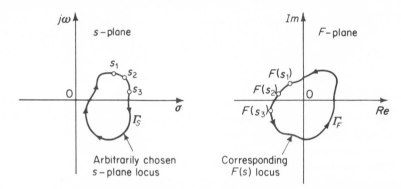

FIG. 7-6. The arbitrary chosen s-plane locus Γ_s, and the corresponding $F(s)$-plane locus Γ_F.

the curve Γ_F mapped by the function $F(s)$ into the F-plane is also a closed one. If, corresponding to the point s_1 in the s-plane, a point $F(s_1)$ is located in the F-plane, as the Γ_s locus is traced starting from the point s_1 in a clockwise direction (arbitrarily chosen) and then returning to s_1 after going through all the points on the Γ_s locus, the corresponding Γ_F locus will start from the point $F(s_1)$ and go through the points $F(s_2)$, $F(s_3)$, . . . , and back to the starting point $F(s_1)$. The direction of traverse of Γ_F may be either clockwise or counterclockwise, depending on the particular function $F(s)$.*

The principle of the argument states:

Let $F(s)$ be a single-valued rational function which is analytic in a specified region in the s-plane except at a finite number of points. Suppose that an arbitrary closed path Γ_s is chosen in the s-plane so that at every point on the Γ_s path $F(s)$ is analytic; the corresponding $F(s)$ locus mapped in the F-plane will *encircle* the origin as many times as the difference between the number of the zeros and the number of the poles of $F(s)$ that are encircled by the s-plane locus Γ_s. In other words,

$$N = Z - P \qquad (7\text{-}44)$$

where

$N =$ number of encirclement of the origin made by the $F(s)$ locus Γ_F in the F-plane

and

$Z =$ number of zeros of $F(s)$ encircled by the s-plane locus Γ_s in the s-plane

$P =$ number of poles of $F(s)$ encircled by the s-plane locus Γ_s in the s-plane

In general, N can be positive $(Z > P)$, zero $(Z = P)$, or negative $(Z < P)$. These three different situations are discussed as follows:

(1) $N > 0(Z > P)$

If the s-plane locus encircles more zeros than poles of $F(s)$ in a certain direction (clockwise or counterclockwise), N is a positive integer; the $F(s)$-plane locus will encircle the origin** N times in the *same* direction as that of Γ_s.

(2) $N = 0(Z = P)$

If the s-plane locus encircles as many poles as zeros, or encircles no poles and zeros of $F(s)$, the F-plane locus Γ_F will not encircle the origin.

(3) $N < 0(Z < P)$

*It is important to note that, although the mapping from the s-plane to the $F(s)$-plane is one-to-one, the reversed process is not a one-to-one correspondence. For example, let

$$F(s) = \frac{K}{(s+a)(s+b)(s+c)}$$

The function $F(s)$ is analytic in the finite s-plane except at the points $s = -a, -b$, and $-c$. For each value of s in the finite s-plane other than the three points $-a, -b$, and $-c$, there is only one corresponding point in the F-plane. But for a given point in the F-plane, there is more than one corresponding point in the s-plane. For $F(s) =$ constant, we can write

$$(s + a)(s + b)(s + c) = K/F(s)$$

The last equation is a cubic equation, which has three roots for each F.

**In the stability studies, the origin in the F-plane is referred to as the "critical point," where $F(s) = 1 + G(s)H(s)$.

If the s-plane locus encircles more poles than zeros of $F(s)$ in a certain direction, N is a negative number; the $F(s)$-plane locus Γ_F will encircle the origin N times in the *opposite* direction from that of Γ_s.

The principle of the argument will become apparent if we consider, for instance, $F(s)$, which is given as

$$F(s) = \frac{(s + z_1)(s + z_2)}{(s + p_1)(s + p_2)(s + p_3)} \tag{7-45}$$

$$F(s) = \frac{\prod\limits_{m=1}^{2} |s + z_m|}{\prod\limits_{n=1}^{3} |s + p_n|} \left[\sum\limits_{m=1}^{2} \underline{/s + z_m} - \sum\limits_{n=1}^{3} \underline{/s + p_n} \right] \tag{7-46}$$

or

$$F(s) = |F(s)| \underline{/F(s)} \tag{7-47}$$

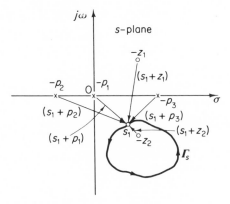

FIG. 7-7. Pole-zero configuration of $F(s)$ and the s-plane locus Γ_s.

Let us assume that the pole-zero configuration of $F(s)$ is as shown in Fig 7-7; Γ_s is the s-plane locus, and s_1 is an arbitrary point on the closed path Γ_s. The factor $(s_1 + z_1)$ can be represented graphically by the vector drawn from z_1 to s_1. Thus, Eq. (7-45) is represented by vectors drawn from the given poles and zeros to the point s_1. Now, the point s_1 is moved along the locus Γ_s in the counterclockwise direction (arbitrarily chosen) until it returns to the starting point; the angles generated by the vectors drawn from the poles and zeros not encircled by Γ_s when s_1 completes one round trip are zero, while the vector $(s_1 + z_2)$ drawn from the zero $-z_2$, which is encircled by the s-plane locus, generates a positive angle (counterclockwise sense) of 2π rad. Then, in Eq. (7-47) the angle of $F(s)$ is

$$\underline{/F(s)} = +2\pi \tag{7-48}$$

which means that the corresponding $F(s)$ locus must go around the origin

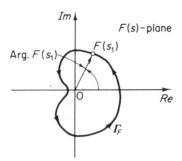

FIG. 7-8. The $F(s)$-plane locus Γ_F corresponding to Γ_s given in Fig. 7-7. Γ_F encircles the origin once in the counterclockwise direction.

2π radians in a counterclockwise direction, such as that which is shown in Fig. 7-8.

In general, if there are N more zeros than poles of $F(s)$ which are encircled by the s-plane locus in a counterclockwise direction,

$$\underline{/F(s)} = 2\pi(Z - P) = 2\pi N \qquad (7\text{--}49)$$

The last equation implies that the F-plane locus will encircle the origin N times in the counterclockwise direction. Conversely, if N more poles than zeros are encircled by the s-plane locus in the counterclockwise direction, the F-plane locus must encircle the origin N times in the clockwise direction, since, in Eq. (7–47),

$$\underline{/F(s)} = 2\pi(Z - P) = 2\pi N$$
$$= \text{negative number} \qquad (7\text{--}50)$$

The application of the argument principle is summarized in Table 7-1.

Table 7-1

Summary of the Argument Principle

$N = Z - P$	Sense of the s-plane locus	F-plane locus	
		No. of encirclements of the origin	Direction of encirclement
$N > 0$	clockwise	N times	clockwise
	counterclockwise		counterclockwise
$N < 0$	clockwise	N times	counterclockwise
	counterclockwise		clockwise
$N = 0$	clockwise	0 times	no encirclement
	counterclockwise		no encirclement

The Nyquist Path

The main objective in the stability studies of feedback control systems is to determine if any of the roots of the characteristic equation ($F(s) = 0$) lies in the right half of the s-plane. It is easy to see that the principle of the argument can be used for this purpose, provided that the s-plane locus is

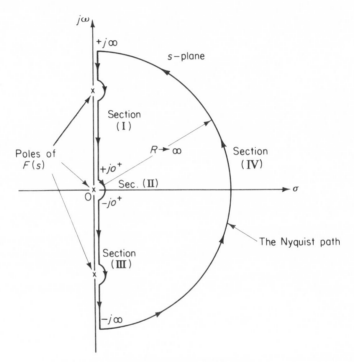

FIG. 7-9. The Nyquist path.

defined as shown in Fig. 7-9. The locus Γ_s is described in a counterclockwise direction so that it *encloses* the entire finite right half of the s-plane; this path is called the *Nyquist path*. For the convenience of analysis, the Nyquist path is divided into four separate sections:

(1) Section I: From $s = +j\infty$ to $+j0^+$ along the $j\omega$ axis.

(2) Section II: From $+j0^+$ to $-j0^+$ along the small semicircle around the origin.

(3) Section III: From $s = -j0^+$ to $s = -j\infty$ along the $-j\omega$ axis.

(4) Section IV: From $-j\infty$ to $+j\infty$ along the semicircle of infinite radius in the right half of the s-plane.

Since the Nyquist path must not pass through any singularity of $F(s)$, the small semicircles along the imaginary axis and at the origin are necessary if $F(s)$ has poles on the $j\omega$ axis and at the origin.

It is apparent that if any pole or zero of $F(s)$ lies in the right half plane in the s-plane, it must be enclosed by the Nyquist path. It is for this reason that the specific path is chosen. Small semicircles on the $j\omega$ axis are necessary to represent cases where poles of $G(s)H(s)$ are found on the $j\omega$ axis, so that a persistent but bounded oscillation exists in the system.

The Nyquist Criterion and the GH-Plot

The Nyquist criterion is a direct application of the principle of the argument when the s-plane locus is the Nyquist path. Once the Nyquist path is specified, the stability of a closed-loop system can be determined by plotting the $F(s) = 1 + G(s)H(s)$ locus when s takes on values along the Nyquist path, and investigating the behavior of the $F(s)$ plot with respect to the origin in the F-plane.

In general, $F(s)$ can be written as

$$F(s) = 1 + G(s)H(s) = \frac{(s + z_1)(s + z_2) \ldots (s + z_m)}{s^j(s + p_1)(s + p_2) \ldots (s + p_n)} \qquad (7\text{-}51)$$

It is important to remember that the poles of $F(s)$ are the same as the poles of $G(s)H(s)$, and the zeros of $F(s)$ are the roots of the characteristic equation, whose location is our main concern in the stability study. Thus, given a feedback control system, if $F(s)$ is of the form given by Eq. (7–51), we can apply the argument principle to determine its stability; the procedure is described as follows:

(1) The Nyquist path is defined as shown in Fig. 7–9.

(2) The $F(s) = 1 + G(s)H(s)$ locus is plotted in the F-plane corresponding to the Nyquist path.

(3) If the poles of $G(s)H(s)$ are all located in the left half of the s-plane, or on the $j\omega$ axis, the closed-loop system is stable, provided the Nyquist plot of $F(s)$ does not encircle the origin. Since, in this case, given that $P = 0$, Eq. (7–44) gives

$$N = Z - P = Z \qquad (7\text{-}52)$$

Therefore, for a stable system, there will be no zero of $F(s)$ for the Nyquist path to enclose. Thus, in Eq. (7–52),

$$N = Z = 0$$

We can also say that, in this case, for stability, the Nyquist plot of $F(s)$ must not enclose the origin in the F-plane, for if $Z \neq 0$, $N = Z$ must be a positive integer and the origin in the F-plane will be encircled in a positive direction (enclosed). However, if some of the poles of $G(s)H(s)$ are in the right half of the s-plane, $P \neq 0$, and then

$$N = Z - P \qquad (7\text{-}53)$$

Since for a stable system Z always must be zero, the condition for a stable system is

$$N = -P \qquad (7\text{-}54)$$

which implies that the Nyquist plot of $F(s)$ must encircle the origin as many times as the number of P. The encirclement, if any, must be made in a negative (clockwise) direction.

Since, in general, the functions $G(s)$ and $H(s)$ are given, rather than $F(s)$, it is easier to plot or sketch the Nyquist plot of $G(s)H(s)$ than the plot of $F(s)$. The difference between the $F(s)$ plot and the $G(s)H(s)$ plot is simply a shift of the imaginary axis. The $(-1, +j0)$ point in the GH-plane corresponds to the origin in the F-plane. Given a certain $F(s)$ plot, as shown in Fig. 7–11, the corresponding GH-plot in the GH-plane will take the form shown in Fig. 7–10.

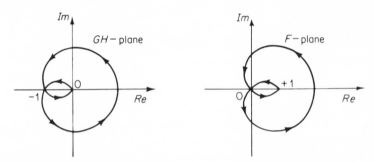

FIG. 7-10. The GH-plane plot.   **FIG. 7-11.** The F-plot.

The Nyquist criterion is normally defined with respect to the GH-plot as:

For a stable closed-loop system, the Nyquist plot of $G(s)H(s)$ should encircle the $(-1, j0)$ point as many times as there are poles of $G(s)H(s)$ in the right half of the s-plane; the encirclements, if there are any, must be made in the clockwise direction. ?

Furthermore, if N=number of encirclements of the critical point $(-1, j0)$ in the GH-plane made by the Nyquist plot of $G(s)H(s)$, with $-N$ for clockwise encirclements, and $+N$ for counterclockwise encirclements,

Z = number of zeros of $1 + G(s)H(s)$ that are in the right half of the s-plane, and

P = number of poles of $1 + G(s)H(s)$ (also the same as for GH) that are in the right half of the s-plane;

$$N = Z - P \qquad (7\text{-}55)$$

For a stable system, Z must be zero; consequently,

$$N = -P \qquad (7\text{-}56)$$

In the majority of cases, $G(s)$ and $H(s)$ are stable functions, so that $P = 0$. Eq. (7–56) becomes

$$N = 0 \qquad\qquad (7\text{-}57)$$

The last equation implies that the Nyquist plot of $G(s)H(s)$ must not encircle the $(-1, j0)$ point in the GH-plane for a system to be stable. However, if, in cases where the GH-plot encircles the critical point $(-1, j0)$, ($N = Z \neq 0$), the encirclement would be made in the counterclockwise direction. For this reason, we can define a Nyquist criterion for a special case which occurs quite frequently; that is, when $P = 0$. The criterion states:

If the loop gain function $G(s)H(s)$ is a stable function, $P = 0$, for a stable closed-loop system, the Nyquist plot of $G(s)H(s)$ must not enclose the critical point $(-1, j0)$.

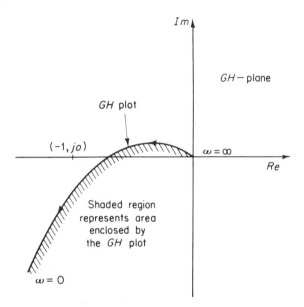

FIG. 7-12. The Nyquist plot.

Also, if $P = 0$, it is necessary only to plot the Nyquist plot of $G(s)H(s)$ corresponding to section (I) on the Nyquist path; that is, from $s = +j\infty$ to $+j0$. For example, the GH-plot given in Fig. 7-12 is plotted only for the frequency range of $\omega = \infty$ to $\omega = 0$, which corresponds to section (I) on the Nyquist path. The region that is *enclosed* by the GH-plot is the area to the left of the path when the path is described from $\omega = \infty$ to $\omega = 0$. Thus, unless it is necessary to know how many zeros of $F(s)$ are located in the right half of the s-plane, the complete Nyquist plot for GH is not required; it is necessary only to investigate whether the $(-1, j0)$ point is to the left or to the right of the GH curve, going from infinite to zero frequency along the GH locus.

7.7 The Application of the Nyquist Criterion

The following examples serve to illustrate the practical application of the Nyquist criterion on the stability of feedback systems.

Example 7-7. Consider a simple feedback control system with $G(s)H(s)$ given as

$$G(s)H(s) = \frac{K}{s(s + a)} \qquad (7\text{–}58)$$

where K and a are constants. It is apparent that $G(s)H(s)$ does not have a pole in the right half of the s-plane; thus, $P = 0$. In this case, to determine the stability of the closed-loop system, it is necessary only to sketch the Nyquist plot of $G(s)H(s)$ that corresponds to $\omega = \infty$ to $\omega = 0^+$ (section I) on the Nyquist path and see if it encloses the -1 point of the GH-plane. To construct the Nyquist plot of $G(s)H(s)$, we shall first determine the behavior of $G(s)H(s)$ at zero and infinite frequencies. When $s = +j\infty$

$$\lim_{s \to j\infty} G(s)H(s) = \lim_{s \to j\infty} \frac{K}{s(s + a)} = \lim_{s \to j\infty} \frac{K}{s^2} = 0\underline{/-180 \deg} \qquad (7\text{–}59)$$

When $s = +j0$

$$\lim_{s = j0} G(s)H(s) = \lim_{s = j0} \frac{K}{s(s + a)} = \lim_{s = j0} \frac{K}{sa} = \infty \underline{/-90 \deg} \qquad (7\text{–}60)$$

The points on the GH plot between zero and infinite frequencies can be obtained by direct computation; for instance, when $\omega = 1$ rad/sec,

$$G(j1)H(j1) = \frac{K}{j1(j1 + a)} = \frac{K}{\sqrt{1 + a^2}} \underline{/-90 \deg - \tan^{-1}\left(\frac{1}{a}\right)} \qquad (7\text{–}61)$$

In general, the application of the Nyquist criterion does not require the exact plot of the GH curve. From Eqs. (7–59) and (7–60), it is known that when the frequency is varied from 0 to ∞, the GH-plot varies from -90 deg to -180 deg; a sketch of GH, as shown in Fig. 7-12, is quite sufficient for the application of the Nyquist criterion.

In Fig. 7-13, since the critical point $(-1, j0)$ is not enclosed by the Nyquist GH-plot, the closed-loop system is stable. Furthermore, the critical point can never be enclosed by the Nyquist plot of this second-order system as long as K is a positive finite number.

It is of interest to sketch the entire Nyquist plot of $G(s)H(s)$ and interpret its significance in the investigation of open- and closed-loop system stability. In order to construct the portion of the GH-plot which corresponds to section II on the Nyquist path, the small semicircle of the Nyquist path is magnified as shown in Fig. 7-14. The points on this semicircle of infinitesimal radius may be represented by a phasor

$$s = \epsilon e^{j\theta} \qquad (7\text{–}62)$$

where $\epsilon(\epsilon \to 0)$ and θ denote the magnitude and phase of the phasor, respectively. As the Nyquist path is described from $+j0^+$ to $-j0^+$ along section

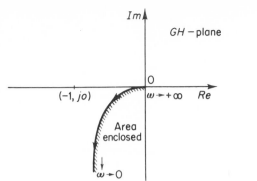

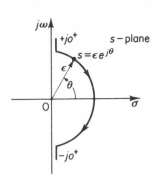

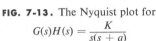

FIG. 7-13. The Nyquist plot for

$$G(s)H(s) = \frac{K}{s(s + a)}$$

FIG. 7-14. Section II of the Nyquist path.

II of the Nyquist path, the phase rotates in the clockwise direction through 180 deg. Also, in going from $+j0^+$ to $-j0^+$, θ is varied from 90 deg to -90 deg through 0 deg. The corresponding plot of $G(s)H(s)$ can be determined simply by substituting Eq. (7–62) into the $G(s)H(s)$ function. Therefore, Eq. (7–58) becomes

$$G(s)H(s)|_{s=\epsilon e^{j\theta}} = \frac{K}{\epsilon e^{j\theta}(\epsilon e^{j\theta} + a)} \tag{7–63}$$

Since ϵ approaches zero, Eq. (7–63) may be simplified to read

$$G(s)H(s)|_{s=\epsilon e^{j\theta}} = \frac{K}{\epsilon a e^{j\theta}} = \infty\, e^{-j\theta} \tag{7–64}$$

Therefore, we have established that the magnitude of $G(s)H(s)$ on section II of the Nyquist path is infinite, and the corresponding phase of $G(s)H(s)$ is opposite to that of s. The phase shift relationships are tabulated in the following as θ is varied from $+90$ deg to -90 deg. It is seen that the phase shift of GH goes from -90 deg to $+90$ deg through a total of 180 deg in the counterclockwise direction. The correspondence of the s-plane locus (section II) and the GH-plane locus is shown in Fig. 7-15.

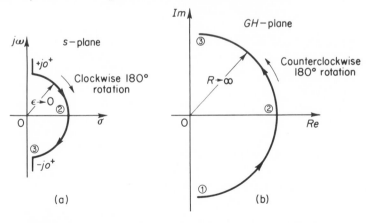

FIG. 7-15. Section II of the Nyquist path and the corresponding GH-plot for the system in Example 7–7. (a) Section II of the Nyquist path; (b) the GH-plot.

θ	90°	60°	30°	0°	−30°	−60°	−90°
$\underline{/GH}$	−90°	−60°	−30°	0°	+30°	+60°	+90°

In general, the GH-plot of section II on the Nyquist path may be determined without going through the detailed steps illustrated above. For instance, in this problem, it is necessary only to investigate the following equation:

$$\lim_{s \to 0} G(s)H(s) = \lim_{s \to 0} \frac{K}{s(s+a)} = \lim_{s \to 0} \frac{K}{sa} \qquad (7\text{-}65)$$

From the last equation, it is clear that the behavior of GH at $s = 0$ is inversely proportional to s. Therefore, as the Nyquist path is described from $+j0^+$ to $-j0^+$ through a clockwise rotation of 180 deg (considered to be -180-deg rotation), the GH-plot must go around the origin of the GH-plane 180 deg in the counterclockwise direction with infinite magnitude. It can be concluded that, in general, if the limit of $G(s)H(s)$ as s approaches 0 takes the form of

$$\lim_{s \to 0} G(s)H(s) = \lim_{s \to 0} K s^n \qquad (7\text{-}66)$$

the GH-plot from $s = +j0^+$ to $s = -j0^+$ will go around the origin of the GH-plane $n \times 180$ deg in the clockwise direction (same direction as that of section II of the Nyquist path) with zero magnitude if n is a positive integer; if n is a negative number, the GH-plot will go around the origin of the GH-plane $n \times 180$ deg in the counterclockwise direction with infinite magnitude.

Exactly the same techinique may be used to sketch the GH-plot which corresponds to section IV of the Nyquist path. At infinite frequency, the large semicircle (section IV) in the s-plane is described in the counterclockwise direction from $s = -j\infty$ to $s = +j\infty$. The behavior of $G(s)H(s)$ at infinite frequency is described by

$$\lim_{s \to \infty} G(s)H(s) = \lim_{s \to \infty} \frac{K}{s(s+a)} = \lim_{s \to \infty} \frac{K}{s^2} \qquad (7\text{-}67)$$

Thus, the behavior of the GH-plot at infinite frequency is proportional to $1/s^2$. When s takes on values along the large semicircle in the s-plane, the corresponding GH-plot must rotate around the origin 2×180 deg clockwise (opposite to the direction of the s-plane trajectory) with zero magnitude in the GH-plane. Thus, the GH-plot of the second-order system which corresponds to section IV of the Nyquist path (Fig. 7-16) is given in Fig. 7-17. The complete Nyquist plot of $G(s)H(s)$ is shown in Fig. 7-18. It is apparent that the complete GH-plot does not encircle the -1 point, which means either that the number of poles and the number of zeros of $F(s) = 1 + G(s)H(s)$ which are located in the right half of the s-plane are both zero, or that the number of poles equals the number of zeros. This is merely an interesting check of the result obtained from Fig. 7-13.

Since $G(s)H(s)$ does not have a finite zero, and since all the poles of $G(s)$

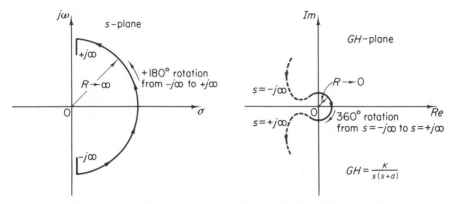

FIG. 7-16. Section IV of the Nyquist path.

FIG. 7-17. The GH-plot corresponding to section IV of the Nyquist path.

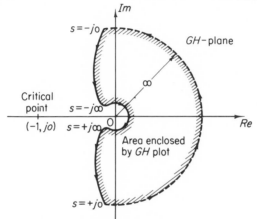

FIG. 7-18. The complete Nyquist plot of $G(s)H(s) = \dfrac{K}{s(s+a)}$

$H(s)$ are located in the left half of the s-plane, by inspection, the complete Nyquist plot of GH given in Fig. 7-18 does not enclose the critical point $(-1, j0)$; thus the closed-loop system is stable.

Example 7-8. Consider a feedback control system with the loop transfer function given as

$$G(s)H(s) = \frac{K}{1 - sT} \qquad (7\text{–}68)$$

where K and T are positive constants. It is apparent that GH has one pole in the right half of the s-plane. The characteristic equation of the closed-loop system is the numerator of

$$1 + G(s)H(s) = \frac{1 + K - sT}{1 - sT} \qquad (7\text{–}69)$$

Thus, the closed-loop system is also unstable, since the closed-loop pole is at $s = (1 + K)/T$. The following conclusions can be reached regarding the behavior of the Nyquist plot of $G(s)H(s)$ based on what we already know about the system.

$G(s)H(s)$	Z	P	$N = Z - P$	Interpretation
	0	1	-1	The $G(s)H(s)$ plot encircles the origin in a clockwise direction.

$1 + G(s)H(s)$	Z	P	$N = Z - P$	Interpretation
	1	1	0	The $G(s)H(s)$ plot does not encircle the $(-1, j0)$ point at all.

The construction of the complete Nyquist plot of GH is summarized as follows:

s	∞	$j\infty$	$-j\infty$	s-plane Nyquist path, section IV $+180°$ rotation
GH	0	$0/90°$	$0/-90°$	GH-plane Nyquist plot, $GH = \dfrac{K}{-sT}\Big\vert_{s \to \infty}$ $-180°$ rotation

s	0	$j0$	$-j0$	s-plane Nyquist path, section II $-180°$ rotation
GH	K	$K/0°$	$K/0°$	GH-plane Nyquist plot, $GH = K/0°$

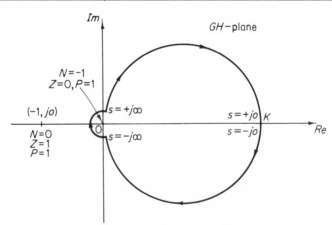

FIG. 7-19. The complete Nyquist plot of $G(s)H(s) = \dfrac{K}{(1 - sT)}$

The complete Nyquist plot of $G(s)H(s)$ is shown in Fig. 7-19; the locus encircles the origin once in the clockwise direction, but never encircles the $(-1, j0)$ point, which checks with the facts predicted.

This example also points out the important fact that the critical point $(-1, j0)$ does not have to be encircled at all by the GH-plot for a closed-loop system to be unstable, if the function $G(s)H(s)$ has poles in the right half of the s-plane. Furthermore, in this case, the critical point must be encircled once in the clockwise direction by the GH-plot if a stable closed-loop system is desired.

Example 7-9. Consider a feedback control system with the loop transfer function $G(s)H(s)$ given as

$$G(s)H(s) = \frac{5}{s(1-s)} \qquad (7\text{-}70)$$

Thus

$$1 + G(s)H(s) = \frac{-s^2 + s + 5}{s(1-s)} \qquad (7\text{-}71)$$

The characteristic equation has one root in the right half of the s-plane and one root in the left half of the s-plane ($s = 0.5 \pm 0.5\sqrt{21}$). The following conclusions can be drawn concerning the characteristics of the Nyquist plot of $G(s)H(s)$, based on what we already know about the system.

$G(s)H(s)$	Z	P	$N = Z - P$	Interpretation
	0	1	-1	The $G(s)H(s)$ plot encircles the origin once in a clockwise direction.

$1 + G(s)H(s)$	Z	P	$N = Z - P$	Interpretation
	1	1	0	The $G(s)H(s)$ plot does not encircle the $(-1, j0)$ point at all.

The construction of the complete Nyquist plot of $G(s)H(s)$ (Fig. 7-20) is summarized as follows:

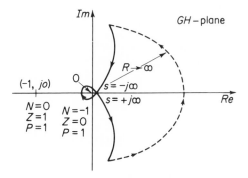

FIG. 7-20. The complete Nyquist plot of

$$G(s)H(s) = \frac{5}{s(1-s)}$$

s	∞	$j\infty$	$-j\infty$	s-plane Nyquist path, section IV 180° rotation
GH	$\dfrac{5}{-s^2}$	$0\underline{/0°}$	$0\underline{/0°}$	GH-plane Nyquist plot, $GH = \left.\dfrac{5}{-s^2}\right\|_{s\to\infty}$ $-360°$ rotation

s	0	$j0$	$-j0$	s-plane Nyquist path, section II $-180°$ rotation
GH	$\dfrac{5}{s}$	$\infty\underline{/-90°}$	$\infty\underline{/+90°}$	GH-plane Nyquist plot, $GH = \left.\dfrac{5}{s}\right\|_{s\to0}$ $+180°$ rotation

Example 7-10. Consider a feedback control system with the loop transfer function $G(s)H(s)$ given as

$$G(s)H(s) = \frac{K}{s(1 + s)(1 + 2s)(1 + 3s)} \qquad (7\text{-}72)$$

By inspection, the properties of the $G(s)H(s)$ plot in the GH-plane are given as follows:

	Z	P	$N = Z - P$	Interpretation
$G(s)H(s)$	0	0	0	The GH-plot does not encircle the origin in the GH-plane.

However, the roots of the characteristic equation are unknown. The poles of $1 + G(s)H(s)$ are known to be located in the left half of the s-plane. The Nyquist criterion will be used to determine the stability of the closed-loop system by determining whether any of the zeros of the function $1 + G(s)H(s)$ is in the right half of the s-plane.

By means of the procedure illustrated in Example 7-7, the construction of the Nyquist plot of $G(s)H(s)$ is summarized as follows:

s	∞	$j\infty$	$-j\infty$	s-plane Nyquist path, section IV $+180°$ rotation
GH	$\dfrac{K}{s^4}$	$0\underline{/-360°}$	$0\underline{/360°}$	GH-plane Nyquist plot, $GH = K/s^4\|_{s\to\infty}$ $-720°$ rotation

s	0	$j0$	$-j0$	s-plane Nyquist path, section II $-180°$ rotation
GH	$\dfrac{K}{s}$	$\infty\underline{/90°}$	$\infty\underline{/90°}$	GH-plane Nyquist plot $GH = K/s\|_{s\to0}$ $+180°$ rotation

The details of the GH-plot at zero and infinite frequencies are given in Fig. 7-21. The complete GH-plot is shown in Fig. 7-22.

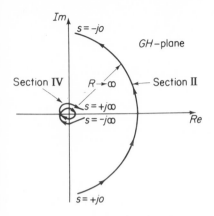

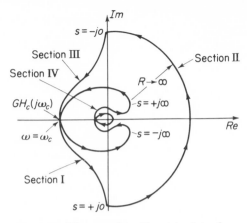

FIG. 7-21. The Nyquist plot of

$$G(s)H(s) = \frac{K}{s(1+s)(1+2s)(1+3s)}$$

at zero and infinite frequencies.

FIG. 7-22. The complete Nyquist plot of

$$G(s)H(s) = \frac{K}{s(1+s)(1+2s)(1+3s)}$$

From Fig. 7-22, it is clear that the Nyquist plot of $G(s)H(s)$ will enclose the $(-1, j0)$ point twice if the value of K is sufficiently large. For a stable closed-loop system, the critical point $(-1, j0)$ must not be enclosed. Substituting $s = j\omega$ into $G(s)H(s)$, we have

$$G(j\omega)H(j\omega) = \frac{K}{j\omega(1+j\omega)(1+j2\omega)(1+j3\omega)}$$

$$= \frac{K}{6\omega^2(\omega^2 - 1) + j\omega(1 - 11\omega^2)} \tag{7-73}$$

When the GH-plot crosses the negative real axis in the GH-plane, the frequency at the crossing is designated as $\omega = \omega_c$, and the imaginary part of $G(j\omega)H(j\omega)$ is zero; thus,

$$1 - 11\omega^2 = 0 \tag{7-74}$$

or

$$\omega = \omega_c = \pm 1/\sqrt{11} \tag{7-75}$$

The frequency ω_c is sometimes called the critical frequency of the system. Substitution of Eq. (7–75) into Eq. (7–73) gives

$$GH_c(j\omega_c) = 121K/60 \tag{7-76}$$

For the closed-loop system to be stable, the magnitude of $GH_c(j\omega_c)$ should be less than one; thus,

$$|GH_c| = 121K/60 < 1 \tag{7-77}$$

or

$$K < 0.495 \tag{7-78}$$

The critical value of K can also be obtained easily by means of the Routh-Hurwitz criterion. The characteristic equation of the system is

$$6s^4 + 11s^3 + 6s^2 + s + K = 0 \tag{7-79}$$

The Routh tabulation is given as follows:

$$
\begin{array}{cccc}
s^4 & 6 & 6 & K \\
s^3 & 11 & 1 & \\
s^2 & \frac{60}{11} & K & \\
s^1 & \dfrac{\frac{60}{11} - 11K}{\frac{60}{11}} & 0 & \\
s^0 & K & 0 &
\end{array}
$$

The conditions of stability are

$$K > 0 \tag{7-80}$$

and

$$\frac{60}{11} - 11K > 0 \tag{7-81}$$

The critical frequency ω_c is obtained by solving for the roots of the auxiliary equation; that is,

$$-\frac{60}{11}\omega^2 + K = 0 \tag{7-82}$$

Hence

$$\omega_c = \pm\sqrt{\frac{11K}{60}} = \pm\frac{1}{\sqrt{11}}\text{rad/sec} \tag{7-83}$$

It was pointed out earlier that if $G(s)H(s)$ does not have any poles in the right half of the s-plane, only the positive frequency locus of GH need be sketched. In this example, all the poles of $G(s)H(s)$ are located in the left half of the s-plane, so it is necessary to sketch only the portion of the Nyquist plot of GH which corresponds to section (I) on the Nyquist path; the Nyquist plot of GH is shown in Fig. 7-23. The region that is enclosed by the Nyquist

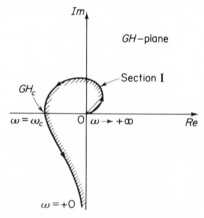

FIG. 7-23. Nyquist plot of
$$G(s)H(s) = \frac{K}{s(1 + s)(1 + 2s)(1 + 3s)}$$
corresponding to section I of the Nyquist path.

plot of GH is indicated in Fig. 7-23 as the shaded area. For a stable system, the critical point $(-1, j0)$ must not be found inside this shaded region.

7.8 The Effects of Additional Poles and Zeros of G(s)H(s) on the Shape of the Nyquist Locus

In this section, we shall investigate the effects on the Nyquist locus when poles and zeros are added to the loop transfer function $G(s)H(s)$. Assume that the loop transfer function of a certain feedback control system is of the form:

$$G(s)H(s) = \frac{K}{1 + sT_1} \qquad (7\text{-}84)$$

The Nyquist locus for positive frequencies of the loop transfer function given in the last equation is shown in Fig. 7-24.

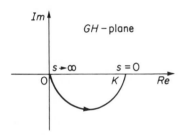

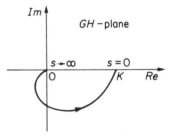

FIG. 7-24. The Nyquist plot of
$$G(s)H(s) = \frac{K}{(1 + sT_1)}$$

FIG. 7-25. The Nyquist plot of
$$G(s)H(s) = \frac{K}{(1 + sT_1)(1 + sT_2)}$$

(1) *Addition of Finite Poles*

Suppose that a pole at $s = -1/T_2$ is added to the $G(s)H(s)$ function given in Eq. (7-84); we then have

$$G(s)H(s) = \frac{K}{(1 + sT_1)(1 + sT_2)} \qquad (7\text{-}85)$$

The Nyquist plot of GH at zero frequency is not affected, since

$$\lim_{s \to 0} G(s)H(s) = K \qquad (7\text{-}86)$$

However, the locus at infinite frequency is

$$\lim_{s \to \infty} G(s)H(s) = \lim_{s \to \infty} \frac{K}{s^2 T_1 T_2} = 0 \underline{/-180 \text{ deg}} \qquad (7\text{-}87)$$

The Nyquist plot of GH for positive frequencies is sketched in Fig. 7-25.

Similarly, by adding one more term $(1 + sT_3)$ in the denominator of Eq. (7–85), the Nyquist locus at infinite frequency is at zero magnitude and an angle of -270 deg, as shown in Fig. 7-26.

In general, we can conclude that the addition of n finite poles, each with a negative real part, to the $G(s)H(s)$ in Eq. (7–84), will result in the GH-plot to go around $(n + 1)\pi/2$ rad in the clockwise direction as ω is varied from zero to infinite frequency (Fig. 7-27).

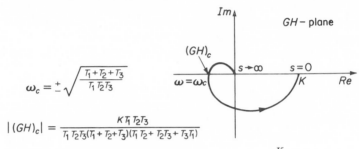

$$\omega_c = \pm\sqrt{\frac{T_1 + T_2 + T_3}{T_1 T_2 T_3}}$$

$$|(GH)_c| = \frac{K T_1 T_2 T_3}{T_1 T_2 T_3 (T_1 + T_2 + T_3)(T_1 T_2 + T_2 T_3 + T_3 T_1)}$$

FIG. 7-26. The Nyquist locus of $G(s)H(s) = \dfrac{K}{(1 + sT_1)(1 + sT_2)(1 + sT_3)}$

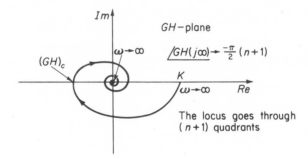

FIG. 7-27. The Nyquist locus of

$$G(s)H(s) = \frac{K}{(1 + sT_1)(1 + sT_2) \cdots (1 + sT_{n+1})}$$

In this case, the Nyquist locus of GH goes through a total of $(n + 1)$ quadrants, or as many quadrants as the number of time constants as the frequency is varied from 0 to ∞.

In general, the effect of adding more finite poles to GH is to make the closed-loop system less stable. The loci shown in Figs. 7-24 and 7-25 represent systems that are always stable. The closed-loop systems which correspond to the GH-plots of Figs. 7-26 and 7-27 may be unstable, however, if $(GH)_c > 1$.

(2) *Addition of Poles at the Origin*

The addition of poles at the origin to the loop transfer function $G(s)H(s)$ also has the effect of making the closed-loop system less stable. If the factor $1/s^n$ is multiplied to the $G(s)H(s)$ of Eq. (7–84), the Nyquist locus at infinite and zero frequencies is rotated by an angle of $n\pi/2$ in the clockwise direction. It was pointed out that the GH-plot will go through as many quadrants in the GH-plane as there are time constants T in the denominator of GH, regardless of the order of the poles at the origin. This fact is helpful in the sketching of the Nyquist locus of the type described in this section. The rule, however, does not apply if there is any term of the form $(1 + sT)$ found in the numerator of $G(s)H(s)$.

Some of the typical Nyquist plots of $G(s)H(s)$ are illustrated in Fig. 7-28.

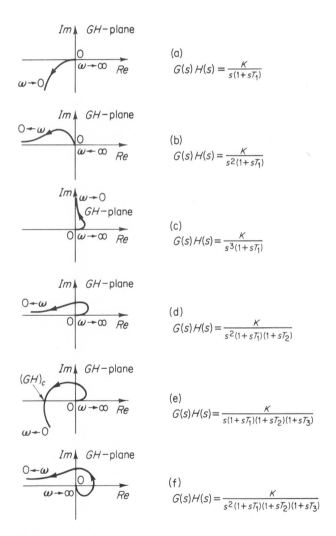

FIG. 7-28. Nyquist loci for several loop transfer functions showing the effect of adding poles to GH.

(3) *Addition of Zeros*

It was pointed out in Chapter 6 that the effect of the derivative control on a closed-loop system is to make the system more stable. In terms of the Nyquist plot, this stabilizing effect is easily shown, since the multiplication of the factor $(1 + sT_d)$ to a $G(s)H(s)$ rotates the GH-plot at ∞ in the counterclockwise direction by 90 deg. For instance, consider the loop transfer function

$$G(s)H(s) = \frac{K}{s(1 + sT_1)(1 + sT_2)} \qquad (7\text{-}88)$$

It is easy to show that the system is stable for all values of $K > 0$ and $K < (T_1 + T_2)/T_1T_2$. Suppose that a zero at $s = -1/T_d$ is added to the loop transfer function in Eq. (7–88) so that

$$G(s)H(s) = \frac{K(1 + sT_d)}{s(1 + sT_1)(1 + sT_2)} \qquad (7\text{-}89)$$

The Nyquist loci for the two $G(s)H(s)$ functions with and without derivative control are shown in Fig. 7–29. It is seen that for the same values of K, T_1, and T_2, the system with derivative control is more stable, because the

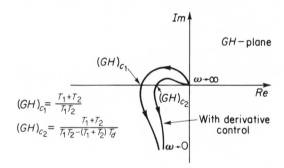

FIG. 7-29. Comparison of Nyquist loci of systems with and without derivative control. $G(s)H(s) = \dfrac{K}{s(1 + sT_1)(1 + sT_2)}$

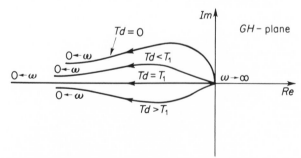

FIG. 7-30. Comparison of Nyquist loci of systems with and without derivative control. $G(s)H(s) = \dfrac{K}{s^2(1 + sT_1)}$

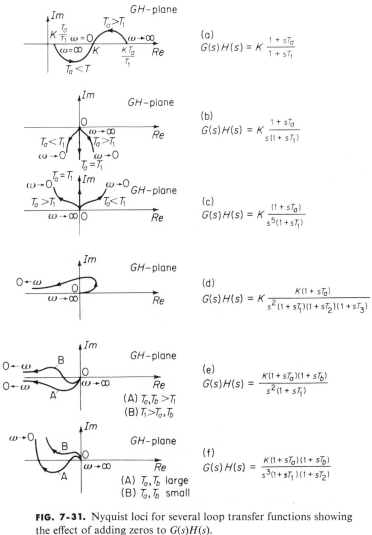

FIG. 7-31. Nyquist loci for several loop transfer functions showing the effect of adding zeros to $G(s)H(s)$.

Nyquist locus is on the right side of the GH-plot of the system without derivative control.

A system that is inherently unstable can be stabilized by adding zeros to the loop transfer function. The system corresponding to the Nyquist plot of Fig. 7-28b is unstable for all positive values of K. With the addition of the derivative control, the loop transfer function of the system is

$$G(s)H(s) = \frac{K(1 + sT_d)}{s^2(1 + sT_1)} \qquad (7\text{--}90)$$

It can readily be shown that the closed-loop system is made stable if the time constant T_d is greater than T_1 (see Fig. 7-30).

Some other Nyquist loci illustrating the effects of adding of zeros to the loop transfer function GH are shown in Fig. 7-31.

7.9 Stability of Discrete-data Control Systems

Just as in the case of designing linear continuous-data systems, one of the most important specifications in the design of discrete-data control systems is stability. A discrete-data system is considered to be stable if the sampled output is bounded when a bounded input is applied. This statement is almost identical to the definition given for a continuous-data system, except that a bounded output at the sampling instants still leaves the possibility of having an unbounded response at all times, although this situation is rare in practice.

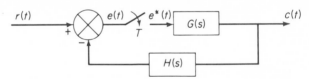

FIG. 7-32. Block diagram of a discrete-data control system.

Consider the block diagram of a discrete-data control system shown in Fig. 7-32. If the z-transform method is valid, the closed-loop transfer function of the system is written as

$$\frac{C(z)}{R(z)} = \frac{G(z)}{1 + GH(z)} \qquad (7\text{--}91)$$

The characteristic equation of the system is

$$1 + GH(z) = 0 \qquad (7\text{--}92)$$

The stability of the closed-loop system is determined by the location of the roots of the characteristic equation. Since the right half of the s-plane corresponds to the exterior of the unit circle, $|z| = 1$, in the z-plane, the stability requirement of the linear discrete-data system states that all the roots of the characteristic equation must lie *inside* the unit circle.

In the preceding sections of this chapter, stability of linear continuous-data systems is investigated by the Routh-Hurwitz criterion and the Nyquist criterion. In this section we shall show that these methods as well as the Bode plot can all be extended to the study of discrete-data control systems.

The Routh-Hurwitz Criterion Applied to Discrete-Data Systems

The attempt to apply the Routh test directly to the z-transform characteristic equation of a discrete-data system meets with one major difficulty. The conventional Routh test is devised to test the roots of a polynomial with respect to the left or right half of the complex s-plane. However, the stability of the discrete-data system concerns the determination of the location of the roots of the characteristic equation with respect to the unit circle in the z-plane. This difficulty is eliminated by modifying the Routh test with the bilinear transformation

$$r = \frac{z+1}{z-1} \tag{7-93}$$

or

$$z = \frac{r+1}{r-1} \tag{7-94}$$

where r is a complex variable; i. e., $r = \sigma_r + j\omega_r$.

The transformation in Eq. (7-93) maps the interior of the unit circle in the z-plane onto the left half of the r-plane. Therefore, the Routh test may be performed on the polynomial in the variable r. The following example illustrates how the modified Routh test is performed for a discrete-data system.

Example 7-11. Let the open-loop transfer function of the discrete-data control system shown in Fig. 7-32 be

$$G(s) = \frac{22.57}{s^2(s+1)} \tag{7-95}$$

and $H(s) = 1$.

If the sampling period is 1 sec, the z-transform of $G(s)$ is

$$G(z) = \frac{22.57(0.368z + 0.264)}{(z-1)^2(z-0.368)} \tag{7-96}$$

The characteristic equation of the system may be written as

$$z^3 + 5.94z^2 + 7.7z - 0.368 = 0 \tag{7-97}$$

Substituting Eq. (7-94) into the last equation yields

$$\left(\frac{r+1}{r-1}\right)^3 + 5.94\left(\frac{r+1}{r-1}\right)^2 + 7.7\left(\frac{r+1}{r-1}\right) - 0.368 = 0 \tag{7-98}$$

which is simplified to

$$14.27r^3 + 2.3r^2 - 11.74r + 3.13 = 0 \tag{7-99}$$

The Routh tabulation of the last equation is

$$r^3 \qquad 14.27 \qquad\qquad -11.74$$

$$r^2 \qquad 2.3 \qquad\qquad 3.13$$

$$r^1 \qquad \frac{-27 - 44.6}{2.3} = -31.1 \qquad 0$$

$$r^0 \qquad 3.13$$

Since there are two changes of sign in the first column of the tabulation, the characteristic equation has two roots in the right half of the r-plane, which correspond to two roots outside the unit circle in the z-plane. This result can be easily checked by solving Eq. (7-97); the three roots of the characteristic equation are at $z = 2$, $z = -3.97$, and $z = 0.032$. When mapped into the r-plane by Eq. (7-94), the three roots of Eq. (7-99) are at $r = 0.333$, $r = 0.6$, and $r = -1.07$. The z-plane roots and the r-plane roots are illustrated in Fig. 7-33.

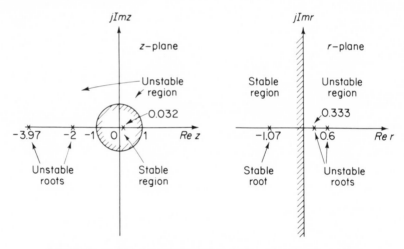

FIG. 7-33. Stable and unstable regions in the z-plane and the r-plane, and the roots of Eq. (7–97).

In principle, the bilinear r-transformation is very simple to apply. In transforming from the z to the r domain, the degree of the polynomial is not altered. However, in the case of higher order systems, the process of simplifying Eq. (7-98) to the form of Eq. (7–99) may be tedious.

There are other analytical methods of testing the roots of a polynomial in z directly. The interested reader may refer to the literature.[6]

The Nyquist Criterion

The stability of a discrete-data control system may be studied by using the Nyquist criterion. In the case of a discrete-data system, the characteristic equation is a function of z. It is apparent that the Nyquist path in the z-plane must be the unit circle $|z| = 1$. Then, the Nyquist plot of $GH(z)$ is the mapping of the unit circle in the z-plane onto the $GH(z)$ plane. The stability of the discrete-data control system is studied by investigating the encirclement of the -1 point by the $GH(z)$ locus in the $GH(z)$ plane. All the properties and rules of Nyquist criterion for continuous-data systems are still valid when applied to the $GH(z)$ plane locus. Actually, the Nyquist locus for discrete-data systems can be sketched by following the same techinques used for continuous-data systems if the bilinear transformation of Eq. (7–94) is applied. With the r-transformation, the Nyquist path in the complex r-plane is, again, composed of the imaginary axis and the semicircle with infinite radius in the right half of the r-plane, as shown in Fig. 7–34.

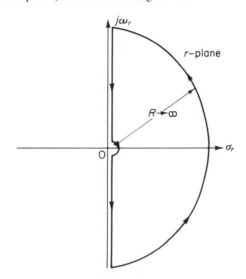

FIG. 7-34. The Nyquist path in the r-plane.

Example 7-12. For the discrete-data control system shown in Fig. 7-32, let

$$G(s) = \frac{K}{s(s + 1)} \qquad (7\text{–}100)$$

and $T = 1.57$ sec. The z-transform of $G(s)$ is

$$G(z) = \frac{0.792Kz}{(z - 1)(z - 0.208)} \qquad (7\text{–}101)$$

Application of the r-transformation to $G(z)$ yields

$$G\left(z = \frac{r + 1}{r - 1}\right) = \frac{0.792K\left(\dfrac{r + 1}{r - 1}\right)}{\left(\dfrac{r + 1}{r - 1} - 1\right)\left(\dfrac{r + 1}{r - 1} - 0.208\right)} = \frac{K(r^2 - 1)}{2(r + 1.525)}$$

$$(7\text{–}102)$$

Since the open-loop system is stable, it is necessary only to construct the Nyquist plot for $G(z)$ corresponding to the positive portion of the imaginary axis in the r-plane. Therefore, when

$$r = j\omega_r = j\infty, \qquad G(z) = \infty \underline{/90°}$$

$$r = 0, \qquad\qquad G(z) = -\frac{K}{3.05}$$

The Nyquist plot of $G(z)$ for $K = 1$ corresponding to values of r from $-j\infty$ to $+j\infty$ is given in Fig. 7–35. It is seen from the Nyquist plot that for $K = 1$, the plot intersects the negative real axis at -0.328. The critical value of K is 3.05; for values of K greater than 3.05, the plot encloses the -1 point and the

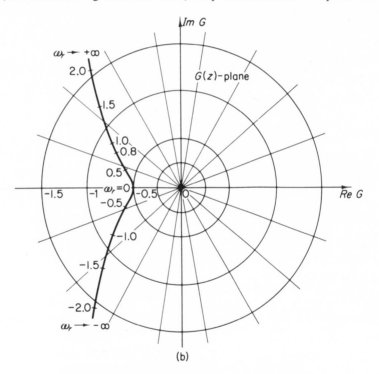

(b)

FIG. 7-35. The Nyquist path and the Nyquist plot of

$$G(z) = \frac{0.792Kz}{(z - 1)(z - 0.208)}$$

system is unstable. It is interesting to note that a second-order system with continuous-data is known to be always stable. However, a second-order system with sampled data has introduced the possibility of becoming unstable.

The relation between the imaginary part of r and the true frequency may be derived as follows:

For $s = j\omega$, $z = e^{Ts} = e^{j\omega T}$, and

$$r = j\omega_r = \frac{z+1}{z-1} = \frac{e^{j\omega T}+1}{e^{j\omega T}-1} \qquad (7\text{-}103)$$

Multiplication of the numerator and denominator of the last equation by $e^{-j\omega T/2}$ yields

$$j\omega_r = \frac{e^{j\omega T/2} + e^{-j\omega T/2}}{e^{j\omega T/2} - e^{-j\omega T/2}} = \frac{2\cos\left(\dfrac{\omega T}{2}\right)}{j2\sin\left(\dfrac{\omega T}{2}\right)} \qquad (7\text{-}104)$$

Hence

$$\omega_r = -\cot\left(\frac{\omega T}{2}\right) \qquad (7\text{-}105)$$

or

$$\omega = -\frac{2}{T}\cot^{-1}\omega_r \qquad (7\text{-}106)$$

From Eq. (7-105),

when $\omega = \omega_s = 2\pi/T,$ $\omega_r = -\cot \pi = \infty$

when $\omega = \omega_s/2 = \pi/T,$ $\omega_r = -\cot(\pi/2) = 0$

when $\omega = 0,$ $\omega_r = -\infty.$

Therefore, when ω_r is varied from $-\infty$ through 0 to $+\infty$, the corresponding variation of the actual frequency ω is only from 0 to the sampling frequency ω_s.

The Bode Diagram

The Bode diagram of a discrete-data control system can be constructed by use of the bilinear transformation in Eq. (7–94). The Bode plot of $G(z)$ is made in terms of the magnitude of $G(z)$ in decibels and the angle of $G(z)$ as a function of ω_r. For example, Eq. (7–102) may be written as

$$G\left(z = \frac{j\omega_r + 1}{j\omega_r - 1}\right) = \frac{K(j\omega_r)^2 - 1}{2(j\omega_r + 1.525)} = \frac{K(j\omega_r + 1)(j\omega_r - 1)}{2(j\omega_r + 1.525)} \qquad (7\text{-}107)$$

or

$$G(z) = \frac{K(j\omega_r + 1)(j\omega_r - 1)}{3.05(0.655 j\omega_r + 1)} \qquad (7\text{-}108)$$

The corner frequencies of the plot are at $\omega_r = 1$ rad/sec, 1 rad/sec, and 1.525 rad/sec. The asymptotes of the magnitude curves of $(j\omega_r - 1)$ and $(j\omega_r + 1)$ are identical, with a slope of $+20$ db/decade of frequency. Thus, the magnitude curve of $(j\omega_r + 1)(j\omega_r - 1)$ has an asymptote with a slope of $+40$ db/decade of frequency. The intersection of the asymptote with the ω_r axis is at $\omega_r = 1$ rad/sec. The only difference between the Bode plots of the two linear terms is in the phase shift curves. The phase shift of $(j\omega_r + 1)$ varies

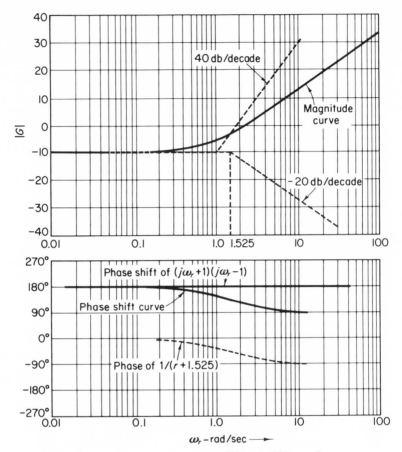

FIG. 7-36. The Bode plot of $G(z) = \dfrac{K(j\omega_r + 1)(j\omega_r - 1)}{3.05(0.655 j\omega_r + 1)}(K = 1)$.

from 0 deg to 90 deg, while the phase of $(j\omega_r - 1)$ varies from 180 deg to 90 deg, as ω_r is varied from 0 to ∞. Thus, the net phase of the product of the two terms is a constant 180 deg. In Fig. 7-36, the Bode plot of Eq. (7–108) is constructed with $K = 1$.

REFERENCES

1. R. J. Schwarz and B. Friedland, *Linear Systems*, McGraw-Hill Book Company, New York, N. Y., 1965.

2. E. J. Routh, *Dynamics of a System of Rigid Bodies*, Chapter 6, part II, Macmillan & Co., Ltd., London, 1905.

3. H. Nyquist, "Regeneration Theory," *Bell System Tech. J.*, Vol. **11**, pp. 126–147, January, 1932.

4. W. R. Evans, "Graphical Analysis of Control Systems," *Trans.*, *AIEE*, Vol. **67**, pp. 547–551, 1948.

5. J. E. Gibson, *Nonlinear Automatic Control*, Chapter 8, McGraw-Hill Book Company, New York, N. Y., 1963.

6. B. C. Kuo, *Analysis and Synthesis of Sampled-data Control Systems*, Prentice-Hall, Inc., Englewood Cliffs, N. J., 1963.

PROBLEMS

7-1. By means of the Routh-Hurwitz criterion, determine the stability of the systems which have the following characteristic equations. In each case, determine the number of roots of the equation which are in the right half of the s-plane.
(a) $s^3 + 20s^2 + 9s + 100 = 0$
(b) $s^3 + 20s^2 + 9s + 200 = 0$
(c) $3s^4 + 10s^3 + 5s^2 + s + 2 = 0$
(d) $s^4 + 2s^3 + 6s^2 + 8s + 8 = 0$
(e) $s^6 + 2s^5 + 8s^4 + 12s^3 + 20s^2 + 16s + 16 = 0$

7-2. The characteristic equations for certain feedback control systems are given below. In each case, determine the values of K which correspond to a stable system.
(a) $s^4 + 22s^3 + 10s^2 + 2s + K = 0$
(b) $s^4 + 20Ks^3 + 5s^2 + (10 + K)s + 15 = 0$
(c) $s^3 + (K + 0.5)s^2 + 4Ks + 50 = 0$

7-3. The conventional Routh-Hurwitz criterion gives only the location of the roots of a polynomial with respect to the right half and the left half of the s-plane. The open-loop transfer function of a unity-feedback control system is given as

$$G(s) = \frac{K}{s(1+Ts)}$$

It is desired that all the roots of the system's characteristic equation lie in the region to the left of the line $s = -a$. This will assure that not only is a stable system obtained, but also that the system has a minimum amount of damping. Extend the Routh-Hurwitz criterion to this case, and determine the values of K and T required so that there are no roots to the right of the line $s = -a$.

7-4. The loop transfer function of a feedback control system is given by

$$G(s)H(s) = \frac{K(s + 1)}{s(1 + Ts)(1 + 2s)}$$

The parameters K and T may be represented in a plane with K as the horizontal axis and T as the vertical axis. Determine the region in which the closed-loop system is stable.

7-5. The open-loop transfer function of a unity-feedback control system is given by

$$G(s) = \frac{K(s + 5)(s + 40)}{s^3(s + 200)(s + 1000)}$$

Discuss the stability of the closed-loop system as a function of K. Determine the values of K which will cause sustained oscillations in the closed-loop system. What are the frequencies of oscillations?

7-6. For the following loop gain functions, sketch the Nyquist diagrams which correspond to the entire Nyquist path. In each case, check the values of N, P, and Z with respect to the origin in the GH-plane. Determine the values of N, P, and Z with respect to the -1 point, and determine if the closed-loop system is stable. Specify in which case it is necessary to sketch only the Nyquist plot for $\omega = 0$ to ∞ (section I) on the Nyquist path to investigate the stability of the closed-loop system.

(a) $G(s)H(s) = \dfrac{50}{s(1 + 0.1s)(1 + 0.2s)}$

(b) $G(s)H(s) = \dfrac{10}{s^2(1 + 0.25s)(1 + 0.5s)}$

(c) $G(s)H(s) = \dfrac{100(1 + s)}{s(1 + 0.1s)(1 + 0.5s)(1 + 0.8s)}$

(d) $G(s)H(s) = \dfrac{5(1 - 0.5s)}{s(1 + 0.1s)(1 - 0.25s)}$

(e) $G(s)H(s) = \dfrac{10}{s(1 + 0.2s)(s - 1)}$

(f) $G(s)H(s) = \dfrac{2.5(1 + 0.2s)}{1 + 2s + s^3}$

7-7. Sketch Nyquist diagrams for the following loop transfer functions. Sketch only the portion which is necessary to determine the stability of the closed-loop system. Determine the stability of the systems.

(a) $G(s)H(s) = \dfrac{100}{s(s^2 + 2s + 2)(s + 1)}$

(b) $G(s)H(s) = \dfrac{50}{s(s + 2)(s^2 + 4)}$

(c) $G(s)H(s) = \dfrac{s}{1 - 0.2s}$

7-8. Figure 7P-8 shows the entire Nyquist plots of the loop gains $G(s)H(s)$ of some

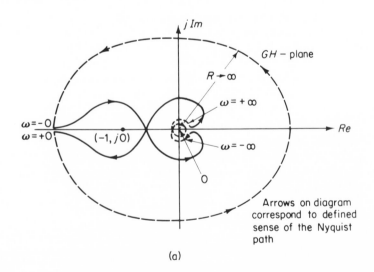

(a)

FIG. 7P-8.

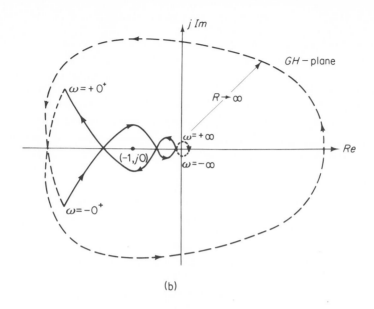

(b)

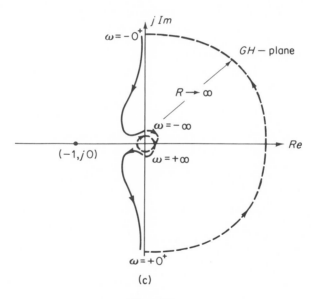

(c)

FIG. 7P-8.

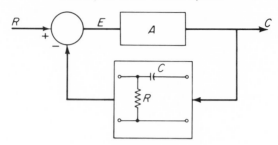

FIG. 7P-10.

feedback control systems. It is known that in each case, the zeros of $G(s)H(s)$ are all located in the left half of the s-plane; i.e., $Z = 0$ with respect to the origin in the GH-plane. Determine the number of poles of $G(s)H(s)$ which are in the right half of the s-plane. State the stability of the open-loop systems. State whether the closed-loop system is stable; if not, give the number of roots of the characteristic equation which are in the right half of the s-plane.

7-9. The characteristic equation of a feedback control system is given by

$$s^3 + 5Ks^2 + (2K + 3)s + 10 = 0$$

Apply the Nyquist criterion to determine the values of K for a stable closed-loop system. Check the answer by means of the Routh-Hurwitz criterion.

7-10. Determine the value of A so that the system shown in Fig. 7P-10 will realize the transfer function of an ideal derivative control $(1 + Ts)$. Sketch the Nyquist diagrams for the transfer function $C(s)/R(s)$ for three different values of A $(A < 1, A = 1, \text{ and } A > 1)$. Investigate the stability of the system in each case.

7-11. The Nyquist criterion was originally devised to investigate the absolute stability of a closed-loop system. By sketching the Nyquist plot of $G(s)H(s)$ which corresponds to the Nyquist path, it is possible to tell whether the system's characteristic equation has roots in the right half of the s-plane.

(a) Define a new Nyquist path in the s-plane which may be used to ensure that all the complex roots of the characteristic equation have damping ratios greater than some value δ_1.

(b) Define a new Nyquist path in the s-plane which may be used to ensure that all the characteristic equation roots are in the left half of the s-plane with real parts greater than α_1.

7-12. For the control system given in Problem 7-5, sketch the Nyquist plot of $G(s)$ and discuss the stability of the closed-loop system as a function of K. Determine the points where the Nyquist plot intersects the negative real axis.

8

Root Locus Technique

8.1 Introduction

Based on the discussions given in the preceding chapters, the fundamental problem of linear feedback control system analysis can be stated as: *Given the open-loop transfer functions G(s) and H(s), determine the closed-loop transfer function C(s)/R(s) from which the performance of the over-all system can be evaluated.*

Similarly, in the design problem, at least in the single-loop case, it is appropriate to state: *Given the desired closed-loop transfer function, determine the corresponding open-loop transfer function of the system.*

In any case, it is desirable to study the relationships between the open-loop and the closed-loop transfer functions of a given feedback control system. More specifically, it is desirable to make a study of the effects of the variations of the parameters of the open-loop transfer function upon the closed-loop transfer function.

As a simple illustration for the discussion given above, let us consider that the open-loop transfer function of a unity-feedback control system is given by

$$G(s) = \frac{K}{s(s+a)} \tag{8-1}$$

where K and a are constants. The closed-loop transfer function of the system is

$$\frac{C(s)}{R(s)} = \frac{K}{s^2 + as + K} \tag{8-2}$$

It is apparent that the system will be unstable if either a or K or both are negative. If no additional compensation elements are allowed to be added, a simple design problem may be formed by determining the proper values of a and K so that the over-all system is *optimum* according to some performance criterion.

Since the dynamic behavior of the system is controlled by the roots of the characteristic equation, it is pertinent to investigate the variation of the roots as a function of a and K.

To simplify the problem further, let us consider that $a = 2$ and K can lie between $-\infty$ and $+\infty$. Then the characteristic equation of the system is

$$s^2 + 2s + K = 0 \tag{8-3}$$

The two roots of Eq. (8–3) are

$$s_1, s_2 = -1 \pm \sqrt{1 - K} \tag{8-4}$$

The variation of the roots when K is varied from $-\infty$ to $+\infty$ is considered in the following:

(1) For $-\infty < K < 0$: The two roots are both real, one being positive, the other negative.

(2) For $K = 0$: $s_1 = 0$, $s_2 = -2$; these roots are the same as the poles of $G(s)$.

(3) For $0 < K < 1$: The two roots are both negative real numbers.

(4) For $K = 1$: There is a double root at $s_1 = s_2 = -1$.

(5) For $1 < K < \infty$: The two roots are complex conjugate pairs with negative real parts equal to -1.

The loci of the two roots when K varies from $-\infty$ to ∞ are given in Fig. 8-1. From the root loci the following information on the system behavior is obtained.

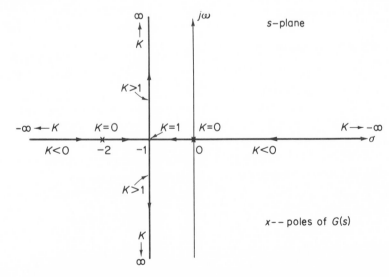

FIG. 8-1. Loci of roots of $s^2 + 2s + K = 0$ as a function of K.

(1) *Stability*

The closed-loop system is unstable for negative values of K, but is stable for all positive values of K.

(2) *Transient Response*

(a) For all values of K between 0 and 1, the system is overdamped $(\delta > 1)$; for $1 < K < \infty$, the system is underdamped $(\delta < 1)$. Critical damping $(\delta = 1)$ occurs when $K = 1$.

(b) The undamped natural frequency ω_n increases with an increase in K.

(c) For all values of $K \geq 1$, the settling time of the step response is constant, since the real parts of the two roots are fixed.

(3) *Frequency Domain Characteristics*

For any given value of K, the roots s_1 and s_2 of the characteristic equation are determined from Fig. 8-1, and the closed-loop transfer function is given by

$$\frac{C(s)}{R(s)} = \frac{K}{(s - s_1)(s - s_2)} \qquad (8\text{-}5)$$

The frequency response of the system can be evaluated from the Bode plot of $C(s)/R(s)$ and the methods described in Chapter 9.

The plot shown in Fig. 8-1 is known as a *root locus diagram* of Eq. (8–3) when K is a variable parameter. The root locus technique was introduced by W. R. Evans in 1948, and the art has been greatly developed and extensively applied to the analysis and design of control systems in recent years.

In control system problems, a root locus diagram is defined as *a plot of the loci of the poles of the closed-loop transfer function (or roots of the characteristic equation) when one or more parameters of the open-loop transfer function are varied from $-\infty$ to $+\infty$.* Usually, when there is only one variable parameter, such as K in Eq. (8–3), and K varies only between 0 and $+\infty$, the plot is called a *root locus diagram.*[1,2] When K varies between 0 and $-\infty$, the plot is called an *inverse root locus diagram.*[3] When more than one parameter is considered to be variable, the plot is referred to as a *root contour diagram.*

8.2 The Root Loci (Definition)

Consider a feedback control system whose closed-loop transfer function is

$$\frac{C(s)}{R(s)} = \frac{G(s)}{1 + G(s)H(s)} \qquad (8\text{-}6)$$

The roots of the characteristic equation are determined from

$$1 + G(s)H(s) = 0 \qquad (8\text{-}7)$$

or

$$G(s)H(s) = -1 \qquad (8\text{-}8)$$

In order to satisfy the last equation, the following conditions must be met:

$$(1) \quad |G(s)H(s)| = 1 \qquad (8\text{-}9)$$

$$(2) \quad \underline{/G(s)H(s)} = (2k + 1)\pi \qquad (8\text{-}10)$$

where $k = 0, \pm 1, \pm 2, \ldots$, all integers.

In feedback control systems without transportation lag, $G(s)H(s)$ is a rational algebraic function, so it can be written as

$$G(s)H(s) = \frac{K(s + z_1)(s + z_2) \cdots (s + z_m)}{(s + p_1)(s + p_2) \cdots (s + p_{m+n})} \qquad (8\text{-}11)$$

The two conditions given in Eqs. (8–9) and (8–10) then become

$$|G(s)H(s)| = \frac{|K| \prod_{i=1}^{m} |s + z_i|}{\prod_{j=1}^{m+n} |s + p_j|} = 1 \qquad (-\infty < K < \infty) \qquad (8\text{-}12)$$

and

$$\underline{/G(s)H(s)} = \underline{/K} + \sum_{i=1}^{m} \underline{/s + z_i} - \sum_{j=1}^{m+n} \underline{/s + p_j} = (2k + 1)\pi \qquad (8\text{-}13)$$

Now the root locus plot of the system in Eq. (8–6) is a plot of all the values of s in the s-plane when K is varied from 0 to $+\infty$. Of course, when K varies between 0 and $-\infty$, the plot is termed an inverse root locus diagram. An alternative way of describing the root locus problem is to say that *for any given value of K, say K_1, between 0 and $+\infty$, any point s_1 in the s-plane which satisfies Eqs. (8–12) and (8–13) is a point on the root loci.*

In other words, a point s_1 in the s-plane is a point on the root loci if it satisfies the following two conditions:

$$\frac{|K| \prod_{i=1}^{m} |s_1 + z_i|}{\prod_{j=1}^{m+n} |s_1 + p_j|} = 1 \qquad (-\infty < K < \infty) \qquad (8\text{-}14)$$

and

$$\sum_{i=1}^{m} \underline{/s_1 + z_i} - \sum_{j=1}^{m+n} \underline{/s_1 + p_j} = (2k + 1)\pi \qquad (0 < K < \infty) \qquad (8\text{-}15)$$

$$= 2k\pi \qquad (-\infty < K < 0) \qquad (8\text{-}16)$$

for $k = 0, \pm 1, \pm 2, \ldots$, all integers.

As an illustration, let

$$G(s)H(s) = \frac{K(s + z_1)}{s(s + p_2)(s + p_3)} \qquad (8\text{-}17)$$

The poles and zeros of $G(s)H(s)$ are assumed to be located as shown in

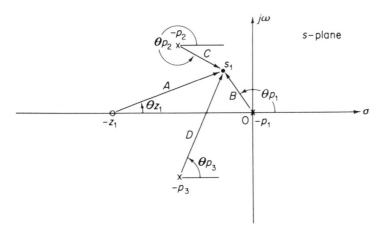

FIG. 8-2. Pole-zero configuration of
$$G(s)H(s) = \frac{K(s + z_1)}{s(s + p_2)(s + p_3)}.$$

Fig. 8–2. Next, we assume an arbitrary point s_1 in the s-plane and draw vectors directed from the poles and zeros of $G(s)H(s)$ to the point s_1. If s_1 is a point on the root loci $(0 < K < +\infty)$ of the closed-loop system, it must satisfy the following two conditions:

$$\frac{|K||s_1 + z_1|}{|s_1||s_1 + p_2||s_1 + p_3|} = 1 \qquad (8\text{–}18)$$

and

$$\underline{/s_1 + z_1} - (\underline{/s_1} + \underline{/s_1 + p_2} + \underline{/s_1 + p_3}) = (2k + 1)\pi \qquad (8\text{–}19)$$

If s_1 is to be a point on the inverse root loci $(-\infty < K < 0)$, it must satisfy Eq. (8–18) and

$$\underline{/s_1 + z_1} - (\underline{/s_1} + \underline{/s_1 + p_2} + \underline{/s_1 + p_3}) = 2k\pi \qquad (8\text{–}20)$$

for $k = 0, +1, \pm 2, \ldots$.

The factor $|s_1 + z_1|$ is recognized as the length of the vector drawn from the zero z_1 to the point s_1, and the factor $|s_1 + p_2|$ is the length of the vector drawn from the pole p_2 to s_1. If, in Fig. 8–2, the vector lengths are represented by A, B, C, and D, Eq. (8–18) becomes

$$\frac{A}{BCD} = \frac{1}{|K|} \qquad (8\text{–}21)$$

The angles θ_{z_1}, θ_{p_1}, θ_{p_2}, and θ_{p_3} are the arguments of the vectors measured with the positive real axis as zero reference. From Eqs. (8–19) and (8–20), it is required that

$$\theta_{z_1} - (\theta_{p_1} + \theta_{p_2} + \theta_{p_3}) = (2k + 1)\pi \qquad (0 < K < \infty) \qquad (8\text{–}22)$$

and

$$\theta_{z_1} - (\theta_{p_1} + \theta_{p_2} + \theta_{p_3}) = 2k\pi \qquad (-\infty < K < 0) \qquad (8\text{–}23)$$

Consequently, given the pole-zero configuration of $G(s)H(s)$, the construction of the root locus diagram of the closed-loop system involves the following two steps:

(1) A search for the s_1 points in the s-plane which satisfy the condition given by Eq. (8–13).

(2) The determination of the value of K ($-K$) at a particular s_1 point on the root loci (inverse root loci) from the relation given by Eq. (8–12).

Although it seems that the search for all the s_1 points in the s-plane which satisfy Eq. (8–13) is an almost impossible task, the actual procedure of the root loci construction is not so formidably complex. Normally, the root loci can be sketched in most cases by following through the rules of construction which will be described in the next section. A special tool called the *Spirule* can also be used to aid in plotting the root locus diagram. It is also common to use analog and digital computers to compute and plot the root locus diagram.

8.3 The Construction of the Root Loci

The following rules of construction are developed from the relation between the poles and zeros of $G(s)H(s)$ and the roots of the characteristic equation. These rules should be regarded only as aids to the construction of the root loci; they do not give the exact plot.

(1) *The $K = 0$ Points on the Root Loci*

The $K = 0$ points of the root loci are at the poles of $G(s)H(s)$.

Proof: Equation (8–12) can be written as

$$\frac{\prod_{i=1}^{m}|(s + z_i)|}{\prod_{j=1}^{m+n}|(s + p_j)|} = \frac{1}{|K|} \tag{8–24}$$

As K approaches zero, the value of Eq. (8–24) approaches infinity, and correspondingly, s approaches the poles of $G(s)H(s)$; i.e., $s \to p_j$. It is apparent that this property applies to both the root loci and the inverse root loci.

Example 8-1. Consider the pole-zero configuration of

$$G(s)H(s) = \frac{K(s + 1)}{s(s + 2)(s + 3)} \tag{8–25}$$

shown in Fig. 8-3. The poles of $G(s)H(s)$ are at $s = 0$, $s = -2$, and $s = -3$; therefore, these three poles also correspond to the $K = 0$ points on the root loci.

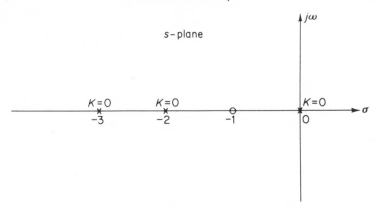

FIG. 8-3. Points at which $K = 0$ on the root loci of

$$G(s)H(s) = \frac{K(s + 1)}{s(s + 2)(s + 3)}$$

(2) *The $K = \pm \infty$ Points on the Root Loci*

The $K = \pm \infty$ points on the root loci are at the zeros of $G(s)H(s)$.

Proof: With reference again to Eq. (8–24), as K approaches plus or minus infinity, the equation approaches zero in value, which requires that s must approach the zeros of $G(s)H(s)$.

Example 8-2. Figure 8-4 shows the pole-zero configuration of Eq. (8–25). According to the property just described, the zeros of $G(s)H(s)$ correspond to the points on the root loci at which $K = \pm \infty$. In this case, there is only one finite zero of $G(s)H(s)$ at $s = -1$, but two other zeros are located at infinity. This is because for a rational function the total number of poles

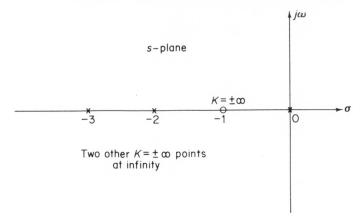

FIG. 8-4. Points at which $K = \pm \infty$ on the root loci of

$$G(s)H(s) = \frac{K(s + 1)}{s(s + 2)(s + 3)}$$

and zeros must be equal if the poles and zeros at infinity are counted.

(3) *Number of Separate Loci*

Let N = number of separate loci.

Z = number of finite zeros of $G(s)H(s)$.

P = number of finite poles of $G(s)H(s)$.

Then,

$$N = Z \quad \text{if} \quad Z > P$$

and

$$N = P \quad \text{if} \quad P > Z$$

Since a complete root locus is formed between each pair of pole and zero of $G(s)H(s)$, the total number of root loci for a given system must be equal to the larger value of P and Z.

Example 8-3. The number of separate loci of the closed-loop system corresponding to

$$G(s)H(s) = \frac{K(s + 1)}{s(s + 2)(s + 3)}$$

is three. In this case, since $P = 3$, $Z = 1$; hence $N = 3$. It is also clear that the characteristic equation of the system is of the third order; thus, there are three sets of roots.

(4) *Symmetry of the Root Loci*

The root loci and the inverse root loci are symmetrical with respect to the real axis of the s-plane.

The proof of this property is self-evident, since, for rational functions, the complex roots must appear in complex conjugate pairs.

(5) *Asymptotes of Root Loci*

For large values of s, the root loci are asymptotic to straight lines with angles given by

$$\theta_k = \frac{(2k + 1)\pi}{P - Z} \tag{8-26}$$

where $k = 0, 1, 2, \ldots$, up to $k = P - Z$ (exclusively).

For inverse root loci,

$$\theta_k = \frac{2k\pi}{P - Z} \tag{8-27}$$

where P and Z are defined as in Rule (4).

The properties of the asymptotes of the root loci near infinity are important, since when $P \neq Z$, $P - Z$ of the loci will approach infinity in the s-plane as s becomes very large.

Proof: From Eq. (8-11), the general form of the loop transfer function of a feedback control system can be written as

$$G(s)H(s) = \frac{K(s^m + a_1 s^{m-1} + \cdots + a_m)}{(s^{m+n} + b_1 s^{m+n-1} + \cdots + b_{m+n})}$$

$$= \frac{K}{\left(\dfrac{s^{m+n} + b_1 s^{m+n-1} + \cdots + b_{m+n}}{s^m + a_1 s^{m-1} + \cdots + a_m} \right)} \tag{8-28}$$

Hence,

$$G(s)H(s) = \frac{K}{s^n + (b_1 - a_1)s^{n-1} + \cdots + R(s)/P(s)} \tag{8-29}$$

where $R(s)$ is a polynomial of degree less than m, and

$$P(s) = s^m + a_1 s^{m-1} + \cdots + a_m \tag{8-30}$$

Then the roots of the characteristic equation are found from

$$s^n + (b_1 - a_1)s^{n-1} + \cdots + R(s)/P(s) = -K \tag{8-31}$$

As s becomes very large, the term $R(s)/P(s)$ approaches zero, and only the first two terms of Eq. (8–31) are considered as significant. Therefore, Eq. (8–31) becomes

$$s^n + (b_1 - a_1)s^{n-1} \simeq -K \tag{8-32}$$

or

$$s\left(1 + \frac{b_1 - a_1}{s}\right)^{1/n} \simeq (-K)^{1/n} \tag{8-33}$$

The factor $\left(1 + \dfrac{b_1 - a_1}{s}\right)^{1/n}$ in Eq. (8–33) is expanded into an infinite series, and Eq. (8–33) becomes

$$s\left(1 + \frac{b_1 - a_1}{ns} + \cdots\right) \simeq (-K)^{1/n} \tag{8-34}$$

Again, if the terms higher than the second are neglected, we get

$$s + \frac{b_1 - a_1}{n} \simeq (-K)^{1/n} \tag{8-35}$$

Now substitute $s = \sigma + j\omega$ into Eq. (8–35), which yields

$$\sigma + j\omega + \frac{b_1 - a_1}{n} \simeq |K^{1/n}|\left[\cos\frac{(2k+1)\pi}{n} + j\sin\frac{(2k+1)\pi}{n}\right]$$
$$(0 < K < \infty) \tag{8-36}$$

and

$$\sigma + j\omega + \frac{b_1 - a_1}{n} \simeq |K^{1/n}|\left[\cos\frac{2k\pi}{n} + j\sin\frac{2k\pi}{n}\right]$$
$$(-\infty < K < 0) \tag{8-37}$$

for $k = 0, \pm 1, \pm 2, \ldots$.

Equating the real and imaginary parts of Eq. (8–36), we have

$$\sigma + \frac{b_1 - a_1}{n} \simeq |K^{1/n}|\cos\frac{(2k+1)\pi}{n} \tag{8-38}$$

and

$$\omega \simeq |K^{1/n}| \sin \frac{(2k+1)\pi}{n} \qquad (8\text{-}39)$$

Solving for $|K^{1/n}|$ from the last two equations, we get

$$|K^{1/n}| \simeq \frac{\omega}{\sin\left(\dfrac{2k+1}{n}\right)\pi} = \frac{\sigma + \dfrac{b_1 - a_1}{n}}{\cos\left(\dfrac{2k+1}{n}\right)\pi} \qquad (8\text{-}40)$$

and solving for ω we have

$$\omega \simeq \tan\left(\frac{2k+1}{n}\right)\pi\left[\left(\sigma + \frac{b_1 - a_1}{n}\right)\right] \qquad (8\text{-}41)$$

Equation (8-41) represents a straight line in the s-plane; the equation is of the form

$$\omega \simeq m(\sigma - \sigma_1) \qquad (8\text{-}42)$$

where m is the slope and σ_1 is the interception on the σ-axis. Thus,

$$m = \tan \frac{(2k+1)\pi}{n} = \tan \frac{(2k+1)\pi}{P-Z} \qquad (8\text{-}43)$$

and

$$\sigma_1 = -\left(\frac{b_1 - a_1}{n}\right) = -\left(\frac{b_1 - a_1}{P-Z}\right) \qquad (8\text{-}44)$$

where $k = 0, 1, 2, \ldots$, up to $k = P - Z$ (exclusively).

Similarly, Eq. (8-37) leads to

$$m = \tan \frac{2k\pi}{P-Z} \qquad (8\text{-}45)$$

and the same expression for σ_1 as in Eq. (8-44), for the inverse root loci.

Therefore, the results in Eqs. (8-43) and (8-45) agree with those of Eqs. (8-26) and (8-27), respectively. The significance of σ_1 in Eq. (8-44) will become apparent in the next rule.

(6) *Intersection of the Asymptotes (Centroid)*

(a) *The intersection of the $n = P - Z$ number of asymptotes lies on the real axis only.*

(b) *The intersection of the asymptotes (centroid) on the real axis is given by*

$$\sigma_1 = -\left(\frac{b_1 - a_1}{n}\right) = \frac{\sum \text{poles of } G(s)H(s) - \sum \text{zeros of } G(s)H(s)}{P-Z} \qquad (8\text{-}46)$$

Proof: The proof of rule (a) is straightforward, since the root loci are symmetrical with respect to the real axis. The proof of Eq. (8-46) follows directly from Eq. (8-44), since, from the laws of algebra,

$b_1 = -\sum$ roots of the denominator of $G(s)H(s) = -\sum$ poles of $G(s)H(s)$
and
$a_1 = -\sum$ roots of the numerator of $G(s)H(s) = -\sum$ zeros of $G(s)H(s)$

It should be noted that Eq. (8–46) is valid for the root loci as well as the inverse root loci.

Example 8-4. Consider a feedback control system with the loop transfer function

$$G(s)H(s) = \frac{K(s + 1)}{s(s + 4)(s^2 + 2s + 2)} \qquad (8\text{--}47)$$

The pole-zero configuration of $G(s)H(s)$ is shown in Fig. 8-5. From the six rules described so far, the following information concerning the root loci and the inverse root loci is obtained:

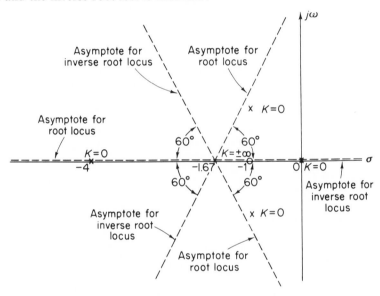

FIG. 8-5. Asymptotes for the complete root loci of
$$G(s)H(s) = \frac{K(s + 1)}{s(s + 4)(s^2 + 2s + 2)}$$

(1) $K = 0$: The $K = 0$ points on the root loci are found at $s = 0$, $s = -4$, $s = -1 + j1$, and $s = -1 - j1$. These are the poles of $G(s)H(s)$.

(2) $K = \pm\infty$: The $K = \pm\infty$ points on the root loci are found at $s = -1$, $s = \infty$, ∞, and ∞. These points correspond to the zeros of $G(s)H(s)$. Notice that three loci end at infinity in the s-plane.

(3) Since $G(s)H(s)$ is of the fourth order, there are four separate loci.

(4) The root loci (for all values of K) have conjugate symmetry.

(5) For large values of s, the root loci are asymptotic to straight lines with angles (with respect to the real axis) given by Eq. (8–26). For

$$k = 0, \qquad \theta_0 = \frac{(2k + 1)\pi}{P - Z} = \frac{180°}{4 - 1} = 60°$$

$$k = 1, \qquad \theta_1 = \frac{(2k + 1)\pi}{P - Z} = \frac{540°}{4 - 1} = 180°$$

$$k = 2, \qquad \theta_2 = \frac{(2k + 1)\pi}{P - Z} = \frac{900°}{4 - 1} = 300°$$

The angles of the asymptotes of the inverse root loci are given by Eq. (8–27). For

$$k = 0, \qquad \theta_0 = \frac{2k}{P - Z} = 0°$$

$$k = 1, \qquad \theta_1 = \frac{2k}{P - Z} = \frac{360°}{4 - 1} = 120°$$

$$k = 2, \qquad \theta_2 = \frac{2k}{P - Z} = \frac{720°}{4 - 1} = 240°$$

(6) The six asymptotic lines (three for the root loci and three for the inverse loci) intersect at

$$\sigma_1 = \frac{\sum \text{poles of } G(s)H(s) - \sum \text{zeros of } G(s)H(s)}{P - Z}$$

$$= \frac{(0 - 4 - 1 + j1 - 1 - j1) - (-1)}{3} = -\frac{5}{3} \qquad (8\text{--}48)$$

Example 8-5. The asymptotes of the root loci $(-\infty < K < \infty)$ for several different feedback control systems are shown in Fig. 8-6.

(7) *Root Loci on the Real Axis*

Root Loci (Positive K): On a given section of the real axis, root loci may be found in the section only if the total number of poles and zeros of $G(s)H(s)$ to the right of the section is odd.

Inverse Root Loci (Negative K): On a given section of the real axis, inverse root loci may be found in the section only if the total number of poles and zeros of $G(s)H(s)$ to the right of the section is even. Alternatively, we can state that inverse root loci will be found in sections of the real axis not occupied by the root loci.

Proof: At any point on the real axis, the angles of the vectors from the complex poles or zeros of $G(s)H(s)$ cancel. The only contribution to the angles in Eq. (8–13) is from the poles and zeros of $G(s)H(s)$ located to the right of the point on the real axis. The requirements on the total number of poles and zeros located to the right of the point in question for the root loci or the inverse root loci to exist are easily verified from Eqs. (8–15)

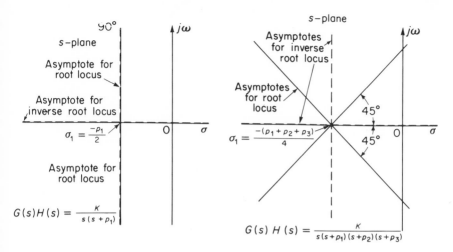

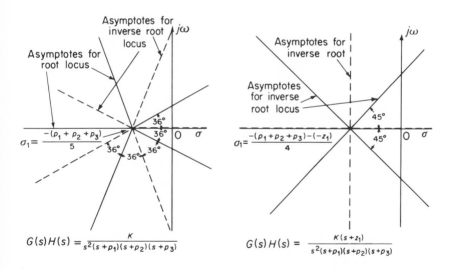

FIG. 8-6. Examples illustrating the asymptotes of root loci.

and (8–16). The following example illustrates how the root loci on the real axis in the s-plane are determined.

Example 8-6. In Fig. 8-7 the root loci and the inverse root loci on the real axis are shown for two different pole-zero configurations. It is apparent that the occurrence of the loci on the real axis is not affected by the complex poles and zeros of $G(s)H(s)$.

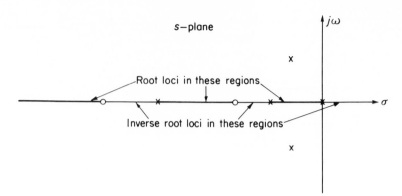

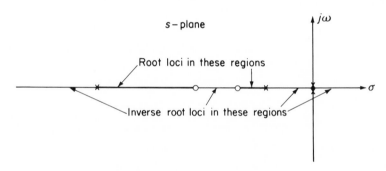

FIG. 8-7. Root loci on the real axis.

(8) *Angles of Departure (from Poles) and the Angles of Arrival (at Zeros) of the Root Loci**

The angles of departure and arrival of root loci can be determined readily from Eq. (8–15). For instance, in the pole-zero configuration of $G(s)H(s)$ given in Fig. 8-8, it is desired to determine the angle at which the root locus leaves the pole at $-1 + j1$. A point s_1, which is very close to the pole at $-1 + j1$, is selected on the root locus; since the point s_1 is assumed to be on the root locus, it must satisfy Eq. (8–15). Thus,

$$-(\theta_{p_1} + \theta_{p_2} + \theta_{p_3} + \theta_{p_4}) = (2k + 1)180° \qquad (8\text{–}49)$$

The θ's in the last equation are measured as shown in Fig. 8-8; we have

$$-135° - 90° - 26.6° - \theta_{p_4} = (2k + 1)180° \qquad (8\text{–}50)$$

from which

---

*Since the complete root loci (for all values of K) are continuous at the poles and zeros of $G(s)H(s)$, it is necessary to determine only the angles of the root loci at these critical points.

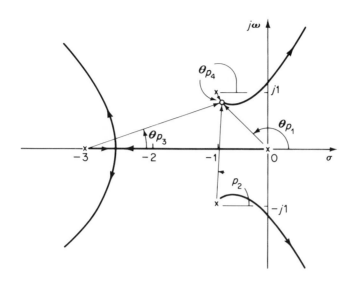

FIG. 8-8. Pole-zero configuration of

$$G(s)H(s) = \frac{K}{s(s + 3)(s^2 + 2s + 2)}$$

$$\theta_{p_4} = -251.6° - (2k + 1)180° = -71.6°$$

Once the angle of the root locus at a pole or zero of $G(s)H(s)$ is determined, the angle of the inverse root locus at the same point differs from that angle by 180 deg. Alternatively, the angles of departure and arrival of inverse root loci can be determined from Eq. (8–16).

(9) *Intersection of the Root Loci with the Imaginary Axis*

The points where the root loci and the inverse root loci intersect the imaginary axis of the s-plane and the corresponding values of K are normally determined by means of the Routh-Hurwitz Criterion.

For more complex systems and for conditional stable systems, the critical values of K and ω are determined more easily with the aid of the Bode plot.

Example 8-7. The pole-zero configuration of the loop transfer function

$$G(s)H(s) = \frac{K}{s(s + 3)(s^2 + 2s + 2)} \qquad (8\text{–}51)$$

is shown in Fig. 8-8. The characteristic equation of the system is

$$s^4 + 5s^3 + 8s^2 + 6s + K = 0 \qquad (8\text{–}52)$$

Applying the Routh-Hurwitz criterion to the last equation, we have the following Routh tabulation:

$$
\begin{array}{ccccc}
s^4 & 1 & 8 & K & \\
s^3 & 5 & 6 & & \\
s^2 & \dfrac{34}{5} & K & & \\
s^1 & \dfrac{\dfrac{204}{5} - 5K}{\dfrac{34}{5}} & 0 & & \text{Coefficients of the auxiliary} \\
& & & & \text{equation} \\
s^0 & K & 0 & &
\end{array}
$$

Thus, the critical value of K is determined by equating the first element of the s^1 row of the above Routh tabulation to zero; that is,

$$
K = \frac{204}{25} = 8.15
$$

To determine the frequency at the intersection on the imaginary axis, we write the auxiliary equation from the Routh tabulation:

$$
\frac{34}{5} s^2 + K = 0 \tag{8–53}
$$

Since K is 8.15 at the critical point, the last equation becomes

$$
170s^2 + 204 = 0 \tag{8–54}
$$

from which

$$
s = \pm j1.095
$$

and

$$
\omega = \pm 1.095 \text{ rad/sec}
$$

(10) *Breakaway Points (Saddle Points) on the Root Loci*

The points on the root loci (all values of K) where multiple roots (roots of an order higher than one) of the characteristic equation are found are called the *breakaway points, or saddle points, of the root loci.* Figure 8-9a illustrates a case in which two separate loci of a root locus plot meet at a point on the real axis in the s-plane, and then break away from the real axis as the value of K is increased further. The point at which the two loci meet and break away is a breakaway point. In this case, the break-away point represents a double root of the characteristic equation. Figure

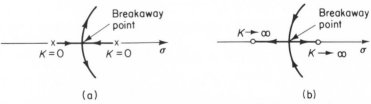

(a)   (b)

FIG. 8-9. Breakaway points on the real axis: (a) Breakaway between poles; (b) Breakaway between zeros.

8-9b shows a similar situation where two loci of complex roots break away at a point on the real axis in the s-plane, and then approach two zeros of $G(s)H(s)$. In general, a breakaway point may involve more than two root loci. For example, in Fig. 8-10, it is shown that four separate loci meet at a point on the real axis and then depart in four different directions. Also, a root locus diagram may have more than one breakaway point, and the breakaway points need not always be on the real axis, However, because of the conjugate symmetry of the root loci, *the breakaway points must either lie on the real axis or occur in complex conjugate pairs.*

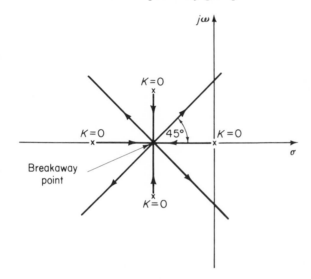

FIG. 8-10. Breakaway point of four separate loci on the real axis.

In Figs. 8-9a and b, the root loci are shown to break away on the real axis at angles of 180 deg apart, whereas in Fig. 8-10 the four loci depart with angles of 90 deg apart. A general statement concerning the angles between the loci at a breakaway point can be made: *The root loci (inverse root loci) must approach and leave a breakaway point on the real axis at an angle of $180°/n$ apart, where n is the number of root loci (inverse root loci) approaching and leaving the point. The same is true for complex breakaway points.* The proof of this statement is not given here.

In general, several graphical and analytical methods of determining the breakaway points on a root locus plot are available. Two analytical methods that seem to be the most powerful and convenient are described below.

Method 1. The breakaway points (real and complex) on a root locus plot for $-\infty < K < \infty$ are obtained as the roots of the equation which is obtained by taking the first derivative of $G(s)H(s)$ with respect to s and setting it equal to zero; i.e.,

$$\frac{d[G(s)H(s)]}{ds} = 0 \tag{8-55}$$

Proof: Let the loop transfer function of a feedback control system be written as

$$G(s)H(s) = \frac{KP(s)}{Q(s)} \tag{8-56}$$

where K is the variable parameter, and $-\infty < K < \infty$. $P(s)$ and $Q(s)$ are polynomials of s, and they do not contain K.

Then the roots of the characteristic equation satisfy the equation

$$Q(s) + KP(s) = 0 \tag{8-57}$$

If we consider that K is varied by an increment ΔK, Eq. (8–57) becomes

$$Q(s) + (K + \Delta K)P(s) = 0 \tag{8-58}$$

Dividing both sides of Eq. (8–58) by $Q(s) + KP(s)$, we have

$$1 + \frac{\Delta KP(s)}{Q(s) + KP(s)} = 0 \tag{8-59}$$

which can be written as

$$1 + \Delta KF(s) = 0 \tag{8-60}$$

where

$$F(s) = \frac{P(s)}{Q(s) + KP(s)} \tag{8-61}$$

Since the denominator of $F(s)$ is the left hand side of Eq. (8–57), at points very close to a characteristic equation root s_i of multiplicity n, which corresponds to a breakaway point of n loci, $F(s)$ can be approximated by

$$F(s) = \frac{A_i}{(s - s_i)^n} = \frac{A_i}{(\Delta s_i)^n} \tag{8-62}$$

where A_i is a constant.

Substituting Eq. (8–62) into Eq. (8–60) gives

$$1 + \frac{\Delta KA_i}{(\Delta s)^n} = 0 \tag{8-63}$$

from which we obtain

$$\frac{\Delta K}{\Delta s} = \frac{-(\Delta s)^{n-1}}{A_i} \tag{8-64}$$

Taking the limit on both sides of the last equation as ΔK approaches zero, we have

$$\lim_{\Delta K \to 0} \left(\frac{\Delta K}{\Delta s}\right) = \frac{dK}{ds} = 0 \tag{8-65}$$

Therefore, at the breakaway points of the root loci, dK/ds is zero.*

---

*The quantity $(ds/s)/(dK/K)$ is defined as the *root sensitivity*[4] of a polynomial with respect to incremental variation of the parameter K. In this case, it is proved that at the breakaway points of the root loci, the roots have infinite sensitivity.

Now writing Eq. (8–57) as

$$K = -\frac{Q(s)}{P(s)} \tag{8-66}$$

and taking the derivative on both sides with respect to s, we have

$$\frac{dK}{ds} = -\left[P(s)\frac{dQ(s)}{ds} - Q(s)\frac{dP(s)}{ds}\right]\frac{1}{[P(s)]^2} \tag{8-67}$$

Now taking the derivative on both sides of Eq. (8–56) with respect to s, we get

$$\frac{d[G(s)H(s)]}{ds} = K\left[Q(s)\frac{dP(s)}{ds} - P(s)\frac{dQ(s)}{ds}\right]\frac{1}{[Q(s)]^2} \tag{8-68}$$

Therefore, the condition stated in Eq. (8–65) is equivalent to

$$Q(s)\frac{dP(s)}{ds} - P(s)\frac{dQ(s)}{ds} = 0 \tag{8-69}$$

or

$$\frac{d[G(s)H(s)]}{ds} = 0 \tag{8-70}$$

It is important to point out that the condition for the breakaway point given by Eq. (8–70) is necessary but not sufficient. In other words, all breakaway points must satisfy Eq. (8–70), but not all the solutions of Eq. (8–70) are breakaway points. In general, the following conclusions can be made with regard to the solutions of Eq. (8–70):

(1) All the real solutions of Eq. (8–70) are breakaway points on the root loci ($-\infty < K < \infty$), since the entire real axis in the s-plane is occupied by the root loci for all values of K.

(2) The complex conjugate solutions of Eq. (8–70) are breakaway points only if the solutions also satisfy the characteristic equation. This uncertainty does not cause any difficulty in using Eq. (8–70) since, usually, the other properties of the root loci are sufficient to provide information on the general location of the breakaway points.

Another disadvantage of the method of locating breakaway points using Eq. (8–55) is that for multiple breakaway points on the root loci, Eq. (8–55) is a high-order polynomial which is usually difficult to solve. However, the method is most convenient if the order of Eq. (8–55) is less than three.

The following examples are devised to illustrate the application of Eq. (8–55).

Example 8-8. The root locus diagram shown in Fig. 8–11 has two breakaway points on the real axis; one between the poles at 0 and -2, the other between the zeros at -4 and $-\infty$. The loop transfer function of the system is

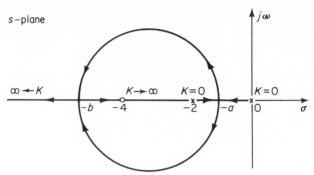

FIG. 8-11. Root loci for system with $G(s)H(s) = \dfrac{K(s + 4)}{s(s + 2)}$

$$G(s)H(s) = \frac{K(s + 4)}{s(s + 2)} \tag{8-71}$$

Using Eq. (8–55), we have

$$\frac{d[G(s)H(s)]}{ds} = \frac{K[s(s + 2) - 2(s + 1)(s + 4)]}{s^2(s + 2)^2} = 0 \tag{8-72}$$

which gives

$$-s^2 - 8s - 8 = 0 \tag{8-73}$$

Solving Eq. (8–73), we find that the breakaway points on the root loci are at $s = -1.172$ and $s = -6.828$.

Example 8-9. Consider the loop transfer function

$$G(s)H(s) = \frac{K(s + 2)}{s^2 + 2s + 2} \tag{8-74}$$

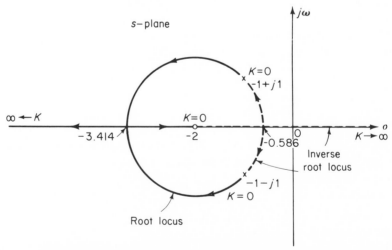

FIG. 8-12. The complete root locus diagram for the system in Example 8-9.

The complete root locus diagram for the closed-loop system is shown in Fig. 8–12. The breakaway points are determined from

$$\frac{d[G(s)H(s)]}{ds} = \frac{K[s^2 + 2s + 2 - 2(s + 1)(s + 2)]}{(s^2 + 2s + 2)^2} = 0 \qquad (8-75)$$

or

$$-s^2 - 4s - 2 = 0 \qquad (8-76)$$

The breakaway points are the roots of Eq. (8–76), and are at $s = -3.414$ and $s = -0.586$. Notice that in this case, $s = -3.414$ is the breakaway point on the root loci, whereas $s = -0.586$ is a breakaway point on the inverse root loci.

Example 8-10. Figure 8-13 shows the root locus diagram of the closed-loop system with

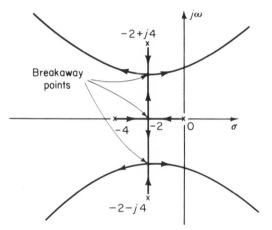

FIG. 8-13. Root loci with breakaway points not located on the real axis.

$$G(s)H(s) = \frac{K}{s(s + 4)(s^2 + 4s + 20)} \qquad (8-77)$$

Taking the derivative of $G(s)H(s)$ with respect to s, we get

$$\frac{d[G(s)H(s)]}{ds} = -\frac{K(4s^3 + 24s^2 + 72s + 80)}{[s(s + 4)(s^2 + 4s + 20)]^2} = 0 \qquad (8-78)$$

Setting the numerator of Eq. (8–78) equal to zero gives

$$s^3 + 6s^2 + 18s + 20 = 0 \qquad (8-79)$$

The roots of Eq. (8–79) are found to be at $s = -2$, $s = -2 + j2.45$, and $s = -2 - j2.45$. In this case, as shown by the root loci in Fig. 8-13, all these three points are breakaway points on the root loci.

Example 8-11. In this example we shall show that sometimes the solutions of Eq. (8–55) are not breakaway points on the root loci.

Consider the loop transfer function

$$G(s)H(s) = \frac{K}{s(s^2 + 2s + 2)} \qquad (8\text{–}80)$$

The complete root locus diagram of the system is shown in Fig. 8-14. It is clear that neither the root loci nor the inverse root loci have a breakaway point in this case. However, applying Eq. (8–55) to Eq. (8–80) gives

$$3s^2 + 4s + 2 = 0 \qquad (8\text{–}81)$$

which has two complex roots at $s = -0.677 + j0.471$ and $s = -0.677 - j0.471$. These two roots do not represent breakaway points on the root loci, since they do not satisfy the characteristic equation of the system for any real values of K.

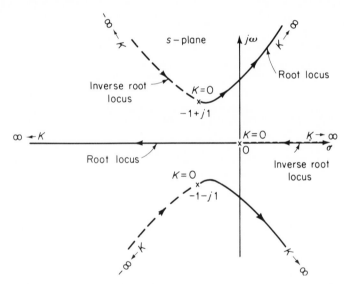

FIG. 8-14. Complete root locus diagram of the system in Example 8–11.

Method 2. An algorithm for finding the breakaway points on the root loci ($-\infty < K < \infty$) was introduced by M. J. Remec.[5] The method is derived from the theory of equations,[6] and the proofs of its necessary and sufficient conditions are given in the literature.[5]

The breakaway point algorithm using a tabulation which resembles the Routh tabulation is described below:

Suggested Procedure

(1) Let the characteristic equation of the closed-loop system be

$$F(s) = a_0 s^n + a_1 s^{n-1} + a_2 s^{n-2} + \cdots + a_{n-1} s + a_n = 0 \qquad (8\text{-}82)$$

(2) Obtain the function $F'(s)$ which is the derivative of $F(s)$ with respect to s. Let $F'(s)$ be of the form

$$F'(s) = b_0 s^{n-1} + b_1 s^{n-2} + \cdots + b_{n-2} s + b_{n-1} \qquad (8\text{-}83)$$

where $b_0 = na_0$, $b_1 = a_1(n-1)$, ..., etc.

(3) Arrange the coefficients of $F(s)$ and $F'(s)$ in two rows as follows:

$$a_0 \quad a_1 \quad a_2 \quad \cdot \quad \cdot \quad \cdot \quad a_{n-1} \quad a_n$$
$$b_0 \quad b_1 \quad b_2 \quad \cdot \quad \cdot \quad \cdot \quad b_{n-1}$$

(4) Form the following array of numbers obtained by the indicated operations. Notice that this is *not* a Routh tabulation, although the cross-multiplication operation is the same as in the Routh case. The example is shown for a fourth-order system.

s^4	a_0	a_1	a_2	a_3	a_4
s^3	b_0	b_1	b_2	b_3	0
s^3	$c_0 = \dfrac{b_0 a_1 - b_1 a_0}{b_0}$	$c_1 = \dfrac{b_0 a_2 - b_2 a_0}{b_0}$	$c_2 = \dfrac{b_0 a_3 - b_3 a_0}{b_0}$		
			$c_3 = \dfrac{b_0 a_4 - a_0 0}{b_0} = a_4$	0	
s^3	b_0	b_1	b_2	b_3	0
s^2	$d_0 = \dfrac{b_0 c_1 - b_1 c_0}{b_0}$	$d_1 = \dfrac{b_0 c_2 - b_2 c_0}{b_0}$	$d_2 = \dfrac{b_0 c_3 - b_3 c_0}{b_0}$		
			$d_3 = \dfrac{b_0 0 - 0 c_0}{b_0} = 0$	0	
s^2	$e_0 = \dfrac{d_0 b_1 - d_1 b_0}{d_0}$	$e_1 = \dfrac{d_0 b_2 - d_2 b_0}{d_0}$	$e_2 = \dfrac{d_0 b_3 - d_3 b_0}{d_0}$	$e_3 = 0$	0
s^2	d_0	d_1	d_2	0	
s^1	$f_0 = \dfrac{d_0 e_1 - d_1 e_0}{d_0}$	$f_1 = \dfrac{d_0 e_2 - d_2 e_0}{d_0}$	$f_2 = 0$	0	
s^1	$g_0 = \dfrac{f_0 d_1 - f_1 d_0}{f_0}$	$g_1 = \dfrac{f_0 d_2 - f_2 d_0}{f_0}$	0		
s^1	f_0	f_1	0		
s^0	$h_0 = \dfrac{f_0 g_1 - f_1 g_0}{f_0}$	0			

Several important features of this tabulation are worth mentioning at this point.

(a) The s^j, $(j = 0, 1, 2, \ldots, n)$ terms assigned to each row of the tabulation are used merely for reference purposes.

(b) The s^j terms repeat for three consecutive rows for $j = (n-1), \ldots, 1$.

(c) If we regard the rows of coefficients in the tabulation that have the same s^j as a *group*, then, it is noticed that the coefficients in the last row of a *group* are always a repeat of those in the first row of the same *group*.

If $F(s)$ has multiple-order roots, a row of the tabulation formed above will contain all zero elements. In other words, the tabulation process will terminate prematurely. *The multiple-order root(s) [breakaway point(s)] is (are) then obtained by solving the equation formed by using the row of coefficients just preceding the row of zeros.*

Let us use the following numerical examples to illustrate the application of the tabulation method of finding the breakaway points on root loci.

Example 8-12. Consider the equation

$$F(s) = (s + 1)^2(s + 2)^2 = s^4 + 6s^3 + 13s^2 + 12s + 4 = 0 \qquad (8\text{-}84)$$

which we know has two double roots at $s = -1$ and $s = -2$. Then

$$F'(s) = 4s^3 + 18s^2 + 26s + 12 \qquad (8\text{-}85)$$

The tabulation using the coefficients of $F(s)$ and $F'(s)$ is made in the following.

s^4	1	6	13	12	4
s^3	4	18	26	12	0
s^3	$\dfrac{(4)(6)-(1)(18)}{4}$	$\dfrac{52-26}{4}$	$\dfrac{48-12}{4}$	4	
s^3	4	18	26	12	
s^2	$-\frac{1}{4}$	$-\frac{3}{4}$	$-\frac{1}{2}$		
s^2	6	18	12		
s^2	$-\frac{1}{4}$	$-\frac{3}{4}$	$-\frac{1}{2}$		
s^1	0	0			

Since there is a row of zero elements in the tabulation before the tabulation process is completed, this indicates that the equation $F(s)$ has multiple-order roots. The equation to be solved now is formed with the coefficients taken from the row just above the row of zeros. Therefore,

$$-\tfrac{1}{4}s^2 - \tfrac{3}{4}s - \tfrac{1}{2} = 0 \qquad (8\text{-}86)$$

or

$$s^2 + 3s + 2 = 0 \qquad (8\text{-}87)$$

The roots of Eq. (8-87) are $s = -1$ and $s = -2$, which are the double roots of $F(s)$.

Example 8-13. The breakaway points of the second-order system considered in Example 8-8 will be found by using the tabulation method. For the $G(s)H(s)$ given in Eq. (8-71), the characteristic equation of the system is

$$F(s) = s^2 + (2 + K)s + 4K = 0 \qquad (8\text{-}88)$$

Then,

$$F'(s) = 2s + (2 + K) \qquad (8\text{-}89)$$

The following breakaway point tabulation is obtained:

s^2	1	$2 + K$	K
s^1	2	$2 + K$	0
s^1	$\dfrac{2 + K}{2}$	$4K$	0
s^1	2	$2 + K$	
s^0	$4K - \dfrac{(2 + K)^2}{4}$	0	

It is noticed that none of the rows can be made to contain all zeros except the last one. Therefore, we set

$$4K - \frac{(2 + K)^2}{4} = 0$$

or   (8-90)

$$-K^2 + 12K - 4 = 0$$

which gives

$$K = 0.344$$

and

$$K = 11.656$$

Therefore, when K equals either one of these two values, the s^0 row of the tabulation will contain all zeros, thus signifying a multiple-order root for $F(s)$. The equation from which the roots (breakaway points) can be obtained is formed by using the coefficients in the row preceding the s^0 row. The equation thus formed is

$$2s + (2 + K) = 0 \qquad (8\text{-}91)$$

Now substituting $K = 0.344$ and $K = 11.656$ into Eq. (8-91), we find the two breakaway points on the root loci at

$$s = -1.172 \qquad (K = 0.344)$$

and

$$s = -6.828 \qquad (K = 11.656)$$

It is apparent that these answers agree with those obtained in Example 8-8. Furthermore, a by-product of the tabulation method is that the values of K at the breakaway point are also determined. In fact, K is always determined first before the breakaway points are found.

Example 8-14. Now consider the root locus problem of Example 8-10. It is found that the root loci for the closed-loop system with $G(s)H(s)$ given by Eq. (8-77) have three breakaway points.

The characteristic equation of the system is

$$F(s) = s^4 + 8s^3 + 36s^2 + 80s + K = 0 \qquad (8\text{–}92)$$

Then,

$$F'(s) = 4s^3 + 24s^2 + 72s + 80 = 0 \qquad (8\text{–}93)$$

In this case, it is possible to divide both sides of Eq. (8–93) by 4. Thus,

$$\frac{F'(s)}{4} = s^3 + 6s^2 + 18s + 20 = 0 \qquad (8\text{–}94)$$

The breakaway point tabulation is formed as follows:

s^4	1	8	36	80	K
s^3	1	6	18	20	0
s^3	2	18	60	K	
s^3	1	6	18	20	
s^2	6	24	$K - 40$	0	
s^2	2	$\left(18 - \dfrac{K-40}{6}\right)$	20	0	
s^2	6	24	$K - 40$	0	
s^1	$\left(10 - \dfrac{K-40}{6}\right)$	$2\left(10 - \dfrac{K-40}{6}\right)$	0	0	
s^1	12	$K' - 40$			
s^1	$\left(10 - \dfrac{K'-40}{6}\right)$	$2\left(10 - \dfrac{K'-40}{6}\right)$			
s^0	$K' - 64$	0			

Notice that the first row of the s^1 group has a common factor $\left(10 - \dfrac{K-40}{6}\right)$ which is a function of K. Therefore, when $K = 100$, the coefficients of this row are zeros. This indicates a premature termination of the tabulation process, and, consequently, $F(s)$ has multiple-order roots. The breakaway points that correspond to $K = 100$ are now found from the equation

$$6s^2 + 24s + (K - 40) = 0 \qquad (K = 100) \qquad (8\text{–}95)$$

or

$$s^2 + 4s + 10 = 0 \qquad (8\text{–}96)$$

Therefore, the two breakaway points occur at $s = -2 + j2.45$ and $s = -2 - j2.45$, which are the roots of Eq. (8–96).

In order to complete the tabulation, we must now consider that $K \neq 100$, so that the coefficients in the subsequent row are finite. In fact, since the multiple roots at $K = 100$ are determined, should there be any additional multiple-order roots, they would have to occur at different values of K than 100. Therefore, in the last three rows of the tabulation, K is replaced by K' to indicate that $K' \neq K$ (= 100). Therefore, the coefficients in the last row of the s^1 group cannot be all zero, since $K' \neq 100$. However, a breakaway point occurs if in the s^0 row, $K' = 64$. The corresponding breakaway point is found by solving the equation

$$\left(10 - \frac{K' - 40}{6}\right)s + 2\left(10 - \frac{K' - 40}{6}\right) = 0 \qquad (K' = 64) \qquad (8\text{-}97)$$

or simply

$$s + 2 = 0 \qquad\qquad (8\text{-}98)$$

Thus,

$$s = -2$$

An alternative method of completing the tabulation after the first row of the s^1 group is to factor out the common factor in that row, and then carry out the tabulation as follows:

s_1	1	2	0	0
s^1	12	$K - 40$	0	0
s^1	1	2	0	0
s^0	$K - 64$	0		

Therefore, the same results, $K = 64$ and $s = -2$, are obtained.

Example 8-15. In this example we shall show that the tabulation method actually indicates explicitly that the root locus diagram in Fig. 8-14 (Example 8-11) does not have any breakaway points.

From Eq. (8–80), the characteristic equation of the system is obtained as

$$F(s) = s^3 + 2s^2 + 2s + K = 0 \qquad (8\text{-}98)$$

Thus,

$$F'(s) = 3s^2 + 4s + 2 \qquad (8\text{-}99)$$

The following tabulation is obtained:

s^3	1	2	2	K
s^2	3	4	2	
s^2	$\frac{2}{3}$	$\frac{4}{3}$	K	
s^2	3	4	2	
s^1	$\frac{4}{9}$	$K - \frac{4}{9}$	0	
s^1	$1 - \dfrac{27K}{4}$	2	0	
s^1	$\frac{4}{9}$	$K - \frac{4}{9}$	0	
s^0	$2 - \dfrac{9}{4}\left(K - \dfrac{4}{9}\right)\left(1 - \dfrac{27K}{4}\right)$	0		

It is clear that only the last row of the tabulation can be made zero for any K. Therefore,

$$2 - \frac{9}{4}\left(K - \frac{4}{9}\right)\left(1 - \frac{27K}{4}\right) = 0 \qquad (8\text{--}100)$$

which is simplified to

$$81K^2 - 48K + 16 = 0 \qquad (8\text{--}101)$$

However, there are no real values of K which will satisfy this equation. Therefore, we conclude that $F(s)$ does not have any multiple-order roots.

A comparison of the two methods of locating the breakaway points on a root locus plot is warranted at this point.

The condition stated in Eq. (8–55) for a breakaway point is necessary but not sufficient. The method involves solving for the possible breakaway points as the roots of Eq. (8–55). For high-order systems, the amount of work involved in solving a high-order equation is excessive. But for systems of the third order or less, the method is most straightforward.

The tabulation method gives a necessary and sufficient condition for breakaway points. In general, the procedure still involves the solving of the roots of a polynomial, but the order of the equation is usually low. The method also gives the values of K at the breakaway points.

It is interesting to note that the tabulation method also is a way of solving the roots of an equation which is known to have multiple-order roots.

(11) *Calculation of K on the Root Loci*

Once we construct the root loci, using the defining equation of Eq. (8–13), we can determine the value of K at any point s_1 on the loci from Eq. (8–12); that is,

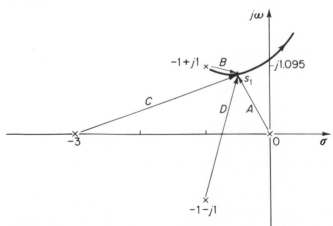

FIG. 8-15. Graphical method of evaluating the values of K on the root loci.

$$|K| = \frac{\prod\limits_{j=1}^{m+n}|s_1 + p_j|}{\prod\limits_{i=1}^{m}|s_1 + z_i|} \tag{8-102}$$

or

$$K = \frac{\text{product of lengths of vectors drawn from the poles of } GH \text{ to } s_1}{\text{product of lengths of vectors drawn from the zeros of } GH \text{ to } s_1} \tag{8-103}$$

Equations (8–102) and (8–103) can be evaluated either graphically or analytically. Usually, if the root locus plot is already drawn accurately, the graphical method is more convenient. For example, in Fig. 8–15, the value of K at the point s_1 is given by

$$K = A \cdot B \cdot C \cdot D \tag{8-104}$$

where A, B, C, and D are the lengths of the vectors drawn from the poles of $G(s)H(s)$ to the point s_1. If s_1 is a point on the root loci, K is positive; if s_1 is a point on the inverse root loci, K is negative.

The value of K at the point where the root loci intersect the imaginary axis is also found in the manner just described. However, the Routh-Hurwitz criterion usually provides a more direct method of computing the critical values of K.

Strictly, the eleven rules on the construction of root locus diagrams just described should be regarded only as important properties of the root loci. Usually, these rules are sufficient for the analyst to make a reasonably accurate sketch of the root locus plot just short of plotting it point by point, if the pole-zero configuration of $G(s)H(s)$ is not too complex. However, in more complicated situations one has to rely on computers as a more dependable means of contructing the root loci.

The following example serves as an illustration on the application of the eleven rules to the construction of a root locus diagram.

Example 8-16. The loop transfer function of a feedback control system is given by

$$G(s)H(s) = \frac{K(s + 3)}{s(s + 5)(s + 6)(s^2 + 2s + 2)} \tag{8-105}$$

The root loci ($-\infty < K < \infty$) of the system are to be constructed, the rules of construction being used.

(1) The $K = 0$ points on the root loci are at $s = 0$, -5, -6, $-1 + j1$, and $-1 - j1$, which are the poles of $G(s)H(s)$.

(2) The $K = \pm\infty$ points on the root loci are at $s = -3$, ∞, ∞, ∞, ∞, which are the zeros of $G(s)H(s)$.

(3) There are five separate root loci.

(4) The root loci must be symmetrical with respect to the real axis.

(5) The angles of the asymptotes of the root loci at infinity are given by

$$\theta_k = \frac{(2k+1)}{P-Z}\pi$$

and that of the inverse root loci are

$$\theta_k = \frac{2k}{P-Z}\pi$$

where $k = 0, 1, 2, 3$, and $P - Z = 5 - 1 = 4$. Hence, the four root loci that approach infinity at $K = +\infty$ should approach with angles of 45 deg, -45 deg, 135 deg, and -135 deg, respectively. The angles of the asymptotes of the inverse root loci as $K \to -\infty$ are 0 deg, 90 deg, 180 deg, and 270 deg.

(6) The intersection of the asymptotes (centroid) is given by

$$\sigma_1 = \frac{\sum \text{poles of } G(s)H(s) - \sum \text{zeros of } G(s)H(s)}{P-Z}$$

$$= \frac{(0-5-6-1+j1-1-j1)-(-3)}{4} = -2.5$$

The results obtained from the last six steps are illustrated in Fig. 8–16.

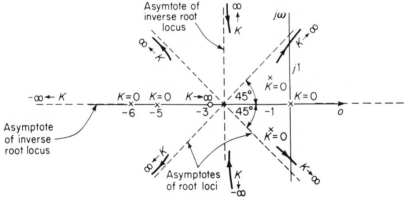

FIG. 8-16. The pole-zero configuration of
$$G(s)H(s) = \frac{K(s+3)}{s(s+5)(s+6)(s^2+2s+2)}$$
and the asymptotes of the root loci.

(7) Root loci on the real axis: There are root loci $(0 < K < \infty)$ on the real axis between $s = 0$ and $s = -3$, $s = -5$ and $s = -6$; there are inverse root loci $(-\infty < K < 0)$ between $s = -3$ and $s = -5$, and between $s = -6$ and $s = -\infty$ (see Fig. 8–17).

(8) Angles of departure: The angle of departure, θ, of the root locus leaving the pole at $-1 + j1$ is determined by using Eq. (8–15). Therefore,

$$\underset{\underset{/s+3}{\uparrow}}{26.6°} - (\underset{\underset{/s}{\uparrow}}{135°} + \underset{\underset{/s+1-j1}{\uparrow}}{90°} + \underset{\underset{/s+5}{\uparrow}}{14°} + \underset{\underset{/s+6}{\uparrow}}{11.4°} + \underset{\underset{/s+1+j1}{\uparrow}}{\theta}) = (2k+1)180° \qquad (8\text{-}106)$$

from which we obtain $\theta = -43.8$ deg (see Fig. 8-18).

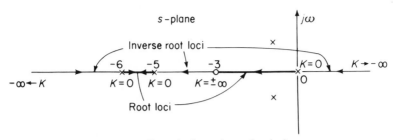

FIG. 8-17. Root loci on the real axis for

$$G(s)H(s) = \frac{K(s + 3)}{s(s + 5)(s + 6)(s^2 + 2s + 2)}$$

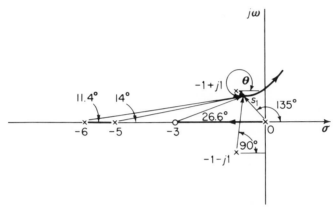

FIG. 8-18. Computation of the angle of departure of the root locus leaving the pole at $-1 + j1$.

(9) The intersection of the root loci with the imaginary axis is determined by the Routh criterion. The characteristic equation of the system is

$$s^5 + 13s^4 + 54s^3 + 82s^2 + (60 + K) + 3K = 0 \qquad (8\text{-}107)$$

The Routh tabulation is

s^5	1	54	$60 + K$
s^4	13	82	$3K$
s^3	47.7	$60 + 0.769K$	0
s^2	$65.6 - 0.212K$	$3K$	0
s^1	$\dfrac{3940 - 105K - 0.163K^2}{65.6 - 0.212K}$	0	0
s^0	$3K$	0	

For a stable system, the quantities of the first column in the Routh tabulation should be greater than zero. Hence,

(a) $65.6 - 0.212K > 0$ or $K < 309$ (8–108)

(b) $3940 - 105K - 0.163K^2 > 0$ or $K < 35$ (positive root)   (8–109)

(c) $K > 0$ (8–110)

Hence, for a stable system, $0 < K < 35$, and the value of K when the root loci cross the imaginary axis is 35. The frequency at the intersection is determined from the auxiliary equation

$$A(s) = (65.6 - 0.212K)s^2 + 3K = 0 \qquad (8\text{–}111)$$

Substituting $K = 35$ into the last equation, we have

$$58.2s^2 + 105 = 0 \qquad (8\text{–}112)$$

which yields

$$s = \pm j1.34$$

(10) Breakaway points: Based on the information obtained from the last nine steps, a trial sketch of the root loci indicates that there is only one breakaway point for the entire root loci, and the point lies between the two poles at $s = -5$ and -6. In this case, since there is only one breakaway point for this fifth-order system, the value of K at the point will be obtained from the s^0 row of the breakaway point tabulation which involves a total of fourteen rows. It is actually simpler to solve Eq. (8–55) by trial and error, since we know that the desired root is between -5 and -6.

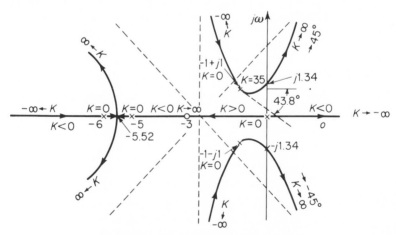

FIG. 8-19. Root loci of system with
$$G(s)H(s) = \frac{K(s + 3)}{s(s + 5)(s + 6)(s^2 + 2s + 2)}$$

Substituting Eq. (8–105) into Eq. (8–55) gives

$$s^5 + 13.5s^4 + 66s^3 + 142s^2 + 123s + 45 = 0 \qquad (8\text{–}113)$$

After a few trial-and-error calculations, the root of Eq. (8–113) that corresponds to the breakaway point is found to be $s = -5.52$.

From the information obtained in the last ten steps, the complete root locus diagram is sketched in Fig. 8–19.

In this section we have described eleven important properties of the root loci. These properties have been regarded as rules when they are used in aiding the construction of the root loci. Of course, there are other properties of the root loci which are not mentioned here. However, in general, if the problem is not too complex, it is found that these eleven rules are adequate in helping to obtain a reasonably accurate sketch of the root loci just short of actually plotting them.

For easy reference, the rules of construction are tabulated in Table 8-1.

Table 8-1

RULES OF CONSTRUCTION OF ROOT LOCI

(1) $K = 0$ points	The $K = 0$ points on the root loci are at the poles of $G(s)H(s)$. (The poles include those in the finite s-plane and those at infinity.)
(2) $K = \pm\infty$ points	The $K = \pm\infty$ points on the root loci are at the zeros of $G(s)H(s)$. (The zeros include those in the finite s-plane and those at infinity.)
(3) Number of separate root loci	Number of root loci $N = Z$ if $Z > P$ Number of root loci $N = P$ if $Z < P$ where P = number of finite poles of $G(s)H(s)$. Z = number of finite zeros of $G(s)H(s)$.
(4) Symmetry of root loci	The root locus plots of systems with rational transfer functions with constant coefficients are symmetrical with respect to the real axis of the s-plane.
(5) Asymptotes of root loci as $s \to \infty$	For large values of s, the root loci (positive K) are asymptotic to straight lines with angles given by $$\theta_k = \frac{(2k + 1)\pi}{P - Z}$$ and for the inverse root loci (negative K), $$\theta_k = \frac{2k\pi}{P - Z}$$ where $k = 0, 1, 2, \ldots$, up to $k = P - Z$ (exclusively).

(6) Intersection of the asymptotes (centroids)	(a) The intersection of the asymptotes lies only on the real axis in the s-plane. (b) The point of intersection of the asymptotes on the real axis is given by (for all values of K) $$\sigma_1 = -\frac{\Sigma \text{ poles of } G(s)H(s) - \Sigma \text{ zeros of } G(s)H(s)}{P - Z}$$
(7) Root loci on the real axis	On a given section of the real axis in the s-plane root loci (positive K) are found in the section only if the total number of real pole and real zeros of $G(s)H(s)$ to the right of the section is *odd*. If the total number of real poles and zeros to the right of the section is even, inverse root loci should be found.
(8) Angles of departure and arrival	The angle of departure of the root locus (positive K) from a pole (or the angle of arrival at a zero) of $G(s)H(s)$ can be determined by assuming a point s_1 which is very close to the pole (or zero) and which is on the root locus associated with the pole (or zero), and applying the following equation: $$\underline{/G(s_1)H(s_1)} = \sum_{i=1}^{m} \underline{/s_1 + z_i} - \sum_{j=1}^{m+n} \underline{/s_1 + p_j} = (2k + 1)\pi$$
(9) Intersection of the root loci with the imaginary axis	The values of ω and K at the crossing points on the imaginary axis of the s-plane may be obtained by use of the Routh-Hurwitz criterion; for more complex cases, the Bode plot of $G(s)H(s)$ should be used.
(10) Breakaway points (saddle points)	The breakaway points on the root loci (all values of K) are determined by finding the roots of $dK/ds = 0$, or $dG(s)H(s)/ds = 0$ (necessary condition only). Alternatively, the breakaway points on the root loci (all values of K) are determined from the breakaway point tabulation by using the coefficients of the characteristic equation $F(s) = 0$ and $F'(s)$ (necessary and sufficient).
(11) Calculation of K on the root loci	The absolute value of K at any point s_1 on the root loci or the inverse root loci is determined from the following equation: $$\|K\| = \frac{1}{\|G(s_1)H(s_1)\|} = \frac{\text{product of all vector lengths drawn from the poles of } G(s)H(s) \text{ to } s_1}{\text{product of all vector lengths drawn from the zeros of } G(s)H(s) \text{ to } s_1}$$

8.4 Relationship Between Root Locus Diagram and Frequency Domain Plots

In Chapter 2 the Bode plot and the polar plot of a transfer function $G(s)H(s)$ are shown to be mappings of the imaginary axis of the s-plane onto the $G(s)H(s)$ plane. These are termed the frequency plots, since the imaginary axis of the s-plane corresponds to the real frequency ω. In the next chapter we shall see that the frequency domain behavior of a feedback control system can be derived from the Bode plot or the polar plot of the open-loop transfer function of the system. Since the root locus diagram can be interpreted as another graphical means of representing $G(s)H(s)$, it is reasonable to expect that these diagrams and plots are somehow related to each other.

In Fig. 8–20, the polar plot of a third-order transfer function is shown to be the mapping of the $j\omega$ axis of the s-plane onto the $G(s)H(s)$ plane. The complete root locus diagram for the same system is shown in Fig. 8-21. Since the points on the root loci satisfy the following relations,

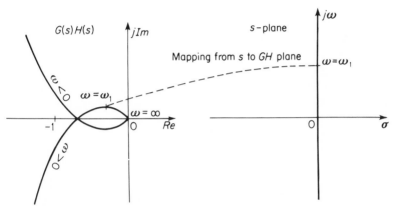

FIG. 8-20. Polar plot of $G(s)H(s) = \dfrac{K}{s(s+a)(s+b)}$ interpreted as a mapping of the $j\omega$ axis of the s-plane onto the $G(s)H(s)$ plane.

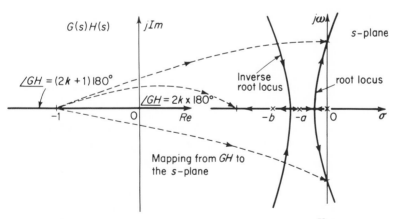

FIG. 8-21. Root locus diagram of $G(s)H(s) = \dfrac{K}{s(s+a)(s+b)}$ interpreted as a mapping of the real axis of the $G(s)H(s)$ plane onto the s-plane.

$$\underline{/G(s)H(s)} = (2k + 1)180° \qquad (k \geq 0)$$
$$\underline{/G(s)H(s)} = 2k \times 180° \qquad (k \leq 0)$$

it is easy to see that the root loci represent a mapping of the real axis of the $G(s)H(s)$ plane onto the s-plane.

In the polar plot, the mapping from the s-plane to the $G(s)H(s)$ plane is single-valued. In other words, for the rational $G(s)H(s)$ function considered, a point $\omega = \omega_1$ on the imaginary axis of the s-plane is mapped onto only one point $G(j\omega_1)H(j\omega_1)$ in the $G(s)H(s)$ plane. However, in the root locus case, which is a reverse process, the mapping is multivalued. For the third-order $G(s)H(s)$ under consideration, each point in the $G(s)H(s)$ plane is mapped onto three points in the s-plane. For instance, the $(-1, j0)$ point of the $G(s)H(s)$ plane corresponds to the two points where the root loci intersect the $j\omega$ axis, and a point on the real axis. Also, the $G(s)H(s) = 0$ point corresponds to $s = \infty$, ∞, ∞ in the s-plane.

The plots in Figs. 8-20 and 8-21 also indicate the fact that the polar plot and the root loci represent the mapping of only a very limited portion of one domain to the other. It would be useful to consider the mapping of points other than those on the $j\omega$ axis in the s-plane and on the real axis of the $G(s)H(s)$ plane to corresponding points in the other plane.

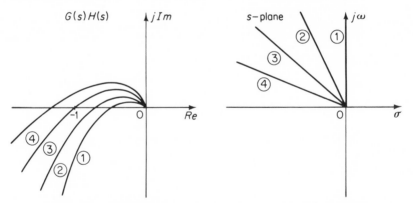

FIG. 8-22. $G(s)H(s)$ plots which correspond to constant damping ratio lines in the s-plane.

Figure 8-22 illustrates the $G(s)H(s)$ plots which correspond to different damping ratio lines in the s-plane. In fact, this represents a practical way of determining the relative stability of a system. As shown by curve (3) in the figure, when the $G(s)H(s)$ curve passes through the $(-1, j0)$ point, it means that the trajectory in the s-plane passes through a root of the characteristic equation. Similarly, the root loci which correspond to straight lines rotated from the real axis in the $G(s)H(s)$ plane are shown in Fig. 8-23. Since these root loci now correspond to points which satisfy

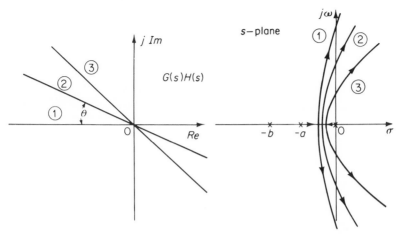

FIG. 8-23. Root loci which correspond to different phase angle loci in the $G(s)H(s)$ plane. (The inverse root loci are not shown).

$$\underline{/G(s)H(s)} = (2k + 1)(180° + \theta) \qquad (K \geq 0)$$

and

$$\underline{/G(s)H(s)} = 2k(180° + \theta) \qquad (K \leq 0)$$

it is apparent that they can be used for systems with transportation lags.

8.5   Some Other Important Properties of the Root Locus

The following properties of the root locus with respect to the open-loop pole-zero configurations are often helpful in the understanding of the root locus technique and its role in the design of feedback control systems.

(1) *The Effect of Adding Open-loop Poles and Zeros*

(a) *Addition of Poles.* Let us start with the pole-zero configuration consisting of two real poles at $s = 0$ and $s = -a$; the root loci are easily constructed, as shown in Fig. 8-24a. An additional pole at $-b$ causes the loci to bend toward the right half of the s-plane, and the breakaway point is also moved to the right (Fig. 8-24b). For instance, if $a = 1$, and $b = 2$, the breakaway point is moved from -0.5 to -0.422. With the addition of another pole at $-c$, the two conjugate loci near the imaginary axis are pushed farther to the right (Fig. 8-24c). Since the conjugate loci contain the roots which control the transient response of the closed-loop system (dominant roots), the system becomes less stable. Figure 8-24d illustrates that the addition of a pair of complex conjugate poles to the basic two-pole configuration will result in a similar effect.

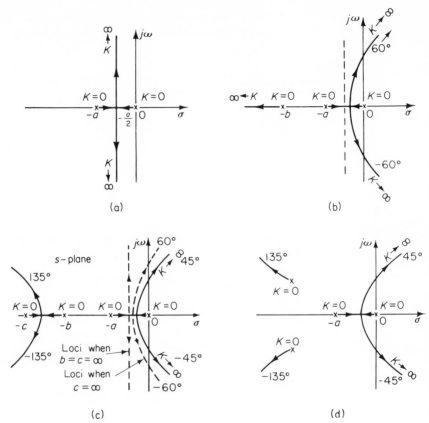

FIG. 8-24. Root locus diagrams showing the effects of adding open-loop poles.

Figure 8-25a shows the root locus diagram of a pair of complex poles; the system is always stable for all positive values of K. With the addition of a real pole at $-b$, the root loci are bent to the right and the system becomes unstable for large values of K (Fig. 8-25b). By adding another real pole at $-c$, it can be shown that the system will be unstable, even for a smaller value of K (Fig. 8-25c).

The root locus diagrams given in Fig. 8-24 and Fig. 8-25 simply verify the well-established fact that the addition of poles to $G(s)H(s)$ reduces the relative stability of the closed-loop system.

(b) *Addition of Zeros.* It was established from previous studies that the addition of zeros to the loop transfer function $G(s)H(s)$ produced more phase lead, which had the tendency to stabilize the closed-loop system. For instance, if a real zero is added at $-b$ to the two-pole configuration

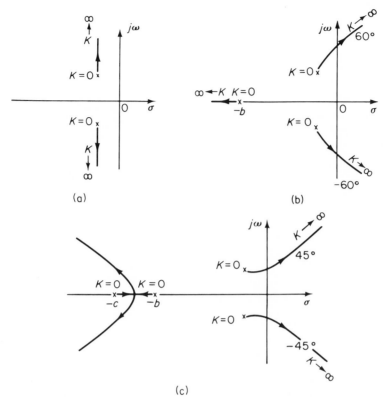

FIG. 8-25. Root locus diagrams showing the effects of adding poles.

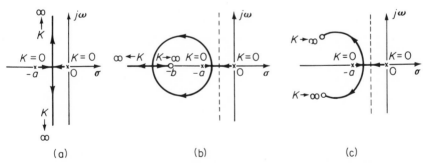

FIG. 8-26. Root locus diagrams showing the effects of adding more zeros.

shown in Fig. 8-26a, the resultant root loci bend toward the left and the stability margin is increased (Fig. 8-26b). Figure 8-26c illustrates that a similar effect will result if a pair of complex conjugate zeros is added to the left of the original loci.

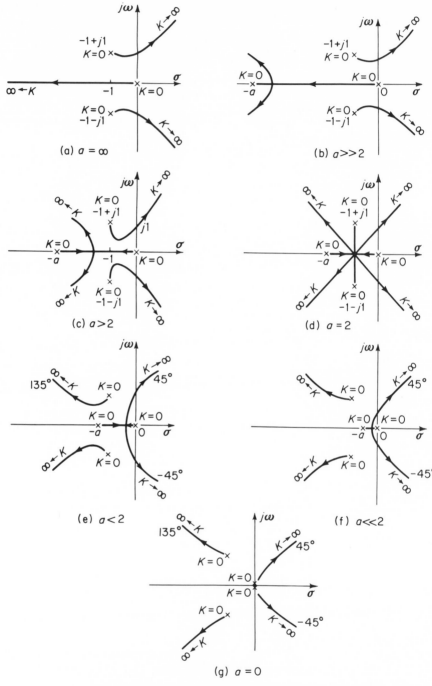

FIG. 8-27. Root locus diagrams for

$$G(s)H(s) = \frac{K}{s(s + a)(s^2 + 2s + 2)}$$

(2) *The Effect of the Movements of Poles and Zeros*

Some of the uncertain factors in the sketching of the root loci can be eliminated if the effects on the root locus configuration due to the movements of some poles and zeros of $G(s)H(s)$ are studied. For instance, given an open-loop transfer function of the form,

$$G(s)H(s) = \frac{K}{s(s + a)(s^2 + 2s + 2)} \tag{8-114}$$

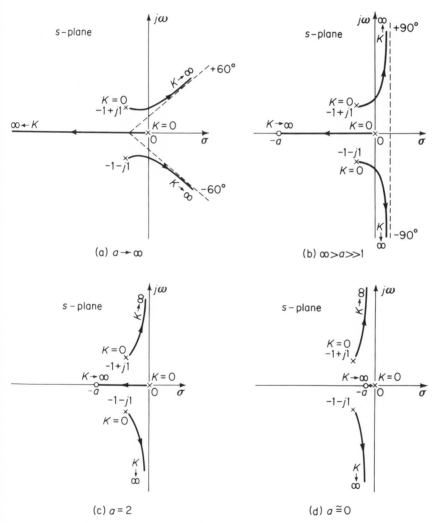

(a) $a \to \infty$

(b) $\infty > a \gg 1$

(c) $a = 2$

(d) $a \cong 0$

FIG. 8-28. Root locus diagrams for
$G(s)H(s) = \dfrac{K(s + a)}{s(s^2 + 2s + 2)}$ when a takes on various values.

If the value of a is chosen close to 2, the rules of root locus construction fail to indicate which pair of loci approaches the right and which pair approaches the left. This uncertainty usually puzzles the beginner. Figure 8-27 shows the change in the root locus configurations as the pole at $-a$ is moved from $-\infty$ to the origin.

When the value of a is infinite, the two loci which start from the complex poles approach infinity asymptotic to $+60$ deg and -60 deg, respectively. When a is a finite number of value greater than 2, the two loci starting from the complex poles approach infinity asymptotic to $+45$ deg and -45 deg, respectively. The other two loci break away along the negative real axis and then approach infinity along $+135$ deg and -135 deg, respectively. A symmetry in the loci with respect to the point $(-2, 0)$ is obtained when $a = 2$. The four loci converge on the point of symmetry at $s = -2$ and then follow the asymptotic lines, as shown in Fig. 8-27d. For values of a less than 2, the two loci originated at the two complex poles approach infinity along $+135$ deg and -135 deg, respectively, and the other two loci are bent toward the right half of the s-plane.

When a zero is moved along the negative real axis toward the origin, as shown in Fig. 8-28, the effect is to pull the loci toward the left. By means of Eq. (8–46), it can be shown that when $a \geq 2$, the characteristic equation roots will always be located in the left half of the s-plane.

The study of the effects and construction of the root locus diagram when poles and zeros are varied in the s-plane can be carried out more effectively by means of the root contour diagrams, which are discussed in Sec. 8-6.

8.6 Root Locus of Conditionally Stable Systems

Consider a unity-feedback control system with the open-loop transfer function

$$G(s) = \frac{K(s + 5)(s + 40)}{s^3(s + 200)(s + 1000)} \tag{8–115}$$

The pole-zero configuration of the last equation is shown in Fig. 8-29.

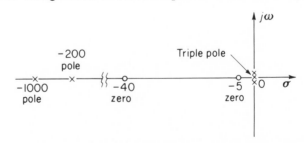

FIG. 8-29. Pole-zero configuration of $G(s) = \dfrac{K(s + 5)(s + 40)}{s^3(s + 200)(s + 1000)}$

From the rules of construction, the following information is obtained concerning the root locus diagram:

(1) The root loci start at $s = 0, 0, 0, -200,$ and -1000.

(2) The root loci end at $s = -5, -40, \infty, \infty, \infty$.

(3) There are five separate root loci.

(4) The root loci are symmetrical with respect to the real axis in the s-plane.

(5) The angles of the asymptotes of the loci are 60 deg, 180 deg, and -60 deg, respectively.

(6) The asymptotes of the loci intersect at $\sigma_1 = -385$.

(7) There is one root locus going from $s = 0$ to $s = -5$, one locus from $s = -200$ to $s = -40$, and one from $s = -1000$ to $-\infty$. Two loci of complex roots that start from the poles at the origin will eventually approach infinity along the 60 deg and the -60 deg asymptotes, respectively.

(8) The two complex root loci leave the poles at the origin at angles of 60 deg and -60 deg, respectively.

(9) The Routh test for critical K: The characteristic equation of the system can readily be shown as

$$s^5 + 1200s^4 + 2 \cdot 10^5 s^3 + Ks^2 + 45Ks + 200K = 0 \qquad (8\text{--}116)$$

The Routh tabulation:

s^5	1	$2 \cdot 10^5$	$45K$
s^4	1200	K	$200K$
s^3	$\dfrac{2.4 \cdot 10^8 - K}{1200}$	$\dfrac{53,800K}{1200}$	0
s^2	$\dfrac{1.7544 \cdot 10^8 K - K^2}{2.4 \cdot 10^8 - K}$	$200K$	
s_1	$\dfrac{-54,000K^3 + 9.534 \cdot 10^{12}K^2 - 11.52 \cdot 10^{18}K}{1200(2.4 \cdot 10^8 - K)}$	0	
s^0	$200K$		

For a stable system, the following conditions are required:

(a) $K < 2.4 \cdot 10^8$ $\qquad\qquad\qquad\qquad\qquad\qquad\qquad\qquad$ (8--117)

(b) $K > 0, \quad K < 1.7544 \cdot 10^8$ $\qquad\qquad\qquad\qquad\qquad$ (8--118)

(c) $-54,000K^2 + 9.534 \cdot 10^{12}K - 11.52 \cdot 10^{18} > 0, \qquad K > 0$ $\quad$ (8--119)

or

$$54,000K^2 - 9.534 \cdot 10^{12}K + 11.52 \cdot 10^{18} < 0 \qquad (8\text{--}120)$$

The solution of the last equation is

$$(K - 1.1 \cdot 10^6)(K - 1.753 \cdot 10^8) < 0$$

from which

$$K > 1.1 \cdot 10^6 \qquad\qquad (8\text{-}121)$$

and

$$K < 1.753 \cdot 10^8 \qquad\qquad (8\text{-}122)$$

The relationships given in Eqs. (8–121) and (8–122) apparently are the more stringent restrictions on K. Since K must lie within a finite range, the system is a conditionally stable system; that is, the system is

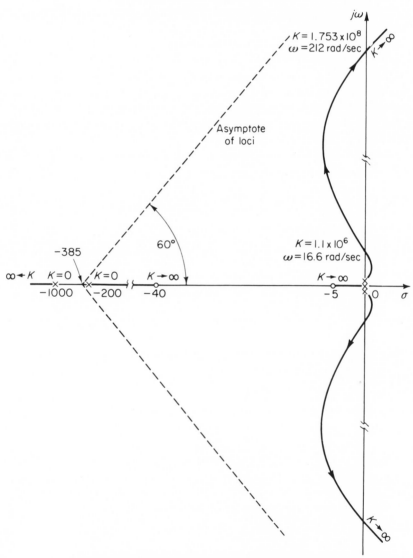

FIG. 8-30. The root loci of $G(s) = \dfrac{K(s + 5)(s + 40)}{s^3(s + 200)(s + 1000)}$

$$\text{unstable for}\quad 0 < K < 1.1 \cdot 10^6 \tag{8–123}$$

$$\text{stable for}\quad 1.1 \cdot 10^6 < K < 1.753 \cdot 10^8 \tag{8–124}$$

$$\text{unstable for}\quad 1.753 \cdot 10^8 < K < \infty \tag{8–125}$$

Substitution of the values of K given by Eqs. (8–121) and (8–122) into the auxiliary equation yields the critical frequencies

$$\omega = 16.6 \text{ rad/sec}$$

and

$$\omega = 212 \text{ rad/sec}$$

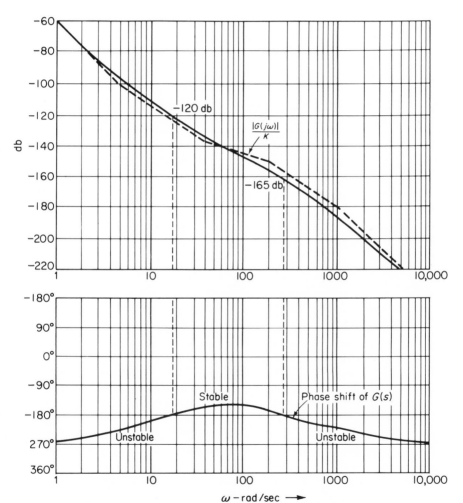

FIG. 8-31. Bode plot of $\dfrac{G(s)}{K} = \dfrac{5 \cdot 40}{200 \cdot 1000}\, \dfrac{[1 + (s/5)][1 + (s/40)]}{s^3[1 + (s/1000)][1 + s/200]}$

The root locus diagram of the system is now sketched, as shown in Fig. 8-30.

The application of the Routh test to determine the critical values of K has presented two major difficulties:

(1) The process was very tedious, and error could very likely have occurred during any step of the numerical computation. There is no way of ascertaining the correctness of the results but to recheck the computation and make sure that there has been no mistake.

(2) In solving Eq. (8–120), it was necessary to use the difference between two large numbers which are almost equal to each other.

A better and easier method could have been used to determine the critical values of K and ω. In Fig. 8-31 the Bode plot of $G(s)/K$ is shown. The phase shift curve intersects the -180 deg axis at $\omega = 20$ rad/sec and $\omega = 220$ rad/sec, and the corresponding values of critical K are 10^6 and $1.75 \cdot 10^8$, which check closely with the values obtained previously. It is easy to see that with the simple sketch of the Bode plot, not only the critical values of K and ω are obtained directly, but the root loci configuration in the vicinity of the imaginary axis in the s-plane is also indicated.

8.7 The Generalized Root Loci (the Root Contours)

Although the root locus technique has been well developed and widely used for the analysis and design of linear feedback control systems, it was originally defined with only the open-loop gain K as the varying parameter; that is, the root locus diagram is defined as a plot of the poles of the closed-loop function $C(s)/R(s)$ as K varies from 0 to ∞. However, in most design problems, the effects on the closed-loop system poles must be studied when parameters other than K are varied; and frequently, there is more than one variable parameter. For instance, in the integral and derivative compensation by the conventional root locus technique, the proper locations of the compensating pole and zero can be determined only by plotting the root loci of all pole and zero combinations. In feedback control systems with multiple feedback loops, the forward path gain K does not appear only as a multiplying factor in the open-loop transfer function; therefore, the conventional root locus technique, again, cannot be applied directly.

In this section, a generalized root locus (root contour) technique will be introduced to construct the root loci when parameters other than K are varied in a feedback control system. The generalized root loci can be sketched simply by following the same rules of construction given in the previous sections. The term "root locus" has been used to represent the conventional plot of the closed-loop function poles when K is the variable parameter. On the other hand, the term "root contour" is used to represent the plot of the closed-loop poles when K is held constant but the open-loop function poles and zeros are varied (due to the variation of parameters other than K). It will be shown in Chapter 10 that, in the design of compensating networks for single-loop or multiple-loop systems, the generalized root loci (root contours) give a clear indication of the proper choice of the parameters of the compensating functions.

Consider that the loop transfer function of a feedback control system is given by

$$G(s)H(s) = \frac{KP(s)}{Q(s)} \qquad (8\text{–}126)$$

where $P(s)$ and $Q(s)$ are polynomials of s. The characteristic equation of the closed-loop system is

$$Q(s) + KP(s) = 0 \qquad (8\text{–}127)$$

Now if a parameter T_i in $P(s)$ or $Q(s)$ is considered as a variable parameter, so that T_i may vary between $-\infty$ and $+\infty$, with K now fixed, Eq. (8–127) can be written as

$$Q(s) + KP(s) = Q_1(s) + T_i P_1(s) = 0 \qquad (8\text{–}128)$$

Therefore, the root loci (root contours) of Eq. (8–128) with T_i as a variable parameter can be sketched from the pole-zero configuration of $P_1(s)/Q_1(s)$ in the same manner as governed by the rules of construction discussed earlier.

As a simple illustration, let us consider the following loop transfer function:

$$G(s)H(s) = \frac{K(s + 2)}{s(s + a)} \qquad (8\text{–}129)$$

It is desired to investigate the variation of the zeros of $1 + G(s)H(s)$ as a function of the pole at $s = -a$, with K considered a fixed quantity.

The characteristic equation of the system is

$$s^2 + as + Ks + 2K = 0 \qquad (8\text{–}130)$$

which can be written as

$$(s^2 + Ks + 2K) + as = 0 \qquad (8\text{–}131)$$

Therefore, $P_1(s) = s$, and $Q_1(s) = s^2 + Ks + 2K$. In other words, we can now formulate an equivalent loop transfer function

$$G_1(s)H_1(s) = \frac{aP_1(s)}{Q_1(s)} = \frac{as}{s^2 + Ks + 2K} \qquad (8\text{–}132)$$

which gives the same characteristic equation as in Eq. (8–130). The root contours when a varies between $-\infty$ and $+\infty$, and for $K = 2$, are con-

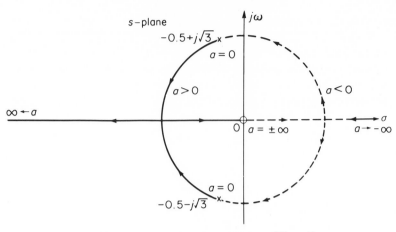

FIG. 8-32. Root contours for $G(s)H(s) = \dfrac{K(s+2)}{s(s+a)}$, $K = 2$.

structed, the pole-zero configuration of Eq. (8–132) being used, and are shown in Fig. 8-32.

As indicated by the above example, the key step in obtaining the equivalent $G_1(s)H_1(s)$ is to *divide both sides of the characteristic equation by the terms that do not contain the variable parameter.*

More examples on the construction of the root contours are given below.

Example 8-17. Consider the loop transfer function

$$G(s)H(s) = \frac{K}{s(1 + T_a s)(s^2 + 2s + 2)} \tag{8-133}$$

The root contours of the closed-loop transfer function with T_a as the variable parameter are desired.

If the conventional root locus plots are used to show the effect of the variation of T_a, Fig. 8-33 illustrates the root loci (K varies) of $G(s)H(s)$ for three different values of T_a. It is apparent that a separate root locus plot is necessary for each value of T_a.

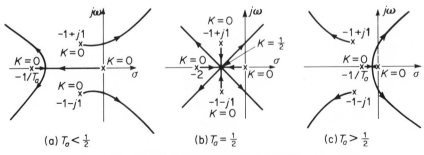

FIG. 8-33. Root loci for $G(s) = \dfrac{K}{s(1 + sT_a)(s^2 + 2s + 2)}$

The characteristic equation of the system is

$$s(1 + T_a s)(s^2 + 2s + 2) + K = 0 \qquad (8\text{-}134)$$

Now dividing both sides of Eq. (8–134) by the terms which do not contain T_a gives

$$1 + \frac{T_a s^2(s^2 + 2s + 2)}{s(s^2 + 2s + 2) + K} = 0 \qquad (8\text{-}135)$$

Therefore,

$$G_1(s)H_1(s) = \frac{T_a s^2(s^2 + 2s + 2)}{s(s^2 + 2s + 2) + K} \qquad (8\text{-}136)$$

The root contours when T_a varies are constructed based on the pole-zero configuration of $G_1(s)H_1(s)$. When $T_a = 0$, the points on the root contours are at the poles of $G_1(s)H_1(s)$, which are the points on the root loci of

$$s(s^2 + 2s + 2) + K = 0 \qquad (8\text{-}137)$$

The root loci of Eq. (8–137) are shown in Fig. 8-34. The $T_a = \pm\infty$ points on the root contours are at the zeros of $G_1(s)H_1(s)$, and these are at $s = 0$, $s = 0$, and $s = -1 \pm j1$. Therefore, the pole-zero configuration of $G_1(s)H_1(s)$ is shown in Fig. 8-35. The root contours for the system are sketched in Fig. 8-36 for three different values of K; when $K = \frac{1}{2}$ and $T_a = \frac{1}{2}$, the characteristic equation has a quadruple root at $s = -1$.

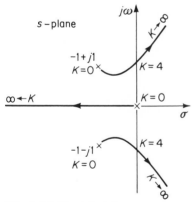

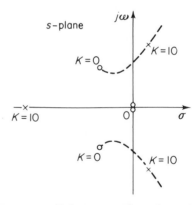

FIG. 8-34. Root loci for
$$s(s^2 + 2s + 2) + K = 0.$$

FIG. 8-35. Pole-zero configuration of
$$G_1(s)H_1(s) = \frac{s^2 T_a(s^2 + 2s + 2)}{s(s^2 + 2s + 2) + K}$$

Example 8-18. As an example illustrating the effect of the variation of a zero of $G(s)H(s)$, consider

$$G(s)H(s) = \frac{K(1 + T_1 s)}{s(s + 1)(s + 2)} \qquad (8\text{-}138)$$

The problem may also be regarded as a study of the effect of derivative

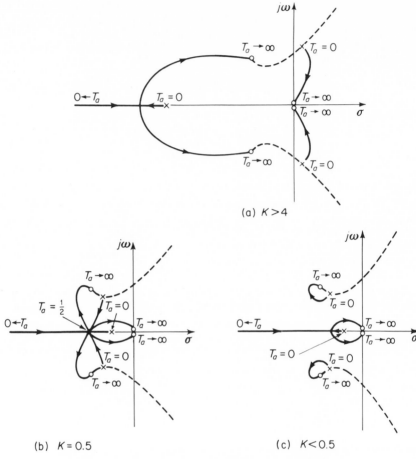

(a) $K > 4$

(b) $K = 0.5$ 　　　　　　　　　　　(c) $K < 0.5$

FIG. 8-36. Root contours for $G_1(s)H_1(s) = \dfrac{K}{s(1 + sT_a)(s^2 + 2s + 2)}$

control as discussed in Sec. 6.8 on the roots of the characteristic equation. The characteristic equation of the system is

$$s(s + 1)(s + 2) + K(1 + T_1 s) = 0 \qquad (8\text{–}139)$$

Dividing both sides of Eq. (8–139) by the terms that do not contain T_1, we get

$$1 + G_1(s)H_1(s) = 1 + \frac{T_1 Ks}{s(s + 1)(s + 2) + K} = 0 \qquad (8\text{–}140)$$

Therefore, the $T_1 = 0$ points on the root contours are at the roots of $s(s + 1)(s + 2) + K = 0$, whose loci are sketched as shown in Fig. 8-37. If we choose $K = 20$, the pole-zero configuration of $G_1(s)H_1(s)$ is shown in

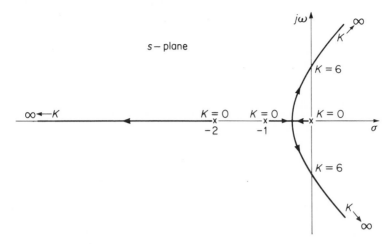

FIG. 8-37. Root loci for $s(s+1)(s+2) + K = 0$.

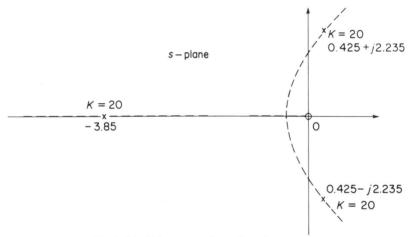

FIG. 8-38. Pole-zero configuration of

$$G_1(s)H_1(s) = \frac{T_1 K s}{s(s+1)(s+2) + K}, \quad K = 20.$$

Fig. 8-38. The root contours for $0 \leq T_1 < \infty$ are sketched in Fig. 8-39 for three different values of K. The intersection of the asymptotes of the root contours is obtained from

$$\sigma_1 = \frac{\sum \text{ poles of } G_1(s)H_1(s) - \sum \text{ zeros of } G_1(s)H_1(s)}{\text{number of poles of } G_1(s)H_1(s) - \text{number of zeros of } G_1(s)H_1(s)}$$

$$= \frac{-3.85 + 0.425 + j2.235 + 0.425 - j2.235}{3 - 1} = -1.5 \qquad (8\text{–}141)$$

The intersection of the asymptotes is always at -1.5 regardless of the value

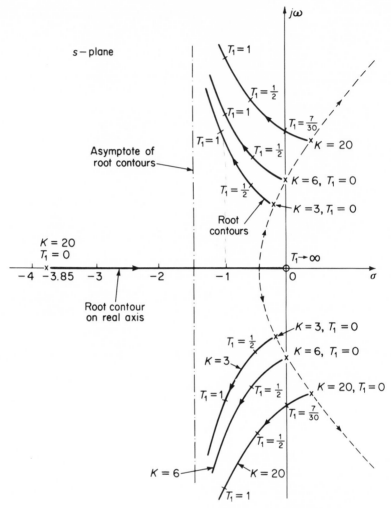

FIG. 8-39. Root contours of $G_1(s)H_1(s) = \dfrac{KT_1s}{s(s+1)(s+2)+K}$

of K. This is due to the fact that the sum of the poles of $G_1(s)H_1(s)$ is always -3.

The root contours shown in Fig. 8-39 verify the well-known fact that the derivative control improves the relative stability of the closed-loop system by moving the characteristic equation roots toward the left in the s-plane. The root contours also indicate an important characteristic of the lead compensation; that is, in certain cases, the contribution to the increase in bandwidth by increasing the value of T_1 far exceeds the improvement made on the relative stability of the system. For $K = 20$, the system is stabilized for all values of T_1 greater than $\frac{7}{30}$; however, the highest damping ratio that the compensated system can have by increasing the value of T_1 is about 30 per cent.

8.8 Root Loci of Discrete-data Control Systems[7]

The root locus technique for continuous-data control systems can be readily applied to discrete-data control systems without requiring any modifications. The characteristic equation of a discrete-data system having a block diagram as shown in Fig. 8-40 can be written as

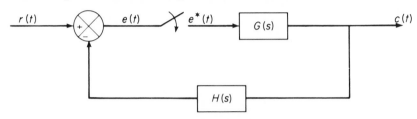

FIG. 8-40. A discrete-data control system.

$$1 + GH^*(s) = 0 \tag{8-142}$$

or

$$1 + GH(z) = 0 \tag{8-143}$$

If Eq. (8-142) is used, the root locus plot is constructed in the s-plane; when Eq. (8-143) is used, the root locus plot will be in the z-plane.

Since

$$GH^*(s) = \frac{1}{T} \sum_{n=-\infty}^{\infty} G(s + jn\omega_s)H(s + jn\omega_s) \tag{8-144}$$

which is an infinite series, the poles and zeros of $GH^*(s)$ in the s-plane will be infinite in number. This usually makes the construction of the root loci of $1 + GH^*(s)$ more difficult. However, as an illustrative example on the difference between the characteristics of the root loci of continuous-data and discrete-data systems, let us consider that the loop transfer function of the system in Fig. 8-40 is

$$G(s)H(s) = \frac{K}{s(s + 1)} \tag{8-145}$$

Then, using Eq. (8-144), we have

$$GH^*(s) = \frac{1}{T} \sum_{n=-\infty}^{\infty} \frac{K}{(s + jn\omega_s)(s + jn\omega_s + 1)} \tag{8-146}$$

which has poles at $s = -jn\omega_s$ and $s = -1 - jn\omega_s$, where n takes on all integers between $-\infty$ and $+\infty$. The pole configuration of $GH^*(s)$ is shown in Fig. 8-41a. Using the same rules as outlined in Sec. 8.3, we draw the

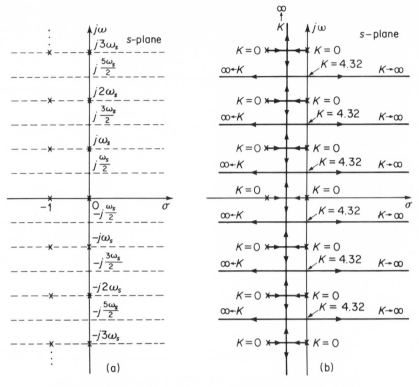

FIG. 8-41. Pole configuration of $GH^*(s)$ and the root locus diagram in the s-plane for the discrete-data system in Fig. 8-40 with

$$G(s)H(s) = \frac{K}{s(s+1)}, \quad T = 1 \text{ sec.}$$

root loci of $1 + GH^*(s) = 0$ when the value of K is varied from 0 to ∞ as shown Fig. 8-41b. Clearly, for more complex pole-zero configurations of $GH^*(s)$ than that of Fig. 8-41a, the construction of the root loci in the s-plane will be more difficult because of the periodic property of $GH^*(s)$.

The root locus diagram of Fig. 8-41b indicates that the second-order control system with sampling ($T = 1$ sec) is unstable for all values of K greater than 4.32. In contrast, it is well-known that the same system without sampling is stable for all finite positive values of K.

The root locus problem is simplified for discrete-data control systems if the root loci are constructed in the z-plane using Eq. (8–143). Since Eq. (8–143) is in general a polynomial in z with constant coefficients, the same rules of construction listed in Sec. 8.3 are directly applicable.

As a simple example illustrating the construction of root loci for discrete-data control systems in the z-plane, let us consider that the z-transform of Eq. (8–145) is taken with $T = 1$ sec. Therefore,

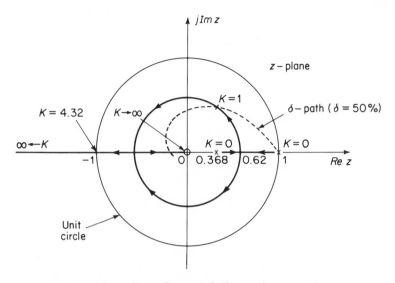

FIG. 8-42. Root locus diagram of discrete-data control system without hold. $G(s)H(s) = \dfrac{K}{s(s+1)}$, $T = 5$ sec.

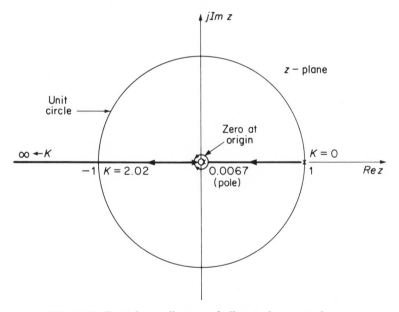

FIG. 8-43. Root locus diagram of discrete-data control system without hold. $G(s)H(s) = \dfrac{K}{s(s+1)}$, $T = 5$ sec.

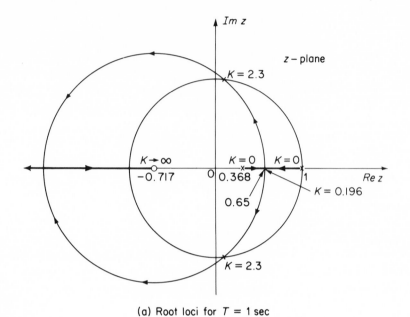

(a) Root loci for $T = 1$ sec

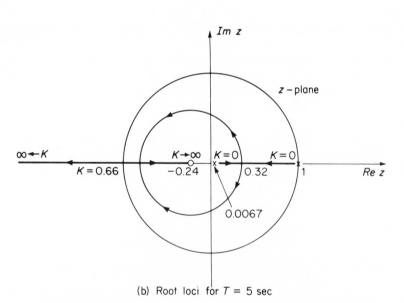

(b) Root loci for $T = 5$ sec

FIG. 8-44. Root locus diagrams of discrete-data control system with sample-and-hold. $G(s)H(s) = \dfrac{K}{s(s+1)}$

$$GH(z) = \mathscr{Z}\left(\frac{K}{s(s+1)}\right) = \frac{0.632Kz}{(z-1)(z-0.368)} \qquad (8\text{-}147)$$

which has a zero at $z = 0$ and poles at $z = 1$ and $z = 0.368$. The root locus diagram for the closed-loop system is constructed in the z-plane as shown in Fig. 8-42. Notice that when the value of K exceeds 4.32, one of the roots of the characteristic equation moves outside the unit circle in the z-plane, and the system becomes unstable.

For the same system, if the sampling period is changed to $T = 5$ sec, the z-transform of the loop transfer function is

$$GH(z) = \frac{0.993Kz}{(z-1)(z-0.0067)} \qquad (8\text{-}148)$$

The root loci for this case are constructed in Fig. 8-43. The reader should not be misled by the fact that the complex conjugate part of the root loci takes the form of a smaller circle than that of the $T = 1$ sec case and conclude that with the same value of K, the system is more stable with $T = 5$ sec. The marginal value of K for stability for $T = 5$ sec is found to be 2.02, as compared to the marginal K of 4.32 for $T = 1$ sec.

The constant damping ratio δ-path (Fig. 6-35) may be superimposed on the root loci to determine the required value of K for a certain specified damping ratio. In Fig. 8-42 the δ-path for $\beta = 30$ deg or $\delta = 50$ per cent is drawn, and the intersection with the root loci gives the value of $K = 1$. This means that for all values of K greater than 1, the damping ratio of the system is greater than 50 per cent.

The effect of the zero-order hold on the general performance of the discrete-data control system may also be studied by means of the root locus plot in the z-plane. If a zero-order hold device is inserted between the sampler and the controlled process $G(s)$ in the system of Fig. 8-41, with $G(s)H(s)$ given still by Eq. (8-145),

$$GH(z) = \frac{K[(T-1+e^{-T})z - Te^{-T}+1-e^{-T}]}{(z-1)(z-e^{-T})} \qquad (8\text{-}149)$$

The root loci of the system with sample-and-hold for $T = 1$ sec and $T = 5$ sec are shown in Fig. 8-44a and Fig. 8-44b, respectively. The marginal value of stability for K is 2.3 for $T = 1$ sec, and 0.66 for $T = 5$ sec.

REFERENCES

1. W. R. Evans, "Graphical Analysis of Control Systems," *Trans. AIEE*, Vol. **67**, pp. 547–551, 1948.

2. W. R. Evans, "Control System Synthesis by Root Locus Method," *Trans. AIEE*, Vol. **69**, pp. 66–69, 1950.

3. K. S. Narendra, "Inverse Root-locus, Reversed Root-locus or Complementary

Root-locus?" *IRE Trans. on Automatic Control*, Vol. **AC-6**, September, 1961, pp. 359–360.

4. J. G. Truxal and I. M. Horowitz, "Sensitivity Considerations in Active Network Synthesis," *Proc. of the Second Midwest Symposium on Circuit Theory*, East Lansing, Mich., December, 1956.

5. M. J. Remec, "Saddle-points of a Complete Root Locus and an Algorithm for Their Easy Location in the Complex Frequency Plane," *Proc. of the National Electronics Conference*, Vol. **21**, pp. 605–608, 1965.

6. C. C. MacDuffee, *Theory of Equations*, pp. 29–104, John Wiley & Sons, Inc., New York, N. Y., 1954.

7. M. Mori, "Root Locus Method of Pulse Transfer Function for Sampled-data Control Systems," *IRE Trans. on Automatic Control*, Vol. **AC-3**, November, 1963, pp. 13–20.

PROBLEMS

8-1. Sketch the root locus diagram for each of the following feedback control systems. In each case determine everything about the locus of roots for $-\infty < K < \infty$ short of actual plotting. Indicate on each locus the starting point, the ending point, and the direction of increasing value of K. The poles and zeros of $G(s)H(s)$ of the systems are given as follows:

(a) Poles at 0, -2, -3; zero at -5.

(b) Poles at 0, 0, -2, -3; zero at -5.

(c) Poles at $-2 + j2$ and -2, $-j2$; zero at -3.

(d) Poles at 0, $-10 + j0$ and $-10 - j10$; zero at -20.

(e) Poles at 0, -20, $-10 + j10$, and $-10 - j10$; no finite zeros.

(f) Poles at -20, $-10 + j10$, and $-10 - j10$; zero at -30.

(g) Poles at 0, 0, -12, and -12; zeros at -4, and -8.

8-2. The open-loop transfer function of a unity-feedback control system is given by

$$G(s) = \frac{K(s + 3)}{s(s^2 + 2s + 2)(s + 5)(s + 6)}$$

(a) Sketch the root locus diagram as a function of K ($-\infty < K < \infty$).

(b) Determine the value of K which makes the relative damping ratio of the closed-loop complex poles equal to 0.4.

8-3. A unity-feedback control system has an open-loop transfer function

$$G(s) = \frac{K(1 + 0.2s)(1 + 0.025s)}{s^3(1 + 0.001s)(1 + 0.005s)}$$

Sketch the complete ($-\infty < K < \infty$) root locus diagram for the system. Indicate the crossing points of the loci on the $j\omega$ axis, and the corresponding values of K and ω at these points.

8-4. A unity-feedback control system has an open-loop transfer function

$$G(s) = \frac{K}{s(1 + 0.02s)(1 + 0.01s)}$$

(a) Sketch the root locus diagram of the system $(0 < K < \infty)$.

(b) Determine the marginal value of K which will cause instability.

(c) Determine the value of K when the system is critically damped.

8-5. The transfer functions of a feedback control system are given as

$$G(s) = \frac{K}{s^2(s + 2)(s + 5)} \quad \text{and} \quad H(s) = 1$$

(a) Sketch the root locus diagram for the system. Indicate the crossing points of the loci on the $j\omega$ axis, and the corresponding values of K and ω at these points (positive values of K only).

(b) The transfer function of the feedback loop element is now changed to $H(s) = (1 + 2s)$. Determine the stability of the modified system as a function of K. Investigate the effect on the root locus diagram due to this change in $H(s)$.

8-6. The characteristic equation of a feedback control system is given by

$$s^3 + 3s^2 + (K + 2)s + 10K = 0$$

Sketch the root locus diagram (positive K only) for this system.

8-7. For the following loop transfer function, sketch the root locus diagram as a function of T (T varies from 0 to ∞). Determine the value of T so that the damping ratio of the complex roots of the characteristic equation is 0.2.

$$G(s)H(s) = \frac{1000(1 + Ts)}{s(1 + 0.1s)(1 + 0.001s)}$$

8-8. For the following loop transfer function, sketch the root locus diagram as a function of T. Determine the value of T so that the damping ratio of the complex roots of the characteristic equation is 0.2.

$$G(s)H(s) = \frac{30}{s(1 + 0.1s)(1 + 0.2s)(1 + Ts)}$$

8-9. For the bridge-T network of Fig. 8P-9,

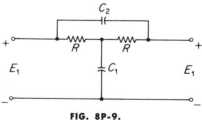

FIG. 8P-9.

(a) Sketch the root locus diagrams of the zeros and poles of E_2/E_1 as a function of C_1 (C_1 varies from 0 to ∞).

(b) Sketch the root locus diagrams of the zeros and poles of E_2/E_1 as a function of C_2.

8-10. The open-loop transfer function of a control system with positive feedback is given by

$$G(s) = \frac{K}{s(s^2 + 4s + 4)}$$

Sketch the root locus diagram of the system as a function of K $(0 < K < \infty)$.

8-11. It is desired that the closed-loop transfer function of a control system be

$$\frac{C(s)}{R(s)} = \frac{1}{(1 + 0.03s)(1 + 0.2s + 0.02s^2)}$$

Determine the open-loop transfer function $G(s)$ of the system. Assume that the system has unity feedback.

8-12. For the sampled-data control system shown in Fig. 8P-12,

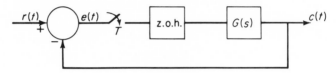

FIG. 8P-12.

$$G(s) = \frac{K}{s(1 + 0.2s)}$$

(a) Sketch the root loci for the system $(0 < K < \infty)$ without the zero-order hold, for $T = 0.1$ sec and $T = 1$ sec. Determine the marginal value of K for stability in each case.

(b) Repeat part (a) when the system has a zero-order hold.

8-13. The following polynomial in z represents the characteristic equation of a certain discrete-data control system. Sketch the root loci $(-\infty < K < \infty)$ for the system. Determine the marginal value of K for stability.

$$z^3 + Kz^2 + 1.5Kz - (K + 1) = 0$$

8-14. Sketch the root loci $(0 \leq K < \infty)$ in the z-plane for the discrete-data control system shown in Fig. 8P-14.

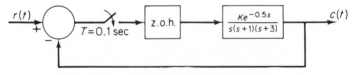

FIG. 8P-14.

9

Frequency Response
of Feedback Control Systems

9.1 Introduction

It was pointed out earlier that time response is usually the information sought in the analysis of a feedback control system. However, analytically, the time response is usually difficult to obtain because of the amount of computation involved. Therefore, the frequency response of a feedback control system is often obtained by means of the graphical methods, such as the Bode plot and Nyquist plot, and then interpretation on the time domain behavior of the system is made based on the time domain-frequency domain relationships.

The starting point in the frequency domain analysis is the transfer function. For a unity-feedback control system, the closed-loop transfer function is

$$\frac{C(s)}{R(s)} = \frac{G(s)}{1 + G(s)} \tag{9-1}$$

Under sinusoidal steady-state conditions, $s = j\omega$, Eq. (9-1) becomes

$$\frac{C(j\omega)}{R(j\omega)} = M(j\omega) = \frac{G(j\omega)}{1 + G(j\omega)} \tag{9-2}$$

When $M(j\omega)$ is written in terms of magnitude and phase, we have

$$M(j\omega) = M(\omega)\underline{/\phi_m(\omega)} \tag{9-3}$$

where

$$M(\omega) = \left|\frac{G(j\omega)}{1 + G(j\omega)}\right| \tag{9-4}$$

and

$$\phi_m(\omega) = \underline{/G(j\omega)} - \underline{/1 + G(j\omega)} \qquad (9\text{-}5)$$

The function $M(j\omega)$ is called the *magnification* of the feedback control system. The significance of $M(j\omega)$ to a control system is similar to the gain or amplification of an electronic amplifier. In an audio amplifier, for instance, an ideal design criterion is that the amplifier must have a flat gain response in the audio frequency range. In control systems, however, the ideal situation sometimes is that the output must follow the input at all times, or simply, the magnitude of $M(j\omega)$ must equal unity for all frequencies. But from the expression of Eq. (9-4), $M(\omega)$ can be unity only when $G(j\omega)$ is infinite. Or, in other words, the loop gain of the system must be infinite at all frequencies. This is, of course, impossible to achieve in practice, nor would it be desirable, since most control systems become unstable for high values of gain. Furthermore, all control systems are subjected to noise. Thus, in addition to responding to the input signal, the systems should be able to reject and suppress noise and unwanted signals. This means that the frequency response of a control system should have a cutoff characteristic in general, and sometimes even band-pass or band-eliminate characteristics.

The phase characteristic of the frequency response is also of importance. The ideal situation is that the phase shift must be a linear function of

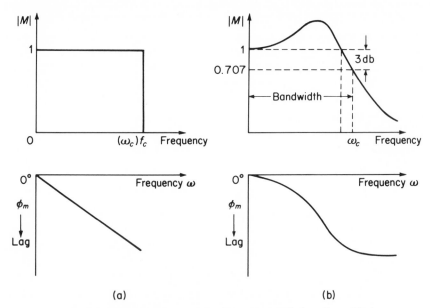

(a)   (b)

FIG. 9-1. Comparison of gain-phase characteristics of an ideal lowpass filter and a typical servo system. (a) Ideal filter; (b) Servo system.

frequency within the frequency band of the input signal. Figure 9-1a shows the gain and phase characteristics of an ideal low pass filter, which is impossible to realize physically. Typical gain and phase characteristics of a control system are shown in Fig. 9-1b. It is seen that the gain decreases as the frequency is increased. This is due to the effect of inertia and inductance in a physical system, so that all responses will cease as the frequency approaches infinity.

9.2 Frequency Domain Specifications

The specifications for the performance of a control system in the frequency domain are commonly given in the following terms:

(1) *Bandwidth.* The bandwidth, *BW*, is defined as the frequency at which the magnitude of $M(j\omega)$ has dropped to 70.7 per cent of its zero frequency level, or 3 db down from the zero frequency level (see Fig. 9-2). In general, the bandwidth indicates the noise filtering characteristics of the system. Also, bandwidth gives a measure of the transient response properties.

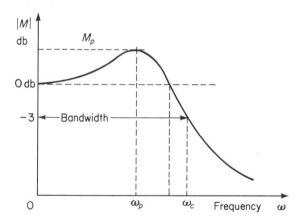

FIG. 9-2. The magnification curve of a servo system.

A large bandwidth usually indicates that higher frequency signals will be passed on to the outputs. Thus, the transient response may have a faster rise time accompanied by a larger overshoot. Conversely, if the bandwidth is small, only low-frequency signals are passed; therefore, the time response will generally be slow and sluggish.

(2) *Peak resonance M_p.* This is defined as the maximum value of $M(\omega)$, which also gives indication on the relative stability of the system. For a second-order system, the step responses and the frequency response curves for various values of ω are shown in Figs. 6-5 and 2-36, respectively. It is apparent that a high M_p corresponds to a large overshoot in the

time response. For design purposes, it is generally accepted that an optimum value of M_p should be somewhere between 1.1 and 1.5.

(3) *Resonant frequency* ω_p. This is the frequency at which the peak resonance M_p occurs.

(4) *Cutoff rate*. Often, the rate of cutoff of the frequency response curve at high frequencies is important, since it indicates the characteristics of the system in distinguishing the signal from noise. However, in general, sharp cutoff characteristics are usually accompanied by large M_p, which means a less stable system.

Other important factors in measuring the relative stability of a control system are the *gain margin* and the *phase margin*. These terms are discussed in the ensuing sections of the chapter.

9.3 M_p and ω_p of a Second-order System

For a second-order feedback control system, the peak resonance M_p and the resonant frequency ω_p are uniquely related to the damping ratio δ and the natural undamped frequency ω_n of the system. Consider the second-order closed-loop transfer function

$$M(j\omega) = \frac{C(j\omega)}{R(j\omega)} = \frac{\omega_n^2}{(j\omega)^2 + 2\delta\omega_n(j\omega) + \omega_n^2}$$

$$= \frac{1}{1 + j2\left(\dfrac{\omega}{\omega_n}\right)\delta - \left(\dfrac{\omega}{\omega_n}\right)^2} \tag{9-6}$$

Normalizing the frequency ω by letting $u = \omega/\omega_n$, the magnitude of $M(j\omega)$ becomes

$$M(u) = \frac{1}{[(1 - u^2)^2 + (2\delta u)^2]^{1/2}} \tag{9-7}$$

and the phase of $M(j\omega)$ is

$$\phi_m(u) = -\tan^{-1}\frac{2\delta u}{1 - u^2} \tag{9-8}$$

The resonant frequency is determined first by taking the derivative of $M(u)$ with respect to u and setting it equal to zero. Thus,

$$\frac{dM(u)}{du} = -\frac{1}{2}[(1 - u^2)^2 + (2\delta u)^2]^{-3/2}(4u^3 - 4u + 8u\delta^2) = 0 \tag{9-9}$$

from which

$$4u^3 - 4u + 8u\delta^2 = 0 \tag{9-10}$$

Therefore,

$$u = 0 \tag{9-11}$$

and

$$u = u_p = \sqrt{1 - 2\delta^2} = \frac{\omega_p}{\omega_n} \tag{9-12}$$

The solution in Eq. (9–11) merely indicates that the slope of the $M(\omega)$ curve is zero at $\omega = 0$; it is not a maximum. From Eq. (9–12), the resonant frequency is given as

$$\omega_p = \omega_n\sqrt{1 - 2\delta^2} \qquad (9\text{–}13)$$

Evidently, Eq. (9–13) is valid only for $1 \geq 2\delta^2$, or $\delta \leq 0.707$, since otherwise ω_p will become imaginary. This means simply that, for all values of $\delta > 0.707$, there is no resonance peak (or $M_p = 1$) in the $M(\omega)$ versus ω curve. The $M(\omega)$ curve is less than one for all values of $\omega > 0$ if the damping ratio δ is greater than 0.707.

Substituting Eq. (9–12) into Eq. (9–7) and simplifying, we get

$$M_p = \frac{1}{2\delta\sqrt{1 - \delta^2}} \qquad (9\text{–}14)$$

It is important to note that M_p is a function of δ only, whereas ω_p is a function of ω_n and δ. The plots of M_p versus δ and u_p versus δ are given in Fig. 9-3 and Fig. 9-4, respectively.

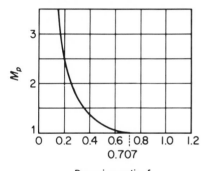

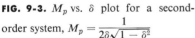

Damping ratio δ

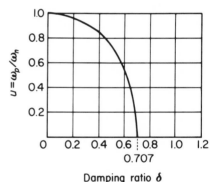

Damping ratio δ

FIG. 9-3. M_p vs. δ plot for a second-order system, $M_p = \dfrac{1}{2\delta\sqrt{1 - \delta^2}}$

FIG. 9-4. u vs. δ plot for a second-order system, $u = \sqrt{1 - 2\delta^2}$.

As an illustrative example, consider the control system given in Sec. 6.7 (Fig. 6-8). The closed-loop transfer function of the system, which was already obtained in Eq. (6–67), is repeated as follows:

$$\frac{\Theta_c(s)}{\Theta_r(s)} = \frac{K_s A K_i n}{R_a B_{me} s(1 + \tau_a s)(1 + \tau_{me} s) + K_b K_i s + K_s A K_i n} \qquad (9\text{–}15)$$

Under sinusoidal steady-state conditions, $s = j\omega$, Eq. (9–15) becomes

$$M(j\omega) = \frac{\Theta_c(j\omega)}{\Theta_r(j\omega)} = \frac{K_s A K_i n}{j\omega R_a B_{me}(1 + j\omega\tau_a)(1 + j\omega\tau) + K_b K_i j\omega + K_s A K_i n} \qquad (9\text{–}16)$$

The magnitude of $M(j\omega)$ is written as

$$M(\omega) = \left| \frac{\Theta_c(j\omega)}{\Theta_r(j\omega)} \right|$$

$$= \frac{K_s A K_i n}{\{[K_s A K_i n - \omega^2(\tau + \tau_a) R_a B_{me}]^2 + \omega^2 [K_b K_i + R_a B_{me} - \omega^2 R_a B_{me} \tau \tau_a]^2\}^{1/2}}$$

(9-17)

The phase of $M(j\omega)$ is

$$\phi_m(\omega) = -\tan^{-1} \frac{\omega(K_b K_i + R_a B_{me} - \omega^2 R_a B_{me} \tau \tau_a)}{K_s A K_i n - \omega^2(\tau + \tau_a) R_a B_{me}}$$

(9-18)

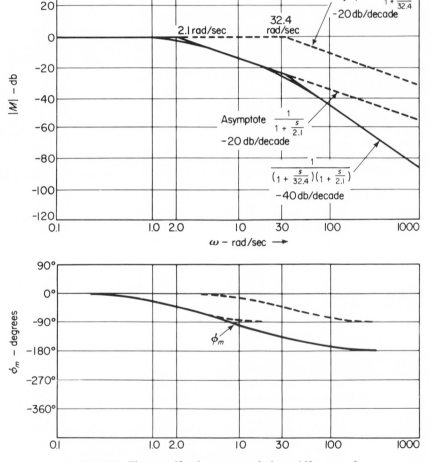

FIG. 9-5. The magnification curve and phase shift curve of

$$M(s) = \frac{1}{\left(1 + \dfrac{s}{32.4}\right)\left(1 + \dfrac{s}{2.1}\right)}$$

From Eq. (9–17) it is seen that the magnitude of $M(j\omega)$ can be greater than unity. Furthermore, if the denominator of Eq. (9–17) becomes zero, the magnitude of $M(j\omega)$ is infinite. Hence, $M(\omega) = \infty$ if

$$\omega^2 = \frac{K_s A K_i n}{(\tau + \tau_a) R_a B_{me}} = \frac{K_b K_i + R_a B_{me}}{R_a B_{me} \tau \tau_a} \qquad (9\text{–}19)$$

By means of the Routh criterion it is easy to show that two of the roots of the characteristic equation will lie on the $j\omega$ axis when

$$(R_a B_{me} \tau \tau_a)(K_s A K_i n) - (K_b K_i + R_a B_{me})(\tau + \tau_a) R_a B_{me} = 0 \qquad (9\text{–}20)$$

which is identical to the condition given by Eq. (9–19). Therefore, when the system goes into sustained oscillation, the magnification $M(\omega)$ of the system is infinite.

Now assume that the motor inductance L_a is zero while all other system parameters are kept unchanged. The closed-loop transfer function becomes

$$\frac{\Theta_c(s)}{\Theta_r(s)} = \frac{5A}{s^2 + 34.5s + 5A} \qquad (9\text{–}21)$$

which is of the second order. For the three different values of A used in Sec. 6.7, the corresponding M_p and ω_p are calculated by means of Eqs. (9–14) and (9–13), respectively, and are tabulated in Table 9-1.

Table 9-1

Gain A	Damping ratio δ	Undamped nat. freq. ω_n rad/sec	Peak M_p	Resonant freq. ω_p rad/sec
13.5	2.0	8.62	—	—
200	0.546	31.6	1.095	21.3
1500	0.2	86.2	2.55	82.6

For $\delta = 0.546$ and $\delta = 0.2$, the $M(\omega)$ versus ω and the phase $\phi_m(\omega)$ versus ω curves may be obtained directly from the normalized plot of the second-order factor given in Figs. 2-36 and 2-37. For a damping ratio of $\delta = 2.0$, the system is overdamped and there is no peak resonance; the closed-loop system response may be obtained from the expression

$$M(j\omega) = \frac{\Theta_c(j\omega)}{\Theta_r(j\omega)} = \frac{1}{(1 + j\omega/32.4)(1 + j\omega/2.1)} \qquad (9\text{–}22)$$

which has two negative corner frequencies—one at $\omega = 32.4$ rad/sec, and the other at $\omega = 2.1$ rad/sec. The $M(\omega)$ versus ω curve is the sum of the two plots for the simple first-order factors. Figure 9-5 illustrates the construction of the $M(\omega)$ versus ω and phase $\phi_m(\omega)$ versus ω curves. The magnitude of $M(j\omega)$ and phase versus ω curves for the three different values of gain A used are plotted in Fig. 9-6. It is seen that the effect of increasing the amplifier gain is to increase M_p and ω_p.

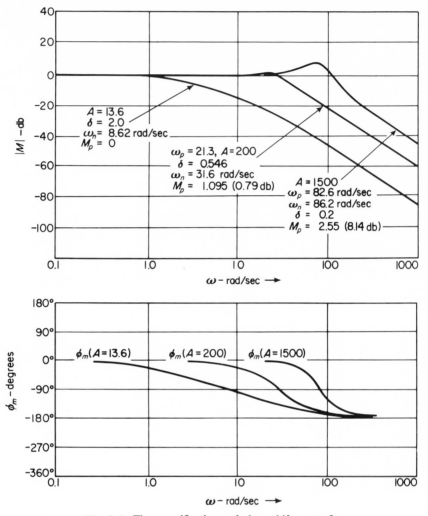

FIG. 9-6. The magnification and phase shift curves for

$$M(s) = \frac{5A}{s^2 + 34.5s + 5A}$$

9.4 Relative Stability—Gain Margin and Phase Margin

Some of the important questions that may be asked about the stability and general performance of a feedback control system are

(1) If the system is stable, how stable is it?

(2) If the system is not stable enough, or if it is unstable, how can the stability condition of the system be improved?

The first question is an analysis problem, whereas the second one is a design problem. Earlier, it was pointed out that the Nyquist plot of the loop transfer function $G(s)H(s)$ can help answer these questions. Therefore, in Fig. 9-7 the concept of relative stability of a closed-loop system is demonstrated by the Nyquist plots of a third-order system for four different values of gain K. The GH-plot in Fig. 9-7a encloses the $(-1, j0)$ point, so the system is unstable and the step response of the system increases with

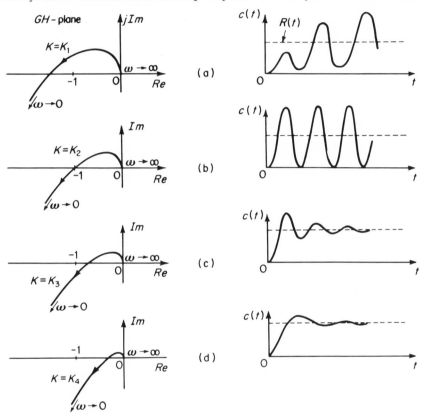

FIG. 9-7. Correspondence of Nyquist plots and transient responses.

time. The GH-plot of Figs. 9-7b goes through the critical point at $(-1, j0)$; this is a borderline case, and the system is said to be between stability and instability. Under this condition, if the system is able to stay operating at the critical point, the time response of the system will be a sinusoidal sustained oscillation. The GH-plots shown in Figs. 9-7c and d do not enclose the critical point. However, the GH-plot in Fig. 9-7c is closer to the critical point; therefore, the output step-response is shown to be more oscillatory and with higher overshoot.

Quantitatively, the distance between the GH-plot and the $(-1, j0)$ point gives measure of the relative stability of the closed-loop system. More specifically, the *gain margin* and the *phase margin* have been generally used to specify the degree of relative stability of a control system.

The Gain Margin

The gain margin is a measure of the closeness of the phase-crossover* point to the critical point. With reference to the $G(s)H(s)$ plot shown in

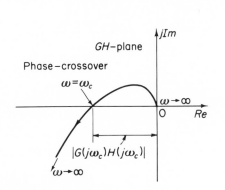

FIG. 9-8. Definition of gain margin.

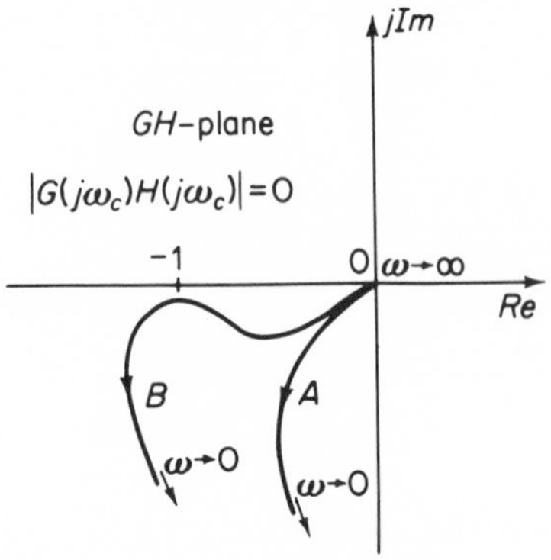

FIG. 9-9. Nyquist plots showing systems with same gain margin but different amount of relative stability.

Fig. 9-8, the phase-crossover frequency is ω_c, and the magnitude of $G(j\omega)H(j\omega)$ at $\omega = \omega_c$ is designated as $|G(j\omega_c)H(j\omega_c)|$. Then the gain margin of the system is defined as

$$\text{Gain margin (G. M.)} = 20 \log_{10} \frac{1}{|G(j\omega_c)H(j\omega_c)|} \text{ db} \qquad (9\text{–}23)$$

On the basis of this definition, it is noticed that in the GH-plot of Fig. 9-8 if the loop gain is increased to the extent that the GH locus passes through the critical point so that $|G(j\omega_c)H(j\omega_c)|$ equals unity, the gain margin is zero db. On the other hand, for a second-order system, the GH locus does not intersect the negative real axis; therefore, $|G(j\omega_c)H(j\omega_c)|$ equals zero, and the gain margin defined by Eq. (9–23) is infinite in decibels. On the basis of the above evaluation, the physical significance of gain margin can be interpreted as follows: *Gain margin is the amount of gain in decibels that can be allowed to increase in the loop before the system reaches instability.* When the GH-plot goes through the $(-1, j0)$ point, the gain margin is zero db, which implies that the loop gain can no longer be increased without causing instability. For a second-order system, the crossover $|G(j\omega_c)H(j\omega_c)|$ on the negative real axis is zero, and the gain margin is infinite decibels; this means that, theoretically, the value of the loop gain can be increased

*See Sec. 2.10 on phase-crossover points.

to infinity before instability occurs. When the critical point is enclosed by the GH-plot, the magnitude of $G(j\omega_c)H(j\omega_c)$ is greater than unity, and the gain margin in decibels becomes negative. However, it should be pointed out that a negative gain margin in decibels does not always correspond to unstable systems. It was learned in Chapter 7 that, for systems with non-minimum phase transfer functions, the stability condition is satisfied only if the Nyquist plot encircles the $(-1, j0)$ point.

The following example illustrates how the gain margin of a control system is determined by the analytical method.

Example 9-1. *Computation of the Gain Margin.* Consider that the loop transfer function of a feedback control system is given by

$$G(s)H(s) = \frac{K}{(1 + s)(1 + 2s)(1 + 3s)} \tag{9-24}$$

It can be shown that the closed-loop system is stable for $-1 < K < 10$. Let us assume that $K = 5$, and the corresponding value of the gain margin is desired. Substituting $K = 5$ and $s = j\omega$ into Eq. (9-24) gives

$$\begin{aligned}
G(j\omega)H(j\omega) &= \frac{5}{(1 - 11\omega^2) + j6\omega(1 - \omega^2)} \\
&= \frac{5[(1 - 11\omega^2) - j6\omega(1 - \omega^2)]}{(1 - 11\omega^2)^2 + 36\omega^2(1 - \omega^2)^2}
\end{aligned} \tag{9-25}$$

Setting the imaginary part of the last equation equal to zero, we have

$$\omega_c = \pm 1 \text{ rad/sec} \tag{9-26}$$

which is not a function of the value of K. Substituting this value of ω_c into Eq. (9-25) gives

$$|G(j\omega_c)H(j\omega_c)| = 0.5 \tag{9-27}$$

Therefore, from Eq. (9-23), the gain margin is

$$\text{G. M.} = 20 \log_{10} \frac{1}{0.5} = 20 \log_{10} 2 = 6 \text{ db} \tag{9-28}$$

which means that the gain K can be increased by 6 db, or a factor of two, before the system reaches instability.

Now let us consider that the value of K is to be determined so that the gain margin of the system is equal to 20 db. From Eq. (9-23),

$$\text{G. M.} = 20 \text{ db} = 20 \log_{10} \frac{1}{|G(j\omega_c)H(j\omega_c)|}$$

from which we get

$$|G(j\omega_c)H(j\omega_c)| = 0.1 \tag{9-29}$$

Also, at the phase crossover, $\omega_c = \pm 1$ rad/sec. Therefore, using Eq. (9-24), we get

$$|G(j\omega_c)H(j\omega_c)| = \frac{K}{10} \tag{9-30}$$

Now equating Eq. (9–29) to Eq. (9–30) gives $K = 1$.

In general, the gain margin is merely one of several essential terms used to indicate the relative stability of a feedback control system. Theoretically, a system with a large gain margin should be more stable than one with a smaller gain margin. However, this statement is not true in general. For all practical purposes, gain margin alone does not sufficiently indicate the relative stability of a system. For instance, the two GH-plots shown in Fig. 9-9 obviously have the same gain margin; that is, they all represent systems with infinite gain margin. However, locus A actually corresponds to a much more stable system than locus B, since, with any slight change in some system parameter (or parameters), it is possible for locus B to pass through or even enclose the $(-1, j0)$ point. The two GH-plots given

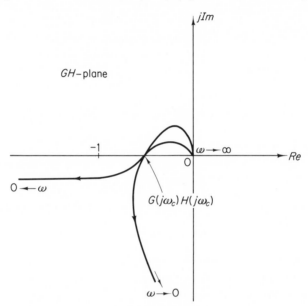

FIG. 9-10. Nyquist plots showing systems with same gain margin but different degree of relative stability.

in Fig. 9-10 also have the same gain margin, but the system corresponding to curve A certainly represents a more stable system.

In order to define adequately the relative stability of a system, the *phase margin* is used to distinguish the degree of stability of cases like those shown in Figs. 9-9 and 9-10.

The Phase Margin

The phase margin is a measure of the closeness of the gain-crossover point to the critical point. Phase margin is defined as the angle through which the Nyquist locus of $G(s)H(s)$ must be rotated in order that the unity magnitude point on the locus passes through the critical point $(-1, j0)$. Figure 9-11 shows that the phase margin is the angle that the unit radius

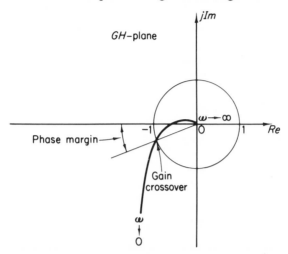

FIG. 9-11. Phase margin measured in the $G(s)H(s)$ plane.

phasor makes with the negative real axis in the GH-plane. The phase margin has the significance of estimating the stability effect of changes of the parameters of the system which affect the phase of $G(s)H(s)$.

The analytical procedure of computing the phase margin involves finding the phase of $G(j\omega)H(j\omega)$ at the gain crossover, then subtracting 180 deg from this phase. Therefore,

$$\text{Phase margin (\Phi. M.)} = \underline{/G(j\omega_h)H(j\omega_h)} - 180° \qquad (9\text{--}31)$$

where ω_h is the gain-crossover frequency. However, the analytical method frequently involves tedious computation so that a graphical method using the Bode plot is usually preferred.

Gain Margin and Phase Margin from the Bode Plot

It is usually preferable to evaluate the gain margin and the phase margin of a control system from its Bode plot. The reason is simply that the Bode plot is very easy to construct, and the gain margin and phase margin are obtained directly from the plot by inspection. As an illustrative example, consider the open-loop transfer function of a unity-feedback system.

$$G(s) = \frac{K}{s(1 + 0.2s)(1 + 0.02s)} \qquad (9\text{--}32)$$

The following steps are followed in constructing the Bode plot of $G(s)$ on semilog coordinates:

(1) The corner frequencies of $G(j\omega)$ are at $\omega = 0$, $\omega = 5$ rad/sec, and $\omega = 50$ rad/sec.

(2) Straight-line asymptotes are drawn for the magnitude curve and the phase curve corresponding to these corner frequencies.

(3) The straight-line asymptotes for the magnitude curve are added, and a smooth curve is sketched representing the actual magnitude curve (see Fig. 9-12).

(4) The actual phase shift curve at the two corner frequencies $\omega = 5$

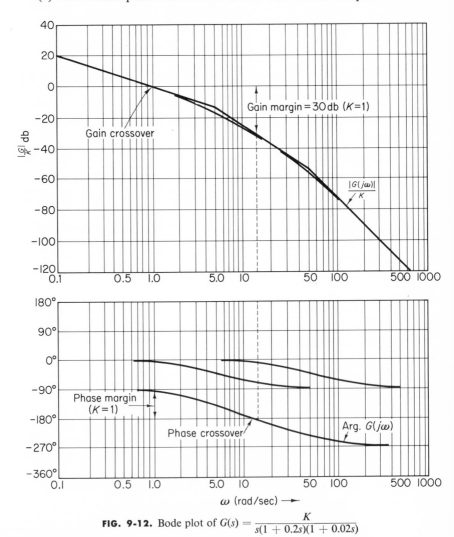

FIG. 9-12. Bode plot of $G(s) = \dfrac{K}{s(1 + 0.2s)(1 + 0.02s)}$

rad/sec, and $\omega = 50$ rad/sec are sketched approximately, based on the straight-line asymptotes. The sum of the three phase curves gives the total phase characteristics of $G(j\omega)$.

It is seen from Fig. 9-12 that the phase curve passes through the -180 deg axis approximately at 15 rad/sec. The magnitude of $|G(j\omega)|/K$ corresponding to this point is -30 db. This means that if the gain K is increased to 30 db, the magnitude curve will cross the 0 db axis (the phase-crossover point), which corresponds to the Nyquist plot of $G(j\omega)$ passing through the $(-1, j0)$ point; the system is on the verge of becoming unstable. From the definition of gain margin, the gain margin in this case is 30 db. Suppose that the next step is to determine the phase margin when K is unity. Remember that the phase margin is defined as the phase difference between the angle of $G(j\omega)$ and -180 deg when the magnitude of $G(j\omega)$ is unity (gain-crossover point). We simply locate the point where the magnitude curve $|G(j\omega)|/K$ crosses the 0 db axis ($\log_{10} 1 = 0$) and the corresponding phase of $G(j\omega)$ is approximately -100 deg. Thus, the phase margin when K is unity is $180° - 100° = 80°$.

The procedure in obtaining the gain margin and the phase margin from the Bode plot may be outlined as follows:

(1) Construct the Bode plot of $|G(j\omega)|/K$ versus ω and Arg $G(j\omega)$ versus ω.

(2) To obtain the gain margin, first locate the point at which the phase curve crosses the -180 deg axis (the phase-crossover point). The magnitude of $|G(j\omega)|/K$ curve in decibels at the phase-crossover point is the gain margin for $K = 1$. For any other value of K, the gain margin is simply the value of K in decibels. For example, in the previous example, if K is set at 10 db, the gain margin is $30 - 10 = 20$ db. Sometimes, the gain margin corresponding to $K = 1$ is called the *gain limit*[1] G_l. Then the gain margin in decibels for any gain K is simply

Gain margin (G.M.) in db = Gain limit G_l in db $-$ Gain K in db   (9–33)

In terms of absolute values, the last equation is written as

$$\text{Gain margin} = \frac{\text{Gain limit}}{K} \qquad (9\text{--}34)$$

Furthermore, if the phase shift curve never crosses the -180 deg axis from above, the system is always stable; e.g., in a second-order system, the phase shift only approaches -180 deg asymptotically as the frequency is increased to infinity.

(3) To obtain the phase margin, first locate the point where the magnitude curve $|G(j\omega)|/K$ crosses the zero decibel axis (the gain-crossover point). The phase angle between the phase curve and the -180 deg axis at the gain-crossover point is the phase margin for $K = 1$. If the phase curve is above the -180 deg axis, the phase margin is positive; otherwise, it is

negative. For any other value of K, the phase margin is obtained by shifting the zero decibel axis to $-K$ in decibels and following the same procedure as outlined above. For instance, in the last example, if $K = 10$ db, the magnitude curve is shifted up by 10 db. This is as if the zero decibel axis were shifted down by 10 db. The new gain-crossover frequency is approximately 3 rad/sec. The phase margin for $K = 10$ db is about 60 deg.

9.5 Conditionally Stable System

Thus far, we have shown that if the gain of a control system is increased sufficiently, the system will become unstable. There is a class of systems, however, in which the system may be stable and unstable for a variety of ranges of gain. It is possible to have a system which is stable only for a finite range (or ranges) of K. This type of system is described as a *conditionally stable system*. The Nyquist locus of a typical conditionally stable system is shown in Fig. 9-13. In this case the regions (2) and (4) on the

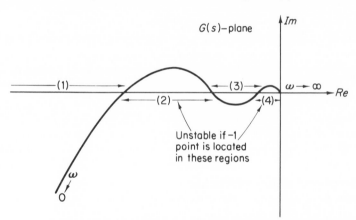

FIG. 9-13. Nyquist plot of a conditionally stable system.

negative real axis apparently correspond to unstable regions. The critical point $(-1, j0)$ must not locate in these regions, or the system will be unstable. Control systems with conditionally stable condition are not desirable in practice, since the system will become unstable when it is first turned on and trying to reach the operating point, say, which corresponds to the $(-1, j0)$ point lying in region (1) of Fig. 9-13. However, a conditionally stable system may be acceptable if some switching scheme can be devised so that the gain K is switched from zero to the proper operating value without going through the values that correspond to unstable operations.

As an illustration of a conditionally stable system, let us consider that a certain unity-feedback control system has the open-loop transfer function

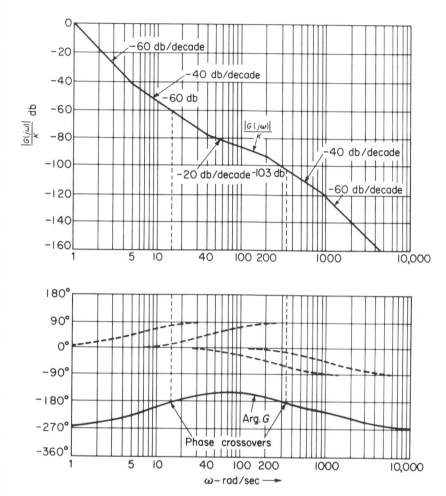

FIG. 9-14. Bode plot of $G(s) = \dfrac{K(1 + 0.2s)(1 + 0.025s)}{s^3(1 + 0.001s)(1 + 0.005s)}$

$$G(s) = \frac{K(1 + 0.2s)(1 + 0.025s)}{s^3(1 + 0.001s)(1 + 0.005s)} \qquad (9\text{--}35)$$

The corner plot of $G(s)$ for $K = 1$ is given in Fig. 9-14 on semilog coordinates. The gain-crossover frequency is approximately 1 rad/sec, and the phase margin is negative. This means that the closed-loop system is unstable even for a very small value of K. There are two phase-crossover points: one at $\omega = 15$ rad/sec, and the other at $\omega = 350$ rad/sec. The phase characteristics between these two frequencies indicate that if the gain crossover lies in this range, the system is stable. From the Bode plot, the range of K for stable operation is found to lie between 60 db and 103 db. For values of K above or below this range, the phase shift exceeds -180 deg, and the

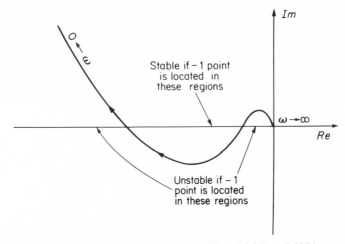

Stable if − 1 point
is located in
these regions

Unstable if − 1
point is located
in these regions

FIG. 9-15. Nyquist plot of $G(s) = \dfrac{K(1 + 0.2s)(1 + 0.025s)}{s^3(1 + 0.001s)(1 + 0.005s)}$

system is unstable. The conditional stable condition of the system is better illustrated if the Nyquist plot of $G(s)$ is sketched as shown in Fig. 9-15.

One important feature of the Bode plot which is useful in the design of control systems is that a definite relation exists between the slope of the magnitude curve at the gain crossover and the relative stability of the system. Specifically, if the slope of the magnitude curve at the gain crossover is −60 db/decade or more, the system is unstable. In general, the smaller the slope of the magnitude curve, the more stable is the system. Figure 9-14 serves as a good example in clarifying this point. At both very low and very high frequencies, the slope of the magnitude curve is −60 db/decade; if the gain crossover falls in either of these two regions, the phase margins are negative and the system is unstable. In the two −40 db/decade sections, the system can be stable only in about half of these regions, but even then the phase margin is still small. If the gain crossover falls within the −20 db/decade section, the phase margin is positive, and the system is rather stable.

9.6 The Constant M Loci in the G-plane

In the previous sections, it has been shown that the maximum resonance peak M_p of the closed-loop frequency response curve is directly related to the maximum overshoot of the transient response. Normally, the magnification curve of $M(\omega)$ versus ω may be constructed by means of the corner plot technique if the closed-loop transfer function $C(j\omega)/R(j\omega)$ is given, and if its numerator and denominator are factored in the standard form of Eq. (2–122). It is not always easy to plot the M versus ω curve, for if the system order is high, the amount of work involved in solving for the roots of the characteristic equation may be quite extensive. However, it will be shown now that the information concerning M_p and the data necessary for plotting the M versus ω curve can be obtained from the Nyquist plot of the open-loop transfer function $G(j\omega)$.

Consider a feedback control system with unity feedback. The closed-loop transfer function is

$$\frac{C(s)}{R(s)} = \frac{G(s)}{1 + G(s)} \tag{9-36}$$

Let the coordinates of the Nyquist plot of $G(s)$ be represented by.

$$G = x + jy \tag{9-37}$$

where it is understood that G, x, and y are functions of s. Then

$$M = M(\omega) = \left|\frac{C(j\omega)}{R(j\omega)}\right| = \left|\frac{G(j\omega)}{1 + G(j\omega)}\right| = \left|\frac{x + jy}{1 + x + jy}\right| = \frac{\sqrt{x^2 + y^2}}{\sqrt{(1 + x)^2 + y^2}} \tag{9-38}$$

which gives

$$M\sqrt{(1 + x)^2 + y^2} = \sqrt{x^2 + y^2} \tag{9-39}$$

or

$$M^2[(1 + x)^2 + y^2] = x^2 + y^2 \tag{9-40}$$

Rearranging the last equation yields

$$(1 - M^2)x^2 + (1 - M^2)y^2 - 2M^2x = M^2 \tag{9-41}$$

Dividing through Eq. (9-41) by $(1 - M^2)$, and adding the term $[M^2/(1 - M^2)]^2$ on both sides of the equation, we have

$$x^2 + y^2 - \frac{2M^2}{1 - M^2}x + \left(\frac{M^2}{1 - M^2}\right)^2 = \frac{M^2}{1 - M^2} + \left(\frac{M^2}{1 - M^2}\right)^2 \tag{9-42}$$

which is simplified to

$$\left(x - \frac{M^2}{1 - M^2}\right)^2 + y^2 = \left(\frac{M^2}{1 - M^2}\right)^2 \tag{9-43}$$

Equation (9-43) represents a circle with the center at $x = M^2/(1 - M^2)$; $y = 0$. The radius of the circle is $r = |M/(1 - M^2)|$. When $M = 1$, we have from Eq. (9-41) $x = -\frac{1}{2}$, which is the equation of a straight line parallel to the y-axis and passing through the point $(-\frac{1}{2}, 0)$ in the G-plane. Therefore, Eq. (9-43) represents the so-called "constant M loci" in the G-plane. The constant M circles for various values of M are defined in Table 9-2 and are constructed in Fig. 9-16. When the value of M becomes infinite, the circles degenerate into a point at $(-1, j0)$. This checks with the well-known fact that when the Nyquist plot of $G(j\omega)$ goes through the $(-1, j0)$ point in the G-plane, the system is on the verge of becoming unstable.

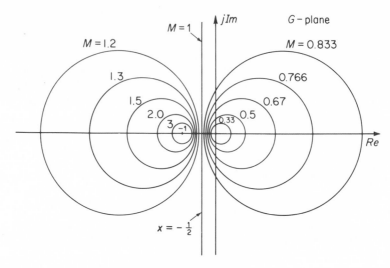

FIG. 9-16. The constant M circles.

Table 9-2

THE CONSTANT M CIRCLES

M	Center $x = \dfrac{M^2}{1 - M^2}, y = 0$	Radius $r = \dfrac{M}{1 - M^2}$
0.3	0.01	0.33
0.5	0.33	0.67
0.7	0.96	1.37
1.0	∞	∞
1.1	−5.76	5.24
1.2	−3.27	2.73
1.3	−2.45	1.88
1.4	−2.04	1.46
1.5	−1.80	1.20
1.6	−1.64	1.03
1.7	−1.53	0.90
1.8	−1.46	0.80
1.9	−1.38	0.73
2.0	−1.33	0.67
2.5	−1.19	0.48
3.0	−1.13	0.38
4.0	−1.07	0.27
5.0	−1.04	0.21
6.0	−1.03	0.17

The constant M loci plot is symmetrical with respect to the $M = 1$ straight line and the real axis. The constant M circles to the left of the $M = 1$ line correspond to values of $M > 1$, and those to the right of the $M = 1$ line are for $M < 1$.

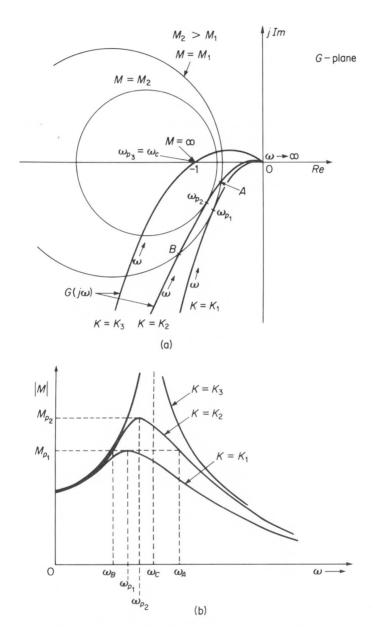

FIG. 9-17. (a) Polar plots of $G(s)$ and constant M loci showing method of determining the resonance peak M_p and the closed-loop frequency response in the G plane; (b) Closed-loop frequency responses.

The intersections of the $G(j\omega)$ plot and the constant M loci give the value of M at the frequency denoted on the G locus. If it is desired to keep the resonance peak M_p of a system less than a certain value, the open-loop locus $G(j\omega)$ must not intersect the corresponding M circle at any point, and at the same time must not enclose the -1 point. The M circle with the smallest radius that is tangent to the $G(j\omega)$ locus gives the value of M_p, and the resonance frequency ω_p is read off at the tangent point on the $G(j\omega)$ locus.

Figure 9-17a shows the Nyquist plot of $G(j\omega)$ for a hypothetical system, together with several of the constant M loci. The resonance peak M_p in the closed-loop gain response for a certain chosen forward gain K_1 is found by locating the smallest circle that is tangent to the G-plot. The resonant frequency is designated as ω_{p1}. If the forward gain is increased to K_2, a constant M circle with a smaller radius, hence with a larger value of M_p, is found tangent to the G-plot. The resonant frequency is shown to be ω_{p2}, which is closer to the phase-crossover frequency ω_c than ω_{p1}. If the value of K is still increased, so that eventually the G-plot passes through the $(-1, j0)$ point which corresponds to $M_p = \infty$ and $\omega_p = \omega_c$, the system is on the verge of becoming unstable. The corresponding values of M_p of the closed-loop frequency response found in the three cases above are sketched in Fig. 9-17b.

The entire closed-loop frequency response curve can also be obtained from the constant M and $G(j\omega)$ loci. The magnitude of M at any frequency is determined by reading the corresponding value of M on the constant M circle which intersects the $G(j\omega)$ locus at that frequency. For instance, when $K = K_2$, the $G(j\omega)$ locus shown in Fig. 9-17b intersects the $M = M_1$ circle at two points, A and B, with frequencies ω_a and ω_b, respectively. This means that at these two frequencies of ω_a and ω_b, the magnitude of the closed-loop frequency response has the same value M_1; these are shown in Fig. 9-17b.

9.7 The Constant Phase Shift Loci in the G-plane

The loci of constant phase shift of the closed-loop system may also be located in the G-plane by means of a method similar to that used for the constant M loci. With reference to Eqs. (9–36) and (9–37) the phase shift of the closed-loop system may be written as

$$\phi = \operatorname{Arg} M(j\omega) = \operatorname{Arg}\left(\frac{x+jy}{1+x+jy}\right) \qquad (9\text{--}44)$$

Hence

$$\phi = \tan^{-1}\left(\frac{y}{x}\right) - \tan^{-1}\left(\frac{y}{1+x}\right) \qquad (9\text{--}45)$$

Taking the tangent of both sides of the last equation and simplifying, we have

$$\tan \phi = \frac{y}{x^2 + x + y^2} \qquad (9\text{-}46)$$

Let $N = \tan \phi$; then Eq. (9-46) reads

$$x^2 + x + y^2 - \frac{y}{N} = 0 \qquad (9\text{-}47)$$

Adding the term $\left(\dfrac{1}{4} + \dfrac{1}{4N^2}\right)$ to both sides of the last equation yields

$$x^2 + x + \frac{1}{4} + y^2 - \frac{y}{N} + \frac{1}{4N^2} = \frac{1}{4} + \frac{1}{4N^2}$$

or

$$\left(x + \frac{1}{2}\right)^2 + \left(y - \frac{1}{2N}\right)^2 = \left(\frac{1}{4} + \frac{1}{4N^2}\right) \qquad (9\text{-}48)$$

which represents a family of circles with centers at $\left(x = -\dfrac{1}{2}, y = \dfrac{1}{2N}\right)$. The radius of any circle corresponding to a given N is represented by

$$r = \sqrt{\frac{N^2 + 1}{4N^2}} \qquad (9\text{-}49)$$

The constant phase shift loci for various values of ϕ are constructed in Fig. 9-18; their results are tabulated in Table 9-3.

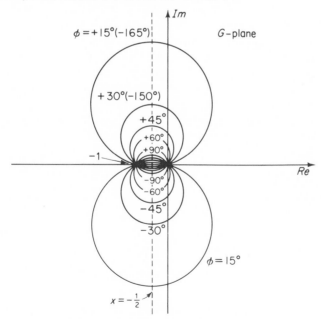

FIG. 9-18. The constant phase angle loci.

Table 9-3

THE CONSTANT N CIRCLES

$\phi = 180°n$ $n = 0, 1, 2 \ldots$	$N = \tan \phi$	Center $x = -\frac{1}{2}, y = \frac{1}{2N}$	Radius $r = \sqrt{\frac{N^2 + 1}{4N^2}}$
−90	−∞	0	0.500
−60	−1.732	−0.289	0.577
−45	−1.000	−0.500	0.707
−30	−0.577	−0.866	1.000
−15	−0.268	−1.866	1.931
0	0	∞	∞
15	0.268	1.866	1.931
30	0.577	0.866	1.000
45	1.000	0.500	0.707
60	1.732	0.289	0.577
90	∞	0	0.500

9.8 The Constant M and N Loci in the Gain-phase Plane (the Nichols Chart)

The constant M and N loci in the polar plane may be used for both the analysis and design of servo systems; however, in general, it is more convenient, especially in design problems, to have the M and N loci constructed in the gain-phase plane (decibel versus phase-shift). A point on a constant M locus in the gain-phase plane may be obtained by drawing a vector directed from the origin of the G-plane to a particular point on a constant M circle; the vector length measured in decibels and its phase angle determine the corresponding point in gain-phase plane. Figure 9-19 illustrates the process of locating three corresponding points on the constant M loci in the gain-phase plane. The critical point $(-1, j0)$ in the G-plane corresponds to the point of zero decibels and -180 deg in the gain-phase plane. By the same method, the constant N loci may also be located in the gain-phase plane. These constant M and N loci were first originated by N. B. Nichols,[2] and are called the "Nichols chart." A typical Nichols chart is constructed in Fig. 9-20 for the phase shift from -180 deg to 0 deg. The chart which corresponds to the phase from -360 deg to -180 deg is a mirror image of that shown in Fig. 9-20 with the mirror placed on the $\phi = -180$ deg axis. In Fig. 9-21 the Nichols chart is shown for -270 deg $< \phi < -90$ deg. It should be reiterated here that the Nichols chart consists simply of the same constant M and N loci originally developed in the polar plot, but now they are drawn in a different set of coordinates, namely magnitude (decibels) versus phase shift.

The following example will illustrate the relationship among the methods of the Bode plot, the Nyquist plot, and the Nichols chart with gain-phase plot.

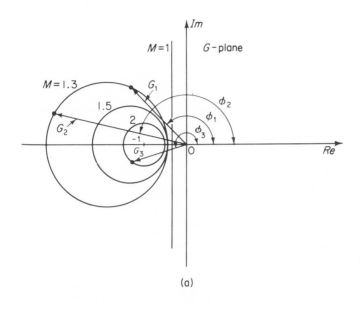

(a)

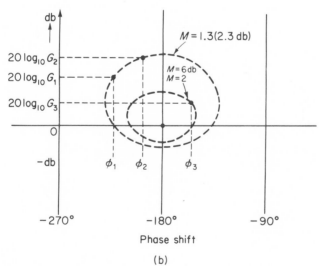

Phase shift

(b)

FIG. 9-19. (a) Constant M circles in the G-plane; (b) Constant M loci (Nichols Chart) for $M = 1.3$ and $M = 2$ in the gain-phase plane.

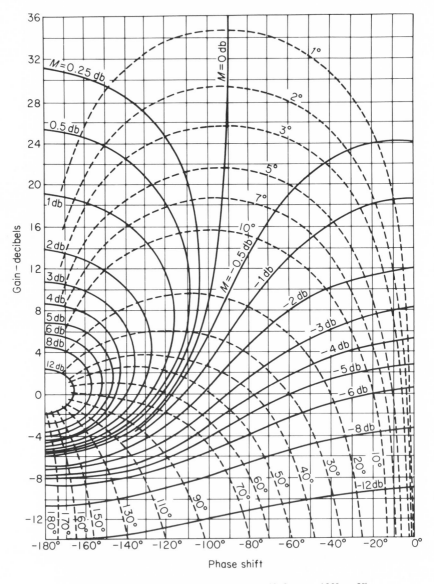

FIG. 9-20. The Nichols chart (for phase shift from $-180°$ to $0°$).

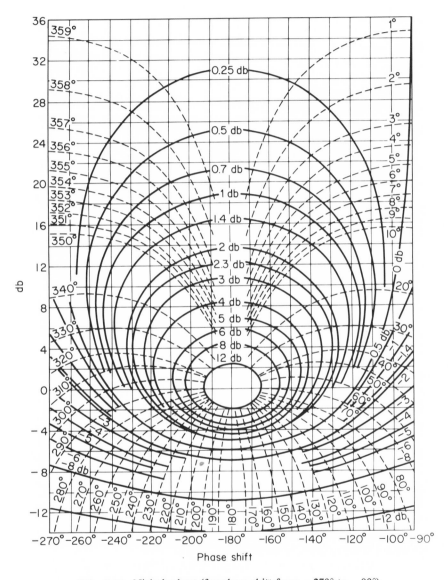

FIG. 9-21. Nichols chart (for phase shift from −270° to −90°).

Example 9-2. The open-loop transfer function $G(s)$ given by Eq. 9–32 is used again in this example. The Bode diagram for $G(s)$ is originally constructed in Fig. 9-12 for $K = 1$. From this Bode plot, it is seen that the following values for gain margin and phase margin are determined for the system when K assumes the values of 1.0, 3.16, and 10.

K	Gain margin (decibels)	Phase margin (degrees)
1 (0 db)	30	82
3.16 (10 db)	20	57
10 (20 db)	10	25

In order to evaluate the closed-loop frequency response, the transfer function $G(s)$ is now constructed in the gain-phase plot by use of the data taken from the Bode diagram of Fig. 9-12. In Fig. 9-22 the gain-phase plots for $G(s)$ are plotted for $K = 1$, 3.16, and 10, respectively. It is important to notice that the three loci have identical forms except for the shift in vertical positions. Thus, it is necessary only to plot $G(s)$ in the gain-phase plane for $K = 1$, for example, and the plot for any other K is obtained simply by shifting the $K = 1$ curve up or down along the vertical axis. For instance, for $K = 10$ db, the $K = 1$ (0 db) curve is shifted up by 10 db.

The gain and phase margins of the closed-loop system are also readily determined from the gain-phase plot by mere inspection. Since the intersection of the G-plot and the zero decibels axis in the gain-phase plane represents the gain crossover, the phase margin is read directly as the phase angle between this intersection and the -180 deg axis. Similarly, the intersection of the $G(s)$ locus and the -180 deg axis in the gain-phase diagram is the phase-crossover point, and gives the gain margin in decibels. The measurement of gain and phase margins in the Nyquist plot, the Bode plot, and the gain-phase plot are illustrated in Fig. 9-23.

The constant M loci in the Nichols chart, superposed on the gain-phase diagram, enables the determination of the closed-loop frequency response of the system. The intersections of the constant M loci give the values of M at the corresponding frequencies ω, read on the $G(s)$ curve. The constant M locus that is tangent only to the G locus gives the resonance peak M_p; the corresponding frequency is ω_p. For $K = 10$ (20 db), the $G(s)$ plot is tangent to the $M = 8$ db locus at $\omega = 7.2$ rad/sec; hence, the resonance peak of the system is $M_p = 8$ db (2.51), and the resonant frequency is 7.2 rad/sec. Similarly, for $K = 3.16$ (10 db), $M_p = 0.7$ db (1.084), and $\omega_p = 3$ rad/sec. For $K = 1$ (0 db), the $G(s)$ locus is not tangent to any constant M locus and there is no resonance.

The *bandwidth* of the closed-loop system can also be determined from the gain-phase diagram and the Nichols chart. It is easy to see that the frequency at the intersection of the $M = 0.707$ (-3 db) locus and the $G(s)$ plot is the bandwidth in rad/sec. Hence, from Fig. 9-23, the following values for the bandwidth are obtained:

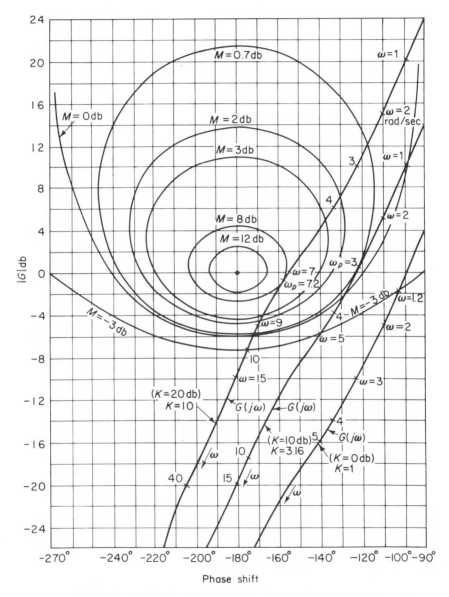

FIG. 9-22. Gain-phase plot for $G(s)$ and the Nichols chart for Ex. 9–2.

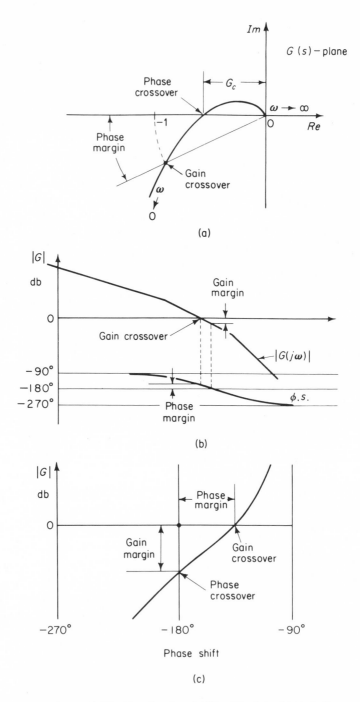

(a)

(b)

(c)

FIG. 9-23. (a) The Nyquist plot of $G(s)$ of Ex. 9–2; (b) Bode diagram of $G(s)$ of Ex. 9–2 (not to scale).

K	Bandwidth (rad/sec)
1	1.2
3.16	5.0
10	10

REFERENCES

1. Y. Chu, "Correlation Between Frequency and Transient Response of Feedback Control Systems," *AIEE Trans. Application and Industry*, Part II, Vol. **72**, 1953, p. 82.

2. H. M. James, N. B. Nichols, and R. S. Phillips, *Theory of Servomechanisms*, McGraw-Hill Book Company, New York, N. Y., 1947.

PROBLEMS

9-1. The pole-zero configuration of a closed-loop transfer function is shown in Fig. 9P-1a.

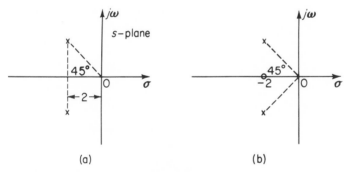

(a)   (b)

FIG. 9P-1.

(a) Compute the bandwidth of the system.

(b) A zero is added to the closed-loop system, as shown in Fig. 9P-1b; how is the bandwidth affected?

(c) Another pole is inserted on the negative real axis in Fig. 9P-1b, but at a distance ten times further from the origin than the zero; how is the bandwidth affected?

9-2. The specification given on a certain second-order feedback control system is that the overshoot of the step response should not exceed 25 per cent.

(a) What are the corresponding limiting values of the damping ratio and peak resonance M_p?

(b) Determine the corresponding values for ω_p and $t_{\max}$.

9-3. For the control system described in Problems 4-8 and 6-7, plot the frequency response ($|M|$ versus ω) curves for $A = 10$, 100, and 1000. Determine the resonance peak M_p and the resonant frequency for each case.

9-4. The closed-loop transfer function of a feedback control system is given by

$$M(s) = \frac{C(s)}{R(s)} = \frac{1}{(1 + 0.01s)(1 + 0.05s + 0.01s^2)}$$

(a) Plot the frequency response curve for the closed-loop system.
(b) Determine the peak resonance peak M_p and the resonant frequency ω_p of the system.
(c) Determine the damping ratio δ and the natural undamped frequency ω_n of the second-order system which will produce the same M_p and ω_p determined for the original system.

9-5. The open-loop transfer function of a unity-feedback control system is

$$G(s) = \frac{K}{s(1 + 0.1s)(1 + s)}$$

(a) Determine the value of K so that the resonance peak M_p of the system is equal to 1.4.
(b) Determine the value of K so that the gain margin of the system is 20 db.
(c) Determine the value of K so that the phase margin of the system is 60 deg.

9-6. The open-loop transfer function of a unity-feedback control system is

$$G(s) = \frac{K(1 + Ts)}{s(1 + s)(1 + 0.01s)}$$

Determine the *smallest* possible value of T so that the system has an infinite gain margin.

9-7. The open-loop transfer function of a unity-feedback control system is

$$G(s) = \frac{K}{s(1 + 0.1s)(1 + 0.001s)}$$

Determine the value of K if the steady-state error of the output position must be less than or equal to 0.1 per cent for a ramp function input. With this value of K, what are the gain margin and the phase margin of the system? Plot $G(s)$ in the gain-phase plot and determine the resonance peak M_p and the resonant frequency ω_p.

9-8. A random compensation network is added to the forward path of the system in Problem 9-7, so that now the open-loop transfer function reads

$$G(s) = \frac{K(1 + 0.0167s)}{s(1 + 0.00222s)(1 + 0.1s)(1 + 0.001s)}$$

where K is determined in part (a) of Problem 9-7. Plot the gain-phase diagram of $G(s)$. Evaluate M_p, ω_p, the gain margin, the phase margin, and the bandwidth of the compensated system.

9-9. For the discrete-data system described in Problem 7-15, plot the closed-loop frequency response. Determine the value of M_p.

9-10. The open-loop transfer function of an error-sampled discrete-data control system with zero-order hold and unity-feedback is

$$G(s) = \frac{1}{s(s + 1)(s + 2)}$$

The sampling period is one second. Determine the phase margin, gain margin, and M_p for the closed-loop system.

10

Design
of Feedback
Control Systems

10.1 Historical Development of Feedback Control
Systems Design

The basic design problem of feedback control systems can be described by the simple block diagram shown in Fig. 10-1. The figure shows a controlled process whose output $c(t)$ is the controlled variable, and the input $m(t)$ is the control signal. The problem is to find an appropriate control signal $m(t)$ so that the controlled variable $c(t)$ will be as desired. The description of the basic design problem is simplified by overlooking the possible existence of external disturbances which act as secondary inputs, and possible saturation effects in system elements which may put a constraint on the magnitude of $m(t)$ or signals at other points of the system. Once the desired $m(t)$ for satisfactory control is determined, a controller is usually needed to generate this $m(t)$ from the reference input and the actual output. The complete system configuration is illustrated by the block diagram of Fig. 10-2. Quite often the design problem is referred to as the design of the transfer function or the contents of the controller.

FIG. 10-1. Block diagram of a controlled process.

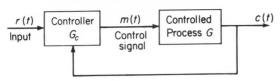

FIG. 10-2. Block diagram of a control system with a controller.

Although only the single input and single output case is illustrated here, the problem description can readily be applied to the multivariable case.

It is interesting to review the history of development of feedback control systems, which may help us gain some perspective on the theory of design of control systems.

The early stage of theoretical development of feedback control systems was characterized by the works of Nyquist, Hall, Nichols, and Bode, who made available such classical methods as the Nyquist plot, Bode diagram, and Nichols chart. A special feature of these methods is that they are all graphical techniques which rely on frequency domain plots. However, it was pointed out earlier that in the design of control systems, it is the time response of $c(t)$ that is of utmost importance, rather than the frequency response. The use of the frequency domain method is simply because the graphical techniques are so convenient to apply.

In the frequency domain design, the design specifications usually are given in terms of gain margin, phase margin, peak resonance, and bandwidth. These criteria, however, should be related to the time domain specifications such as rise time, delay time, setting time, overshoot, etc., which are more direct measurements of the system's output response.

The use of the frequency domain specifications results in a designed system which may be acceptable for the purpose of the controlled process, but it is very seldom the best by any standards. For instance, the gain margin and phase margin are measures of the relative stability of a control system. A gain margin of 20 db or a phase margin of 45 deg does not tell how good a control system really is in carrying out its prescribed objectives. In using the peak resonance M_p as a design criterion, it is generally accepted that a satisfactory range of M_p should be between 1.1 and 1.5, since the corresponding step response usually exhibits reasonable values for response time and overshoot.

In attempting to arrive at an acceptable system using the frequency domain design, the designer must first choose a suitable system configuration and the elements of the controller. For instance, Fig. 10-3a shows the block diagram of a system with the controller located in the forward path. This is a very common practice, and the system is said to have a cascade or series compensation. Figure 10-3b shows another scheme of compensation by

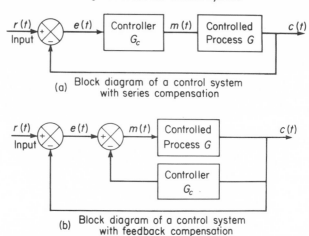

(a) Block diagram of a control system with series compensation

(b) Block diagram of a control system with feedback compensation

FIG. 10-3. Block diagrams of control systems with two different schemes of compensation.

having the controller in the feedback path, and this is often referred to as the feedback compensation. In general, other more complicated configurations, such as having controllers in both the forward path and the feedback path, may be used if necessary. In practice, the controllers or compensators used in control systems may take a great variety of forms. For instance, they may be passive networks in the form of low-pass filters, high-pass filters, or band-pass filters, or they may be networks with active elements. The proper selections of the system configuration as well as the contents of the controller depend to a great extent on the experience and ingenuity on the part of the designer. Therefore, the frequency domain design is very much a trial-and-error proposition. This is a distinct disadvantage of the method, since it does not indicate whether a solution actually exists for the problem. It may be entirely possible that the design requirements are so stringent or may even be contradictory so that they cannot be satisfied by any system configuration or controllers that are physically realizable.

Evan's introduction of the root locus technique in 1950 made possible the design of feedback control systems to be carried out in the s-plane. The main advantage of the root locus method is due to the fact that information on frequency response as well as transient response can be derived directly from the pole-zero configuration in the s-plane. With the knowledge of the closed-loop poles and zeros, the transient response is determined readily by means of inverse Laplace transform, and the frequency response is easily obtained from the Bode plot. However, the root locus design is still basically a trial-and-error procedure, and it relies on the reshaping of the root loci in order to get a satisfactory pole-zero configuration for the closed-loop transfer function.

The work by Norbert Wiener[1] in the late 1940's opened a new horizon to the design of feedback control systems. Wiener introduced not only the statistical considerations of control systems but also the idea of the performance index. For the first time, the design engineer was able to start from a set of design criteria and work toward the designed system by means of a completely analytical procedure. He is also able to design a control system which is optimum or the best possible with respect to a given performance criterion. In many practical applications of control systems, the actual signals and disturbances subjected by a control system may be random in nature. Unlike the deterministic signals, such as the step function and the sinusoidal function considered in the preceding chapters, random signals can be adequately described only by their statistical properties. For instance, in the problem of controlling the antenna of a radar system, the wind force acting on the antenna is best described by some probabilistic function, rather than by a sine wave or any other deterministic signals. The main difference between a deterministic signal and a random signal is that the magnitude of the former signal is fixed at any time, whereas the magnitude of the latter can only be described as what is the probability that it will lie in a certain range at a given time.

The principle of Wiener's optimization technique is demonstrated by the block diagram shown in Fig. 10-4. The design objective is to determine the transfer function $M(s)$ of the system such that the error between the desired output and the actual output is minimized. In Wiener's statistical design technique, the mean-square value of the error $e(t)$ is used as the performance index. The reason for using the mean-square error as the performance index is that the minimization of this particular performance index induces an analytical design procedure which makes use of the mathematical functions already defined in the theory of probability and statistics. However, it is apparent that a system which is optimum in the sense of minimum mean-square error may be ideal only for certain applications

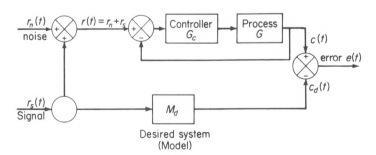

Desired system
(Model)

FIG. 10-4. Block diagram of control system design by means of Wiener's optimization technique.

but not for the others. In fact, the mean-square error criterion places heavier emphasis on large errors than on smaller ones.

In reality, the configuration shown in Fig. 10-4 can be used for the analytical design of systems with random inputs as well as systems with deterministic inputs. When the input signal is considered to be deterministic, other performance indices such as those listed below can be handled mathematically:

$$\int_0^t e^2(t)\,dt, \qquad \int_0^t |e(t)|\,dt, \qquad \int_0^t t\,|e(t)|\,dt$$

The reason that Wiener's work and the analytical design principle are so important is not so much because the techniques have found significant applications in control practice, but because these represent a revolution in design principle from the conventional trial-and-error methods.

At about the same time of the development of the analytical design, Truxal[2] proposed a synthesis procedure through pole-zero configuration in the s-plane. The synthesis procedure still makes use of the conventional design specifications such as the relative damping ratio, error constants, bandwidth, etc., and the signals are necessarily deterministic. Based on these specifications, the closed-loop transfer function is determined, and then the corresponding open-loop transfer function is found. The advantage of this synthesis over the frequency domain design is that the designer is able to determine if the given set of specifications are compatible at the beginning of the design so that the amount of guesswork and trial and error is cut to a minimum. Also, Truxal's synthesis procedure starts with the closed-loop transfer function and then works towards the transfer function of the controller, whereas the frequency domain design starts out with the controller and then works toward the closed-loop transfer function to see if it satisfies the design specifications.

It is very difficult to say when the modern control systems theory was inaugurated. In fact, the mathematical foundation of certain aspects of modern control theory can be traced far back to works that were conducted some seventy years ago. For instance, Liapunov's method[3] on stability was based on his Ph. D. thesis, which was completed in 1892. The linear programming technique, which has significant impact on modern control theory and practice, was developed around 1939. These significant contributions, among many others, did not become widely known until recent years simply because they were much too far ahead of their time.

The launch of the space age has placed a challenge to the control engineer to find new methods of designing more complicated control systems and meeting more rigid requirements. The control engineer soon discovered that the conventional design was no longer adequate and rigorous enough to handle the complicated problems encountered in modern fire control systems, autopilot systems, missile guidance systems, spacecraft rendezvous problems. Consequently, many of the mathematical contributions which have been long neglected were rediscovered and made applicable to the practical control problems. In a sense, the old control systems design problem is truly an engineering endeavor, but the modern control design contains, first, the development and formulation of the mathematical theory, and second, the application of the mathematical principles to practical design problems. Indeed, at present, many areas of the advanced control theory are still at the theoretical stage. This is why it is generally recognized that a gap now exists between the theory and practice of modern control theory.

The objective of modern control design can be described by two words: *optimal control*. In other words, a system is to be designed so that it is optimum in some prescribed sense. For instance, with reference to the block diagram of the multivariable controlled process shown in Fig. 10-1, one of the common problems in optimal control is to determine the control signal vector $\mathbf{m}(t)$ over the interval $t_0 \leq t < t_f$ so that the state vector $\mathbf{x}(t)$ is brought from the initial state $\mathbf{x}(t_0)$ to the desired final state $\mathbf{x}(t_f)$ in the shortest possible time, subjected to the given controlled process and possibly other constraints. The problem is usually referred to as the *minimal-time optimization*. Another optimization problem often encountered is the determination of the desired set of control signal vector $\mathbf{m}(t)$ so that a given performance index I is maximized or minimized. The performance index may assume the form

$$I = \int_{t_0}^{t_1} f[\mathbf{x}(t), \mathbf{m}(t)] \, dt \qquad (10\text{--}1)$$

where f is a functional relationship.

The extensive use of applied mathematics in modern control theory has made it difficult for one to make a quick transition from the conventional design to the modern. The conventional design is characterized by such terms as *transfer function, poles and zero, frequency response, Bode plots, Nichols charts, root loci, gain margin*, and *phase margin*. In the optimal control literature we will find a set of new terms such as *state variables, state equations, state transition matrix, Pontryagin's maximum principle*,[4] *Liapunov's methods, gradient technique, linear programming*, and *dynamic programming*.

In this section we have given a brief discussion on the historical development of control systems theory. The discussion and references made here are by no means exhaustive. It is hoped that these introductory remarks will give the reader a general idea of the basic problems involved in the design of feedback control systems before we enter the subject of design. The remaining part of this chapter will contain subjects on the design methods in the frequency domain and the s-plane. An introduction to the optimal control is given in Chapter 11.

10.2 Considerations in the Design of A-C and D-C Control Systems

Before we begin the discussion on the design of feedback control systems, it is important to survey the nature of the systems that are to be designed. It was pointed out in Chapter 1 that many control systems are of the a-c or carrier type, in which the signals are transmitted as the envelopes of modulated carrier signals. For a d-c system, however, the signals in the system are unmodulated. Not all systems are purely d-c or a-c; some systems may employ both d-c and a-c components, and the signals are converted from d-c to a-c and vice versa by means of modulators and demodulators. Therefore, compensating networks acting as controllers should be designed to operate on either d-c signals or a-c signals, as the case may be. For a d-c or unmodulated signal, the frequency range usually lies between 0 and 20 cycles per second. For a suppressed carrier signal, the carrier frequency is usually 60 cps, 400 cps, or higher. The frequency spectra of a typical d-c signal and a suppressed carrier signal are illustrated in Fig. 10-5.

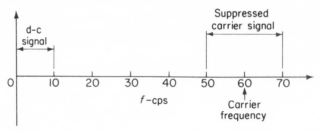

FIG. 10-5. Frequency spectrum of d-c signal and suppressed carrier signal in servo systems.

The compensation networks which are used to operate on d-c signals (hereafter called d-c compensation networks) are usually R-C networks with phase-lead, phase-lag, or combinations of phase-lead and phase-lag proper-

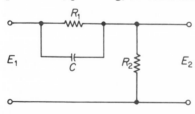

FIG. 10-6. Phase lead network as d-c compensating network.

ties. Figure 10-6 shows the circuit diagram of a typical phase-lead network which can be used for d-c compensation. In general, d-c networks are relatively easy to adjust and design.

The design of networks for the compensation of a-c signals is necessarily different from that of the d-c networks. The following discussion should help to explain the basic problems involved in designing a-c compensation networks.

If $e_s(t)$ is an error signal, and $\sin \omega_c t$ is the carrier signal, the actuating signal which appears at the rotor terminals of a synchro control transformer of a servo system is described by

$$e(t) = e_s(t) \sin \omega_c t \tag{10-2}$$

For the purpose of sinusoidal analysis, we may assume that $e_s(t)$ varies sinusoidally with time; thus, Eq. (10–2) becomes

$$e(t) = \sin \omega_s t \sin \omega_c t \tag{10-3}$$

where, normally, $\omega_s \ll \omega_c$. By use of familiar trigonometric relations, we obtain

$$e(t) = \tfrac{1}{2}[\cos (\omega_c - \omega_s)t - \cos (\omega_c + \omega_s)t] \tag{10-4}$$

This actuating signal is called a suppressed-carrier signal, since it is clear that $e(t)$ no longer contains the carrier frequency ω_c, but only the two side bands $\omega_c + \omega_s$ and $\omega_c - \omega_s$.

Let us assume now that this actuating signal is applied to the input of a compensating network; at the output of the network, we expect that the error signal $e_s(t)$ (envelope of the suppressed-carrier wave) is multiplied by a constant K and shifted in phase by an angle ϕ. In other words, the output of the compensator should give

$$e(t) = K \sin (\omega_s t + \phi) \sin \omega_c t \tag{10-5}$$

It can be easily shown that Eq. (10–5) can be written as

$$e(t) = \tfrac{1}{2} K\{\cos [(\omega_c - \omega_s)t - \phi] - \cos [(\omega_c + \omega_s)t + \phi]\} \tag{10-6}$$

Therefore, in order that the output follow Eq. (10–6), the a-c compensating network must multiply the upper side band by K and shift it by an angle $+\phi$, and multiply the lower side band by K, but shift it by an angle of $-\phi$. Unless the lower and the upper side bands are shifted by an equal angle in opposite sense, the resulting envelope will be distorted. Passive networks which have the properties described above are of the bridged-T or twin-T type. Figure 10-7a shows a twin-T network which may be used for the compensation of a-c or carrier systems. It can be shown that, if $4C_1R_2 > C_2R_1$, the amplitude and phase characteristics of the network are of the forms shown in Fig. 10-7b. It will be shown later that bridged-T networks may also be used efficiently to compensate d-c servo systems. By properly adjusting the network parameters, it is possible to have the two complex zeros of the network cancel the unwanted poles that give excessive oscillatory response in the original system. These poles sometimes occur in systems due to effects such as structural resonances; the compensating

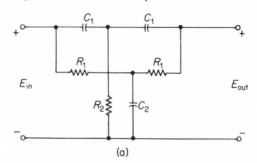

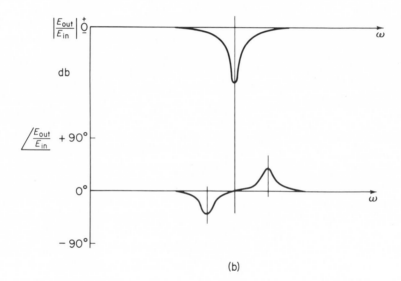

FIG. 10-7. (a) Twin-T network; (b) Magnitude and phase characteristics of twin-T network when $4R_2C_1 > R_1C_2$.

networks are designed so that they automatically adjust to cancel these resonances.

10.3 Frequency Domain Design of Feedback Control Systems

The frequency domain design technique has been well developed in the past twenty years. The method is still in popular use today, simply because it is straightforward and simple to carry out.

Let us begin by considering the transfer function of a controlled process to be

$$G_p(s) = \frac{K}{s(1 + 0.1s)(1 + 0.2s)} \qquad (10\text{-}7)$$

Let us assume that the steady-state performance requirement on the closed-loop system specifies that the velocity error constant K_v should not be less than 30 sec^{-1}, and the requirement on relative stability or transient behavior is given in terms of the peak resonance $M_p \leq 1.25$. If we construct a unity-feedback control system, using $G_p(s)$ in Eq. (10-7) as its open-loop transfer function, from the definition of K_v, we have

$$K_v = \lim_{s \to 0} sG(s) = \lim_{s \to 0} \frac{K}{(1 + 0.1s)(1 + 0.2s)} = k \qquad (10\text{-}8)$$

Therefore, to satisfy $K_v \geq 30$ sec^{-1}, K must be at least 30. However, applying the Routh-Hurwitz criterion to the characteristic equation of the system indicates that the system is unstable for all values of K greater than 15. This means that some kind of compensation scheme should be applied to the system so that the steady-state and the relative stability requirements can be satisfied simultaneously.

The characteristics of the frequency domain design are best illustrated by the Nyquist plot of $G_p(s)$ shown in Fig. 10-8. When $K = 30$, the system is unstable, and the Nyquist plot is shown to enclose the $(-1, j0)$ point. For $M_p = 1.25$, the Nyquist plot of $G_p(s)$ must be tangent to the constant M circle for $M = 1.25$ from below. If K is the only parameter which we can adjust to achieve the objective of $M_p = 1.25$, Fig. 10-8 shows that the desired K is 3. However, with this value of K, the velocity error constant is only 3 sec^{-1}. One of the methods that can be used to satisfy the steady-state and transient requirements simultaneously is to reshape the Nyquist locus so that the high frequency portion of the locus follows the $K = 3$ plot and the low frequency portion follows the $K = 30$ locus. Since the error constant is taken as a limit as s approaches zero, the zero frequency behavior of the open-loop transfer function governs the steady-state behavior of the system. The significance of this locus reshaping is that the compensated locus as shown in Fig. 10-8 will be tangent to the $M = 1.25$ circle at a relatively high frequency, while the zero frequency gain is maintained at 30 to satisfy the steady-state requirement. When we inspect the loci of Fig. 10-8, it is clear that there are two alternate approaches in arriving at the compensated locus:

(1) Starting from the $K = 30$ locus and reshaping the locus in the region near the resonant frequency ω_p, while the low frequency portion is unaltered.

(2) Starting from the $K = 3$ locus and reshaping the low frequency region to obtain $K_v = 30$ while keeping the locus near ω_p relatively unchanged.

In the first approach, the high frequency portion of the $G_p(s)$ locus is pushed toward the counterclockwise direction, which means that more phase

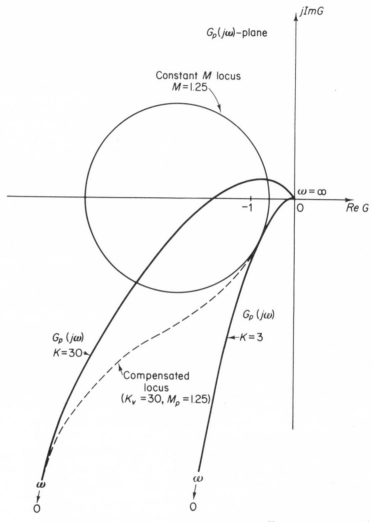

FIG. 10-8. Nyquist plots of $G_p(s) = \dfrac{K}{s(1 + 0.1s)(1 + 0.2s)}$.

is added to the system in the positive direction in the proper frequency range. This scheme is called the *phase-lead compensation*. The second approach apparently involves the shifting of the low frequency part of the $K = 3$ locus in the clockwise direction. This is often referred to as the *phase-lag compensation*, since more phase lag is introduced to the system in the low frequency range.

One should not jump to the conclusion that a given system can always be compensated satisfactorily by either of the two schemes mentioned above. It will be shown that, for systems with certain characteristics, satisfactory compensation cannot be accomplished by phase-lead networks. This, however, does not mean that proper compensation may then be achieved by using phase-lag networks, for it is quite common that neither scheme is feasible and some combination of lead and lag characteristics is needed.

The designer is usually interested in ascertaining the best compensation scheme for the particular system on which he is working. Unfortunately, the design technique in the frequency domain does not give an answer to this question. Judging from the nature of the system, the designer must depend considerably on his past experience to decide which compensation he should use, and then try it. If the scheme does not work, he simply must try something else.

Series Compensation with D-C Networks

In Fig. 10-9a is shown a typical d-c servo system employing a d-c compensation network. The equivalent block diagram of the system is shown in Fig. 10-9b with the typical signal waveforms illustrated at significant points of the system. The open-loop transfer function of the system without compensation is

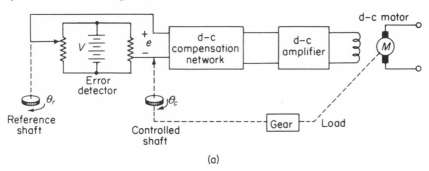

(a)

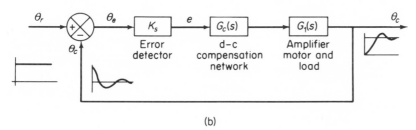

(b)

FIG. 10-9. A d-c servo system employing a d-c compensation network.

$$G(s) = K_s G_1(s)$$

and that of the compensated system is

$$G_c(s)G(s) = K_s G_c(s)G_1(s)$$

where $G_c(s)$ is the transfer function of the compensation network.

It is also quite common to replace the potentiometers in the system of Fig. 10-9 by a pair of synchros whose output is then the sine wave carrier modulated by the error signal $\theta_e(t)$. However, a demodulater must be inserted between the synchro output and the compensation network if the d-c network, d-c amplifier, and d-c motor are still used. This a-c–d-c system is shown in Fig. 10-10a. In Fig. 10-10b is shown the equivalent block diagram of the system. The transfer function $G_1(s)$ includes the demodulator, the error detector, the amplifier, the motor, and the other elements involved before compensation is added.

In Fig. 10-11 is given the schematic and block diagrams of an all a-c servo system employing a d-c compensation network. Evidently, a demodulator should be inserted in front of the d-c compensation network, and a modulator must be used to convert the d-c output signal from the network back into an a-c signal, which is to be amplified by an a-c amplifier. Since the

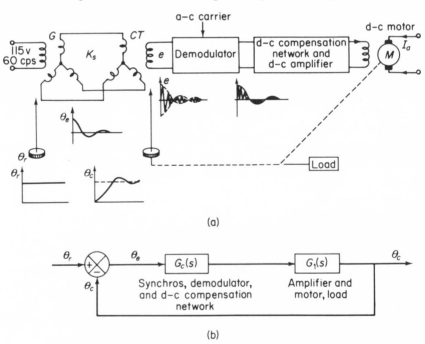

(a)

(b)

FIG. 10-10. An ac-dc servo system employing a d-c compensation network.

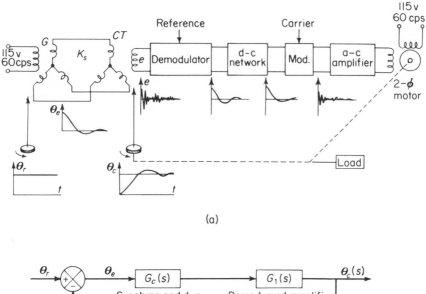

(a)

(b)

FIG. 10-11. An a-c system employing a d-c compensation network.

transfer functions of modulators and demodulators are usually mere constants, the system may be represented by an equivalent block diagram similar to those of the previous systems, as shown in Fig. 10-11b.

We can conclude that, when d-c compensation networks are applied to servo systems of any kind, the design techniques are the same, provided that the transfer functions of all the modulators used are taken into consideration.

(I) Phase-lead Compensation

In Chapter 6 a simple phase-lead compensation network with the transfer function $(1 + sT)$ was described under the name of derivative control. However, in practice, $(1 + sT)$ cannot be realized by passive networks; thus it is often called the transfer function of an ideal phase-lead network. A practical and simple phase-lead network* is shown in Fig. 10-12. The transfer function of the network is

---

*Although the network configuration is even simpler if, in Fig. 9-10, $R_1 = \infty$, such a network will block d-c signals completely and cannot be used in the forward path of a servo system.

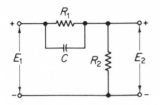

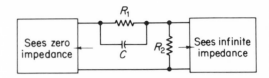

FIG. 10-12. Passive phase-lead network.

FIG. 10-13. Assumption of zero source impedance and infinite output impedance when deriving the transfer function given in Eq. (10–10).

$$\frac{E_2(s)}{E_1(s)} = \frac{R_2 + R_1 R_2 C_s}{R_1 + R_2 + R_1 R_2 C_s} \tag{10–9}$$

or

$$\frac{E_2(s)}{E_1(s)} = \frac{R_2}{R_1 + R_2} \frac{1 + R_1 C_s}{1 + \dfrac{R_1 R_2}{R_1 + R_2} C_s} \tag{10–10}$$

If we let

$$a = \frac{R_1 + R_2}{R_2} \quad (a > 1) \tag{10–11}$$

and

$$T = \frac{R_1 R_2}{R_1 + R_2} C \tag{10–12}$$

then

$$\frac{E_2(s)}{E_1(s)} = \frac{1}{a} \frac{1 + aTs}{1 + Ts} \tag{10–13}$$

It should be pointed out here that the transfer function E_2/E_1 given in Eq. (10–13) is derived under the assumption that the source impedance which the lead network sees is zero, and the output load impedance is infinite (Fig. 10-13). This assumption is, of course, made in general in the derivation of the transfer function of any four-terminal network.

Characteristics of R-C Phase-lead Network

(1) Pole-zero Configuration

The transfer function of the phase-lead network has a real zero at $s = -1/aT$, and a real pole at $s = -1/T$ (Fig. 10-14). By varying the values of a and T, the pole and zero may be located at any point on the negative real axis in the s-plane. It is seen that for $a > 1$ the zero is always located to the right of the pole, and the distance between them is determined by the constant a.

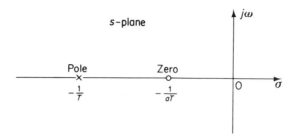

FIG. 10-14. The pole-zero configuration of
$$\frac{E_2}{E_1} = \frac{1}{a}\frac{1 + aTs}{1 + Ts}.$$

(2) Polar Plot of the R-C Phase-lead Network

Since, in general, the attenuation $(1/a)$ produced by the lead network is compensated by the amplifier gain of the servo system, it is necessary to investigate only the function

$$a\frac{E_2(s)}{E_1(s)} = \frac{1 + aTs}{1 + T_s} \tag{10-14}$$

The polar plot of Eq. (10–14) is shown in Fig. 10-15 for several different values of a. For any particular value of a, the angle between the tangent line drawn from the origin to the semicircle and the real axis gives the maximum phase shift (phase lead) ϕ_m obtainable from the network. The frequency at the tangent point ω_m represents the frequency at which ϕ_m occurs. It is seen that, as a increases, the maximum phase lead ϕ_m also increases, approaching a limit of 90 deg as a approaches infinity. The frequency ω_m decreases with the increase in a.

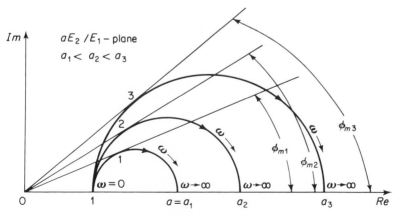

FIG. 10-15. Polar plot of $a\frac{E_2}{E_1} = \frac{1 + aTs}{1 + Ts}$.

(3) *Bode Plot of the Phase-lead Network*

In terms of the Bode plot, the lead network has two corner frequencies: a positive corner frequency at $\omega = 1/aT$ and a negative corner at $\omega = 1/T$. The Bode plot of aE_2/E_1 is sketched in Fig. 10-16.

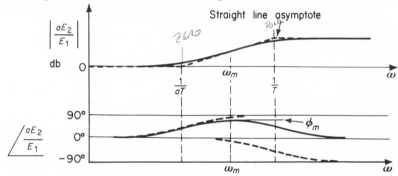

FIG. 10-16. Bode plot of the phase-lead network.

Analytically, ϕ_m and ω_m may be related to the circuit parameters a and T. Since ω_m is at the geometric mean of the two corner frequencies, we can write

$$\log \omega_m = \frac{1}{2}\left(\log \frac{1}{aT} + \log \frac{1}{T}\right) \tag{10-15}$$

Hence

$$\omega_m = \frac{1}{\sqrt{aT}} \tag{10-16}$$

To determine the maximum phase lead ϕ_m, we first write the phase shift of aE_2/E_1 as

$$\phi = \text{Arg}\left(a\frac{E_2}{E_1}\right) = \tan^{-1} aT\omega - \tan^{-1} T\omega \tag{10-17}$$

from which

$$\tan \phi = \frac{aT\omega - T\omega}{1 + (aT\omega)(T\omega)} \tag{10-18}$$

When $\phi = \phi_m$,

$$\omega = \omega_m = \frac{1}{\sqrt{aT}} \tag{10-19}$$

Hence

$$\tan \phi_m = \frac{(a-1)\dfrac{1}{\sqrt{a}}}{1+1} = \frac{a-1}{2\sqrt{a}} \tag{10-20}$$

Referring to the triangle shown in Fig. 10-17, we have

$$\sin \phi_m = \frac{a-1}{a+1} \qquad (10\text{–}21)$$

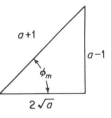

FIG. 10-17.

Equation (10–21) is a very important and useful relationship in the frequency domain design of feedback control systems, since a is determined once the required phase lead ϕ_m is given.

Design of Phase-lead Compensation by Bode Plot Method

The Bode plot method is generally preferred in the frequency domain design of series compensation of feedback control systems because the effect of the compensation network is easily obtained by adding its magnitude and phase shift curves, respectively, to that of the original system. For the phase-lead compensation employing the R-C network shown in Fig. 10-12, the general outline of the design procedure is given as follows:

(1) The magnitude and phase versus frequency curves are plotted for $G(s)$ of the uncompensated system with the gain constant K set according to the steady-state error requirement.

(2) The phase margin and gain margin of the original system are read from the Bode plot, and the additional amount of phase lead needed to provide the specified phase margin is determined. From the maximum phase lead required, ϕ_m is estimated accordingly, and Eq. (10–21) gives the corresponding value of a.

(3) Once a is determined, it is necessary only to obtain the value of T and the design is completed. The corner frequencies of the lead network $(1/aT, 1/T)$ are usually so placed that ϕ_m is located at the new gain-crossover frequency.

(4) The Bode plot of the compensated system is investigated to check that all the performance specifications are met; if not, a new value of ϕ_m must be estimated.

(5) If the specifications are all satisfied, the transfer function of the phase lead network is determined from the values of a and T.

Example 10-1. Consider a feedback control system with the open-loop transfer function

$$G_1(s) = \frac{K}{s(s+1)} \qquad (10\text{–}22)$$

which could be the transfer function of a linearized servo system employing a two-phase servomotor. The transfer function of the modulators used to adapt d-c compensation may be assumed to be unity.

The specifications are

(1) The phase margin of the system must be greater than 45 deg.

(2) When the input is a step velocity (ramp) function, the steady-state error of the output in position should be less than 0.1 deg per deg/sec of the final output velocity.

From the second requirement, we recall that the velocity constant K_v was defined as

$$K_v = \frac{\text{output velocity}}{\text{steady-state error}} = \frac{1}{0.1} = 10 \text{ sec}^{-1} \qquad (10\text{--}23)$$

Also

$$K_v = \lim_{s \to 0} sG_1(s) = K = 10 \text{ sec}^{-1} \qquad (10\text{--}24)$$

which implies that if the steady-state error is to be as specified, the forward path gain must be greater than 10.

The following steps are followed in the design of the phase-lead compensation network:

(1) The Bode diagram of $G_1(s)$ with $K = 10$ is plotted, as shown in Fig. 10-19.

(2) The phase margin read at the gain crossover ($\omega_c = 3.16$ rad/sec) is 18 deg. The damping ratio δ and the resonance peak M_p at this gain are computed to be 15.8 per cent and 3.2, respectively. Since the phase margin is less than 45 deg, more phase lead should be added to the system. Let us assume that we choose to use the phase-lead network given in Fig. 10-12. The block diagram of the compensated system is shown in Fig. 10-18.

(3) Since the desired phase margin is 45 deg and the present phase margin with $K = 10$ is only 18 deg, the phase-lead network must provide at least an additional phase lead of 27 deg in the vicinity of the resonant frequency. However, by inserting the compensation network, the magnitude curve of the Bode plot is also affected. The gain crossover is normally shifted to a higher frequency. Although it is possible to adjust the corner frequencies $1/aT$ and $1/T$ so that the maximum phase lead ϕ_m falls exactly at the new gain-crossover frequency, the original phase curve at this point is no longer 18 deg; it may be decreased to a low value, for example, 15 deg.* Thus,

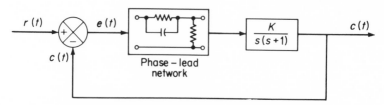

FIG. 10-18. Feedback control system with phase-lead compensation.

*This is, indeed, the main difficulty encountered in the phase-lead compensation. If the phase shift decreases rapidly with increasing frequency near the gain-crossover frequency, phase-lead compensation becomes ineffective.

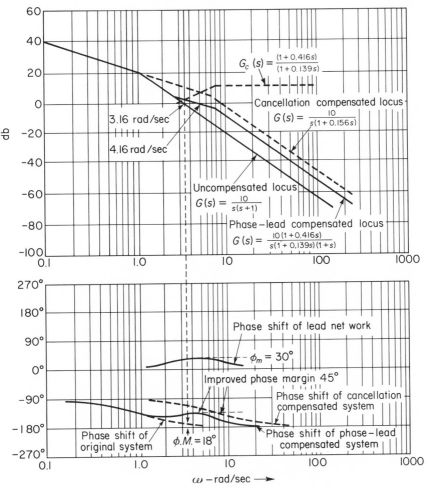

FIG. 10-19. Bode plots of $G(s)$ of system given in Example 10–1.

in estimating the necessary amount of phase lead, it is essential to include a little safety factor to account for this error. Instead of selecting $\phi_m = 27$ deg, we let $\phi_m = 30$ deg. From Eq. (10–21), we have

$$\sin \phi_m = \sin 30° = 0.5 = \frac{a-1}{a+1} \qquad (10\text{–}25)$$

from which

$$a = 3 \qquad (10\text{–}26)$$

(4) To determine the proper location of the two corner frequencies $1/aT$ and $1/T$: It is known that the maximum phase lead ϕ_m occurs at the geometric mean of the two corner frequencies $1/aT$ and $1/T$. To achieve

maximum phase margin with a already determined, apparently, the maximum phase lead ϕ_m provided by the lead network should occur at the new gain-crossover frequency ω_c', which is not known. Thus, the problem now is to locate the two corner frequencies $1/aT$ and $1/T$, so that $\omega_m = \omega_c'$. This may be obtained graphically as follows:

(a) The zero frequency attenuation of the lead network is calculated:

$$20 \log a = 20 \log 3 = 9.55 \, db \qquad (10\text{--}27)$$

(b) The geometric mean ω_m of the corner frequencies $1/aT$ and $1/T$ must be located at the frequency at which the magnitude of $G_1(j\omega)$ in decibels is equal to the negative value in decibels of one half of this attenuation; i.e.,

$$|G_1(j\omega)| = \frac{-9.55}{2} = -4.78 \, db \qquad (10\text{--}28)$$

From the Bode plot shown in Fig. 10-19, $\omega_m = 4.16$ rad/sec. Thus

$$1/T = \sqrt{a}\, \omega_m = \sqrt{3} \times 4.16 = 7.2 \, \text{rad/sec} \qquad (10\text{--}29)$$

and

$$1/aT = 2.4 \, \text{rad/sec} \qquad (10\text{--}30)$$

The new gain-crossover frequency is at

$$\omega_c' = \omega_m = 4.16 \, \text{rad/sec} \qquad (10\text{--}31)$$

A check of the compensated Bode plot shows that the phase margin of the compensated system is approximately 45 deg. The design has been done here with the straight-line asymptotic plots rather than the exact curves for the magnitude plots.

(5) The transfer function of the phase-lead network is simply

$$\frac{E_2(s)}{E_1(s)} = \frac{1}{a} \frac{1 + aTs}{1 + Ts} = \frac{1}{3} \frac{1 + 0.416s}{1 + 0.139s} \qquad (10\text{--}32)$$

If the amplifier gain is increased by a factor of 3, the open-loop transfer function of the compensated system becomes

$$G(s) = G_c(s)G_1(s) = \frac{10(1 + 0.416s)}{s(1 + 0.139s)(1 + s)} \qquad (10\text{--}33)$$

In Fig. 10-20 the magnitude versus phase shift plot of the original and the compensated systems are plotted on the Nichols chart. These plots are obtained by taking the values of magnitude and phase shift directly from the Bode diagrams (exact values rather than asymptotes are used) shown in Fig. 10-19. From the Nichols chart, the resonance peak M_p without compensation is found to be 10 db or 3.2 in magnitude, which checks with the value computed previously. The M_p after compensation is found to be

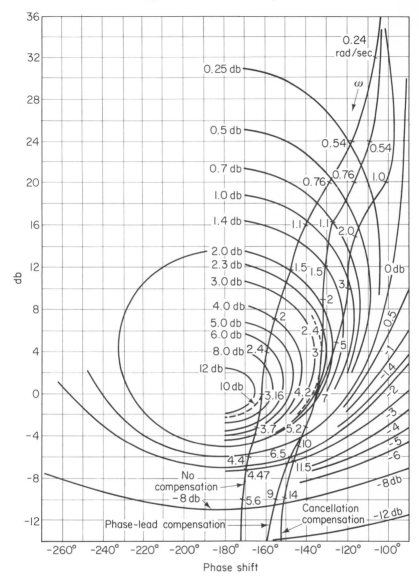

FIG. 10-20. Plots of $G(s)$ in db versus phase shift for system in Example 10–1.

2.7 db or 1.36, which shows quite an improvement on the system's stability. One more important point is that the resonant frequency of the system is decreased from 3.16 rad/sec to approximately 3 rad/sec and the bandwidth is increased from 4.47 rad/sec to 6.7 rad/sec. On the basis of the band-width-rise time relationship, we know that the rise time is shortened by the phase-lead compensation. From the magnitude versus phase shift curves and the Nichols chart, the closed-loop frequency responses for before and after compensation are shown in Fig. 10-21. It is also interesting to investigate the effect of the phase-lead compensation on the root locus diagram of the system, which is shown in Fig. 10-22.

Example 10-2. Let us consider a third-order servo system with the open-loop transfer function

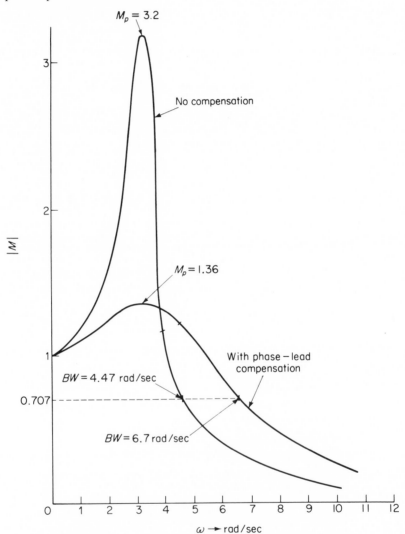

FIG. 10-21. Closed-loop frequency responses of system given in Example 10–1.

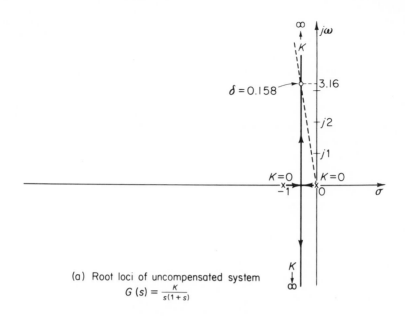

(a) Root loci of uncompensated system
$$G(s) = \frac{K}{s(1+s)}$$

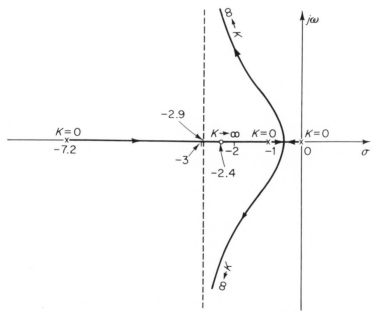

(b) Root loci of phase − lead compensated system
$$G(s) = \frac{K(1+0.416s)}{s(1+0.139s)(1+s)}$$

FIG. 10-22. Root locus diagrams of system in Example 10–1.

445

$$G_1(s) = \frac{K}{s(1 + 0.1s)(1 + 0.001s)} \tag{10-34}$$

The specifications are

(1) The phase margin of the system must be greater than or equal to 45 deg.

(2) For a velocity input, the steady-state error in the output position must be less than or equal to 0.1 per cent of the final output velocity.

From the second requirement

$$K = K_v \geq 1000 \text{ sec}^{-1} \tag{10-35}$$

which means that the gain constant of the system must be set at 1000 to meet the minimum steady-state error requirement.

The following steps are followed in the design of the compensation of the control system:

(1) As the first step, the Bode diagram of $G_1(s)$ is plotted for $K = 1000$ (Fig. 10-24).

(2) The phase margin read at the gain-crossover frequency $\omega_c = 100$ rad/sec is very close to 0 deg. (The critical value of K for absolute stability determined from the Routh criterion is 1010.) This means that the pair of complex conjugate roots of the characteristic equation is practically on the $j\omega$ axis in the s-plane, and that the corresponding resonance peak M_p is almost infinite.

(3) Since additional phase is required to realize the specified phase margin, we assume that a first trial is to use the phase-lead network given in Fig. 10-12 for series compensation (with no assurance that it will work). The configuration of the compensated system is shown in Fig. 10-23.

Evidently, the phase-lead network must provide at least an additional phase of 45 deg. However, anticipating that the new gain-crossover frequency after compensation will be somewhat higher, and, at the same time, that the original phase shift decreases with the increase in frequency, it is necessary to estimate a higher value for ϕ_m; for example, 50 deg.

From Eq. (10–21), we have

$$\sin \phi_m = \sin 50° = 0.765 = \frac{a - 1}{a + 1} \tag{10-36}$$

which gives

$$a = 7.5 \tag{10-37}$$

(4) The proper location of the two corner frequencies $1/aT$ and $1/T$ is determined as follows:

(a) The attenuation of the phase-lead network is calculated:

$$20 \log a = 20 \log 7.5 = 17.5 \text{ db} \tag{10-38}$$

(b) The new gain crossover must be placed at the frequency at which

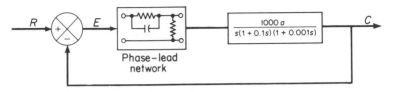

FIG. 10-23. Feedback control system with phase-lead compensation.

the magnitude of $G_1(j\omega)$ is equal to one half of the negative value in decibels of this attenuation; i.e.,

$$|G_1(j\omega)| = -17.5/2 = -8.75 \text{ db} \qquad (10\text{--}39)$$

From the Bode plot constructed in Fig. 10-24, ω_m is 164.5 rad/sec; from which we obtain

$$1/aT = 60 \text{ rad/sec} \qquad (10\text{--}40)$$

Hence

$$1/T = 60a = 450 \text{ rad/sec} \qquad (10\text{--}41)$$

The new gain-crossover frequency is at

$$\omega_c' = \omega_m = 164.5 \text{ rad/sec} \qquad (10\text{--}42)$$

Hence, the transfer function of the phase-lead network is

$$\frac{E_2(s)}{E_1(s)} = \frac{1}{a}\frac{1 + aTs}{1 + Ts} = \frac{1}{7.5}\frac{1 + 0.0167s}{1 + 0.00222s} \qquad (10\text{--}43)$$

and the open-loop transfer function of the compensated system is

$$G(s) = \frac{1000(1 + 0.0167s)}{s(1 + 0.00222s)(1 + 0.1s)(1 + 0.001s)} \qquad (10\text{--}44)$$

A check of the Bode plot of the compensated system finds that the phase margin of the system is close to 45 deg, which is the desired value. The magnitude versus phase shift plot on the Nichols chart (Fig. 10-25) shows that the resonant peak M_p of the compensated system is 3.3 db or 1.46 in magnitude. The bandwidth of the system, however, is increased from 150 rad/sec to 300 rad/sec.

The Nichols chart is used as an aid to the construction of the root locus diagram of the compensated system (Fig. 10-26). The loci of the complex roots of the original system intersect the imaginary axis at $\omega = \pm 100$ rad/sec ($K = 1010$); these intersections correspond to the point at which the magnitude versus phase shift curve passes through the -180 deg axis on the Nichols chart. For the compensated system, the magnitude versus phase shift curve intersects the -180 deg axis at $\omega = 612$ rad/sec and the corresponding magnitude is -17.25 db, which means that, for $K = 1000$, the gain margin is 17.25 db. By using Eq. (9–32) the marginal gain of stability (gain limit) of the compensated system is

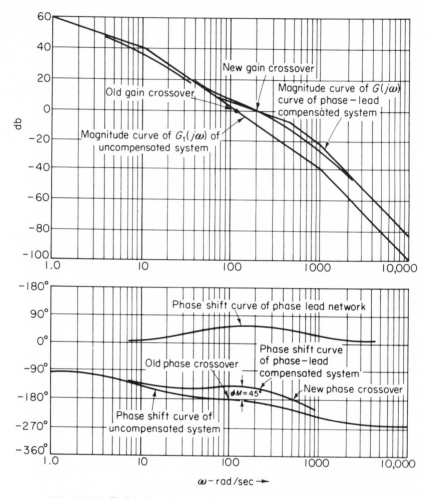

FIG. 10-24. Bode plots of control system given in Example 10–2.

$$G_{\text{lim}} = 17.25 + 60 = 77.25 \text{ db} \qquad (10\text{–}45)$$

or

$$|G_{\text{lim}}| = 7320 \qquad (10\text{–}46)$$

which is the value of K where the two complex loci cross the $j\omega$ axis. The frequency at this point is 612 rad/sec.

The Effect and Limitations of the Phase-lead Compensation

From the results obtained in the last two examples, we may summarize the general effect of the phase-lead compensation on the performance of servo systems as follows:

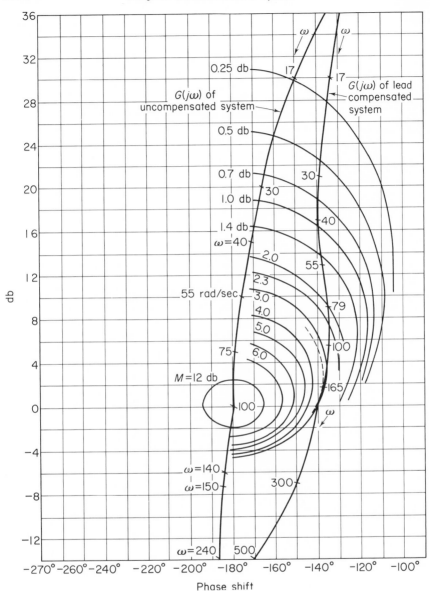

FIG. 10-25. Magnitude versus phase shift plot of $G(s)$ for Example 10–2.

Frequency Response

(1) The phase shift in the vicinity of the resonant frequency is increased in the positive direction.

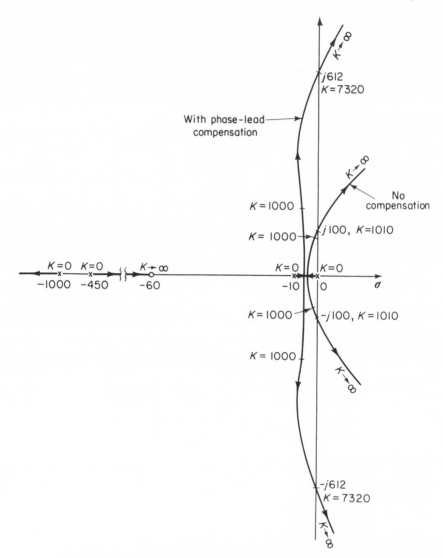

FIG. 10-26. Root locus diagrams of system given in Example 10–2.

(2) For a given relative stability, the velocity constant usually is increased.

(3) For a given gain constant K, the slope of the magnitude curve on the Bode plot is reduced at the gain crossover; thus, the relative stability of the system is usually improved. That is, the phase margin is increased and the resonance peak M_p is reduced.

(4) The bandwidth is usually increased.

Time Response

(1) The overshoot is reduced.

(2) The rise time is faster.

However, it was mentioned previously that satisfactory compensation cannot always be accomplished by means of the phase-lead network. The examples given here represent two of the few types of systems on which the phase-lead compensation is effective and practical. The successful application of the phase-lead compensation is limited by the following considerations:

(1) Bandwidth considerations: For unstable systems, the additional phase lead necessary to obtain a certain specified phase margin is large. This requires a large value for a; the bandwidth of the compensated system is large accordingly, and the transmission of noise may become objectionable. In practice, the value of a is seldom chosen greater than 15; sometimes two or more cascaded lead compensators are used to achieve large phase leads.

(2) For systems with low or negative damping ratios, if the phase shift decreases rapidly near the gain crossover, phase lead compensation becomes ineffective because the additional phase lead at the new gain crossover is added to a much smaller phase angle than that at the old gain crossover. The desired phase margin may be realized only by using a very large value for a. The property of this rapid change in phase in general may be attributed to systems with the following characteristics:

(a) Two simple negative corners placed close to each other near the gain-crossover frequency ω_c.

(b) A simple double corner $1/(1 + Ts)^2$ placed near the gain-crossover frequency ω_c.

(c) A complex corner $\omega_n^2/(s^2 + 2\delta\omega_n s + \omega_n^2)$ placed near the gain-crossover frequency ω_c.

Example 10-3. Let

$$G_1(s) = \frac{K}{s(1 + 0.2s)(1 + 0.1s)} \tag{10-47}$$

be the uncompensated open-loop transfer function of a feedback control system. The frequency domain specifications are as follows:

(1) $K_v = 10$.

(2) Phase margin ≥ 40 deg.

Figure (10-27) gives the Bode plot of $G_1(s)$ when K is set equal to 10. The phase margin at this gain is approximately -3 deg and the system is unstable. (The marginal value of K for stability is 7.) The rapid change in phase at the gain-crossover frequency ($\omega_c = 7$ rad/sec) indicates that the phase-lead compensation is ineffective. To illustrate the point, phase-lead

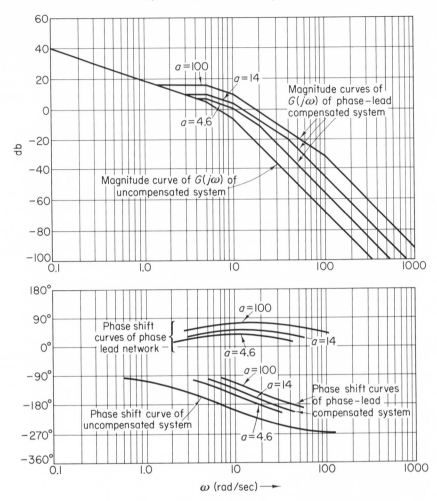

FIG. 10-27. Bode plots of control system given in Example 10–3.

networks with $a = 4.6$, 14, and 100 are used to compensate the system. The results are tabulated in Table 10-1. It is seen from these results that a phase margin of 40 deg can only be realized by an a greater than 100. The corresponding bandwidth may not be too excessive, but the value of a is certainly too large. The desired specifications can be achieved for this system if one of the three following courses is followed:

(1) Use two cascaded lead compensators.

(2) Use a lag compensating network.

(3) Use auxiliary feedback loop, such as a rate feedback.

Table 10-1

a	$1/aT$	$1/T$	ϕ_m	ω_m	Gain crossover ω_c	Bandwidth	Phase margin
4.6	4.78	22	40°	10.3	10.3	16 rad/sec	19°
14	3.2	44.8	60°	12	12	19 rad/sec	28°
100	1.7	170	78.8°	17	17	27 rad/sec	38°

Phase-lead Compensation by Root Locus Method

The phase-lead compensation can also be effected in the s-plane; specifically, the root contour method described previously will be shown as a convenient tool in the design of feedback control systems. Consider the system given in Example 10-1. The open-loop transfer function of the compensated system is of the form

$$G(s) = \frac{10(1 + saT)}{s(1 + s)(1 + sT)} \tag{10-48}$$

where the values of T and a are to be determined.

The root contours of the compensated system (T and a are the variable parameters) are constructed as follows:

(1) For the uncompensated system, the characteristic equation is

$$s^2 + s + 10 = 0 \tag{10-49}$$

and the roots are at $s_{1,2} = -0.5 \pm j3.12$.

(2) Consider that the system is compensated by the lag factor $1/(1 + sT)$; in other words, $a = 0$ for the phase-lead network. The characteristic equation of the partially compensated system is

$$s(s + 1)(1 + sT) + 10 = 0 \tag{10-50}$$

which can be written as

$$1 + G_1 H_1 = 1 + \frac{Ts^2(s + 1)}{s^2 + s + 10} \tag{10-51}$$

The root contours represented by the last equation with T as the varying parameter are constructed in Fig. 10-28. These contours begin at the poles of $G_1 H_1$ and end at the zeros of $G_1 H_1$. As the value of T is increased, the two roots of the characteristic equation move into the right half of the s-plane. The closed-loop system is unstable for all values of T greater than 0.111.

(3) The system is compensated by the phase-lead network ($a \neq 0$, $T \neq 0$). In this case, T is kept constant while a is considered a variable parameter. The characteristic equation of the compensated system is

$$s(s + 1)(1 + sT) + 10(1 + saT) = 0 \tag{10-52}$$

which can be written as

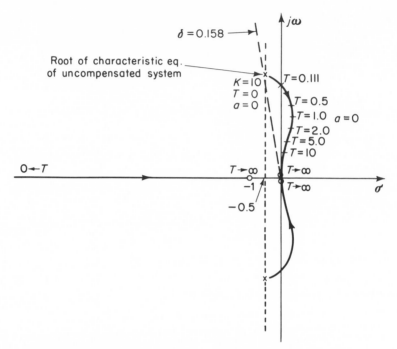

FIG. 10-28. Root contours of the control system given in Example
10–1 when $a = 0$, but T is the varying parameter ($K = 10$).

$$1 + G_2 H_2 = 1 + \frac{10aTs}{s(1 + sT)(1 + s) + 10} \qquad (10\text{–}53)$$

Thus, when a varies, the root contours start at the poles of $G_2 H_2$, which
are the points on the root contours of $1 + G_1 H_1$ shown in Fig. 10-28 and
end at the zero of $G_2 H_2$ ($s = 0$). The root contours of the phase-lead compensated system are shown in Fig. 10-29. From these root contours, we can
see that for effective phase-lead compensation, the value of T must be small.
For large values of T, the bandwidth of the system increases very rapidly
as a is increased, while very little improvement is made on the damping
ratio. On the other hand, T cannnot be too small, for in trying to realize
the complex roots with a prescribed damping ratio, the real root on the
negative real axis will be very close to the origin.

As a second example, let us consider the control system given in Example
10-2. The open-loop transfer function of the phase-lead compensated system
is

$$G(s) = \frac{1000(1 + saT)}{s(1 + 0.1s)(1 + 0.001s)(1 + sT)} \qquad (10\text{–}54)$$

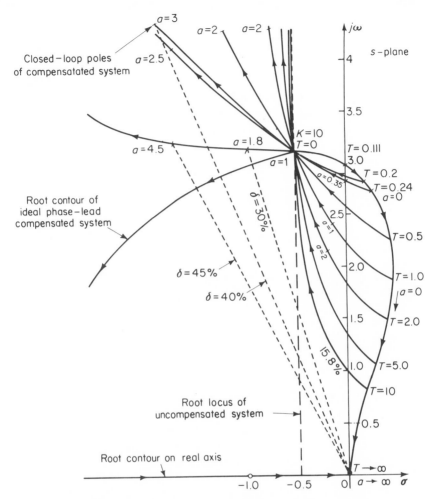

FIG. 10-29. Root contours of system given in Example 10–1 with phase lead compensation $G_c(s) = \dfrac{1 + saT}{1 + sT}$.

The root contours of the compensated system are obtained in the same way as that described previously.

(1) The roots of the characteristic equation of the uncompensated system are shown in Fig. 10-30.

(2) When $a = 0$, but T is the varying parameter,

$$1 + G_1 H_1 = 1 + \frac{Ts^2(1 + 0.1s)(1 + 0.001s)}{s(1 + 0.1s)(1 + 0.001s) + 1000} \tag{10–55}$$

and the root contours of which are sketched in Fig. 10-31.

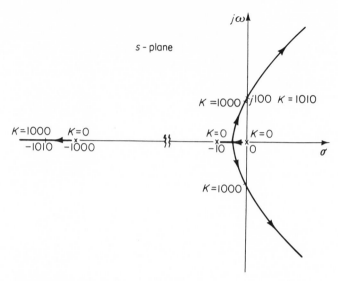

FIG. 10-30. Root loci of uncompensated system in Example 10–2 ($K = 10$).

(3) When a varies from 0 to ∞, it can readily be shown that the root contours of the compensated system are described by

$$1 + G_2 H_2 = 1 + \frac{1000 T a s}{s(1 + 0.1s)(1 + 0.001s)(1 + sT) + 1000} \qquad (10\text{–}56)$$

and are sketched in Fig. 10-32 for various values of T.

From the root contours shown in Fig. 10-32, it is seen that the value of T should not be too large, or the phase-lead compensation becomes ineffective. Since the two contours near the $j\omega$ axis bend into the right half of the plane, there is an upper bound for the value of a above which the compensated system will become unstable. It is clear that for large values of T, not only are the root contours very close to the $j\omega$ axis (low damping), but the stable range of a is also very small. On the other hand, the value of T should not be too small, for, although a more stable system is possible, the value of a is necessarily large and the bandwidth is increased accordingly. Furthermore, if a is large, the real zero along the real axis will move toward the origin and the oscillation of the response will be damped out more slowly.

The root contours can also be used to explain the cases for which the phase-lead compensation is entirely ineffective. For instance, consider the transfer function

$$G(s) = \frac{10(1 + sTa)}{s(1 + 0.2s)(1 + 0.5s)(1 + sT)} \qquad (10\text{–}57)$$

We shall construct the root contour diagrams of the system to show

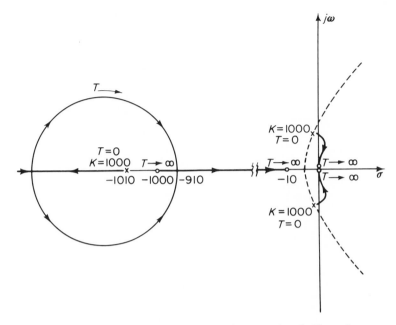

FIG. 10-31. Root contours of the control system given in Example 10–2 when $a = 0$, but T is the varying parameter.

that the phase-lead compensation is ineffective in improving the perform-ance of this system.

(1) For the uncompensated system, the roots of the characteristic equation are shown in Fig. 10-33 for $K = 10$. The two complex roots are in the right half of the plane and the system is unstable.

(2) When $a = 0$, but T varies from 0 to ∞, the root contours of the compensated system are described by

$$1 + G_1 H_1 = 1 + \frac{Ts^2(1 + 0.2s)(1 + 0.5s)}{s(1 + 0.2s)(1 + 0.5s) + 10} \qquad (10\text{--}58)$$

The root contours are sketched in Fig. 10-34.

(3) When the value of a is varied from 0 to ∞, the root contours of the compensated system are described by

$$1 + G_2 H_2 = 1 + \frac{10Tas}{s(1 + 0.2s)(1 + 0.5s)(1 + Ts)} \qquad (10\text{--}59)$$

The root contours are sketched in Fig. 10-35.

From the root contours shown in Fig. 9-35, it is easy to see that the value of T should be kept small. Large values of T do not make the system stable. However, as T decreases, the root contours move very slowly into the left half of the s-plane, and then bend back into the right half of the

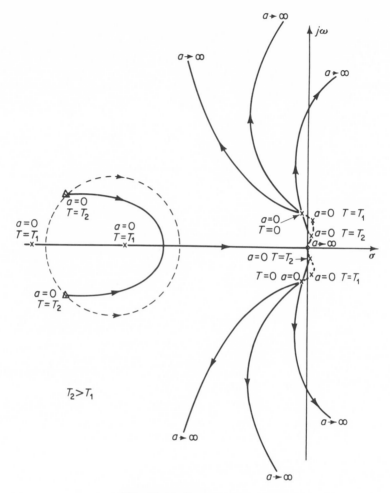

FIG. 10-32. Root contours of

$$G(s) = \frac{10(1 + saT)}{s(1 + 0.1s)(1 + 0.0001s)(1 + Ts)} \quad \text{(Example 10–2).}$$

plane. The bandwidth of the system increases very rapidly with the increase in the value of a. All these observed phenomena are due to the fact that the two poles of G_2H_2 are close to the $j\omega$ axis; the poles have the effect of pushing the root contours toward the right half of the s-plane.

Similarly, the root contour diagram can be used to show why the phase-lead network is not recommended to compensate systems with complex open-loop poles. Consider a feedback control system with the open-loop transfer function

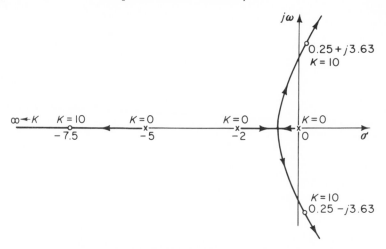

FIG. 10-33. Root loci of uncompensated system,

$$G(s) = \frac{K}{s(1 + 0.2s)(1 + 0.3s)}.$$

$$G_1(s) = \frac{K}{s(s^2 + 2\delta\omega_n s + \omega_n^2)} \qquad (10\text{--}60)$$

and $\delta < 1$.

The root loci of the system are shown in Fig. 10-36.

The transfer function of the phase-lead compensated system is

$$G(s) = G_c(s)G_1(s) = \frac{K(1 + sTa)}{s(1 + sT)(s^2 + 2\delta\omega_n s + \omega_n^2)} \qquad (10\text{--}61)$$

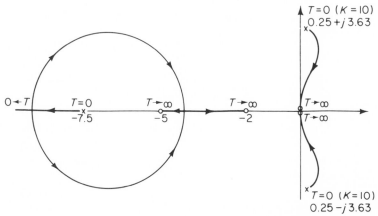

FIG. 10-34. Root contours of $1 + G_1H_1 = 1 + \dfrac{Ts^2(1 + 0.2s)(1 + 0.5s)}{s(1 + 0.2s)(1 + 0.5s) + 10}$.

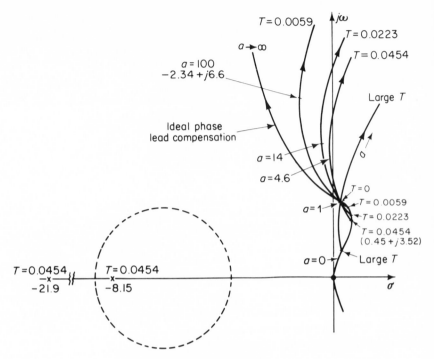

FIG. 10-35. Root contours of

$$1 + G_2H_2 = 1 + \frac{10Tas}{s\,(1+0.2s)\,(1+0.5s)\,(1+Ts)}.$$

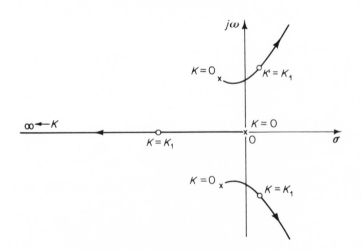

FIG. 10-36. Root loci of system with

$$G_1(s) = \frac{K}{s(s^2 + 2\delta\omega_n s + \omega_n^2)}.$$

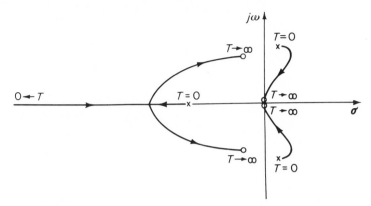

FIG. 10-37. Root contour of system represented by Eq. (10-61) with $a = 0$, but T is a varying parameter.

For any fixed K, and for $a = 0$, the root contours of the partially compensated system are sketched in Fig. 10-37. It is apparent that for small values of T, the system can be stabilized only at the expense of large a and large bandwidth. When the value of T is large, the roots on the two contours of the left half of the plane move toward the $j\omega$ axis and push the compensated contours toward the right half of the plane (Fig. 10-38).

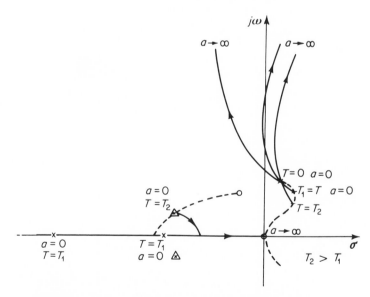

FIG. 10-38. Root contours of system represented by Eq. (10-61). The contours indicate that the phase-lead network is ineffective to compensate systems with complex open-loop poles.

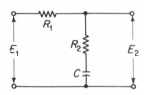

FIG. 10-39. Passive phase-lag network.

(II) *Phase-lag Compensation*

Figure 10-39 shows a simple R-C network, which is often used for the phase-lag compensation of feedback control systems. If we assume that the input impedance of the network is zero and that the output impedance which the network sees is infinite, the transfer function of the lag network is

$$\frac{E_2(s)}{E_1(s)} = \frac{1 + R_2 C s}{1 + (R_1 + R_2) C s} \tag{10-62}$$

Let

$$aT = R_2 C \tag{10-63}$$

and

$$a = R_2/(R_1 + R_2) \qquad (a < 1) \tag{10-64}$$

Equation (10–62) becomes

$$\frac{E_2(s)}{E_1(s)} = \frac{1 + aTs}{1 + Ts} \tag{10-65}$$

Characteristics of the R-C Passive Phase-lag Network

(1) *Pole-zero Configuration*

The transfer function of the phase-lag network has a real zero at $s = -1/aT$ and a real pole at $s = -1/T$, as shown in Fig. 10-40. Since a is less than unity, the pole is always located to the right of the zero, and the distance between them is determined by a.

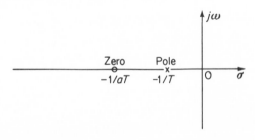

FIG. 10-40. Pole-zero configuration of $(1 + aTs)/(1 + Ts)$.

(2) *Polar Plot of the R-C Phase-lag Network*

The polar plot of the transfer function represented by Eq. (10–65) is given in Fig. 10-41 for three different values of a. Just as in the case of the phase-lead network, for any given a, the angle between the tangent line drawn from the origin to the semicircle and the real axis gives the maximum

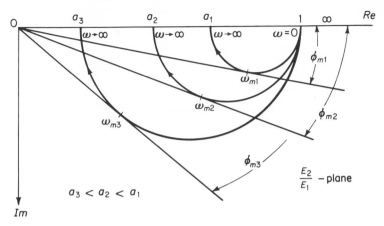

FIG. 10-41. Polar plot of $\dfrac{E_2}{E_1} = \dfrac{1 + aTs}{1 + Ts}$ $(a < 1)$.

phase lag ϕ_m obtainable from the network. As a is decreased, the maximum phase lag ϕ_m increases, approaching the limit of -90 deg as a approaches infinity. The frequency ω_m decreases with the increase in a.

(3) *The Bode Plot of the Phase-lag Network*

The Bode plot of the phase-lag network has two corner frequencies—a positive corner at $\omega = 1/aT$, and a negative corner at $\omega = 1/T$. These is no attenuation at zero frequency.

Since the transfer functions of the phase-lead and phase-lag networks are identical in form except for the value of the constant factor a, the maximum phase lag of the lag network can readily be shown to be

$$\sin \phi_m = \frac{a - 1}{a + 1} \tag{10–66}$$

The design of the phase-lag compensation of feedback control systems, however, does not rely on this maximum phase shift; rather, it utilizes the attenuation of the lag network at high frequencies. It has been pointed out that, for the phase-lead compensation, the function of the lead network is to increase the phase shift of the system at the vicinity of the gain-crossover frequency while the magnitude curve of the Bode plot is kept relatively unchanged. But usually the gain-crossover frequency on the magnitude curve is moved to a higher value as a consequence of the phase-lead network. The design of the lead compensation is, essentially, to find a compromise between the increase in bandwidth and the desired amount of relative stability (phase margin). In the phase-lag compensation, the phase-lag network is used to move the gain crossover to a lower frequency while keeping the phase shift curve of the Bode plot relatively unchanged at the crossover frequency.

Design of Phase-lag Compensation by Bode Plot Method

Just as in the case of the phase-lead compensation, the Bode plot is a very convenient tool in the design of the phase-lag compensation in the frequency domain. The design procedure may be outlined as follows:

(1) The Bode plot of the magnitude and phase shift of the open-loop transfer function $G_1(s)$ versus frequency is plotted; $G_1(s)$ is the transfer function of the uncompensated system. The gain constant K is set according to the steady-state error requirement.

(2) The phase margin and the gain margin of the original system are obtained from the Bode plot. For a certain specified phase margin, the frequency corresponding to this phase margin is found on the Bode plot; the magnitude curve must pass through the zero decibel axis at this frequency in order to realize the desired phase margin. In other words, the gain crossover of the compensated system must be located at the frequency at which the specified phase margin is found.

(3) To bring the magnitude curve down to 0 db at the new prescribed gain-crossover frequency ω_c', the phase-lag network must provide the amount of attenuation equal to the gain $|G_1(j\omega)|$ at the new gain crossover. Or

$$|G_1(j\omega_c')| = -20 \log a \text{ db} \qquad (10\text{--}67)$$

from which

$$a = 10^{-|G_1(j\omega_c')|/20} \qquad (a < 1) \qquad (10\text{--}68)$$

(4) a having been determined (Eq. 10–68), it is necessary only to select the proper value for T to complete the design. Up to this step, we have assumed that although the gain-crossover frequency is moved by attenuating the gain at ω_c, the original phase shift curve is not affected. This is not

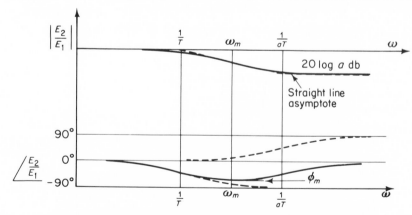

FIG. 10-42. Bode plot of the phase lag network $\dfrac{E_2}{E_1} = \dfrac{1 + aTs}{1 + Ts}$

possible, however, since any modification of the magnitude curve will bring corresponding change to the phase shift curve, and vice versa. With reference to the phase characteristics of the phase-lag network given in Fig. 10-42 it is apparent that, if the upper corner frequency $1/aT$ of the network is placed far below the new gain-crossover frequency ω_c', the phase shift at ω_c' of $G_1(s)$ will not be appreciably affected by the lag network. Usually the upper corner frequency $1/aT$ is placed at a frequency about one decade below the new gain crossover; i.e.,

$$\frac{1}{aT} = \frac{\omega_c'}{10} \text{rad/sec} \qquad (10\text{--}69)$$

from which

$$\frac{1}{T} = \frac{\omega_c'}{10} a \text{ rad/sec} \qquad (10\text{--}70)$$

(5) The Bode plot of the compensated system is investigated to see if the performance specifications are met.

(6) If all the specifications are satisfied, the values of a and T may be substituted into Eq. (10–65) and the transfer function of the phase-lag network is obtained.

Example 10-4. Consider the system given in Example 10-3 for which the phase-lead compensation is ineffective. The transfer function of the uncompensated system is (Fig. 10-43)

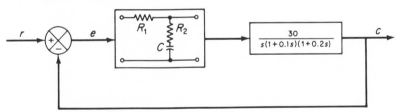

FIG. 10-43. Feedback control system with phase-lag compensation (Example 10-4).

$$G_1(s) = \frac{K}{s(1 + 0.1s)(1 + 0.2s)} \qquad (10\text{--}71)$$

The specifications are as follows:

(1) $K_v = 30 \text{ sec}^{-1}$.

(2) Phase margin ≥ 40 deg.

If it is decided that the phase-lag compensation is to be used, the design procedure is as follows:

(1) The Bode plot of $G_1(s)$ is plotted in Fig. 10-44 for $K = 30$.

(2) The phase margin read at the gain-crossover frequency ($\omega_c = 11$ rad/sec) is -25 deg, and the system is unstable. The required phase margin is 40 deg, which can be obtained if the gain-crossover frequency is moved

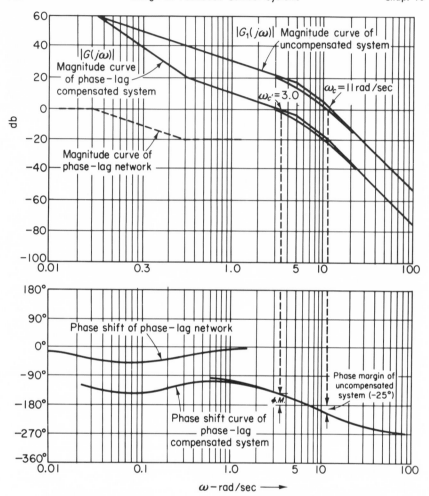

FIG. 10-44. Bode plots of open-loop transfer functions of system given in Example 10–4.

to about 3.3 rad/sec. This means that the phase-lag network must reduce the magnitude of $G_1(j\omega)$ to zero decibels, while it does not appreciably affect the phase shift curve in the vicinity of this new gain-crossover frequency. Since actually a small negative phase shift is still introduced by the lag network at ω_c', it is a safe measure to choose the new gain-crossover at a frequency somewhat less than 3.3 rad/sec; 3.0 rad/sec,* for example.

(3) From the magnitude curve, the gain of $G_1(j\omega)$ at $\omega_c' = 3$ rad/sec is

*In other words, it is the same as selecting a safer phase margin of 45 deg.

20 db, which means that the lag network must provide 20 db of attenuation at this frequency. Hence, from Eq. (10–68),

$$a = 10^{-|G_1(j\omega_c')|/20} = 10^{-1} = 0.1 \qquad (10\text{–}72)$$

The last equation implies that the two corners of the lag network must be placed at a distance of one decade apart in order to produce the required attenuation of 20 db.

(4) The upper corner frequency of the network, $1/aT$, is placed at the frequency one decade below the new gain-crossover frequency. Thus,

$$\frac{1}{aT} = \frac{\omega_c'}{10} = \frac{3}{10} = 0.3 \text{ rad/sec} \qquad (10\text{–}73)$$

which gives

$$T = 33.3 \text{ sec} \qquad (10\text{–}74)$$

The lower corner frequency is

$$1/T = 0.03 \qquad (10\text{–}75)$$

(5) The Bode plot of the compensated system is plotted in Fig. 10-44. It is seen that the phase margin of the compensated system is approximately 40 deg.

(6) The transfer function of the phase-lag network is

$$\frac{E_2(s)}{E_1(s)} = \frac{1 + saT}{1 + sT} = \frac{1 + 3.33s}{1 + 33.3s} \qquad (10\text{–}76)$$

and the open-loop transfer function of the compensated system is

$$G(s) = G_c(s)G_1(s) = \frac{30(1 + 3.33s)}{s(1 + 0.1s)(1 + 0.2s)(1 + 33.3s)} \qquad (10\text{–}77)$$

The magnitude versus phase shift curve of the compensated system is plotted on the Nichols chart, as shown in Fig. 10-45. It is seen that the resonant peak M_p is approximately 3 db, or a magnitude of 1.41. The bandwidth of the system is reduced from 15 rad/sec to 5.5 rad/sec.

The root locus diagrams of the system with and without the phase-lag compensation are sketched in Fig. 10-46. It is important to note that the shape of the original root loci is hardly affected by the phase-lag compensating dipole at all. However, the critical value of K for stability is increased by a factor of 10, which is the distance between the compensating pole and zero on the Bode plot; that is, $a^{-1} = 10$. The uncompensated system becomes unstable for all values of K greater than 15, whereas the phase-lag compensated system will be unstable only when K is greater than 150. The compensated and the uncompensated loci cross the imaginary axis of the s-plane at approximately the same point ($\omega = 7.07$ rad/sec), since it is clear from the Bode plot in Fig. 10-44 that the phase crossover is not much affected by the phase-lag characteristic.

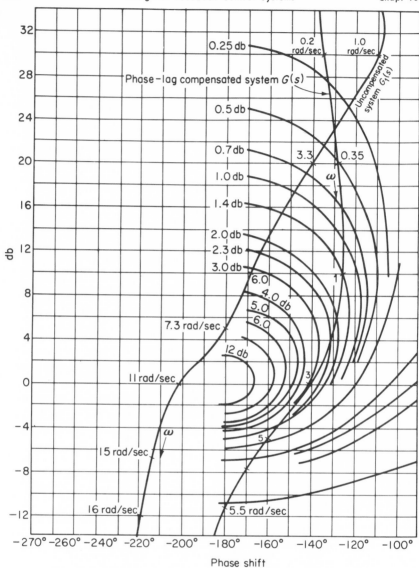

FIG. 10-45. Magnitude (db) versus phase shift of open-loop transfer function given in Example 10-4.

When K is equal to 30, the roots of the characteristic equation of the compensated system are at -11.9, -0.34, and $-1.38 \pm j3.1$. The closed-loop transfer function of the compensated system can be written as

$$\frac{C(s)}{R(s)} = \frac{150(s + 0.3)}{(s + 0.34)(s + 11.9)(s + 1.38 - j3.1)(s + 1.38 + j3.1)} \quad (10\text{--}78)$$

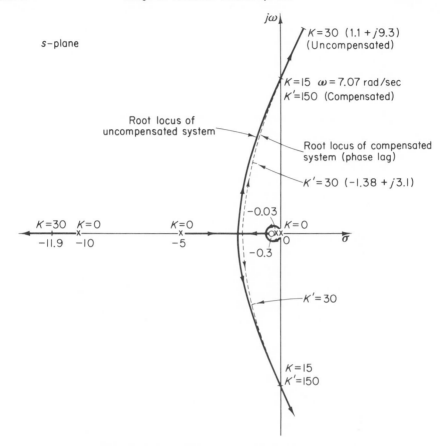

FIG. 10-46. Root locus diagrams for system in Example 10–4. Uncompensated system:
$$G_1(s) = K/s(1 + 0.1s)(1 + 0.2s)$$
Phase-lag compensated system:
$$G(s) = K(1 + 3.33s)/s(1 + 0.1s)(1 + 0.2s)(1 + 33.3s)$$

Its pole-zero configuration is shown in Fig. 10-47. It can readily be shown
that, since the real zero at -0.3 and the real pole at -0.34 are very close
together, they do not affect the transient response appreciably. Thus, the
time response of the compensated system may be approximated by the
three closed-loop poles at $s = -11.9$ and $s = -1.38 \pm j3.1$.

The Effect of the Phase-lag Compensation

From the results of the last example, the effect of the phase-lag compensation on servo system performance may be summarized as follows:
Frequency Response

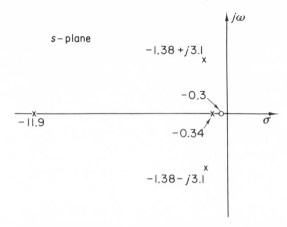

FIG. 10-47. Closed-loop poles and zeros of phase-lag compensated system in Example 10–4 ($K = 30$).

(1) For a given relative stability, the velocity constant is increased.

(2) The gain-crossover frequency is decreased; thus, the bandwidth of the system is reduced.

(3) For a given gain K, the magnitude curve of $G_1(s)$ is attenuated at the low frequencies, thus allowing the improvement of the phase margin and resonance peak of the system.

(4) The time response usually is slower with the lag compensation since the natural undamped frequency ω_m and the bandwidth are decreased.

Phase-lag Compensation by Root Locus Method

Since the transfer functions of the phase-lead and the phase-lag networks are of the same form, for the same uncompensated system, the root contour diagram may be used for either type of compensation. For the phase-lead network, the portions of the root contours corresponding to $a > 1$ are used, and those for $a < 1$ are used for the phase-lag design. To clarify this point, let us consider the second-order control system given in Example 9-1. The open-loop transfer function of the compensated system is

$$G(s) = \frac{10(1 + saT)}{s(s + 1)(1 + sT)} \tag{10–79}$$

where, if $a < 1$, the compensation is of the phase-lag type, and if $a > 1$, the compensation is of the phase-lead type. The root contour diagram of the compensated system when a and T are variable parameters was given in Fig. 10-29. From this root contour diagram, the significance of the difference between phase-lead and phase-lag compensation in terms of the root locations is evident. Figure 10-48 shows the two regions in which the roots of the characteristic equation are found corresponding to $a < 1$ (phase-lag)

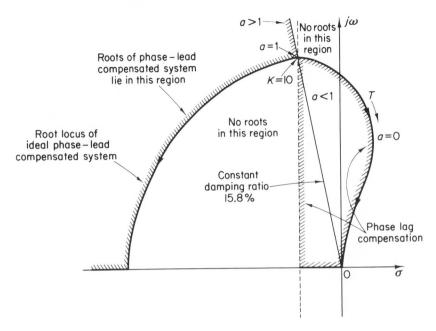

FIG. 10-48. Regions in the s-plane indicating the locations of the characteristic equation roots of phase-lag and phase-lead compensations (Example 10–1).

and $a > 1$ (phase-lead), respectively. The straight line drawn from the origin through the $a = 1$ point represents the constant damping of 15.8 per cent, which is the damping ratio of the original uncompensated system. If the complex roots of the compensated system are to have a higher damping ratio, they must be located to the left of the $\delta = 15.8$ per cent line. From Fig. 10-48, the following facts concerning the phase-lead and phase-lag design are obtained:

(1) Improper phase-lag design may make the system less stable or even unstable. For this particular system, the value of T should be greater than 5 if the damping of the system is to be improved.

(2) Improper phase-lead compensation may also cause the system to be less stable than the original system, although it will not cause the system to become unstable.

(3) Since the distance from the complex roots to the origin in the s-plane indicates the bandwidth of the system, the effects of the lag and lead compensations on the bandwidth are apparent.

The servo system given in Example 10-4 serves a better purpose in the illustration of the phase-lag compensation by the root contour technique. The open-loop transfer function of the compensated system is

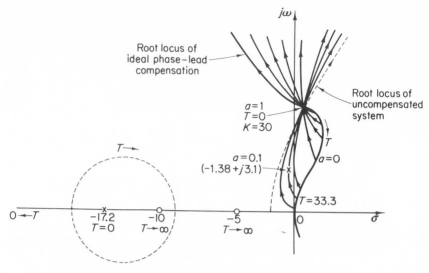

FIG. 10-49. Root contours of
$$G(s) = \frac{30(1 + saT)}{s(1 + 0.1s)(1 + 0.2s)(1 + sT)}$$
(Only the two dominant root contours are shown in the diagram.)

$$G(s) = \frac{30(1 + saT)}{s(1 + 0.1s)(1 + 0.2s)(1 + sT)} \qquad (10\text{–}80)$$

where the compensation is of the phase-lag type if $a < 1$, and is of the phase-lead type if $a > 1$. The root contours of the compensated system when a and T are varied from 0 to ∞ are given in Fig. 10-49. The regions of the characteristic equation roots for lead and lag compensations are shown in Fig. 10-50. Since the root contours for $a > 1$ move rapidly upward when a is increased, the lead compensation is apparently ineffective in this case. It is also evident that, for proper phase-lag compensation, the value of T should be large. Small values of T may not even bring the roots back into the left half of the s-plane for any value of $a < 1$. Furthermore, for large values of T, the contours travel into the left half of the s-plane, but they eventually go back to the right half of the s-plane; for each T, there is an optimum value of a which yields a maximum possible damping to the system.

(III) *Lag-lead Compensation*

We have shown in the preceding sections that the phase-lead compensation usually improves the rise time and overshoot but increases the bandwidth of a feedback control system, and that the phase-lag compensation improves the steady-state response or the stability margin, but often results in longer rise time because of reduced bandwidth. Therefore, in regard to

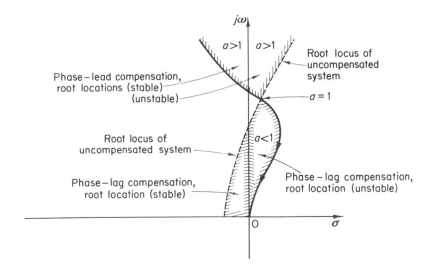

FIG. 10-50. Regions of the characteristic equation roots (dominant roots) for phase-lead and phase-lag compensation of system given in Example 10–4.

the effects of phase-lead and phase-lag compensations, we can say that each has its advantages and disadvantages. However, there are many systems which cannot be satisfactorily improved by the use of either scheme. We have illustrated before that feedback systems with certain characteristics cannot be effectively improved by a phase-lead network alone. Furthermore, more stringent specifications may also make the use of pure phase-lag, as well as pure phase-lead, compensation inadequate.

A more practical and versatile arrangement is, therefore, to use a combination of the lead and lag networks. As a matter of fact, the combination of lead and lag networks, hereafter called the lag-lead compensation, contains all the advantages of both schemes, but some of the undesirable features in each are eliminated in the combined structure.

The transfer function of a lag-lead network can be written as

$$\frac{E_2(s)}{E_1(s)} = \frac{(1 + sT_1a)(1 + sT_2b)}{\underbrace{(1 + sT_1)}_{\text{phase-lead}}\underbrace{(1 + sT_2)}_{\text{phase-lag}}} \qquad (a > 1), (b < 1) \qquad (10\text{–}81)$$

where the attenuation factor $1/a$ is not shown in the equation if we assume that adequate gain is available in the forward path of the system to compensate the loss.

Usually it is not necessary to cascade the lead and lag networks of Figs. 10-12 and 10-39 for the realization of Eq. (10-81). A network which has the lag-lead characteristic, but a lesser number of elements, is depicted in Fig. 10-51. The transfer function of the network shown in Fig. (10-51) is

$$\frac{E_2(s)}{E_1(s)} = \frac{(1 + R_1 C_1 s)(1 + R_2 C_2 s)}{1 + (R_1 C_1 + R_1 C_2 + R_2 C_2)s + R_1 R_2 C_1 C_2 s^2} \tag{10-82}$$

Comparing Eq. (10-81) with Eq. (10-82), we have

$$aT_1 = R_1 C_1 \tag{10-83}$$

$$bT_2 = R_2 C_2 \tag{10-84}$$

$$T_1 T_2 = R_1 R_2 C_1 C_2 \tag{10-85}$$

From Eqs. (10-89) and (10-90), we have

$$abT_1 T_2 = R_1 R_2 C_1 C_2 \tag{10-86}$$

Hence

$$ab = 1 \tag{10-87}$$

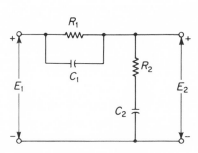

FIG. 10-51. A lag-lead network.

This means that we do not have an independent choice of a and b. Once the value of b is determined, a is equal to the reciprocal of b (or vice versa).

The design of a lag-lead compensation is illustrated by the following example.

Example 10-5. In this example, we shall again consider the system used in Examples 10-3 and 10-4. The open-loop transfer function of the uncompensated system is repeated here as

$$G_1(s) = \frac{K}{s(1 + 0.1s)(1 + 0.2s)} \tag{10-88}$$

The performance specifications are as follows:

(1) $K_v = 30 \sec^{-1}$.

(2) Phase margin ≥ 40 deg.

(3) After transients, the amplitude of the steady-state error due to sinusoidal inputs of three units in amplitude and up to 0.1 rad/sec in frequency must not exceed 0.01 unit.

We see now that, in addition to the K_v and phase margin requirements, a third condition on the steady-state error due to low frequency signals has been added. At very low frequencies, the magnitude of the open-loop transfer function is much greater than unity; hence,

$$\left|\frac{E(j\omega)}{R(j\omega)}\right|_{\omega=0.1} = \left|\frac{1}{1 + G(j\omega)}\right|_{\omega=0.1} = \left|\frac{1}{G(j\omega)}\right|_{\omega=0.1} \tag{10-89}$$

From condition (3), we have

$$\left|\frac{E(j\omega)}{R(j\omega)}\right|_{\omega=0.1} \leq \frac{1}{300} \tag{10-90}$$

Therefore,

$$|G(j\omega)|_{\omega=0.1} \geq 300 \tag{10-91}$$

In other words, the magnitude of $G(j\omega)$ must exceed approximately 50 db at 0.1 rad/sec.

From Fig. 10-44 we see that the magnitude of $G(j\omega)$ of the phase-lag compensated system is equal to 40 db at 0.1 radian per second. We have also demonstrated in Example 10-3 that a phase-lead compensation is ineffective in this case. At this point, a lag-lead compensation seems to be the next choice. No definite procedure can be prescribed for the design of the lag-lead network. Usually a trial-and-error procedure, using the Bode plot, may provide a proper design arrangement.

We shall first determine the lag portion of the compensation by selecting proper values for T_2 and b. As a first trial, we shall move the gain crossover of $G_1(j\omega)$ from 12 rad/sec to 3 rad/sec. This corresponds to improving the phase margin from -25 deg (unstable) to 30 deg (or equivalently improving the gain margin from -10 db to $+10$ db). The lower corner of the lag network, $1/T_2$, is placed at 0.1 rad/sec, where the magnitude of $G_1(j\omega)$ is 50 db, provided that the asymptotic curves are acceptable as the final design. Since the attenuation provided by the lag network at high frequencies is 20 db, b is equal to 0.10 (Eq. 10-68). The upper corner of the lag network must then be placed at 1.0 rad/sec. The transfer function of the lag network is, therefore,

$$\frac{1 + 0.1s}{1 + s} \tag{10-92}$$

The phase-lead portion of the compensation can be effected in much the same way as described in Sec. (1). Since b is equal to 0.10, from Eq. (10-87), a must be 10. This determines the distance between the two corners in the phase-lead network. The zero frequency attenuation of the lead network is

$$20 \log a = 20 \log 10 = 20 \text{ db} \tag{10-93}$$

By the same method described in Eqs. (10-28) through (10-31), we obtain

$$\omega_m = 7 \text{ rad/sec} \tag{10-94}$$

$$1/T_1 = 22 \text{ rad/sec} \tag{10-95}$$

and

$$1/aT_1 = 2.2 \text{ rad/sec} \tag{10-96}$$

The transfer function of the lag-lead network is

$$\frac{E_2(s)}{E_1(s)} = \frac{(1 + 0.1s)(1 + 22s)}{(1 + s)(1 + 2.2s)} \tag{10-97}$$

The Bode plots of the compensated and the uncompensated systems are depicted in Fig. 10-52. From the compensated diagram, it is clear that all

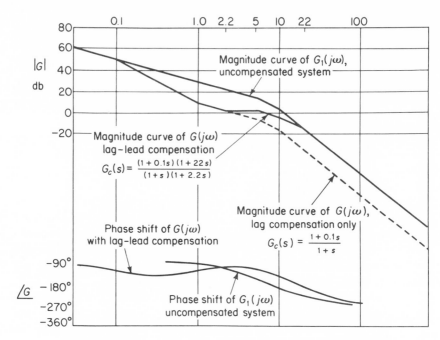

FIG. 10-52. Bode diagram for system in Example 9–5 with lag-lead compensation.

the specified requirements are satisfied. The phase margin of the system is approximately 50 deg. Also, the effects of the lag and lead compensations at the high frequencies cancel each other so that the bandwidth of the system is hardly affected.

(4) *Bridged-T Network Compensation*

Many servo systems possess open-loop transfer functions which contain one or more pairs of complex conjugate poles. It was shown that the simple phase-lead network does not give satisfactory compensation to third- (or higher-) ordered systems with complex open-loop poles, especially if these poles are close to the imaginary axis. We may suggest the use of a compensation transfer function with two zeros and two poles. The zeros are so selected that they will cancel the undesired complex poles of the original system, and the poles are placed at more desirable locations in the s-plane. For instance, if the open-loop transfer function of the uncompensated system is

$$G_1(s) = \frac{K}{s(s^2 + s + 10)} \tag{10–98}$$

the suggested form of the compensation transfer function is

$$G_c(s) = \frac{s^2 + s + 10}{s^2 + 2\delta\omega_n s + \omega_n^2} \tag{10–99}$$

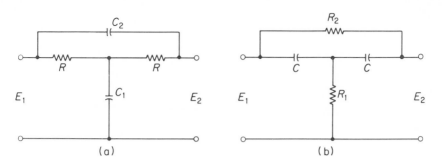

FIG. 10-53. Two basic types of bridged-T network. (a) Type 1 network; (b) Type 2 network.

where the constants δ and ω_n are determined according to the system performance specifications. Although Eq. (10–99) can be realized by various types of passive networks, the bridged-T networks have the advantage of containing only R-C elements. The configurations of the two basic types of bridged-T R-C networks are shown in Fig. 10-53. In the following, the network shown in Fig. 10-53a is referred to as bridged-T type 1, and that shown in Fig. 10-53b is referred to as type 2.

With the assumption of zero input source impedance and infinite output load impedance, the transfer function of the bridged-T type 1 network is found to be

$$\frac{E_2(s)}{E_1(s)} = \frac{1 + 2RC_2s + R^2C_1C_2s^2}{1 + R(C_1 + 2C_2)s + R^2C_1C_2s^2} \qquad (10\text{–}100)$$

and that of the bridged-T type 2 network is

$$\frac{E_2(s)}{E_1(s)} = \frac{1 + 2R_1Cs + C^2R_1R_2s^2}{1 + C(R_1 + 2R_2)s + C^2R_1R_2s^2} \qquad (10\text{–}101)$$

When the last two equations are compared, it is apparent that the two networks have similar characteristics. If R, C_1, and C_2, in Eq. (10–100) are replaced by C, R_2, and R_1, respectively, Eq. (10–100) becomes the transfer function of the type 2 network given by Eq. (10–101).

Root Contours of the Poles and Zeros of E_2/E_1 When the Network Elements Are Varied

It is necessary to find out the behavior of the zeros and poles of the transfer functions given in Eq. (10–100) and Eq. (10–101) when the network parameters are varied. Due to the similarity of the two networks, only the type 1 will be analyzed here.

Equation (10–100) can also be written as

$$\frac{E_2(s)}{E_1(s)} = \frac{s^2 + \dfrac{2}{RC_1}s + \dfrac{1}{R^2 C_1 C_2}}{s^2 + \dfrac{C_1 + 2C_2}{RC_1 C_2}s + \dfrac{1}{R^2 C_1 C_2}} \tag{10-102}$$

If both the numerator and the denominator of the last equation are written in the standard form of a quadratic equation,

$$s^2 + 2\delta\omega_n s + \omega_n^2 = 0 \tag{10-103}$$

We have, for the numerator,

$$\omega_{nz} = \pm\frac{1}{R\sqrt{C_1 C_2}} \tag{10-104}$$

$$\delta_z = \sqrt{\frac{C_2}{C_1}} \tag{10-105}$$

and for the denominator,

$$\omega_{np} = \pm\frac{1}{R\sqrt{C_1 C_2}} \tag{10-106}$$

$$\delta_p = \frac{C_1 + 2C_2}{2\sqrt{C_1 C_2}} = \frac{1 + 2C_2/C_1}{2\sqrt{C_2/C_1}} = \frac{1 + 2\delta_z^2}{2\delta_z} \tag{10-107}$$

By means of the root contour technique, the loci of the zeros and poles of E_2/E_1 given by Eq. (10–102) when C_1, C_2, and R vary individually are given in Fig. 10-54. When R is the varying parameter, the numerator and denominator of Eq. (10–102) contain R in the form of R^2, and the root contour method cannot be applied directly. However, the equations are of the second order, and the roots can be solved easily. It is seen from the zero and pole loci shown in Fig. 10-54 that the two zeros of the bridged-T network type 1 can be either real or complex. For complex zeros, C_2 must be greater than C_1. The poles can be found only on the negative real axis.

The natural undamped frequency and the damping ratio of the type 2 network may be obtained by replacing R, C_1, and C_2 in Eq. (10–104) through Eq. (10–107) by C, R_2 and R_1, respectively. Thus,

$$\omega_{nz} = \pm\frac{1}{C\sqrt{R_2 R_1}} \tag{10-108}$$

$$\delta_z = \sqrt{\frac{R_1}{R_2}} \tag{10-109}$$

$$\omega_{np} = \pm\frac{1}{C\sqrt{R_2 R_1}} \tag{10-110}$$

$$\delta_p = \frac{R_2 + 2R_1}{2\sqrt{R_2 R_1}} \tag{10-111}$$

The loci given in Fig. 10-54 can likewise be used for the type 2 bridged-T network if corresponding symbols are altered.

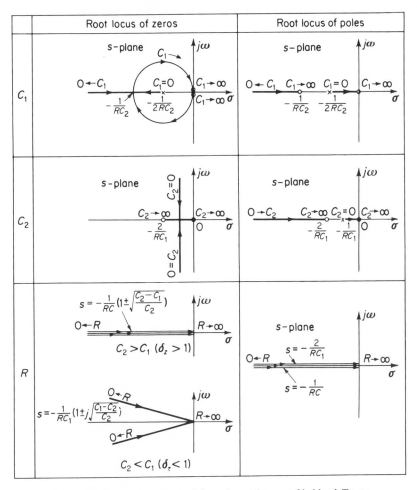

Root locus of zeros	Root locus of poles

FIG. 10-54. Root contours of the poles and zeros of bridged-T type 1 network.

*Example 10-6.** The control system shown in Fig. 10-55 is selected to demonstrate the use of the bridged-T network for servo compensation. The root locus diagram of the uncompensated system is shown in Fig. 10-56.

Evidently, the uncompensated system has a very small damping ratio and the response will be quite oscillatory. The bridged-T network used to compensate this system should possess a pair of complex zeros that will cancel the poles of the original open-loop function. Let us select the type 1 network first; the transfer function is of the form

*This example is taken from Rosenstein Chandaket, "Notes on Bridged-T Complex Conjugate Compensation and Four-terminal Network Loading," *AIEE Transactions, Applications and Industry,* July, 1959.

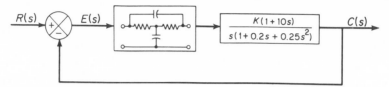

FIG. 10-55. Feedback control system with bridged-T compensation.

$$\frac{E_2(s)}{E_1(s)} = \frac{s^2 + 0.8s + 4}{s^2 + 2\delta_p\omega_{np}s + \omega_{np}^2} \qquad (10\text{--}112)$$

Since

$$\omega_{nz} = \frac{1}{R\sqrt{C_2C_1}} = \sqrt{4} = 2 \qquad (10\text{--}113)$$

and

$$\delta_z = \sqrt{\frac{C_2}{C_1}} = 0.2 \qquad (10\text{--}114)$$

from Eq. (10–110) and Eq. (10–111) we have

$$\omega_{np} = \omega_{nz} = 2 \qquad (10\text{--}115)$$

and

$$\delta_p = \frac{1 + 2\delta_z^2}{2\delta_z} = \frac{1 + 0.08}{0.4} = 2.7 \qquad (10\text{--}116)$$

The transfer function of the bridged-T type 1 network is

$$\frac{E_2(s)}{E_1(s)} = \frac{s^2 + 0.8s + 4}{s^2 + 10.8s + 4} = \frac{s^2 + 0.8s + 4}{s(s + 0.384)(s + 10.42)} \qquad (10\text{--}117)$$

The root locus diagram of the compensated system is shown in Fig. 10-57. It is apparent that the system is much improved by the bridged-T compensation.

Although this analysis is made on the basis of exact cancellation of the unwanted poles, an impossibility in physical systems, the root loci clearly

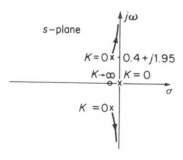

FIG. 10-56. Root loci for system with
$$G_1(s) = \frac{K(1 + 10s)}{s(1 + 0.2s + 0.25s^2)}.$$

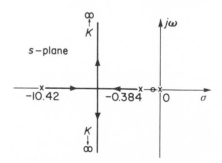

FIG. 10-57. Root loci of bridged-T compensated system (Example 9–6).

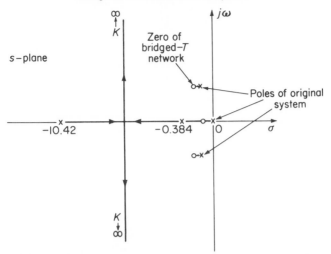

FIG. 10-58. Root loci of compensated system in Example 9–6 when pole-zero concellation is inexact.

show that it is not necessary to cancel the poles of $G_1(s)$ exactly. Figure 10-58 illustrates the root locus diagram with the poles and zeros close together. The system will have essentially the same performance characteristics, because the transient terms due to the closed-loop complex dipole are very small and will not affect the time response significantly.

Feedback Compensation

In general, it is common to introduce compensating networks and elements into the feedback paths of a control system. A typical application of the feedback compensation is a system with tachometer feedback or rate feedback, in which the tachometer is used to feed back a signal proportional to the first derivative of the output variable. In the following example, the root contour technique will be used to design a system with feedback compensation which involves several unknown parameters.

Example 10-7. A multiple-loop system with a tachometer and a phase-lead network in the feedback path is shown in Fig. 10-59.

Normally, the constants T_2, K_1, and K_2 of the system are not given and must be determined to satisfy the given design specifications.

The construction of the root contours and root loci when the above-mentioned three parameters are considered to be the variable parameters is described as follows:

(1) As a first step, the feedback loop with the lead network and the tachometer is opened. In other words, the system is considered first without any compensation. The characteristic equation of the uncompensated system is readily obtained as

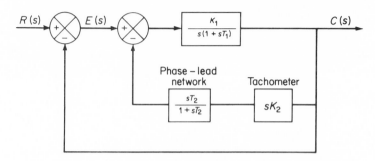

FIG. 10-59. Control system with tachometric and phase-lead feed-back.

$$T_1 s^2 + s + K_1 = 0 \qquad (10\text{--}118)$$

in which the value of T_1 is assumed to be given, but K_1 can be varied from 0 to ∞. The root loci of Eq. (10–118) corresponding to the uncompensated system are given in Fig. 10-60.

Let us assume that the velocity constant K_v of the compensated system is specified to be 20. The open-loop transfer function of the compensated system is

$$\frac{C(s)}{E(s)} = \frac{K_1(1 + sT_2)}{s(1 + sT_1)(1 + sT_2) + K_1 K_2 T_2 s^2} \qquad (10\text{--}119)$$

Thus, to realize $K_v = 20$, K_1 must equal 20. The two roots of Eq. (10–118) when $T_1 = 1$ are found to be at $s = -0.5 + j4.44$ and $s = -0.5 - j4.44$.

(2) The second step is to close the tachometric feedback path, but let $T_2 = 0$. The characteristic equation of the system with only tachometric feedback is

$$s(1 + sT_1) + sK_1 K_2 + K_1 = 0 \qquad (10\text{--}120)$$

or

$$1 + \frac{sK_1 K_2}{s(1 + sT_1) + K_1} \qquad (10\text{--}121)$$

Thus, the root contours when K_2 varies from 0 to ∞ must start at the points on the root loci given in Fig. 10-60, and end at $s = 0$. For $K_1 = 20$ and $T_1 = 1$, the root contours start at $s = -0.5 + j4.44$ and $s = -0.5 - j4.44$. The root contours are sketched in Fig. 10-61.

(3) The last step in the construction of the root contours of the entire system is to consider the phase-lead network together with the tachometer $(T_2 \neq 0)$.

The characteristic equation of the completely compensated system is

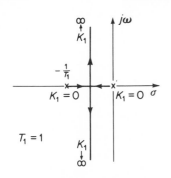

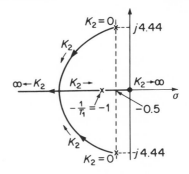

FIG. 10-60. Root loci of the control system shown in Fig. 10–59 with the tachometric feedback loop opened.

FIG. 10-61. Root contours of system shown in Fig. 10–59 with only tachometric feedback $(T_2 = 0, T_1 = 1, K_1 = 20)$.

$$s(1 + sT_1)(1 + sT_2) + K_1K_2T_2s^2 + K_1(1 + sT_2) = 0 \qquad (10\text{--}122)$$

Rearranging, we have

$$[s(1 + sT_1) + K_1] + sT_2 + [s(1 + sT_1) + sK_1K_2 + K_1] = 0 \qquad (10\text{--}123)$$

The last equation can also be written as

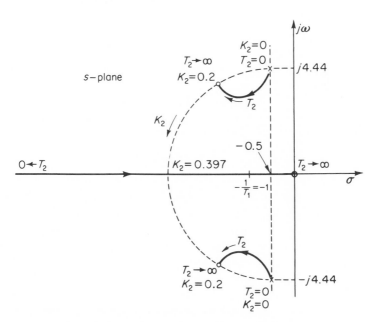

FIG. 10-62. Root contours of phase-lead network and tachometer feedback compensated system given in Example 10–7 $(K_1 = 20, T_1 = 1, K_2 = 0.2)$.

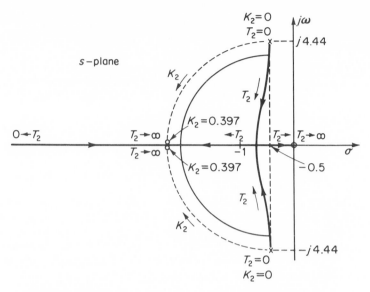

FIG. 10-63. Root contours of phase-lead network and tachometer feedback compensated system given in Example 10–7. ($K_1 = 20$, $T_1 = 1$, $K_2 = 0.397$).

$$1 + \frac{sT_2[s(1 + sT_1) + sK_1K_2 + K_1]}{s(1 + sT_1) + K_1} = 0 \qquad (10\text{–}124)$$

The root contours of Eqs. (10–122) or (10–123), when T_2 is varied from 0 to ∞, must start at the poles and end at the zeros of

$$\frac{sT_2[s(1 + sT_1) + sK_1K_2 + K_1]}{s(1 + sT_1) + K_1} \qquad (10\text{–}125)$$

Note also that one of the zeros of Eq. (10–125) is at $s = 0$ and that the rest of the zeros are the same as the roots of Eq. (10–120); the poles of Eq. (10–125) are the same as the roots of Eq. (10–118). For $T_1 = 1$ and $K_1 = 20$, the roots of Eq. (10–118) are at $s = -0.5 + j4.44$ and $s = -0.5 - j4.44$; thus, the root contours, when T_2 varies, must start at these two points. The root contours of Eq. (10–120), when K_2 varies, are sketched in Fig. 10-61, and the ending points of the root contours when T_2 varies must be found on these contours. For $K_2 = 0.25$ and $K_2 = 0.397$, the root contours when T_2 is varied are shown in Figs. 10-62 and 10-63, respectively.

REFERENCES

1. J. G. Truxal, *Automatic Feedback Control System Synthesis*, Chapter 1, McGraw-Hill Book Company, New York, N. Y., 1955.

2. H. M. James, N. B. Nichols, and R. S. Phillips, *Theory of Servomechanisms*, MIT Radiation Laboratory Series, Vol. **25**, McGraw-Hill Book Company, New York, N. Y., 1947.

3. B. C. Kuo, *Analysis and Synthesis of Sampled-data Control Systems*, Prentice-Hall, Inc., Englewood Cliffs, N. J., 1963.

PROBLEMS

10-1. The open-loop transfer function of a gun-director control system is given by

$$G(s) = \frac{K}{s(1 + 0.2s)(1 + 0.5s)} \qquad H(s) = 1$$

The maximum output velocity of the system is specified as 2 rpm, and the permissible steady-state error in the output position is to be within 2 deg.

(a) Determine the smallest value of K which will satisfy the specification given above. With this value of K, analyze the system performance by evaluating the system gain margin, the phase margin, the resonance peak, and the bandwidth.

(b) A lead compensation with transfer function $(1 + 0.4s)/(1 + 0.08s)$ is now inserted in the forward path of the system. Evaluate the values of the gain margin, the phase margin, M_p, and the bandwidth of the system. Make comments on the effects of the lead compensation on the system performance.

(c) Sketch the root locus diagrams for the compensated and the uncompensated systems.

10-2. A unity-feedback control system has the open-loop transfer function

$$G(s) = \frac{K}{s(1 + 0.1s)(1 + 0.0005s)}$$

The following specifications on system performance are given:

(a) The velocity error constant $K_v \geq 1000$ sec^{-1}.

(b) The phase margin must be at least 45 deg.

Design a series compensating network so that the compensated system will satisfy these specifications. Compare the following quantities of the compensated and the uncompensated systems: gain margin, phase margin, M_p, and bandwidth.

10-3. A simple feedback control system is shown in Fig. 10P-3 in block diagram form. The system must meet the following performance specifications:

(a) Acceleration constant $K_a = 5$ sec^{-2}.

(b) The resonance peak $M_p \leq 1.5$.

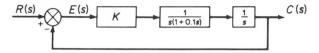

FIG. 10P-3.

Design a series phase-lead compensation to satisfy these requirements. Sketch the root locus diagrams for the uncompensated and the compensated systems. What are the values of the damping ratio and the bandwidth of the compensated system?

10-4. The open-loop transfer function of a unity-feedback control system is

$$G(s) = \frac{8}{s(1 + 0.1s + 0.01s^2)}$$

(a) Determine the stability of the system.

(b) Design a series compensation so that the system has a peak resonance of approximately 1.5. Plot the frequency response curves (M versus ω) for the uncompensated and the compensated systems.

10-5. A voltage regulator has an open-loop transfer function

$$G(s) = \frac{K}{(1 + 0.5s)(1 + 0.25s)} \qquad H(s) = 1$$

The output voltage is to be regulated at $1000\ v \pm 0.5\ v$. Design a series compensating network for the system so that not only is the steady-state requirement met, but also the peak resonance of the system is not greater than 1.5.

10-6. The block diagram in Fig. 10P-6 shows the basic components of a control system before compensation. The system must meet the following specifications:

(a) Velocity constant $K_v = 20\ \text{sec}^{-1}$.

(b) Phase margin ≥ 45 deg.

Design a series compensating network to satisfy these requirements.

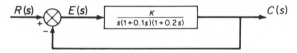

FIG. 10P-6.

10-7. The feedback control system described in Problem 10-4 is to be compensated by inserting a bridge-T network in the forward path. Assuming that perfect cancellation of the undesirable poles of $G(s)$ by the zeros of the network is possible, determine the per cent overshoot of the compensated system. Plot the frequency response curve (M versus ω) for the compensated system.

10-8. Tachometer feedback is employed frequently to permit the stabilization of

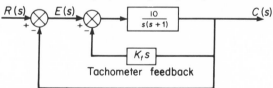

FIG. 10P-8.

servomechanisms. In Fig. 10P-8 is shown a typical application of this type of feedback. Choose the tachometer constant K_t to result in a relative damping ratio of 50 per cent. How does the tachometric feedback affect the bandwidth of the system?

10-9. For the multiple-loop feedback control system of Fig. 10-59 (Example 10-7), given $K_1 = 20$ and $K_2 = 0.2$, determine the value of T_2 so that the relative damping of the closed-loop system is critical.

10-10. The block diagram of a control system is shown in Fig. 10P-10. By means of the root contour method, show the effect of variation in the value of T on the location of the closed-loop poles.

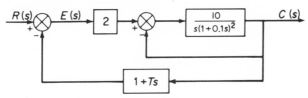

FIG. 10P-10.

10-11. The system described in Problem 10-3 is to be compensated by an inner positional feedback loop, as shown in Fig. 10P-11. The velocity error constant of the system is to be 5 sec^{-1}. Sketch the root contour diagram of the compensated system as a function of K_1. Determine the maximum value of the damping ratio of the complex closed-loop poles obtainable by varying the value of K_1. What is the value of M_p for this value of K_1?

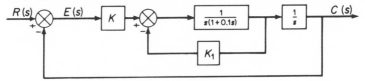

FIG. 10P-11.

10-12. The system described in Problem 10-3 is now to be compensated by a tachometric feedback loop, as shown in Fig. 10P-12. $K_a = 5$ sec^{-2}. Sketch the root contour diagram for the compensated system as a function of K_1. Determine the value of K_1 so that the damping ratio of the complex closed-loop poles is 50 per cent. What are the bandwidth and M_p with this value of K_1?

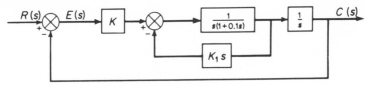

FIG. 10P-12.

11

Introduction
to Optimal Control

11.1 *Introduction*

From the discussions given in the last chapter we realize that the conventional design of feedback control systems has many disadvantages. Two of the most important disadvantages of the design are that the method is not rigorous and that it relies heavily on trial-and-error procedures. In contrast, the optimal control design is aimed at obtaining a system which is the best possible with respect to some performance index or criterion. Two of the more important design criteria used in optimal control are time optimality and optimization with respect to a performance index I which may be a function of the control signal $\mathbf{m}(t)$ and the state variable $\mathbf{x}(t)$. In the design of a time-optimal problem, the design objective is to find a set of control signals $\mathbf{m}(t)$ for $t_0 \leq t < t_f$ which will bring the state $\mathbf{x}(t)$ of the system from the initial state $\mathbf{x}(t_0)$ to the final state $\mathbf{x}(t_f)$ in the shortest possible time. Although it may seem that the statement of the problem involves only the open-loop system configuration shown in Fig. 10-1, in reality, in order to obtain the desired $\mathbf{m}(t)$ to accomplish the stated objective, a controller which depends upon the output signal and/or the state variables of the system must be employed in the form shown in Fig. 10-2, thus forming a closed-loop system. However, since the optimal control theory usually refers to the open-loop configuration of Fig. 10-1, it may give one the misconception that we are working with an open-loop system. The performance index I can assume a variety of forms. In general, it may be written as

$$I = \int_{t_0}^{t_f} f[\mathbf{x}(t), \mathbf{m}(t), t]\, dt \tag{11-1}$$

The optimization problem is to find the desired $\mathbf{m}(t)$ so that I is maximized or minimized with respect to the given process. It is interesting to note that the minimal-time control problem can also be formulated from the performance index viewpoint. If we let

$$I = \int_{t_0}^{t_f} dt = t_f - t_0 \tag{11-2}$$

then minimizing I is equivalent to minimizing $t_f - t_0$.

11.2 Controllability and Observability of Linear Control Systems

The concepts of controllability and observability introduced first by Kalman[1,2] play an important role in both theoretical and practical aspects of modern control theory. The conditions on controllability and observability often govern the existence of a solution to an optimal control problem, particularly in multivariable systems.

General Concepts of Controllability and Observability

The concept of controllability can be stated with reference to the block diagram of Fig. 11-1. The controlled process G is said to be completely controllable if *every* state variable of G can be affected or controlled in finite time by some unconstrained input signal $\mathbf{m}(t)$. Intuitively, we understand that if any one of the state variables is independent of the input signal $\mathbf{m}(t)$, then there is no way of driving this particular state variable to a desired state in finite time by means of some control effort. Therefore, this particular state variable is said to be uncontrollable, and the system is said to be not completely controllable or simply uncontrollable.

The concept of observability is quite similar to that of controllability. Essentially, the process G is completely observable if every state variable of the process eventually affects some of the process's outputs. In other words, it is often desirable to obtain information on the state variables from measurements of the outputs and the inputs. If any one of the states cannot be observed from the measurements of outputs, then the state is said to be unobservable and the system is not completely observable or is simply unobservable.

FIG. 11-1. Block diagram of a controlled process.

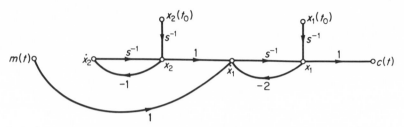

FIG. 11-2. State transition signal flow graph of a controlled process which is not completely controllable.

The descriptions of controllability and observability given above are only general in nature. Before giving the formal definitions of the subjects, let us first consider some simple illustrative examples on the ideas. Figure 11-2 shows the state transition signal flow graph of a certain controlled process or system with two state variables. Since the input $m(t)$ (a single input in this case) affects only the state variable $x_1(t)$, we say that $x_2(t)$ is uncontrollable. In other words, it would be impossible to make $x_2(t)$ change from an initial state $x_2(t_0)$ to a desired state $x_2(t_f)$ in a finite time interval $t_f - t_0$ by means of any input $m(t)$. In this case, $x_2(t)$ depends solely on its initial condition $x_2(t_0)$. Given any $x_2(t_0)$, $x_2(t)$ is simply

$$x_2(t) = e^{-(t-t_0)} x_2(t_0) \tag{11-3}$$

for $t \geq t_0$. Therefore, it takes an infinite amount of time for this transient response of $x_2(t)$ to damp out. Under this circumstance we say that $x_2(t)$ is not controllable, and the system is not completely controllable or is simply uncontrollable.

In Fig. 11-3 is shown the state transition signal flow graph of another controlled process. It is seen that the state variable $x_2(t)$ is not connected to the output $y(t)$ in any way. Therefore, if once we have measured $y(t)$, we can observe the state variable $x_1(t)$, since $y(t) = x_1(t)$. However, the state variable $x_2(t)$ cannot be observed from the information on $y(t)$. Thus the process is described as not completely observable or simply unobservable.

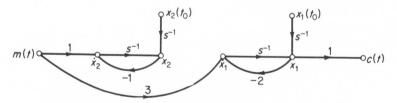

FIG. 11-3. State transition signal flow graph of a controlled process which is not completely observable.

Definitions of Controllability[2,3]

Consider that the system shown in Fig. 11-1 is an nth order linear multi-variable time-invariant system and is described by the following dynamic equation:

State equation: $\dot{\mathbf{x}}(t) = \mathbf{A}\mathbf{x}(t) + \mathbf{B}\mathbf{m}(t)$ (11-4)

Output equation: $\mathbf{c}(t) = \mathbf{D}\mathbf{x}(t) + \mathbf{E}\mathbf{m}(t)$ (11-5)

where
$$\mathbf{x}(t) = n \times 1 \text{ state vector}$$
$$\mathbf{m}(t) = r \times 1 \text{ input vector}$$
$$\mathbf{c}(t) = p \times 1 \text{ output vector}$$
$$\mathbf{A} = n \times n \text{ constant matrix}$$
$$\mathbf{B} = n \times r \text{ constant matrix}$$
$$\mathbf{D} = p \times r \text{ constant martix}$$
$$\mathbf{E} = p \times n \text{ constant matrix}$$

The state $x_i(t)$ $(i = 1, 2, \ldots, n)$ of the process G is said to be controllable at $t = t_0$ if there exists a piecewise continuous input $\mathbf{m}(t)$ which will drive the state to any final state $x_i(t_f)$ for some finite time $(t_f - t_0) \geq 0$. If every state of the process is controllable in some finite time interval, then the process G is said to be completely controllable (completely state-controllable) or simply controllable (state-controllable).

We shall show that the condition of controllability depends on the matrices $\mathbf{A}$ and $\mathbf{B}$ of the process.

The solution of Eq. (11-4) is

$$\mathbf{x}(t) = \mathbf{\Phi}(t - t_0) + \int_{t_0}^{t} \mathbf{\Phi}(t - \tau)\mathbf{B}\mathbf{m}(\tau) \, d\tau \qquad (11\text{-}6)$$

for $t \geq t_0$. Without losing any generality we can assume that the desired final state for some finite $t_f \geq t_0$ is $\mathbf{x}(t_f) = \mathbf{0}$. Then Eq. (11-6) gives

$$\mathbf{x}(t_0) = -\int_{t_0}^{t_f} \mathbf{\Phi}(t_0 - \tau)\mathbf{B}\mathbf{m}(\tau) \, d\tau \qquad (11\text{-}7)$$

The state transition matrix can be written as

$$\mathbf{\Phi}(t) = e^{\mathbf{A}t} = \sum_{k=0}^{n-1} \alpha_k(t)\mathbf{A}^k \qquad (11\text{-}8)$$

where $\alpha_k(t)$ is a scalar function of t. Therefore, Eq. (11-7) becomes

$$\mathbf{x}(t_0) = -\int_{t_0}^{t_f} \sum_{k=0}^{n-1} \alpha_k(t_0 - \tau)\mathbf{A}^k\mathbf{B}\mathbf{m}(\tau) \, d\tau$$
$$= -\sum_{k=0}^{n-1} \mathbf{A}^k\mathbf{B} \int_{t_0}^{t_f} \alpha_k(t_0 - \tau)\mathbf{m}(\tau) \, d\tau \qquad (11\text{-}9)$$

Equation (11-9) can be written as

$$\mathbf{x}(t_0) = -[\mathbf{B} \quad \mathbf{AB} \quad \mathbf{A}^2\mathbf{B} \quad \cdots \quad \mathbf{A}^{n-1}\mathbf{B}] \begin{bmatrix} \mathbf{U}_0 \\ \mathbf{U}_1 \\ . \\ . \\ . \\ \mathbf{U}_{n-1} \end{bmatrix} = -\mathbf{SU} \quad (11\text{-}10)$$

where

$$\mathbf{U}_k = \int_{t_0}^{t_f} \alpha_k(t_0 - \tau)\mathbf{m}(\tau)\, d\tau \qquad (r \times 1 \quad \text{matrix}) \qquad (11\text{-}11)$$

$$\mathbf{S} = [\mathbf{B} \quad \mathbf{AB} \quad \mathbf{A}^2\mathbf{B} \quad \cdots \quad \mathbf{A}^{n-1}\mathbf{B}] \quad (n \times nr) \qquad (11\text{-}12)$$

$$\mathbf{U} = [\mathbf{U}_0 \quad \mathbf{U}_1 \quad \mathbf{U}_2 \quad \cdots \quad \mathbf{U}_{n-1}]' \quad (nr \times 1) \qquad (11\text{-}13)$$

where the prime in Eq. (11–13) denotes the matrix transpose.

Equation (11–10) can be interpreted as: Given any initial state $\mathbf{x}(t_0)$, find the control vector $\mathbf{m}(t)$ so that the final state is $\mathbf{x}(t_f) = \mathbf{0}$ for finite $t_f - t_0$. Therefore, a unique solution exists if and only if there is a set of n linearly independent column vectors in the matrix

$$\mathbf{S} = [\mathbf{B} \quad \mathbf{AB} \quad \mathbf{A}^2\mathbf{B} \quad \ldots \quad \mathbf{A}^{n-1}\mathbf{B}] \qquad (11\text{-}14)$$

In particular, if the process has only one input, $r = 1$, $\mathbf{S}$ is an $n \times n$ square matrix. Then Eq. (11–10) represents a set of n linear independent equations if $\mathbf{S}$ in Eq. (11–14) is nonsingular, or, the determinant of $\mathbf{S}$ is nonzero.

Based on the foregoing discussion, we state that the system of Eq. (11–4) is completely controllable if $\mathbf{S}$ in Eq. (11–14) contains n linearly independent column vectors, or, alternatively, $\mathbf{S}$ has a rank n.

Example 11-1. Consider the system shown in Fig. 11-2 which was reasoned earlier to be uncontrollable. Let us try to arrive at the same answer, using the condition of Eq. (11–14). The state equations of the system are written from Fig. 11-2.

$$\begin{bmatrix} \dfrac{dx_1(t)}{dt} \\ \dfrac{dx_2(t)}{dt} \end{bmatrix} = \begin{bmatrix} -2 & 1 \\ 0 & -1 \end{bmatrix} \begin{bmatrix} x_1(t) \\ x_2(t) \end{bmatrix} + \begin{bmatrix} 1 \\ 0 \end{bmatrix} m(t) \qquad (11\text{-}15)$$

Therefore, from Eq. (11–14),

$$\mathbf{S} = [\mathbf{B} \quad \mathbf{AB}] = \begin{bmatrix} 1 & -2 \\ 0 & 0 \end{bmatrix} \qquad (11\text{-}16)$$

which is singular, and the system is uncontrollable.

Example 11-2. Determine the controllability of the system which is described by the state equation

$$\begin{bmatrix} \dfrac{dx_1(t)}{dt} \\[2mm] \dfrac{dx_2(t)}{dt} \end{bmatrix} = \begin{bmatrix} 0 & 1 \\ -1 & 0 \end{bmatrix} \begin{bmatrix} x_1(t) \\ x_2(t) \end{bmatrix} + \begin{bmatrix} 0 \\ 1 \end{bmatrix} m(t) \qquad (11\text{--}17)$$

From Eq. (11–14),

$$\mathbf{S} = [\mathbf{B} \quad \mathbf{AB}] = \begin{bmatrix} 0 & 1 \\ 1 & 0 \end{bmatrix} \qquad (11\text{--}18)$$

which is nonsingular. Therefore, the system is completely controllable.

An Alternative Definition of Controllability

If it is assumed that the eigenvalues (characteristic roots) of $\mathbf{A}$ are distinct (different) and are denoted by λ_i, $i = 1, 2, \ldots, n$, then there exists an nth order nonsingular matrix $\mathbf{P}$ which transforms $\mathbf{A}$ into a diagonal matrix Λ, such that

$$\mathbf{P}^{-1}\mathbf{AP} = \Lambda = \begin{bmatrix} \lambda_1 & 0 & 0 & \cdots & 0 \\ 0 & \lambda_2 & 0 & \cdots & 0 \\ 0 & 0 & \lambda_3 & \cdots & 0 \\ \cdot & \cdot & \cdot & \cdots & \cdot \\ \cdot & \cdot & \cdot & \cdots & \cdot \\ 0 & 0 & 0 & \cdots & \lambda_n \end{bmatrix} \qquad (11\text{--}19)$$

The matrix $\mathbf{P}$ is formed from the eigenvectors of $\mathbf{A}$; that is, if $\mathbf{X}_i$ ($i = 1, 2, \ldots, n$) is the eigenvector associated with the eigenvalue λ_i, then

$$\mathbf{P} = [\mathbf{X}_1 \quad \mathbf{X}_2 \quad \cdots \quad \mathbf{X}_i \quad \cdots \quad \mathbf{X}_n] \qquad (11\text{--}20)$$

The eigenvector of the eigenvalue λ_i is a vector $\mathbf{X}_i$ which satisfies the matrix equation

$$(\lambda_i \mathbf{I} - \mathbf{A})\mathbf{X}_i = \mathbf{0} \qquad (11\text{--}21)$$

In determining the eigenvectors, in general, we can always select the first element of any $\mathbf{X}_i$ to be unity. Therefore, it can be shown that if $\mathbf{A}$ has eigenvalues, a general form for $\mathbf{P}$ is

$$\mathbf{P} = \begin{bmatrix} 1 & 1 & 1 & \cdots & 1 \\ \lambda_1 & \lambda_2 & \lambda_3 & \cdots & \lambda_n \\ \lambda_1^2 & \lambda_2^2 & \lambda_3^2 & \cdots & \lambda_n^2 \\ \cdot & \cdot & \cdot & \cdots & \cdot \\ \lambda_1^{n-1} & \lambda_2^{n-1} & \lambda_3^{n-1} & \cdots & \lambda_n^{n-1} \end{bmatrix} \qquad (11\text{--}22)$$

which is the well-know Vandermonde matrix.

As a simple illustration of diagonalizing $\mathbf{A}$, let us consider the state equation of Eq. (11–15), in which

$$\mathbf{A} = \begin{bmatrix} -2 & 1 \\ 0 & -1 \end{bmatrix}$$

The eigenvalues of $\mathbf{A}$ are $\lambda_1 = -2$ and $\lambda_2 = -1$. Substituting $\lambda_1 = -2$ into Eq. (11–21), we have

$$\begin{bmatrix} \lambda_1 + 2 & -1 \\ 0 & \lambda_1 + 1 \end{bmatrix} \begin{bmatrix} x_1 \\ x_2 \end{bmatrix} = \begin{bmatrix} 0 & -1 \\ 0 & -1 \end{bmatrix} \begin{bmatrix} x_1 \\ x_2 \end{bmatrix} = \mathbf{0} \qquad (11\text{--}23)$$

which corresponds to $x_2 = 0$. Since x_1 is not specified by Eq. (11–23), we can choose x_1 to be unity, and the eigenvector associated with $\lambda_1 = -2$ is

$$\mathbf{X}_1 = \begin{bmatrix} 1 \\ 0 \end{bmatrix} \qquad (11\text{--}24)$$

For $\lambda = \lambda_2 = -1$, Eq. (11–21) gives

$$\begin{bmatrix} \lambda_2 + 2 & -1 \\ 0 & \lambda_2 + 1 \end{bmatrix} \begin{bmatrix} x_1 \\ x_2 \end{bmatrix} = \begin{bmatrix} 1 & -1 \\ 0 & 0 \end{bmatrix} \begin{bmatrix} x_1 \\ x_2 \end{bmatrix} = \mathbf{0} \qquad (11\text{--}25)$$

which corresponds to $x_1 - x_2 = 0$ or $x_1 = x_2$. For simplicity, we can choose $x_1 = x_2 = 1$. Therefore, the eigenvector associated with $\lambda_2 = -1$ is

$$\mathbf{X}_2 = \begin{bmatrix} 1 \\ 1 \end{bmatrix} \qquad (11\text{--}26)$$

Now, using Eq. (11–20), we obtain the matrix $\mathbf{P}$ as

$$\mathbf{P} = [\mathbf{X}_1 \quad \mathbf{X}_2] = \begin{bmatrix} 1 & 1 \\ 0 & 1 \end{bmatrix} \qquad (11\text{--}27)$$

From Eq. (11–19), we have

$$\mathbf{P}^{-1}\mathbf{A}\mathbf{P} = \begin{bmatrix} 1 & -1 \\ 0 & 1 \end{bmatrix} \begin{bmatrix} -2 & 1 \\ 0 & -1 \end{bmatrix} \begin{bmatrix} 1 & 1 \\ 0 & 1 \end{bmatrix} = \begin{bmatrix} -2 & 0 \\ 0 & -1 \end{bmatrix} = \begin{bmatrix} \lambda_1 & 0 \\ 0 & \lambda_2 \end{bmatrix}$$
$$(11\text{--}28)$$

which is the desired result.

When $\mathbf{A}$ has multiple-order eigenvalues, a nonsingular matrix $\mathbf{P}$ for the diagonalization of $\mathbf{A}$ may not exist. For instance, let

$$\mathbf{A} = \begin{bmatrix} -1 & -1 \\ 0 & -1 \end{bmatrix} \qquad (11\text{--}29)$$

whose eigenvalues are $\lambda_1 = \lambda_2 = -1$. Then,

$$\lambda\mathbf{I} - \mathbf{A} = \begin{bmatrix} \lambda + 1 & 1 \\ 0 & \lambda + 1 \end{bmatrix} \begin{bmatrix} x_1 \\ x_2 \end{bmatrix} = \mathbf{0} \qquad (11\text{--}30)$$

When $\lambda = -1$, Eq. (11–30) becomes

$$\begin{bmatrix} 0 & 1 \\ 0 & 0 \end{bmatrix} \begin{bmatrix} x_1 \\ x_2 \end{bmatrix} = \mathbf{0} \qquad (11\text{--}31)$$

The two eigenvectors which satisfy Eq. (11–31) are

$$\mathbf{X}_1 = \mathbf{X}_2 = \begin{bmatrix} a \\ 0 \end{bmatrix} \qquad (11\text{–}32)$$

where a can be any number. Since $\mathbf{X}_1 = \mathbf{X}_2$, $\mathbf{P}$ will be a singular matrix; therefore, $\mathbf{A}$ in Eq. (11–29) cannot be diagonalized. In this case $\mathbf{A}$ can be diagonalized only if $\mathbf{X}_1$ and $\mathbf{X}_2$ are linearly independent. We shall discuss an alternative method of determining controllability when $\mathbf{A}$ cannot be diagonalized in a later section.

Once the matrix $\mathbf{P}$ is found, let the new state vector be defined as

$$\mathbf{y}(t) = \mathbf{P}^{-1}\mathbf{x}(t) \qquad (11\text{–}33)$$

Substituting Eq. (11–33) into Eqs. (11–4) and (11–5), the new state equation in vector-matrix form is

$$\dot{\mathbf{y}}(t) = \Lambda\mathbf{y}(t) + \Gamma\mathbf{m}(t) \qquad (1\text{–}34)$$

and the new output equation is

$$\mathbf{v}(t) = \mathbf{F}\mathbf{y}(t) + \mathbf{E}\mathbf{m}(t) \qquad (11\text{–}35)$$

where

$$\Gamma = \mathbf{P}^{-1}\mathbf{B} \qquad (11\text{–}36)$$

$$\mathbf{F} = \mathbf{D}\mathbf{P} \qquad (11\text{–}37)$$

Equation (11–34) and (11–35) are often referred to as the normalized or canonical form dynamic equations.

Since Λ is a diagonal matrix, the matrix equation in Eq. (11–34) represents a set of first-order differential equations which are of the form:

$$\dot{y}_i(t) = \lambda_i y_i(t) + \sum_{k=1}^{r} \Gamma_{ik} m_k(t) \qquad (i = 1, 2, \ldots, n) \qquad (11\text{–}38)$$

where Γ_{ik} denotes the ikth element of the matrix Γ. It is easy to see that if any one row of Γ contains all zeros, the corresponding state will not be controlled by any of the inputs, and the state is uncontrollable. Therefore, an alternative definition of controllability for a system with distinct eigenvalues (or multiple eigenvalues but with $\mathbf{A}$ which can be diagonalized) is given as follows:

The process G is said to be completely controllable if the matrix Γ has no rows which are zero.

It is apparent that this alternate definition of controllability is not as simple to apply as the condition given by Eq. (11–14), since it involves the diagonalization of $\mathbf{A}$ and the determination of the matrix $\mathbf{P}$.

The condition on controllability by examining the rows of $\Gamma = \mathbf{P}^{-1}\mathbf{B}$ applies only to a system with matrix $\mathbf{A}$ which can be diagonalized. However, when $\mathbf{A}$ has multiple-order characteristic roots and cannot be diagonalized, we can transform $\mathbf{A}$ into the Jordan canonical form (rather than a diagonal matrix). For instance, if $\mathbf{A}$ has four eigenvalues, $\lambda_1, \lambda_1, \lambda_1, \lambda_2$, three of which are equal, then there is a nonsingular 4×4 matrix $\mathbf{P}$ which transforms $\mathbf{A}$ into the Jordan canonical form

$$\Lambda = \mathbf{P}^{-1}\mathbf{A}\mathbf{P} = \begin{bmatrix} \lambda_1 & 1 & 0 & 0 \\ 0 & \lambda_1 & 1 & 0 \\ 0 & 0 & \lambda_1 & 0 \\ \hdashline 0 & 0 & 0 & \lambda_2 \end{bmatrix} \qquad (11\text{–}39)$$

Then the dynamic equations in the Jordan canonical form are

State equation $\dot{\mathbf{y}}(t) = \Lambda\mathbf{y}(t) + \Gamma\mathbf{m}(t)$ (11–40)

Output equation: $\mathbf{v}(t) = \mathbf{F}\mathbf{y}(t) + \mathbf{E}\mathbf{m}(t)$ (11–41)

where

$$\Gamma = \mathbf{P}^{-1}\mathbf{B} \qquad (11\text{–}42)$$

$$\mathbf{F} = \mathbf{D}\mathbf{P} \qquad (11\text{–}43)$$

The matrix Λ in Eq. (11–39) is shown to be partitioned into a 2×2 diagonal matrix. The submatrices on the main diagonal of the partitioned matrix are called the *Jordan blocks*. Then the condition of controllability of the system of Eq. (11–40) is that all the elements of Γ that correspond to the last row of each Jordan block are nonzero. The reason for this condition is that the last row of each Jordan block will always correspond to a state equation which is similar to Eq. (11–38). The elements in the other rows of Γ need not all be nonzero, because the corresponding state variables are not uncoupled.

Example 11-3. Consider the system of Example 11–1. The $\mathbf{A}$ and $\mathbf{B}$ matrices are

$$\mathbf{A} = \begin{bmatrix} -2 & 1 \\ 0 & -1 \end{bmatrix} \qquad \mathbf{B} = \begin{bmatrix} 1 \\ 0 \end{bmatrix}$$

Let us test the controllability of the system by checking the rows of the matrix Γ in Eq. (11–36). We have shown earlier that $\mathbf{A}$ can be diagonalized by the matrix

$$\mathbf{P} = \begin{bmatrix} 1 & 1 \\ 0 & 1 \end{bmatrix}$$

Therefore,

$$\Gamma = \mathbf{P}^{-1}\mathbf{B} = \begin{bmatrix} 1 & -1 \\ 0 & 1 \end{bmatrix}\begin{bmatrix} 1 \\ 0 \end{bmatrix} = \begin{bmatrix} 1 \\ 0 \end{bmatrix} \qquad (11\text{–}44)$$

The transformed state equation which corresponds to Eq. (11–34) now reads

$$\dot{\mathbf{y}}(t) = \begin{bmatrix} -2 & 0 \\ 0 & -1 \end{bmatrix}\mathbf{y}(t) + \begin{bmatrix} 1 \\ 0 \end{bmatrix}m(t) \qquad (11\text{–}45)$$

Since the second row of Γ is zero, the state variable $y_2(t)$, or $x_2(t)$, is uncontrollable, and the system is uncontrollable.

Example 11-4. Determine the controllability of the system which is described by the state equation

$$\begin{bmatrix} \dfrac{dx_1(t)}{dt} \\[2mm] \dfrac{dx_2(t)}{dt} \end{bmatrix} = \begin{bmatrix} 0 & 1 \\ -1 & 0 \end{bmatrix} \begin{bmatrix} x_1(t) \\ x_2(t) \end{bmatrix} + \begin{bmatrix} 0 \\ 1 \end{bmatrix} m(t) \tag{11-46}$$

From Eq. (11-14),

$$\mathbf{S} = [B \quad AB] = \begin{bmatrix} 0 & 1 \\ 1 & 0 \end{bmatrix} \tag{11-47}$$

which is nonsingular. Therefore, the system is completely controllable.

Let us now transform Eq. (11-46) into a canonical form state equation and then check the controllability of the system from the rows of Γ. The eigenvalues of $\mathbf{A}$ are $\lambda_1 = j$ and $\lambda_2 = -j$, since the characteristic equation is

$$s^2 + 1 = 0 \tag{11-48}$$

Since the eigenvalues of $\mathbf{A}$ are distinct, $\mathbf{A}$ can be transformed into a diagonal matrix $\Lambda = \mathbf{P}^{-1}\mathbf{A}\mathbf{P}$. From Eq. (11-20),

$$\mathbf{P} = \begin{bmatrix} 1 & 1 \\ j & -j \end{bmatrix} \tag{11-49}$$

Thus,

$$\Lambda = \mathbf{P}^{-1}\mathbf{A}\mathbf{P} = \begin{bmatrix} \dfrac{1}{2} & \dfrac{1}{2j} \\[2mm] \dfrac{1}{2} & -\dfrac{1}{2j} \end{bmatrix} \begin{bmatrix} 0 & 1 \\ -1 & 0 \end{bmatrix} \begin{bmatrix} 1 & 1 \\ j & -j \end{bmatrix} = \begin{bmatrix} j & 0 \\ 0 & -j \end{bmatrix} \tag{11-50}$$

which agrees with the form for Λ given by Eq. (11-19).

From Eq. (11-42),

$$\Gamma = \mathbf{P}^{-1}\mathbf{B} = \begin{bmatrix} \dfrac{1}{2} & \dfrac{1}{2j} \\[2mm] \dfrac{1}{2} & -\dfrac{1}{2j} \end{bmatrix} \begin{bmatrix} 0 \\ 1 \end{bmatrix} = \begin{bmatrix} \dfrac{1}{2j} \\[2mm] -\dfrac{1}{2j} \end{bmatrix} \tag{11-51}$$

Since all the rows of Γ are nonzero, the system is completely controllable.

Definitions of Observability

With reference to the system G described by Eqs. (11-4) and (11-5), *the state $x_i(t)$ ($i = 1, 2, \ldots, n$) is said to be observable if given any input $\mathbf{m}(t)$ for $t_0 \le t < t_f$, the matrices $\mathbf{A}$, $\mathbf{B}$, $\mathbf{D}$, and $\mathbf{E}$ and the output $\mathbf{c}(t)$ for $t_0 \le t < t_f$ is sufficient to determine $\mathbf{x}(t_0)$. If every state of the system is observable for* *some finite time t_f, then we say that the system is completely observable, or simply observable.*

We can show that the condition of observability depends on the matrices $\mathbf{A}$ and $\mathbf{D}$ of the process.

Substituting Eq. (11-6) into Eq. (11-5), we get

$$\mathbf{c}(t) = \mathbf{D}\Phi(t - t_0)\mathbf{x}(t_0) + \mathbf{D} \int_{t_0}^{t} \Phi(t - \tau)\mathbf{B}\mathbf{m}(\tau)\, d\tau + \mathbf{E}\mathbf{m}(t) \quad (11\text{-}52)$$

Based on the definition of observability, it is apparent that the observability of $\mathbf{x}(t_0)$ depends essentially on the first term on the right side of Eq. (11-52). Therefore, the output when $\mathbf{m}(t) = \mathbf{0}$ is

$$\mathbf{c}(t) = \mathbf{D}\Phi(t - t_0)\mathbf{x}(t_0) \quad (11\text{-}53)$$

and, using Eq. (11-8), we have

$$\begin{aligned}
\mathbf{c}(t) &= \mathbf{D} \sum_{k=0}^{n-1} \alpha_k(t - t_0)\mathbf{A}^k \mathbf{x}(t_0) \\
&= \sum_{k=0}^{n-1} \alpha_k(t - t_0)\mathbf{D}\mathbf{A}^k \mathbf{x}(t_0)
\end{aligned} \quad (11\text{-}54)$$

Based on the relationship of Eq. (11-54), we can state that knowing the output $\mathbf{c}(t)$ over the interval $t_0 \leq t < t_f$, $\mathbf{x}(t_0)$ is uniquely determined from Eq. (11-54) if and only if $\mathbf{x}(t_0)$ is a linear combination of the vector $(D_j \mathbf{A}^k)'$, $k = 0, 1, 2, \ldots, n - 1, j = 1, 2, \ldots, p$, where D_j denotes the $1 \times n$ matrix formed from elements in the jth row of $\mathbf{D}$. Since $(D_j \mathbf{A}^k)' = (\mathbf{A}')^k D_j'$, if we let $\mathbf{T}$ be the $n \times np$ matrix defined by

$$\mathbf{T} = [\mathbf{D}' \quad \mathbf{A}'\mathbf{D}' \quad (\mathbf{A}')^2\mathbf{D}' \quad \ldots \quad (\mathbf{A}')^{n-1}\mathbf{D}'] \quad (11\text{-}55)$$

then the system is completely observable if and only if there is a set of n linearly independent column vectors in $\mathbf{T}$. In particular, if the system has only one output, $\mathbf{D}$ is a $1 \times n$ matrix; $\mathbf{T}$ is an $n \times n$ square matrix. Then the system is completely observable if $\mathbf{T}$ is nonsingular.

Example 11-5. Consider the system shown in Fig. 11-3, which was reasoned earlier to be unobservable. The dynamic equations of the system are written directly from Fig. 11-3.

State equation:

$$\begin{bmatrix} \dfrac{dx_1(t)}{dt} \\ \dfrac{dx_2(t)}{dt} \end{bmatrix} = \begin{bmatrix} -2 & 0 \\ 0 & -1 \end{bmatrix} \begin{bmatrix} x_1(t) \\ x_2(t) \end{bmatrix} + \begin{bmatrix} 3 \\ 1 \end{bmatrix} m(t) \quad (11\text{-}56)$$

Output equation:

$$c(t) = [1 \quad 0] \begin{bmatrix} x_1(t) \\ x_2(t) \end{bmatrix} \quad (11\text{-}57)$$

Therefore,

$$\mathbf{D} = [1 \quad 0] \qquad \mathbf{D}' = \begin{bmatrix} 1 \\ 0 \end{bmatrix}$$

$$\mathbf{A}'\mathbf{D}' = \begin{bmatrix} -2 & 0 \\ 0 & -1 \end{bmatrix} \begin{bmatrix} 1 \\ 0 \end{bmatrix} = \begin{bmatrix} -2 \\ 0 \end{bmatrix}$$

and from Eq. (11–55),

$$\mathbf{T} = [\mathbf{D}' \quad \mathbf{A}'\mathbf{D}'] = \begin{bmatrix} 1 & -2 \\ 0 & 0 \end{bmatrix} \tag{11-58}$$

Since $\mathbf{T}$ is singluar, the system is unobservable.

   Example 11-6. A controlled process is described by the folowing dynamic equations. Determine its controllability and observability.

$$\begin{bmatrix} \dfrac{dx_1(t)}{dt} \\[2ex] \dfrac{dx_2(t)}{dt} \end{bmatrix} = \begin{bmatrix} 1 & -1 \\ 1 & 1 \end{bmatrix} \begin{bmatrix} x_1(t) \\ x_2(t) \end{bmatrix} + \begin{bmatrix} 2 & -1 \\ 1 & 0 \end{bmatrix} \begin{bmatrix} m_1(t) \\ m_2(t) \end{bmatrix} \tag{11-59}$$

$$\begin{bmatrix} c_1(t) \\ c_2(t) \end{bmatrix} = \begin{bmatrix} 1 & 0 \\ -1 & 1 \end{bmatrix} \begin{bmatrix} x_1(t) \\ x_2(t) \end{bmatrix} \tag{11-60}$$

$$\mathbf{AB} = \begin{bmatrix} 1 & -1 \\ 1 & 1 \end{bmatrix} \begin{bmatrix} 2 & -1 \\ 1 & 0 \end{bmatrix} = \begin{bmatrix} 1 & -1 \\ 3 & -1 \end{bmatrix} \tag{11-61}$$

Thus,

$$\mathbf{S} = [\mathbf{B} \quad \mathbf{AB}] = \begin{bmatrix} 2 & -1 & 1 & -1 \\ 1 & 0 & 3 & -1 \end{bmatrix} \tag{11-62}$$

which has two independent columns, (or a rank of two) and the system is completely controllable.

   For the test of observability, we compute

$$\mathbf{A}'\mathbf{D}' = \begin{bmatrix} 1 & 1 \\ -1 & 1 \end{bmatrix} \begin{bmatrix} 1 & -1 \\ 0 & 1 \end{bmatrix} = \begin{bmatrix} 1 & 0 \\ -1 & 2 \end{bmatrix} \tag{11-63}$$

Thus,

$$\mathbf{T} = [\mathbf{D}' \quad \mathbf{A}'\mathbf{D}'] = \begin{bmatrix} 1 & -1 & 1 & 0 \\ 0 & 1 & -1 & 2 \end{bmatrix} \tag{11-64}$$

which has a rank of two, and the system is completely observable.

An Alternative Definition of Observability

   If $\mathbf{A}$ is diagonalized as in Eq. (11–19) with distinct entries, then the system is completely observable if the matrix $\mathbf{F}$ in Eq. (11–35) has no zero columns. The reason behind this is that if the jth column of $\mathbf{F}$ contains all zeros,

$(j = 1, 2, \ldots , n)$ the state variable y_j will not appear in Eq. (11–35) and is not related to the output $\mathbf{v}(t)$. The states that correspond to zero columns of $\mathbf{F}$ are said to be unobservable and those corresponding to nonzero columns are called observable.

Let us consider the system of Example 11–5, using the alternative test of observability just described. Since $\mathbf{A}$ is already a diagonal matrix, the condition of observability requires that $\mathbf{D}$ must not contain zero columns. However, in this case, the second column of $\mathbf{D}$ is zero; therefore, $x_2(t)$ is not observable and the system is unobservable.

11.3 State Controllability Versus Output Controllability[4]

The concept of controllability defined in the preceding sections is defined only with reference to the state of a system. Essentially, a system is controllable if every desired transition of the state of the process can be effected in finite time by some unconstrained control inputs. Therefore, strictly, the controllability with respect to the state should be referred to as *state controllability*. However, in the design of control systems one is often concerned with the outputs of the system. It is necessary, therefore, to define the concept of *output controllability*. Furthermore, it will be shown that the condition of state controllability does not necessarily lead to the answer on output controllability.

Definition of Output Controllability

A system is said to be completely output controllable if there exists an unconstrained piecewise continuous input $\mathbf{m}(t)$ *which will drive the output* $\mathbf{c}(t)$ *from* $t = t_0$ *to any final output* $\mathbf{c}(t_f)$ *for some finite time* $t_f - t_0 \geq 0$.

Consider that an nth order linear time-invariant system G is described by the dynamic equations of Eqs. (11–4) and (11–5). Then the system is completely output controllable if and only if the $p \times (n + 1)r$ matrix

$$[\mathbf{DB} \quad \mathbf{DAB} \quad \mathbf{DA}^2\mathbf{B} \quad \ldots \quad \mathbf{DA}^{n-1}\mathbf{B} \quad \mathbf{E}] \tag{11–65}$$

has a set of p linearly independent columns, where p = number of outputs. The proof of this condition of output controllability can be carried out in the same way as that of Eq. (11–14).

Example 11-7. Consider a linear control system whose input-output relationship is described by the following differential equation:

$$\frac{d^2c(t)}{dt^2} + 3\frac{dc(t)}{dt} + 2c(t) = \frac{dm(t)}{dt} + m(t) \tag{11–66}$$

First we shall show that the state controllability and observility of the system depend on how the state variables are defined.

If we let $x_1(t) = c(t)$ and $x_2(t) = \dot{x}_1(t)$, the dynamic equations of the system are written as

$$\begin{bmatrix} \dot{x}_1(t) \\ \dot{x}_2(t) \end{bmatrix} = \begin{bmatrix} 0 & 1 \\ -2 & -3 \end{bmatrix} \begin{bmatrix} x_1(t) \\ x_2(t) \end{bmatrix} + \begin{bmatrix} 0 \\ 1 \end{bmatrix} m(t) \qquad (11\text{--}67)$$

$$c(t) = \begin{bmatrix} 1 & 1 \end{bmatrix} \begin{bmatrix} x_1(t) \\ x_2(t) \end{bmatrix} \qquad (11\text{--}68)$$

Therefore, using Eq. (11–14), we have

$$\mathbf{S} = [\mathbf{B} \quad \mathbf{AB}] = \begin{bmatrix} 0 & 1 \\ 1 & -3 \end{bmatrix} \qquad (11\text{--}69)$$

which is nonsingular. Thus, the system is state controllable for the state variables $x_1(t)$ and $x_2(t)$.

Let us define the state variables as

$$y_1(t) = c(t)$$

and

$$y_2(t) = \dot{c}(t) - m(t)$$

Then the dynamic equations of the system become

$$\begin{bmatrix} \dot{y}_1(t) \\ \dot{y}_2(t) \end{bmatrix} = \begin{bmatrix} 0 & 1 \\ -2 & -3 \end{bmatrix} \begin{bmatrix} y_1(t) \\ y_2(t) \end{bmatrix} + \begin{bmatrix} 1 \\ -2 \end{bmatrix} m(t) \qquad (11\text{--}70)$$

$$c(t) = \begin{bmatrix} 1 & 0 \end{bmatrix} \begin{bmatrix} y_1(t) \\ y_2(t) \end{bmatrix} \qquad (11\text{--}71)$$

In this case,

$$\mathbf{S} = [\mathbf{B} \quad \mathbf{AB}] = \begin{bmatrix} 1 & -2 \\ -2 & 4 \end{bmatrix} \qquad (11\text{--}72)$$

which is a singular matrix, and the system is not state controllable for the state variables $y_1(t)$ and $y_2(t)$. Thus we have demonstrated that state controllability of a system depends on how the state variables are defined.

Now let us investigate the observability of the system under the different definitions of the state variables. From Eqs. (11–67) and (11–68), we get

$$\mathbf{T} = [\mathbf{D}' \quad \mathbf{A}'\mathbf{D}'] = \begin{bmatrix} 1 & -2 \\ 1 & -2 \end{bmatrix} \qquad (11\text{--}73)$$

which is singular. Therefore, the system is not observable. In other words, not all the states $x_1(t_0)$ and $x_2(t_0)$ can be determined from the knowledge of the output $c(t)$ for $t_0 \leq t < t_f$.

For Eqs. (11–70) and (11–71),

$$\mathbf{T} = [\mathbf{D}' \quad \mathbf{A}'\mathbf{D}'] = \begin{bmatrix} 1 & 0 \\ 0 & 1 \end{bmatrix} \qquad (11\text{--}74)$$

which is nonsingular. Therefore, the state variables $y_1(t)$ and $y_2(t)$ are observable and the system is completely observable.

We conclude that the system characterized by Eqs. (11–67) and (11–68) is state controllable but not observable. The system characterized by Eqs. (11–70) and (11–71) is observable but not state controllable.

Now let us investigate the output controllability of the system. For Eqs. (11–67) and (11–68), we have

$$[\mathbf{DB} \quad \mathbf{DAB} \quad \mathbf{E}] = [1 \quad -2 \quad 0] \tag{11-75}$$

which is of rank 1. Thus the system is output controllable. For Eqs. (11–70) and (11–71),

$$[\mathbf{DB} \quad \mathbf{DAB} \quad \mathbf{E}] = [1 \quad -2 \quad 0] \tag{11-76}$$

and the system is also output controllable. It should be apparent that the two answers came out to be the same, since the output of the system is independent of how the state variables are chosen.

11.4 Relationship Between Controllability, Observability, and Transfer Functions

The concepts of controllability and observability can be related to the concept of transfer functions, which is well known in the studies of linear systems.

Let us focus our attention to the system of Example 11–7. The transfer function of the system is obtained by taking the Laplace transform on both sides of Eq. (11–66) and assuming that $x_1(0) = 0$ and $x_2(0) = 0$. Therefore,

$$\frac{C(s)}{M(s)} = \frac{s + 1}{s^2 + 3s + 2} = \frac{(s + 1)}{(s + 2)(s + 1)} = \frac{1}{(s + 2)} \tag{11-77}$$

which has an identical pole and zero at $s = -1$. In Example 11–7 we have demonstrated that the system is either not state controllable or not observable, depending on the ways state variables are defined. We shall prove in the following that this phenomenon will occur whenever the input-output transfer function has identical poles and zeros which lead to pole-zero cancellation.

Consider that an nth order system with a single input and single output and distinct characteristic roots is described by the state equation

$$\dot{\mathbf{x}}(t) = \mathbf{A}\mathbf{x}(t) + \mathbf{B}m(t) \tag{11-78}$$

The output equation is

$$c(t) = \mathbf{D}\mathbf{x}(t) \tag{11-79}$$

Let the $\mathbf{A}$ matrix be diagonalized by an $n \times n$ Vandermonde matrix $\mathbf{P}$ of Eq. (11–22), so that the state equation in canonical form is

$$\dot{\mathbf{z}}(t) = \mathbf{\Lambda}\mathbf{z}(t) + \mathbf{\Gamma}m(t) \tag{11-80}$$

where $\Lambda = \mathbf{P}^{-1}\mathbf{A}\mathbf{P}$. The output equation is transformed into

$$c(t) = \mathbf{F}\mathbf{z}(t) \qquad (11\text{--}81)$$

where $\mathbf{F} = \mathbf{D}\mathbf{P}$. The state variables $\mathbf{x}(t)$ and $\mathbf{z}(t)$ are related by

$$\mathbf{x}(t) = \mathbf{P}\mathbf{z}(t) \qquad (11\text{--}82)$$

Since Λ is a diagonal matrix, the ith equation of Eq. (11–80) is

$$\dot{z}_i(t) = \lambda_i z_i(t) + \gamma_i m(t) \qquad (11\text{--}83)$$

where λ_i is the ith characteristic root of $\mathbf{A}$, and γ_i is the ith element of Γ which is $n \times 1$ in this case. Taking the Laplace transform on both sides of Eq. (11–83) and assuming zero initial states, we obtain the transfer function relation between $Z_i(s)$ and $M(s)$ as

$$Z_i(s) = \frac{\gamma_i}{s - \lambda_i} M(s) \qquad (11\text{--}84)$$

The transformed version of the output equation in Eq. (11–81) is

$$C(s) = \mathbf{F}Z(s) = \mathbf{D}\mathbf{P}Z(s) \qquad (11\text{--}85)$$

Now if it is assumed that

$$\mathbf{D} = [d_1 \quad d_2 \quad \ldots \quad d_n] \qquad (11\text{--}86)$$

then

$$\mathbf{D}\mathbf{P} = [f_1 \quad f_2 \quad \ldots \quad f_n] \qquad (11\text{--}87)$$

where

$$f_i = d_1 + d_2\lambda_i + \ldots + d_n\lambda_i^{n-1} \qquad (11\text{--}88)$$

for $i = 1, 2, \ldots, n$. Therefore, Eq. (11–85) can be written as

$$C(s) = [f_1 \quad f_2 \quad \cdots \quad f_n]Z(s)$$

$$= [f_1 \quad f_2 \quad \cdots \quad f_n] \begin{bmatrix} \dfrac{\gamma_1}{s - \lambda_1} \\ \dfrac{\gamma_2}{s - \lambda_2} \\ \vdots \\ \dfrac{\gamma_n}{s - \lambda_n} \end{bmatrix} M(s) \qquad (11\text{--}89)$$

For an nth order system, the input-output transfer function can be written as

$$\frac{C(s)}{M(s)} = \frac{K(s - a_1)(s - a_2) \cdots (s - a_m)}{(s - \lambda_1)(s - \lambda_2) \cdots (s - \lambda_n)} \quad (n > m) \qquad (11\text{--}90)$$

For distinct characteristic roots, Eq. (11–90) is expanded by partial fraction expansion into

$$\frac{C(s)}{M(s)} = \sum_{i=1}^{n} \frac{\sigma_i}{s - \lambda_i} \tag{11-91}$$

where σ_i denotes the residue of $C(s)/M(s)$ at $s = \lambda_i$.

It was established earlier that for the system described by Eq. (11–80) to be state controllable, all the rows of Γ must be nonzero; i.e., $\gamma_i \neq 0$ for $i = 1, 2, \ldots, n$. If $C(s)/M(s)$ has one (or more) pair of identical pole and zero, for instance in Eq. (11–90), $a_1 = \lambda_1$, then in Eq. (11–91), $\sigma_1 = 0$. Now comparing Eq. (11–89) with Eq. (11–91), we see that in general

$$\sigma_i = f_i \gamma_i \tag{11-92}$$

Therefore, when $\sigma_i = 0$, γ_i will be zero if $f_i \neq 0$, and the state $z_i(t)$ is uncontrollable.

For observability, it was established earlier that $\mathbf{F}$ must not have columns containing zeros. Or, in the present case, $f_i \neq 0$ for $i = 1, 2, \ldots, n$. However, from Eq. (11–92),

$$f_i = \frac{\sigma_i}{\gamma_i} \tag{11-93}$$

When the transfer function has an identical pair of pole and zero at $a_i = \lambda_i$, $\sigma_i = 0$. Therefore, $f_i = 0$ if $\gamma_i \neq 0$.

The discussions given above lead to the following conclusion on the relationship between the transfer function and the controllability and observability of a linear system.

If the input-output function of a system has pole-zero cancellation, the system will either be uncontrollable or unobservable, depending on how the state variables are defined.

If the input-output transfer function of a system does not have pole-zero cancellation, the system can always be represented by state equations as a completely controllable and observable system.

11.5 A Practical Illustration of the Concept of Controllability

Controllability and observability have both theoretical and practical significance. Although it is true that practically all physical systems are controllable and observable, when one works with linearized mathematical models of control systems difficulty may arise if the models do not satisfy the conditions of controllability and observability. In this section we shall demonstrate that when a system is controllable a piecewise continuous input exists which will drive the system from one state to another in finite time.

The block diagram of a second-order feedback control system is shown in Fig. 11-4. It is apparent that the over-all system is controllable and observable, since the closed-loop transfer function

FIG. 11-4. A second-order feedback control system.

$$\frac{C(s)}{R(s)} = \frac{2500}{s^2 + 20s + 2500} \tag{11-94}$$

does not have identical poles and zeros.

Let us assume that the design objective is to drive the system's output $c(t)$ from $c(t) = 0$ at $t = 0$ to $c(t) = 1$ for some finite time $t_f \geq 0$, and stays there for all $t \geq t_f$. The problem is to find an input $r(t)$, defined for $0 \leq t \leq t_f$, such that the stated objective is achieved.

The state equations of the system are written as

$$\dot{x}_1(t) = x_2(t) \tag{11-95}$$

$$\dot{x}_2(t) = -0.008x_1(t) - x_2(t) + 0.0004r(t) \tag{11-96}$$

and the output equation is

$$c(t) = x_1(t) \tag{11-97}$$

With reference to the state space diagram shown in Fig. 11-5, the problem can be stated as the determination of an input which will effect the state transition from the initial state $(0, 0)$ to the $(1,0)$ in the (x_1, x_2) plane in finite time duration t_f.

A single-step function input cannot satisfy the design requirement, since it is well known that the step response of the linear system approaches its final value only asymptotically as time increases to infinity. Now let us try the signal which is a combination of two step functions as shown in Fig. 11-6. The first step function is applied at $t = 0$; the amplitude k is so chosen that the overshoot in the corresponding step response is unity. At precisely the moment of the peak overshoot, $c(t) = x_1(t) = 1$ and $\dot{c}(t) = x_2(t) = 0$, the input is shifted from k to unity, and the state of the system will stay at

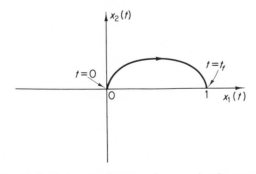

FIG. 11-5. State space diagram of a second-order system.

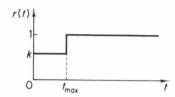

FIG. 11-6. Input signal for the system shown in Fig. 11-4.

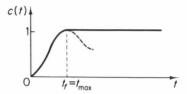

FIG. 11-7. Output of the system in Fig. 11-4.

$x_1 = 1$ and $x_2 = 0$ for all time thereafter. This scheme is known as the *posicast control*, a concept which was first introduced by Smith.[5]

The design problem is now reduced to finding the optimum value of k and the time t_{max} at which the input switches. The damping ratio of the system is .2. From Eq. (6–39), the per cent overshoot for $\delta = 0.2$ is found to be 53 per cent. Thus, when the input step function has an amplitude of $1/1.53 = 0.65$, the maximum overshoot of the output will be unity. The time at which c_{max} is obtained is calculated from Eq. (6–35).

$$t_{max} = \frac{\pi}{\omega_n\sqrt{1 - \delta^2}} = \frac{\pi}{50\sqrt{1 - 0.04}} = 0.064 \text{ sec} \qquad (11–98)$$

Now at $t = t_{max}$ the input step function is shifted from a magnitude of 0.65 to 1.0, and the system output will stay at unity for all $t \geq t_{max}$. Therefore, $t_f = t_{max} = 0.064$ sec. The output response of the system is sketched as shown in Fig. 11-7.

11.6 Controllability and Observability of Discrete-data Systems[6,7]

Controllability of Discrete-data Systems

Consider that a discrete-data system is described by the following state transition equation

$$x[(k + 1)T] = \Phi(T) x(kT) + \Theta(T) m(kT) \qquad (11–99)$$

where $m(kT)$ is an $r \times 1$ input vector, and $m_i(kT)$, $i = 1, 2, \ldots, r$ is a constant for $kT \leq t < (k + 1)T$. $\Phi(T)$ is an $n \times n$ coefficient matrix, and $\Theta(T)$ is an $n \times r$ input matrix.

The condition of controllability of the discrete-data system is defined as:

Given $\Phi(T)$ and $\Theta(T)$, there exists a set of control signals $m(kT)$, defined over the interval $0 \leq t < NT$, which will bring the states from $x(0)$ to $x(NT)$ in N sampling instants, where N is a finite positive integer.

The solution of Eq. (11–99) is

$$\mathbf{x}(kT) = \mathbf{\Phi}^k(T)\mathbf{x}(0) + \sum_{i=0}^{k-1} \mathbf{\Phi}^{k-i-1}(T)\mathbf{\Theta}(T)\mathbf{m}(iT) \qquad (11\text{--}100)$$

or

$$\mathbf{x}(kT) = \mathbf{\Phi}(kT)\mathbf{x}(0) + \sum_{i=0}^{k-1} \mathbf{\Phi}[(k-i-1)T]\mathbf{\Theta}(T)\mathbf{m}(iT) \qquad (11\text{--}101)$$

Assuming that the state of the process is to reach the equilibrium state $\mathbf{x}(NT)$ = 0 in N sampling instants, and solving for $\mathbf{x}(0)$ in Eq. (11-101), we get

$$\mathbf{x}(0) = -\mathbf{\Phi}(-NT) \sum_{i=0}^{N-1} \mathbf{\Phi}[(N-i-1)T]\mathbf{\Theta}(T)\mathbf{m}(iT) \qquad (11\text{--}102)$$

or

$$\mathbf{x}(0) = -\sum_{i=0}^{N-1} \mathbf{\Phi}[(-i-1)T]\mathbf{\Theta}(T)\mathbf{m}(iT) \qquad (11\text{--}103)$$

If we set

$$\mathbf{S}_i(T) = \mathbf{\Phi}[(-i-1)T]\mathbf{\Theta}(T) \qquad (11\text{--}104)$$

Eq. (11–103) becomes

$$\mathbf{x}(0) = -\sum_{i=0}^{N-1} \mathbf{S}_i(T)\mathbf{m}(iT) \qquad (11\text{--}105)$$

which represents a set of n simultaneous equations. Given the initial state $\mathbf{x}(0)$, the solution for the control vector $\mathbf{m}(iT)$, $i = 0, 1, 2, \ldots, (N-1)$ exists only if the n equations represented by Eq. (11-105) are all linearly independent. In other words, the necessary and sufficient condition for the initial state $\mathbf{x}(0)$ to reach $\mathbf{x}(NT)$ for a finite N is that all the vectors

$$\mathbf{S}_0(T) = \mathbf{\Phi}(-T)\mathbf{\Theta}(T)$$
$$\mathbf{S}_1(T) = \mathbf{\Phi}(-2T)\mathbf{\Theta}(T)$$
$$\cdot$$
$$\cdot \qquad\qquad\qquad\qquad\qquad\qquad (11\text{--}106)$$
$$\cdot$$
$$\mathbf{S}_{N-1}(T) = \mathbf{\Phi}(-NT)\mathbf{\Theta}(T)$$

are linearly independent.

Now consider that the system has only one input so that $\mathbf{m}(iT)$ becomes a scalar. Then, Eq. (11-105) can be expanded into the following form:

$$\mathbf{x}(0) = -\mathbf{S}_0(T)m(0) - \mathbf{S}_1(T)m(T) - \cdots - \mathbf{S}_{N-1}(T)m[(N-1)T] \qquad (11\text{--}107)$$

or

$$\begin{bmatrix} x_1(0) \\ x_2(0) \\ \cdot \\ \cdot \\ \cdot \\ x_n(0) \end{bmatrix} = - \begin{bmatrix} s_{01} & s_{11} & s_{21} & \cdots & s_{N-1,1} \\ s_{02} & s_{12} & s_{22} & \cdots & s_{N-1,2} \\ \cdot & \cdot & \cdot & \cdots & \cdot \\ \cdot & \cdot & \cdot & \cdots & \cdot \\ s_{0n} & s_{1n} & s_{2n} & \cdots & s_{N-1,n} \end{bmatrix} \begin{bmatrix} m(0) \\ m(T) \\ \cdot \\ \cdot \\ m[(N-1)T] \end{bmatrix} \qquad (11\text{--}108)$$

If the values of $m(iT)$ are not restricted, given $x_1(0), x_2(0), \ldots, x_n(0)$, which define n independent equations in Eq. (11–108), provided that the

$S_i(T)$'s are linearly independent, we need n unknowns in $m(0), m(T), \ldots,$ $m(n-1)T$, which form the control law. It is easy to see that with no restrictions placed on the values of $m(iT)$, an nth order linear system needs n sampling periods ($N = n$) to bring any initial state $x(0)$ to the equilibrium state $x(NT) = 0$.

If fewer than n control signals are used, it is apparent that the initial state $x(0)$, which can be brought to the equilibrium state in NT periods, will be restricted to a finite set. However, if the magnitude of $m(iT)$ is restricted by $|m(iT)| \le M$, then

$$N = n + p \tag{11-109}$$

where p is the number of m's which are subjected to magnitude saturation. This conclusion is self-evident, since for an nth order system we need a total n controllable signals in m in order to solve Eq. (11-108), and if p of these $m(iT)$ signals are fixed by the saturation limit, additional P variable ones must be made available. On the basis of this discussion, we realize that the effect of saturation of the control signal is the increase in the period of reaching equilibrium state.

Example 11-8. Consider that a controlled process is described by the transfer function

$$\frac{C(s)}{M(s)} = \frac{1}{s(s+1)}$$

The control signal $m(t)$ is the output of a sample-and-hold device; i.e., $m(t) = m(kT)$ for $kT \le t < (k+1)T$. The sampling period is assumed to be one second. The problem is to find the control law $m(iT)$, $i = 0, 1, \ldots,$ $N-1$, for $N =$ minimum, so that the system can be brought from any initial state $x(0)$ to the equilibrium state $x(NT)$. Defining the state variables as $x_1(t) = c(t)$ and $x_2(t) = \dot{x}_1(t)$, we write the state equations of the system as

$$\begin{bmatrix} \dot{x}_1(t) \\ \dot{x}_2(t) \end{bmatrix} = \begin{bmatrix} 0 & 1 \\ 0 & -1 \end{bmatrix} \begin{bmatrix} x_1(t) \\ x_2(t) \end{bmatrix} + \begin{bmatrix} 0 \\ 1 \end{bmatrix} m(t) \tag{11-110}$$

from which we have

$$\Phi(T) = \begin{bmatrix} 1 & 1 - e^{-T} \\ 0 & e^{-T} \end{bmatrix} \tag{11-111}$$

and

$$\boldsymbol{\theta}(T) = \int_0^T \Phi(T-\tau)\mathbf{B}\, d\tau = \begin{bmatrix} T + e^{-T} - 1 \\ 1 - e^{-T} \end{bmatrix} \tag{11-112}$$

Since the system is of the second order, it should not take more than two sampling periods to bring the system to its equilibrium point; i.e., $N = 2$. Evaluating the vectors in Eq. (11-106), we have

$$S_0(T) = \Phi(-T)\Theta(T) = \begin{bmatrix} -0.72 \\ 1.72 \end{bmatrix} \tag{11-113}$$

$$S_1(T) = \Phi(-2T)\Theta(T) = \begin{bmatrix} -3.67 \\ 4.67 \end{bmatrix} \tag{11-114}$$

Now since

$$[S_0(T) \quad S_1(T)] = \begin{bmatrix} -0.72 & -3.67 \\ 1.72 & 4.67 \end{bmatrix} \tag{11-115}$$

is nonsingular, the system is controllable in two sampling instants. For $N = 2$, Eq. (11-108) gives

$$\begin{bmatrix} x_1(0) \\ x_2(0) \end{bmatrix} = - \begin{bmatrix} -0.72 & -3.67 \\ 1.72 & 4.67 \end{bmatrix} \begin{bmatrix} m(0) \\ m(1) \end{bmatrix} \tag{11-116}$$

Solving for the control signals from the last equation yields

$$\begin{bmatrix} m(0) \\ m(1) \end{bmatrix} = - \begin{bmatrix} -0.72 & -3.67 \\ 1.72 & 4.67 \end{bmatrix}^{-1} \begin{bmatrix} x_1(0) \\ x_2(0) \end{bmatrix} \tag{11-117}$$

$$= \begin{bmatrix} -1.58 & -1.237 \\ 0.582 & 0.2 \end{bmatrix} \begin{bmatrix} x_1(0) \\ x_2(0) \end{bmatrix} \tag{11-118}$$

Equation (11-118) gives the results of the desired control signal at $t = 0$ and $t = 1$ in terms of the initial state at $t = 0$. However, the design of the optimum system can be obtained by expressing the control signals as functions of the state variables at the corresponding sampling instants. Using Eq.(3-76), we can write Eq. (11-105) as

$$x(kT) = - \sum_{i=0}^{N-1} S_i(T) m[(i+k)T] \tag{11-119}$$

Therefore, the results of Eq. (11-118) can also be written as

$$m(kT) = [1 \quad 0] [-S_0(T) \quad -S_1(T)]^{-1} x(kT)$$

$$= [1 \quad 0] \begin{bmatrix} -1.58 & -1.237 \\ 0.582 & 0.2 \end{bmatrix} \begin{bmatrix} x_1(kT) \\ x_2(kT) \end{bmatrix}$$

$$= 1.58 x_1(kT) - 1.237 x_2(kT) \tag{11-120}$$

for $k = 0, 1$.

The block diagram of the optimum system is shown in Fig. 11-8. The difficulty encountered in practice with this type of optimization scheme is that sometimes the state variables are not accessible for measurement. Then it is necessary to use an estimator to estimate the state vector $x(t)$, so that the desired control signal $m(kT)$ may be obtained.

If we wish the system to reach the equilibrium state of $x(NT) = 0$ in one sampling period ($N = 1$), then from Eq. (11-107),

$$x(0) = -S_0(T)m(0) \tag{11-121}$$

or

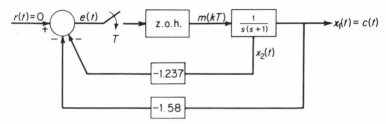

FIG. 11-8. Block diagram of optimum system with state variable feedback so that the system will reach equilibrium in two sampling periods.

$$\begin{bmatrix} x_1(0) \\ x_2(0) \end{bmatrix} = - \begin{bmatrix} -0.72 \\ 1.72 \end{bmatrix} m(0) \qquad (11\text{–}122)$$

However, it is apparent that Eq. (11–122) is satisfied only if $x_1(0) = -(0.72/1.72)x_2(0) = -0.417x_2(0)$, which represents a straight line with slope of -0.417 in the state space of x_1 versus x_2, as shown in Fig. 11-9. In other words, only the initial states that lie on this line can be brought to the equilibrium state $\mathbf{x} = \mathbf{0}$ in one sampling period.

The second-order system can be brought to the desired equilibrium state in two sampling periods from any initial state only if there is no constraint placed on the magnitude of $m(t)$. In practice, however, all control systems have saturation effects when the magnitudes of signals become large. When the control signal subjects to saturation restrictions,

$$|m(kT)| \le M \qquad (11\text{–}123)$$

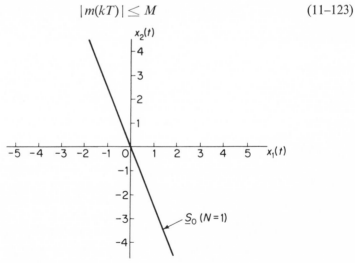

FIG. 11-9. Trajectory of controllable states for a second order system with $N = 1$. (No saturation).

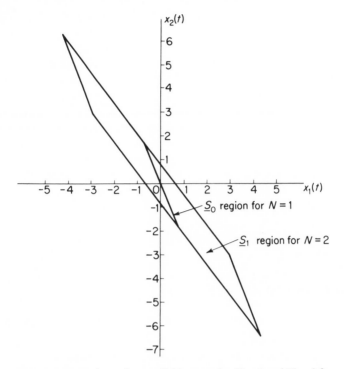

FIG. 11-10. Regions of controllable states for $N = 1$ and $N = 2$ for a second-order process. (With saturation, $|m(kT)| \leq 1$).

the conditions obtained in Eq. (11–118) must be restricted also. For instance, if $M = 1$, from Eq. (11–122) the controllable state for $N = 1$ is

$$|x_1(0)| \leq 0.72$$

$$|x_2(0)| \leq 1.72$$

These restrictions cut the line of controllable states for $N = 1$ shown in Fig. 11-9 down to one with a finite length, as shown in Fig. 11-10. The controllable states for $N = 2$, when $M = 1$, are determined from Eq. (11–118), the four possible combinations of $m(0) = +1$, -1, and $m(1) = +1$, -1 being used. Therefore, the boundaries of the region of controllable states for $N = 2$ are given by the following equations:

$$m(0) = +1 \qquad -1.58x_1(0) - 1.237x_2(0) = 1 \qquad (11\text{--}124)$$

$$m(0) = -1 \qquad -1.58x_1(0) - 1.237x_2(0) = -1 \qquad (11\text{--}125)$$

$$m(1) = +1 \qquad 0.582x_1(0) + 0.24x_2(0) = +1 \qquad (11\text{--}126)$$

$$m(1) = -1 \qquad 0.582x_1(0) + 0.24x_2(0) = -1 \qquad (11\text{--}127)$$

and the region is sketched as shown in Fig. 11-10 as a convex polygon. The conclusion is that when $|m(kT)| \leq 1$, only the initial states found on or inside the convex polygon described by Eqs. (11-124) through (11–127) can be brought to the equilibrium state of $\mathbf{x}(NT) = 0$ for $N \leq 2$. For $N = 1$, the initial state has to lie on the line described by Eq. (11–122).

The procedure of deriving the regions of controllable states for N greater than 2 follows essentially the same as that described above. For $N=3$, it is easy to see that the boundary of the convex polygon is formed by six straight lines. In general, for control in N sampling instants, the convex polygon of the region of control is described by Eq. (11–105), When $m(kT)$, $k = 0, 1, 2, \ldots, N - 1$, takes on the values of $+1$ and -1, there are a total of $2N$ combinations, thus leading to $2N$ straight-line equations.

Although the equilibrium state considered in this illustrative example is the origin of the state plane, generality is not lost when a nonzero final state is considered. For instance, if the equilibrium state is to be at $\mathbf{x}(NT) = [1 \quad 0]'$, which corresponds to a response with no overshoot, due to a unit-step function input, the control region shown in Fig. 11-10 is simply shifted to the right by one unit.

Observability of Discrete-data Systems

Consider that a discrete-data system is described by the following equations:

$$\mathbf{x}[(k + 1)T] = \mathbf{\Phi}(T)\,\mathbf{x}(kT) + \mathbf{\Theta}(T)\mathbf{m}(kT) \qquad (11–128)$$

and

$$\mathbf{c}(kT) = \mathbf{D}\mathbf{x}(kT) + \mathbf{E}\mathbf{m}(kT) \qquad (11–129)$$

The state $\mathbf{x}(kT)$ *is said to be observable if given any input* $\mathbf{m}(kT)$ *for* $0 \leq k \leq N$, *the matrices* $\mathbf{\Phi}(T)$, $\boldsymbol{\theta}(T)$, $\mathbf{D}$, *and* $\mathbf{E}$ *and the output* $\mathbf{c}(kT)$ *for* $0 \leq k \leq N$ *is sufficient to determine* $\mathbf{x}(kT)$. *If every state of the system is observable for some finite* N, *then we say that the system is completely observable, or simply observable.*

Notice that the definition of observability given above for discrete-data systems is completely analogous to that for continuous-data systems. Since observability is independent of the input, we can let $\mathbf{m}(kT) = \mathbf{0}$. Substituting the solution of Eq. (11–128), with $\mathbf{m}(kT) = 0$, into Eq. (11–129), we get

$$\mathbf{c}(kT) = \mathbf{D}(kT)\,\mathbf{x}(0) \qquad (11–130)$$

or

$$\mathbf{c}(NT) = \mathbf{D}(k + N)T\,\mathbf{x}(kT) \qquad (11–131)$$

Assuming that $\mathbf{c}(NT)$ is measured, then to observe the state variables $x_1(kT)$, $x_2(kT), \ldots, x_n(kT)$, we need $n = N$ independent equations in Eq. (11–131). Therefore, observability of the system requires that the following matrix has a set of $n = N$ independent column vectors.

$$[\mathbf{D}' \quad \mathbf{\Phi}(T)'\mathbf{D}' \quad \mathbf{\Phi}(2T)'\mathbf{D}' \quad \ldots \quad \mathbf{\Phi}[(N - 1)T]'\mathbf{D}'] \qquad (11–132)$$

Notice that the matrix in Eq. (11–132) is of the same form as that of Eq. (11–55) which is used for the observability of continuous-data systems.

Controllability and Observability Versus Sampling Period[8]

Investigating Eqs. (11–106) and (11–132), it is apparent that when

$$\Phi(T) = \Phi(2T) = \ldots = \Phi(NT) \qquad (11\text{–}133)$$

the discrete-data system will be neither controllable nor observable. It is interesting to point out that in certain systems, the condition of Eq. (11–133) depends on the sampling period T. Let us consider that the transfer function of a linear process is described by

$$G(s) = \frac{\omega}{s^2 + \omega^2} \qquad (11\text{–}134)$$

Ordinarily, in a continuous-data system, $G(s)$ represents a completely controllable and observable system. With sampled data ,the control signal to the process is $m(t) = m(kT)$ for $kT \le t < (k+1)T$, where T is the sampling period.

The state transition matrix of $G(s)$ is

$$\Phi(t) = \begin{bmatrix} \cos \omega t & \dfrac{1}{\omega} \sin \omega t \\ -\omega \sin \omega t & \cos \omega t \end{bmatrix} \qquad (11\text{–}135)$$

Therefore, when $t = T = 2n\pi/\omega$, $\Phi(T) = \Phi(2T) = \ldots = \Phi(NT)$, for $n =$ positive integer, and the discrete-data system is uncontrollable and unobservable.

In terms of transfer function concept, the z-transform of Eq. (11–134) is

$$G(z) = \frac{z \sin \omega T}{z^2 - 2z \cos \omega T + 1} \qquad (11\text{–}136)$$

When $T = 2n\pi/\omega$, $G(z)$ becomes

$$G(z) = 0 \qquad (11\text{–}137)$$

This shows that the sampled output of the process is zero, whereas the true output is an undamped sinusoid.

REFERENCES

1. R. E. Kalman, "On the General Theory of Control Systems," *Proc. First International Congress of Automatic Control*, Moscow, USSR, 1960.

2. R. E. Kalman, Y. C. Ho, and K. S. Narendra, "Controllability of Linear Dynamical Systems," *Contributions to Differential Equations*, Vol. 1, No. 1, John Wiley & Sons, Inc., 1961.

3. E. G. Gilbert, "Controllability and Observability in Multivariable Control Systems," *Journal on Control*, Series A, Vol. 1, No. 2, SIAM, 1963.

4. E. Kreindler and P. E. Sarachik, "On the Concept of Controllability and Observability of Linear Systems," *IEEE Trans. on Automatic Control*, Vol. AC-9, April, 1964, pp. 129–136.

5. O. J. M. Smith, *Feedback Control Systems*, Chapter 10, McGraw-Hill Book Company, New York, N. Y., 1958.

6. C. A. Desoer and J. Wing, "A Minimal Time Discrete System," *IRE Trans. on Automatic Control*, Vol. AC-6, May, 1961, pp. 111–125.

7. J. T. Tou, *Modern Control Theory*, McGraw-Hill Book Company, New York, N. Y., 1964.

8. R. E. Kalman, "Mathematical Description of Linear Dynamical Systems," *Journal on Control*, Series A, Vol. 1, No. 2, SIAM, 1963.

PROBLEMS

11-1. Determine the controllability and observability of the systems which are described by the following dynamic equations.

(a)

$$\begin{bmatrix} \dfrac{dx_1(t)}{dt} \\ \dfrac{dx_2(t)}{dt} \end{bmatrix} = \begin{bmatrix} 2 & 2 \\ 0 & 0 \end{bmatrix} \begin{bmatrix} x_1(t) \\ x_2(t) \end{bmatrix} + \begin{bmatrix} 1 \\ 1 \end{bmatrix} m(t)$$

$$c(t) = [1 \quad 0] \begin{bmatrix} x_1(t) \\ x_2(t) \end{bmatrix}$$

(b)

$$\begin{bmatrix} \dfrac{dx_1(t)}{dt} \\ \dfrac{dx_2(t)}{dt} \end{bmatrix} = \begin{bmatrix} 1 & 0 \\ 1 & 0 \end{bmatrix} \begin{bmatrix} x_1(t) \\ x_2(t) \end{bmatrix} + \begin{bmatrix} 1 & 0 \\ 0 & -1 \end{bmatrix} \begin{bmatrix} m_1(t) \\ m_2(t) \end{bmatrix}$$

$$c(t) = [0 \quad 1] \begin{bmatrix} x_1(t) \\ x_2(t) \end{bmatrix}$$

11-2. Determine the conditions on b_1, b_2, d_1, d_2 so that the system is completely controllable and observable.

$$\begin{bmatrix} \dfrac{dx_1(t)}{dt} \\ \dfrac{dx_2(t)}{dt} \end{bmatrix} = \begin{bmatrix} 1 & 1 \\ 0 & 1 \end{bmatrix} \begin{bmatrix} x_1(t) \\ x_2(t) \end{bmatrix} + \begin{bmatrix} b_1 \\ b_2 \end{bmatrix} m(t)$$

$$c(t) = [d_1 \quad d_2] \begin{bmatrix} x_1(t) \\ x_2(t) \end{bmatrix}$$

11-3. Determine the state controllability of the following systems.

(a) $\dfrac{C(s)}{M(s)} = \dfrac{K}{s^3 + 2s^2 + 2s + 1}$

(b) $\dfrac{C(s)}{M(s)} = \dfrac{2s+1}{s^2+2.5s+1}$

11-4. A single-variable controlled process has the transfer function

$$\frac{C(s)}{M(s)} = G(s) = \frac{1}{s(s+1)}$$

The sampling period is one second and the initial conditions of the system are assumed to be zero. The control signal $m(t)$ is bounded by $|m(t)| \leq M = 1$. Determine the optimum control sequence $m(0), m(T), \ldots, m(N-1)T$, so that the output will follow a unit step input for minimum NT.

11-5. A discrete-data control system is shown in Fig. 11P-5. Determine the transfer function of the digital controller so that the signal $x(t)$ will follow a unit step input in the shortest possible time NT. What is this minimum N? Assume zero initial state, and $T = 0.5$ sec.

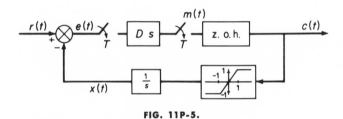

FIG. 11P-5.

11-6. Consider that a second-order process is described by the state equations

$$\frac{dx_1}{dt} = x_2$$

$$\frac{dx_2}{dt} = -x_2 + m$$

and the output equation is

$$c(t) = x_1(t).$$

Determine the optimum control signal sequence $m(0), m(T), \ldots, m(N-1)T$, so that the output will follow a unit ramp input after a minimum number of sampling periods. Assume that $x_1(0) = 1$ and $x_2(0) = 0$. $T = 1$ sec.

Laplace transform $F(s)$	Time function $f(t)$
$\dfrac{1}{s}$	$u(t)$ (unit step function)
$\dfrac{1}{s^2}$	t
$\dfrac{n!}{s^{n+1}}$	t^n (n = integer)
$\dfrac{1}{s + a}$	e^{-at}
$\dfrac{1}{(s + a)(s + b)}$	$\dfrac{e^{-at} - e^{-bt}}{b - a}$
$\dfrac{\omega_n{}^2}{s^2 + 2\delta\omega_n s + \omega_n{}^2}$	$\dfrac{\omega_n}{\sqrt{1 - \delta^2}}\, e^{-\delta\omega_n t} \sin \omega_n\sqrt{1 - \delta^2}t$
$\dfrac{1}{(1 + sT)^n}$	$\dfrac{1}{T^n(n - 1)!}\, t^{n-1}e^{-t/T}$
$\dfrac{\omega_n{}^2}{(1 + Ts)(s^2 + 2\delta\omega_n s + \omega_n{}^2)}$	$\dfrac{T\omega_n{}^2 e^{-t/T}}{1 - 2\delta T\omega_n + T^2\omega_n{}^2} + \dfrac{\omega_n e^{-\delta\omega_n t} \sin(\omega_n\sqrt{1 - \delta^2}t - \phi)}{\sqrt{(1 - \delta^2)(1 - 2\delta T\omega_n - T^2\omega_n{}^2)}}$, where $\phi = \tan^{-1}\dfrac{T\omega_n\sqrt{1 - \delta^2}}{1 - T\delta\omega_2}$
$\dfrac{\omega_n}{(s^2 + \omega_n{}^2)}$	$\sin \omega_n t$
$\dfrac{\omega_n}{(1 + Ts)(s^2 + \omega_n{}^2)}$	$\dfrac{T\omega_n}{1 + T^2\omega_n{}^2} e^{-t/T} + \dfrac{1}{\sqrt{1 + T^2\omega_n{}^2}} \sin(\omega_n t - \phi)$ where $\phi = \tan^{-1}\omega_n T$
$\dfrac{\omega_n{}^2}{s(s^2 + 2\delta\omega_n s + \omega_n{}^2)}$	$1 + \dfrac{1}{\sqrt{1 - \delta^2}} e^{-\delta\omega_n t} \sin(\omega_n\sqrt{1 - \delta^2}t - \phi)$ where $\phi = \tan^{-1}\dfrac{\sqrt{1 - \delta^2}}{-\delta}$
$\dfrac{\omega_n{}^2}{s(s^2 + \omega_n{}^2)}$	$1 - \cos \omega_n t$
$\dfrac{1}{s(1 + Ts)}$	$1 - e^{-t/T}$
$\dfrac{1}{s(1 + Ts)^2}$	$1 - \dfrac{t + T}{T} e^{-t/T}$
$\dfrac{\omega_n{}^2}{s(1 + Ts)(s^2 + 2\delta\omega_n s + \omega_n{}^2)}$	$1 - \dfrac{T^2\omega_n{}^2}{1 - 2T\delta\omega_n + T^2\omega_n{}^2} \epsilon^{-t/T} + \dfrac{e^{-\delta\omega_n t} \sin(\omega_n\sqrt{1 - \delta^2}t - \phi)}{\sqrt{1 - \delta^2(1 - 2\delta T\omega_n + T^2\omega_n{}^2)}}$ where $\phi = \tan^{-1}(\sqrt{1 - \delta^2}/ - \delta) + \tan^{-1}[T\omega_n\sqrt{1 - \delta^2}/(1 - T\delta\omega_n)]$
$\dfrac{\omega_n{}^2}{s^2(s^2 + 2\delta\omega_n s + \omega_n{}^2)}$	$t - \dfrac{2\delta}{\omega_n} + \dfrac{1}{\omega_n\sqrt{1 - \delta^2}} e^{-\delta\omega_n t} \sin(\omega_n\sqrt{1 - \delta^2}t - \phi)$ where $\phi = 2\tan^{-1}(\sqrt{1 - \delta^2})/ - \delta$

Laplace transform $F(s)$	Time function $f(t)$
$\dfrac{\omega_n{}^2}{s^2(1+Ts)(s^2+2\delta\omega_n s+\omega_n{}^2)}$	$t - T - \dfrac{2\delta}{\omega_n} + \dfrac{T^3\omega_n{}^2}{1-2\delta\omega_n T + T^2\omega_n{}^2}\,\epsilon^{-t/T}$ $$+ \dfrac{e^{-\delta\omega_n t}\sin\,(\omega_n\sqrt{1-\delta^2}\,t-\phi)}{\omega_n\sqrt{(1-\delta^2)}(1-2\delta\omega_n T + T^2\omega_n{}^2}$$ where $\phi = 2\tan^{-1}(\sqrt{1-\delta^2}/-\delta) +$ $\tan^{-1}\,[T\omega_n\sqrt{1-\delta^2}/(1-T\omega_n\delta)]$
$\dfrac{1}{s^2(1+Ts)^2}$	$t - 2T + (t+2T)\epsilon^{-t/T}$
$\dfrac{\omega_n{}^2(1+as)}{s^2+2\delta\omega_n s+\omega_n{}^2}$	$\omega_n\sqrt{\dfrac{1-2a\delta\omega_n+a^2\omega_n{}^2}{1-\delta^2}}\,\epsilon^{-\delta\omega_n t}\sin\,(\omega_n\sqrt{1-\delta^2}\,t+\phi)$ where $\phi = \tan^{-1}\dfrac{a\omega_n\sqrt{1-\delta^2}}{1-a\delta\omega_n}$
$\dfrac{\omega_n{}^2(1+as)}{(s^2+\omega_n{}^2)}$	$\omega_n\sqrt{1+a^2\omega_n{}^2}\sin\,(\omega_n t+\phi)$ where $\phi=\tan^{-1}a\omega_n$
$\dfrac{\omega_n{}^2(1+as)}{(1+Ts)(s^2+2\delta\omega_n s+\omega_n{}^2)}$	$\dfrac{\omega_n}{\sqrt{1-\delta^2}}\sqrt{\dfrac{1-2a\delta\omega_n+a^2\omega_n{}^2}{1-2T\delta\omega_n+T^2\omega_n{}^2}}\,\epsilon^{-\delta\omega_n t}\sin\,(\omega_n\sqrt{1-\delta^2}\,t+\phi)$ $$+\dfrac{(T-a)\omega_n{}^2}{1-2T\delta\omega_n+T^2\omega_n{}^2}\,\epsilon^{-t/T}$$ where $\phi = \tan^{-1}\dfrac{a\omega_n\sqrt{1-\delta^2}}{1-a\delta\omega_n} - \tan^{-1}\dfrac{T\omega_n\sqrt{1-\delta^2}}{1-T\delta\omega_n}$
$\dfrac{\omega_n{}^2(1+as)}{(1+Ts)(s^2+\omega_n{}^2)}$	$\dfrac{\omega_n{}^2(T-a)}{1+T^2\omega_n{}^2}\,\epsilon^{-t/T} + \dfrac{\omega_n\sqrt{1+a^2\omega_n{}^2}}{\sqrt{1+T^2\omega_n{}^2}}\sin\,(\omega_n t+\phi)$ where $\phi = \tan^{-1}a\omega_n - \tan^{-1}\omega_n T$
$\dfrac{\omega_n{}^2(1+as)}{s(s^2+2\delta\omega_n s+\omega_n{}^2)}$	$1 + \dfrac{1}{\sqrt{1-\delta^2}}\sqrt{1-2a\delta\omega_n+a^2\omega_n{}^2}\,\epsilon^{-\delta\omega_n t}$ $$\sin\,(\omega_n\sqrt{1-\delta^2}\,t+\phi)$$ where $\phi = \tan^{-1}\dfrac{a\omega_n\sqrt{1-\delta^2}}{1-a\delta\omega_n} - \tan^{-1}\dfrac{\sqrt{1-\delta^2}}{-\delta}$
$\dfrac{\omega_n{}^2(1+as)}{s(1+Ts)(s^2+\omega_n{}^2)}$	$1 + \dfrac{T\omega_n{}^2(a-T)}{1+T^2\omega_n{}^2}\,\epsilon^{-t/T} - \sqrt{\dfrac{1+a^2\omega_n{}^2}{1+T^2\omega_n{}^2}}\cos\,(\omega_n t+\phi)$ where $\phi = \tan^{-1}a\omega_n - \tan^{-1}\omega_n T$
$\dfrac{\omega_n{}^2(1+as)}{s(1+Ts)(s^2+2\delta\omega_n s+\omega_n{}^2)}$	$1 + \sqrt{\dfrac{1-2a\delta\omega_n+a^2\omega_n{}^2}{(1-\delta^2)(1-2T\delta\omega_n+T^2\omega_n{}^2)}}\,\epsilon^{-\delta\omega_n t}$ $$\sin\,(\omega_n\sqrt{1-\delta^2}\,t+\phi)+\dfrac{\omega_n{}^2T(a-T)}{1-2T\delta\omega_n+T^2\omega_n{}^2}\,\epsilon^{-t/T}$$ $\phi = \tan^{-1}[a\omega_n\sqrt{1-\delta^2}[(1-a\delta\omega_n)] -$ $\tan^{-1}\,[T\omega_n\sqrt{1-\delta^2}/(1-T\delta\omega_n)] - \tan^{-1}(\sqrt{1-\delta^2}/-\delta)$
$\dfrac{1+as}{s^2(1+Ts)}$	$t + (a-T)(1-\epsilon^{-t/T})$
$\dfrac{s\omega_n{}^2}{s^2+2\delta\omega_n s+\omega_n{}^2}$	$\dfrac{\omega_n{}^2}{\sqrt{1-\delta^2}}\,\epsilon^{-\delta\omega_n t}\sin\,(\omega_n\sqrt{1-\delta^2}\,t+\phi)$ where $\phi = \tan^{-1}\dfrac{\sqrt{1-\delta^2}}{-\delta}$

Laplace transform $F(s)$	Time function $f(s)$
$\dfrac{s}{s^2 + \omega_n{}^2}$	$\cos \omega_n t$
$\dfrac{s}{(s^2 + \omega_n{}^2)^2}$	$\dfrac{1}{2\omega_n} t \sin \omega_n t$
$\dfrac{s}{(s^2 + \omega_{n1}{}^2)(s^2 + \omega_{n2}{}^2)}$	$\dfrac{1}{\omega_{n2}{}^2 - \omega_{n1}{}^2} (\cos \omega_{n1} t - \cos \omega_{n2} t)$
$\dfrac{s}{(1 + Ts)(s^2 + \omega_n{}^2)}$	$\dfrac{-1}{(1 + T^2\omega_n{}^2)} \epsilon^{-t/T} + \dfrac{1}{\sqrt{1 + T^2\omega_n{}^2}} \cos (\omega_n t - \phi)$ where $\quad \phi = \tan^{-1} \omega_n T$
$\dfrac{1 + as + bs^2}{s^2(1 + T_1 s)(1 + T_2 s)}$	$t + (a - T_1 - T_2) + \dfrac{b - aT_1 + T_1{}^2}{T_1 - T_2} \epsilon^{-t/T} - $ $\dfrac{b - aT_2 + T_2{}^2}{T_1 - T_2} \epsilon^{-t/T_2}$
$\dfrac{\omega_n{}^2(1 + as + bs^2)}{s(s^2 + 2\delta\omega_n s + \omega_n{}^2)}$	$1 + \sqrt{\dfrac{(1 - a\delta\omega_n - b\omega_n{}^2 + 2b\delta^2\omega_n{}^2)^2 + \omega_n{}^2(1 - \delta^2)(a - 2b\delta\omega_n)^2}{(1 - \delta^2)}}$ $\epsilon^{-\delta\omega_n t} \sin (\omega_n\sqrt{1 - \delta^2} t + \phi)$ $\phi = \tan^{-1} \dfrac{\omega_n\sqrt{1 - \delta^2}(a - 2b\delta\omega_n)}{b\omega_n(2\delta^2 - 1) + 1 - a\delta\omega_n} - \tan^{-1}\dfrac{\sqrt{1 - \delta^2}}{-\delta}$
$\dfrac{s^2}{(s^2 + \omega_n{}^2)^2}$	$\dfrac{1}{2\omega_n} (\sin \omega_n t + \omega_n t \cos \omega_n t)$

Index

519